ENGINEERING MANUFACTURING METHODS

ENGINEERING

MANUFACTURING METHODS

GILBERT S. SCHALLER

Professor of Mechanical Engineering
University of Washington

McGRAW-HILL BOOK COMPANY, Inc.

New York   Toronto   London

1953

ENGINEERING MANUFACTURING METHODS

Library of Congress Catalog Card Number: 51-12948

II

THE MAPLE PRESS COMPANY, YORK, PA.

Dedicated to

DOLLY,
JOHNNY and GIL

PREFACE

Engineering industry is continuing the trend toward specialization in its endeavor to produce a quality end product at a satisfactory cost. This challenging objective poses the vital problem of material selection coupled with economical manufacturing methods to every level of the industrial organization. Decisions on these fundamentals are no longer the province of any one department; rather, they are best reached by the combined thinking of the entire organization. Considered judgment combined with open-mindedness are requisites to correct decisions.

This text is intended to provide a survey of engineering manufacturing methods in a manner that will afford the student some insight into their potentialities. The selection of the best method or the most efficient machine tool for a specific undertaking should result from the evaluation of all pertinent factors.

The text content has evolved from the author's teaching material modified by his experience in engineering industry. There is little that is actually new in the text. However, the light metals are given attention commensurate with their increasing importance in engineering manufacture. Foundry subjects are approached from the viewpoint of the production of economical quality castings. The chapters on welding are of such scope as to include all the salient features of this pertinent phase of manufacturing methods. Emphasis in the treatment of machining is placed on fundamentals with special attention to those machine tools and methods that are of widest usage.

The author acknowledges the profound assistance given him by many professional engineering societies and trade associations. They have been most generous in permitting the inclusion of material from their publications on standards and other pertinent information; individual acknowledgments are included in the text.

To the many companies which have contributed photographs to illustrate the text, the author expresses his sincere thanks. The numerous courtesies extended by publishers and copyright owners are appreciated.

This text could not have been written without the help of many individuals. The author wishes to take this means of recognizing the valuable assistance rendered to him by his colleagues in the Mechanical Engineering Department of the University of Washington. He is especially appreciative of the efforts of Profs. William A. Snyder, Blake Mills, Jr., and K. E. H. Moltrecht, in offering suggestions for, and revi-

sion of, the manuscript.   He is sincerely grateful for the encouragement
and generous cooperation given him by Prof. B. T. McMinn, department
chairman.   His secretary, Gladys Olcott Fraley, rendered invaluable
service in editing and preparing the manuscript, as did Lois Luft in
providing library reference service.   Many of the photographs were
made possible through the efforts of Whitey Marten, ably assisted by
K. W. MacFarlane.   Ed Boyle, Master Molder, Puget Sound Naval
Shipyard, graciously supplied data on insulated risers, while E. J. McAfee,
Master Patternmaker, contributed information on plastic foundry
patterns.   Now that the text is finished, the author expresses the wish
that his efforts will, in a measure at least, bring some satisfaction to the
many whose inspiration and encouragement made its completion possible.

Gilbert S. Schaller

Seattle, Wash.
October, 1952

CONTENTS

CHAPTER 1

ENGINEERED MANUFACTURING

The word manufacturing is generally applied to any activity which produces a satisfactory end product from materials by a systemetized method or combination of methods. The terms manufacturing, production, and building, which on occasion are used interchangeably, are not, strictly speaking, synonymous. It would seem more accurate to associate the first two with industrial plants whose products are of a serialized nature and to reserve the last for establishments where individual or small group orders predominate. It is in the latter group that chief reliance for success is placed on the ability of the artisan rather than on the potentialities of the combination of engineering, tooling, and equipment that characterizes the former.

Specialization in Industry. The distinction between manufacturing and production on the one hand, and building on the other, should be sharply drawn, especially in view of the trend toward integration and mass production in industry. This development, which has been under way for a considerable period, has led to the necessity for specialization all along the line. Whether or not this is desirable is open to question when all aspects of the situation are examined. However, one inescapable conclusion is that the specialist is in the ascendancy at the expense of the broadly trained individual. A continuation of this trend may well result in a defeat for the objective sought because of the appalling price of intradependence that specialization exacts.

There seems to be little need to enter into the continuing controversy of education versus practical experience. These are not in conflict at all; rather they are complementary in the sense that either one can be much more rapidly attained by an individual if he is in possession of the other. Universities and colleges generally recognize this fact by offering programs that strike a balance between classroom courses and laboratory classes. That well-established industries take a similar view is evidenced by the training programs offered for the graduate who enters their employ. The objective, in any case, is a training in fundamentals of such quality and magnitude as to give the individual a solid foundation on which he can develop.

Manufacturing Costs. The problems that must be solved in a manufacturing program are far from routine. As competition becomes more intense the matter of cost grows in importance. The truth is that cost has become the dominant factor in every phase of manufacturing, from methods through marketing. Cognizance must be taken of cost in designing the product; in fact the subordination of functionality and service of a product to the cost position seems to be indicated. It is impossible to overemphasize the power that design of the product exercises over the manufacturing cost of that product.

The Designer's Responsibilities. It is within the province of the designer to call into play any manufacturing method or any engineering material that he deems necessary or desirable. The limitations confronting him stem from the availability of material and equipment, or in some cases, the necessity of using excess inventoried material. Too, he may find that his manufacturing organization is incapable of performing its function owing to inability, lack of required equipment, or both. Yet, severe as these limitations may be, they are sometimes secondary to the limitations of the designer himself. In order to make the most of his capabilities, a designer must have a sound working knowledge of current manufacturing methods and engineering materials. The importance of modernity is continually dictated by the competitive position imposed through the workings of our enterprise system. Regardless of how well a product sells or how profitable its manufacture proves to be, competition arises; the greater the sale and the more extensive the profits, the more competition is engendered. Such a continuing cycle is a strong stimulant to the originator as it is to his emulator. As this competition intensifies, it usually resolves itself into a situation in which manufacturing methods emerge as the main point of issue. The philosophy of following or copying competition for your own product is at best a passive one and will ultimately lead to a second-rate position. A study of the development of any of the sturdy American industries will reveal this continuing striving for survival and its reward of leadership.

Organizational Responsibilities. The management organization charged with the responsibility of keeping the company in a position of competitive leadership is confronted with a task that runs the full gamut of engineering. Their problem is that of knowing and applying accepted manufacturing methods and engineering materials; yet as challenging as this may prove to be, they have the further mandate of anticipating future developments by their competition, since it is axiomatic that a static policy is, in effect, an invitation to retrogression. The company policy should be definite in delineating the lines of authority and, equally important, of responsibility. The ideal solution involves the employment of all the ability that can be mustered within the organization.

There should be no reluctance about consulting the shop, nor should there be any jealousies between the different branches of management. Differences of opinion should be tolerated for the very good reason that a fuller examination of the problem under discussion will result. However, these differences should be resolved and the final solution reached through a program of logical reasoning rather than in a spirit of preemptoriness.

Development of the Individual. It is not an easy matter to make a decision on the manufacturing method or on the best engineering material to be employed for a given design. When the decision is solely the responsibility of one person, he will, being human, invoke the solution he is most familiar with and the one he knows most about. Obviously, this will not always be the best solution, for the very sound reason it cannot take into account possibilities existing beyond his capabilities. It is a strong human trait to repeat actions that have previously proved successful in similar circumstances. The possible advantage to be gained from experimenting with a new method or a different material is sacrificed for the security of proved solutions. The factual knowledge of the college classroom is frequently of questionable assistance for the reason that it has become obsolete even though only a short time, seemingly, has elapsed since its acquisition. This is far from comforting knowledge to the graduate; yet an early realization of the situation will prove helpful in steering him into channels of current information. Undoubtedly his best plan of action is to affiliate with a professional society in his field of major interest. That society's publications will provide a current source of information of great potential value. Specific questions directed to the editors or to the secretary of the society will be given definite answers. In addition, there is a wide choice of periodicals covering every conceivable phase of manufacturing methods and engineering materials. The local library will prove most helpful. There remain, too, publications, governmental agencies, private bureaus, and educational institutions all of which will prove to be valuable sources of information.

Product Development. It is an accepted practice in industry to place great reliance on salesmen and manufacturer's agents for current information on consumer interest. However, it is an unfortunate fact that in far too many instances the urge to sell overcomes all other considerations and an overwhelming representation is made for a product that is not necessarily factual. It is also deplorable that sometimes individuals within an organization become enamored of a material different from one that they have been currently using and decide that this new material must be substituted throughout the product, only to find the substitution a grievous mistake as evidenced by unreliable service or outright failures.

The Approach to Manufacturing Methods. Change in manufacturing methods does not necessarily denote progress. Changes must be made, but not merely for the sake of change. Such action should be taken only after all the facts bearing on the situation have been gathered and analyzed thoroughly. The direction that a change is to follow may seem a reversal of the going trend. An outstanding example is the introduction of cast camshafts as well as cast crankshafts as replacements for forgings in the motorcar industry. The cast camshaft has established a fine reputation from the standpoint of cost as well as of service. The casting comes to the machine shop in such form that roughing operations are reduced; thus a substantial saving in machining time is achieved.

Finding a best product usually results from conflicting views on manufacturing methods. Especially noteworthy in this connection is the employment of welding in one of its branches as a new method of joining. Weldments have replaced both castings and forgings in many manufactured products. The prominence that welding has achieved does not necessarily indicate that this manufacturing method has made obsolete all prior methods of fastening or joining metals; nor is it to be understood that weldments are to replace forgings and castings in general. The considered view recognizes that there is a best method and a best material for each individual design. This desirable solution should be sought on a factual basis.

Selection of Engineering Materials. There is little justification for speaking of an "age" insofar as engineering materials are concerned. The history of product development is replete with examples of one material being supplanted by another, only to have the former develop in public favor to the point where a demand, quite apart from sound engineering or manufacturing methods, arises for it.

During the war years there was a rather widespread interest in the possibility of the manufacture of aluminum alloy automobile bodies. The fact that was overlooked or perhaps completely unknown was that aluminum alloy bodies had been used on motorcars almost from the beginning of their manufacture; yet today this material is not used on production models of American motorcars owing to the cost of manufacture.

Product Manufacturing. The objective of every producer is to create a product that will give satisfactory service and at the same time return a profit. This fundamental of manufacturing has been grasped and exploited to its fullest by successful manufacturers; yet the casualty list among manufacturers over the years is an appalling one. Every failure is an expensive experience that reaches through our entire society. Much research has been devoted toward ascertaining the reason for such a substantial number of failures. The statistical data compiled from these efforts indicate that in the majority of cases the concept of the product has been faulty. Public acceptance or rejection can generally be traced to the engineering of the product both as to manufacturing methods and as to materials used. The choice of a manufacturing method must become a matter of paramount concern to the engineering department; nothing should be left to chance or to personal opinion. Designs should be definite to the point where there can be no misunderstanding by the shop.

The inauguration of a complete system of checks and instructions will place responsibility where it belongs and enable each individual to devote his entire effort to doing the job before him with all of his energy and ability. Engineering for functionality has always been of chief interest; now the necessity of engineering for manufacturing is definitely in the ascendancy and is a factor that must be acknowledged and dealt with by management.

Outlook for Engineering Manufacture. The first half of the twentieth century has demonstrated that product manufacturing is never static. Improved materials are being combined with revised production techniques adapted to the continually changing requirements in consumer demand. The trend toward greater production per man-hour is especially marked. Fundamental developments in the concept of machine performance are indicated by the increasing acceptance of transfer-type machines in all realms of engineering manufacture. This course of action undoubtedly has social implications for our entire way of life.

Survey Questions

1-1. What is the distinguishing characteristic of job-lot manufacturing?

1-2. List the important advantages of specialization in industry.

1-3. To what extent does the designer control manufacturing costs?

1-4. How does a successful manufacturing organization function?

1-5. By whom is company policy formulated?

1-6. Offer suggestions for the continuing education of an engineering graduate.

1-7. What advantages result from membership in a professional engineering society?

1-8. Where is information for product development best obtained?

1-9. Under what circumstances should changes in currently used manufacturing methods be made?

1-10. How should the selection of an engineering material be approached?

1-11. What is a major cause of business failure?

1-12. Explain the meaning of "engineering a product."

1-13. The objective of increased production per man-hour can lead to several results. Discuss some of the far-reaching results that this objective will produce.

1-14. Should management concern itself with the social problems that result from increasing mechanization of industry generally?

CHAPTER 2

MATERIALS IN MANUFACTURING

The selection of an engineering material is usually approached either from the standpoint of functionality or from that of first cost of the chosen material. A close examination of any successful product which has been in continuous production over a period of time will show continual revision in the direction of lowered man-hour production time. Paralleling this favorable development will be found changes in the engineering materials providing for better manufacturing results.

Selection of Engineering Materials. The conclusion seems clear that engineering materials must be given a closer correlation with manufacturing methods. This need becomes more pressing as competition develops in industry. A pertinent, and for the most part an overlooked, development is the change in the supply or availability situation as it applies to engineering materials. It is hazardous to use the present situation as a guide for forecasting the future. Nonetheless, there seems to be sufficient evidence at hand to indicate that some of the standard materials of the past will be forced to share their popularity with others that are developing and making their bid for recognition. The designer is already confronted with this evolution and is being forced to consider the use of different engineering materials or of familiar materials in different applications. A striking example of the latter situation is the case of gray cast iron.

Here is a manufacturing material that has been basic from the beginning of the building of machinery. In fact history proves the great antiquity of gray-iron castings in almost every ramification of manufacturing. The idea of bulk and weight has been associated with this material, an idea that continues to persist in some quarters even though it is no longer founded on fact. Recently, gray cast iron has been the beneficiary of research and re-evaluation. Metallurgists have discovered its versatility and have uncovered potentialities that had never before been connected with it. Through a program of development, parts of which border on the spectacular, gray cast iron is now being produced at a price and in a quality that places it in direct competition with steel as well as with other materials. In the continuing search for something new it is repeatedly discovered that what was considered commonplace has properties previously overlooked or underevaluated.

The practice of making repeated changes in steel specifications from the commoner carbon steels to the complex alloy steels has long been popular. The scarcities in certain alloying elements occurring during the war focused attention on the necessity for conservation of those dwindling resources. This challenge was met in a most gratifying fashion through the program which led to the development of the National Emergency (N.E.) series of steels. Once the consumer became accustomed to these substitute steels, he was quick to note that here was a trend toward the use of lower amounts of alloying elements. This raised the question whether or not alloy steels were actually necessary in many of the applications where their use had become general. The trend is continuing, since it has proved itself from the standpoint of cost, in which manufacturing methods loom importantly.

When materials of engineering are discussed it is usual to consider the metallic alloys. These in turn are divided into the general groupings of ferrous and nonferrous materials. It should be added, though, that there is some interest in the noble metals, especially silver, for use in manufacturing. However, no listing or consideration of the subject is complete unless the nonmetals are given their rightful place. The strides being made by ceramics, glass, plastics, synthetics, and processed woods are little short of phenomenal. Plastics have made the greatest development in engineering manufacture and, for that reason they are detailed later in this chapter.

Ferrous Metals

Pig Iron. A study of the materials in manufacture should start with the ferrous group, since they are most widely used and are produced in the greatest tonnage (Fig. 2-1). Pig iron is the basis of the far-reaching series of ferrous alloys. However, in a more restricted sense, pig iron is associated with the foundry as the base for cast iron. When considered from this standpoint, the term pig iron ASTM designation A43-49T, which constitutes the tentative specification for Foundry Pig Iron, lists a total of 308 grades on the basis of chemical composition. These grades are arranged in the following groupings: low-phosphorus, intermediate low-phosphorus, Bessemer, malleable, Foundry Northern low-phosphorus, Foundry Northern high-phosphorus, Foundry Southern, silvery, and charcoal pig irons. These specifications give accurate limits for silicon, sulfur, phosphorus, and manganese contents. Although carbon is a most important element, its percentages are not given in this specification because it is not controllable within narrow limits.

Fig. 2-1. Casting pig iron on a pig-casting machine at the Ironton Works of the Columbia-Geneva Steel Division of the U.S. Steel Co. The resulting pigs weigh from 50 to 100 lb each. (*Courtesy of Columbia-Geneva Steel Division of the U.S. Steel Co., San Francisco.*)

CAST IRON

Cast iron is defined in ASTM designation A196-47T as:

Essentially an alloy of iron, carbon, and silicon in which the carbon is present in excess of the amount which can be retained in solid solution in austenite at the eutectic temperature. When cast iron contains a specially added element or elements in amounts sufficient to produce a measurable modification of the physical properties of the section under consideration, it is called alloy cast iron. Silicon, manganese, sulfur, and phosphorus as normally obtained from raw materials are not considered as alloy additions.

This definition of cast iron, in which alloy cast iron is specifically noted, covers the further modifications more familiarly known as chilled iron, inoculant, gray cast iron, ductile cast iron, white cast iron, mottled cast iron, malleable cast iron, and pearlitic malleable cast iron. Each of these is characterized by distinguishing chemical, physical, and mechanical properties.

Chilled Iron. Chilled iron is produced in the foundry in a manner similar to gray cast iron with the added feature that the part of the casting to be chilled is subjected to accelerated cooling. This is accomplished by placing a metal adjunct, termed "chill," in such a position in the mold that the molten metal lying in contact with it is caused to cool at a greater rate than the remainder of the casting which is in contact with the sand in the mold. The effect obtained is, in essence, a quenching operation that prevents the precipitation of major amounts of graphitic carbon, with the result that combined carbon Fe_3C predominates. Since there is but little graphite present, the fracture is white and the section that was subjected to the chill is extremely hard (Fig. 2-2). The purpose of chilling is to produce a very hard surface that is wear-resistant. Perhaps the most widely used product whose manufacture includes the process of chilling is cast iron car wheels; the treads of these are chilled in order to withstand wear from the railroad rails as well as from the brake shoes.

Fig. 2-2. Section through a cast-iron railroad-car wheel showing chilled tread. (Courtesy of Griffin Wheel Co., Chicago.)

Gray Cast Iron. This most interesting and versatile material has been and continues to be the subject of study and research. An exhaustive treatment of gray cast iron in its engineering and metallurgical aspects has been written by John Bolton.[1] The interested student will find a study of this treatise most rewarding.

It is the accepted practice to classify gray iron castings on the basis of minimum tensile strengths. The established classification, found in ASTM specification A48-48, is shown in Table 2-1:

TABLE 2-1

Class no.	Tensile strength, min., psi
20	20,000
25	25,000
30	30,000
35	35,000
40	40,000
50	50,000
60	60,000

Even though the groupings show no. 60 as the maximum tensile strength, higher values are regularly produced through the addition of alloying elements. It is not difficult to produce gray cast iron of 75,000 psi tensile strength. Some interesting research is under way in the

[1] Gray Cast Iron, The Penton Publishing Co., Cleveland, 1937.

direction of modification of structure by processing and alloying; this has already resulted in gray cast irons approaching 100,000 psi in tensile strength.

The classifications for minimum tensile strength do not include chemical compositions for the reason that the elements comprising gray cast iron vary widely in their effects on the final structure. These effects occur chiefly as the result of the combinations that are possible with such a wide range of variability.

Carbon and silicon exert the greatest influence on machinability; a highly graphitic structure is regarded as being easiest to machine, while a white cast iron possessing a structure in which iron carbide predominates is most difficult. The machinability of gray iron castings is predicted by a study of their structure. Structure has been recognized as of such importance that an ASTM specification A247-47 has been developed in conjunction with the American Foundrymen's Society (AFS). The specification embodies two charts, one portraying graphite flake *size* and the other, graphite flake *type*.

Any discussion of gray cast iron should refer to the fact that it can be cast into almost any conceivable shape. Moldenke in his "Principles of Iron Founding"[1] states that lace curtains were actually reproduced in cast iron in Belgium. Individual castings have been made in sizes weighing from a few ounces to hundreds of tons. They have been produced in such a wide range of application as to extend from cannon balls to the dome on the Capitol in Washington, D.C. It is little wonder that gray cast iron is so popular as a manufacturing material.

Cast iron can be successfully welded by any of the commonly used non-pressure-welding methods, but the oxyacetylene torch has been the most prominent. The electric carbon arc process has been outmoded largely because of the development of suitable metal arc electrodes which are gaining in favor. Braze welding remains a reliable method of joining broken cast-iron parts. It can be stated that the welding of cast iron is almost always for the purpose of reclamation. Cast-iron weldments are scarce for the reason that a part can be cast as an entity to better advantage and with greater facility.

Nodular Cast Iron. Inoculated gray cast iron has taken many forms. Some of these, such as acicular cast iron, have proven their worth in critical applications as diesel crankshafts. A further development in inoculation has resulted in a group of cast irons wherein the graphite is of a nodular character in the "as cast" condition. Cerium additions were originally used to achieve the inoculating effect. Further progress has seen magnesium or magnesium and nickel as the inoculating agency. Inoculants are added to the molten metal as ladle additions prior to

[1] McGraw-Hill Book Company, New York, 1917.

pouring.   The resultant structure is one that has the graphite constituent in the form of nodules.

Nodular cast iron includes a group of materials that are capable of wide variation in mechanical properties resulting from base iron composition and inoculating procedure.   There are no standard specifications as yet covering this type of cast iron.   Two general trends are noticeable. In one of these, high tensile strengths are secured in the as-cast condition, while in the other, ductility is impressive although heat treatment is generally required to develop its maximum values.   It remains to be seen just where nodular cast iron will find its major field of utility and to what extent it will displace currently used ferrous castings.

Malleable Cast Iron.   Malleable cast iron is divided technically into two classifications, viz., malleable iron castings, covered by ASTM specification A47-48, and pearlitic malleable iron castings, specification A220-48T.

In specification A47-48 the mechanical properties are as follows:

	Grade no. 32510	Grade no. 35018
Tensile strength, min., psi...............	50,000	53,000
Yield point, min., psi...................	32,500	35,000
Elongation in 2 in. min., per cent........	10	18

The irons covered by the above specification must be made by either the air-furnace, the open-hearth, or the electric-furnace process.   In addition to these, there is Cupola malleable, which is covered by ASTM specification A197-47.

Pearlitic Malleable Cast Iron.   The products known as pearlitic malleable resulted from an interesting development in the field of malleable iron castings, which involved the use of alloying elements or a shorter annealing cycle, or a combination of both.   As noted in ASTM specification A220-48T, the materials in this grouping exhibit higher strengths and lower ductility values than the standard malleable cast irons.

	Grade no. 43010	Grade no. 48005	Grade no. 60003	Grade no. 70002
Tensile strength, min., psi..........	60,000	70,000	80,000	90,000
Yield strength, min., psi............	43,000	48,000	60,000	70,000
Elongation in 2 in., min., per cent...	10	5	3	2

Malleable cast irons have excellent machinability and ductility (Fig. 2-3). The superiority of the standard group in this connection to the pearlitic is due to the fact that in the latter there is some retained iron carbide, whereas in the former the total carbon content has been reduced to temper carbon of the characteristic nodular form. Machining may be entirely eliminated for certain designs in standard malleable cast iron, since the ductility of the material is such that it can be coin-pressed.

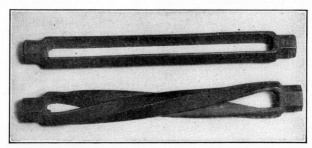

Fig. 2-3. Malleable-iron casting for a turnbuckle. Note ductility exemplified by lower view.

This method is limited to production runs because of the rather specialized tooling requirements.

WROUGHT IRON

The ferrous material of antiquity is known to industry as wrought iron. Indications are that this material was produced originally directly from iron ore in a hearth. The next development was the use of pig iron for the basic charge in the puddling process. The current production method is known in industry as the Aston or Byers process. The original work on this process was started in 1918; it developed into a commercial operation in 1930.

In colonial America, as elsewhere at that time, the ferrous materials in common usage were cast iron and wrought iron. Since there have been many designs inspired by the work of the artisans of those early times, the term "wrought iron" has come to be very widely used; in fact it is not at all uncommon to encounter products being offered today under the name of wrought iron that are produced from steel or even gray cast iron. The point to note here is that the term wrought iron is used sometimes in the sense of a manufacturing method rather than in its proper province as the designation of a ferrous material.

The definition of wrought iron that is accepted as authoritative is given in ASTM designation A81-33: "a ferrous material, aggregated from a solidifying mass of pasty particles of highly refined metallic iron, with which, without subsequent fusion, is incorporated a minutely and uniformly distributed quantity of slag."

It will be noted from this definition that wrought iron is never in a molten state during its production, a fact which readily explains that wrought iron is a material that can only appear in end-product form as the result of mechanical working.

The property of corrosion resistance is always associated with wrought iron and it has been widely accepted that here this material is pre-eminent.   There is now cause to question whether wrought iron is not being pressed by steel in many applications, although it seems to be agreed that when it comes to resistance to corrosion of the pitting type, the fibrous slag content of wrought iron places it in a position of supe-riority.   Its use in boiler stay bolts and hold-down bolts as well as in some locomotive parts is traditional and constitutes an acknowledgement of the properties inherent in wrought iron.

STEEL

The importance of steel to society or, more properly, the dependence of society upon steel as a basic material is an ever increasing one.   Steel possesses so many qualities that it occupies the position of being the most versatile and most widely used engineering material.

The beginning of the modern steel industry dates from the invention of the steel converter.   This revolutionary method made its appearance around 1856.   While Sir Henry Bessemer is generally acknowledged as the inventor, valid claims to priority on the converter have been advanced for William Kelly of Eddyville, Kentucky.   It seems reasonable to assume that these men, working independently and in ignorance of each other's experiments, achieved the same results concurrently.

Cementation Steel.   The earliest steels were made from wrought-iron bars by cementation.   In that method, the iron bars were packed in a container along with a carbon-yielding agent.   This sealed package was subjected to an elevated temperature for a considerable period of time, until the carbon had penetrated through the bar thereby changing it into steel.   A revised application of this method is used currently in heat treatment and is known as carburizing.   Owing to a lack of control, coupled with the variability of the raw material used, cementation steel proved to be of erratic quality.

Crucible Steel.   The lack of consistency in cementation steel led to a search for corrective measures that ended with an entirely new steel-making method.   In the crucible process, as developed by Huntsman in England in 1742, bars of carefully selected cementation steel were cut into small pieces and placed in a crucible.   When the latter was filled, a lid was luted into position and the crucible placed into a pit furnace, there to remain until its charge was melted.   The molten metal was poured into ingots which, upon cooling, were forged into the desired shape. The processing has been revised in that pieces of wrought iron are used for the charge and carbonaceous material is added prior to melting. Crucible steel proved to be so homogeneous in quality that its manufacture has endured, in a measure at least, up to the present time. From the standpoint of quality, it shares its position only with electric-furnace steels.

Steel Making. The impressive steel-making industry was built on converter steel, even though the open-hearth process (Fig. 2-4) is now the leader from a tonnage standpoint. Recently the electric arc and still more recently the electrical induction furnace have added their

Fig. 2-4. Open-hearth charging floor at the Bethlehem Pacific Coast Steel Co.'s South San Francisco Works. (*Courtesy of Bethlehem Pacific Coast Steel Corp., San Francisco.*)

influence to the steel-making industry, until the production has exceeded the imposing total of 100 million tons of ingots per year. All the ingot steel is destined for further processing and, therefore, represents a production exclusive of the steel-casting industry, which has also attained a heavy production volume.

Steel is shaped into end products by all manufacturing methods excepting only die castings. In order to meet this range of requirements, steels of widely varying chemical properties and microstructure are now regularly produced. Metallurgical control is of fundamental importance. The necessity of close control is strikingly portrayed by the requirements imposed through the recently developed cold strip mill (Fig. 2-5) whose operating speeds may exceed 4,000 fpm on the finishing pass.

The methods of manufacture, some of which were mentioned earlier, can be summarized as follows:

Cementation steel
Crucible steel
Converter steel { Acid (American) bessemer
                 { Basic bessemer
Open-hearth steel { Acid open-hearth
                   { Basic open-hearth
Electric-furnace { Acid electric
                 { Basic electric
Electric induction furnace steel
Duplexed steel { Cupola melted gray iron, refined in side blow converter
               { Molten pig partially refined in converter, finished in open-hearth

Of greater interest is the classification of steel on the basis of its composition, inasmuch as end-use is closely related to this feature.   Any listing

Fig. 2-5. Continuous-type cold reduction sheet mill. Main drive has 5 motors, totaling 15,500 hp. Capacity is about 450 net tons of cold reduced steel per 8-hr shift. (*Courtesy of Columbia-Geneva Steel Division of the U.S. Steel Co., San Francisco.*)

of this classification must consider both the wrought, or mechanically worked, steels and the cast steels.

A simplified grouping on this basis follows:

Ingot iron: A highly refined open-hearth steel whose total impurities are 0.15% max.

Plain carbon steels { Dead soft—C (0.10% max.)
                     { Low carbon (mild)—C (0.10%–0.30%)
                     { Medium carbon—C (0.30%–0.65%)
                     { High carbon—C (0.85%–1.50%)

Alloy steels { Low-alloy, high-strength structurals (total alloys range from 1–2%)
             { Low-alloy steels (alloys total 8% max.)
             { High-alloy steels (alloys total 8% min.)

In manufacturing, steels are processed either at room temperature or at elevated temperatures. On that basis, the following grouping is obtained:

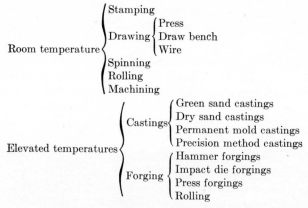

Perhaps there has been too much stress on the traditional approach when choosing a steel for a given design. The principal emphasis is placed on the mechanical properties of a given steel although the design may require only one or a combination of a few of these; the result is a program of trial-and-error selection. It is an established fact that the mechanical properties of steel are dependent primarily upon its microstructure. In consequence, the composition of a steel, which usually is given greatest emphasis, should be interpreted only in light of its effect on microstructure. The carbon content of a steel, coupled with phase transformations the steel may undergo during any heat treatment, is the determinant of the microstructure.

Steel Compositions. The designer must specify an engineering material that is suitable for the projected component. His specification will serve best when it is confined to a recognized engineering standard. There are several such standards for steels, any one of which will prove satisfactory. American Society for Testing Materials (ASTM) specifications are fundamental. Society of Automotive Engineers (SAE) classifications afford a ready means of showing composition. Another specification of a similar nature is the American Iron and Steel Institute (AISI) classification. The designation numbers used by the SAE and AISI systems are identical. The point of difference is that the AISI employs a pattern of letter prefixes indicating the method of steel manufacture, as follows:

B—Acid Bessemer carbon steel

C—Basic open-hearth carbon steel

D—Acid open-hearth carbon steel

E—Electric-furnace steel

No prefix—Basic open-hearth alloy steel

When AISI designations are used, both the composition and the method of steel manufacture are incorporated in one specification. Basic open-hearth alloy steel has the same designations in the AISI and SAE classifications.

Steel Selection. In a broad sense, steels are grouped into plain carbon and alloy classifications. There are several types of each, although carburizing as well as deep-hardening steels are available in each group. The plain carbon steels were developed first. They are less costly than the alloy steels and if correctly specified and properly processed are capable of satisfactory performance. Plain carbon steels are sometimes overlooked because of the more imposing mechanical properties possessed by most alloy steels. A careful evaluation of plain carbon steels, as to both properties and processing capabilities, will frequently result in a lower manufacturing cost for the end product. This situation is becoming increasingly important, since the supply of alloying elements is growing critical. It is impossible to generalize on the subject of plain carbon versus alloy steel. In each case the design should be studied and an economy survey made in order to arrive at the best solution. Among the several factors entering into such a study, the matter of availability deserves especial attention.

Alloy Steels. The range of composition in this classification extends from the low-alloy high-strength structurals to the highly alloyed stainless and heat-resisting groups. An alloy steel is considered to be one in which manganese exceeds 1.65 per cent or silicon exceeds 0.60 per cent. Both elements are constituents of plain carbon steel and for that reason are considered as alloying elements only when present in the percentages given. In addition to these two, aluminum, boron, chromium, cobalt, copper, columbium, molybdenum, nickel, titanium, tungsten, vanadium, and zirconium are regarded as alloying elements in these steels. The content of any alloying element or elements can be found by reference to the specification of an individual alloy steel. The compositions have been developed to impart specific properties. The degree to which an alloying element is present in a steel varies within a given classification. The effect of each alloy or combination of alloying elements is well-known and forms the basis of the property classifications of alloy steel.

The composition range for alloying elements as well as basic elements must be closely controlled within a given steel specification. Quality requirements are rigid. Special property and quality requirements have resulted in recognized classifications such as aircraft, axle shaft, bearing, cold heading, and hardenability, among others. Each of these types has its specific field of application and degree of excellence. The designer should take cognizance of the possibilities of all types as a means toward developing a satisfactory product.

H-steels. Alloy steels are available whose hardenability can be specified within standard limits. The limits are referred to as hardenability bands; their values are given in Rockwell C points. H-steels are designated by numbers of the SAE-AISI classification with the letter *H* appearing as a suffix. There is some modification in analysis of these steels over their standard alloy steel counterparts in order that the steel maker can meet the specified hardenability requirements. The development of H-steels is of significance since it affords a reliable means of meeting hardenability specifications in a design. It is sound procedure to consult with the steel producer because of his records on every heat of steel. Precautions of this nature are valuable in eliminating variability in the end product.

Stainless and Heat-resisting Steels. Steels in these classifications are increasing in importance, paralleling the development of process-industry equipment and high-temperature applications. The application of these, the most highly alloyed types of steel, is in corrosion and/or heat resistance. The development of jet engines and gas turbines has intensified interest in these steels. Experience gained from exhaust stacks and similar aircraft engine components indicates that these are the most satisfactory steels for meeting corrosion and high-temperature conditions. Further research is necessary because the properties of the established stainless and heat-resisting steels are not entirely equal to the severity of modern jet and turbine requirements.

These steels are available in wrought form where they are, for the most part, identified under brand names. Corrosion-resistant castings are produced for chemical plants, pulp and paper mills, oil refining, food processing and other services that require resistance to corrosion or heat. Their classification is not identical with the wrought types. The latter are designated as follows under the AISI classification:

    3XX—Cr-Ni steels, austenitic
    4XX—Cr steels, martensitic
    4XX—Cr steels, ferritic
    5XX—low Cr steels, heat resisting

The range of properties inherent in this classification offers the designer an opportunity to select a steel to meet his needs. The martensitic steels are heat-treatable, while the others are susceptible to work-hardening. Machinability is developed in these types by special chemical analysis and also through further alloying elements. A similar situation obtains for weldability, although a low carbon content is especially desirable in order to avoid intergranular corrosion adjacent to the welds. Stabilized stainless steels are specified for welding where service conditions are severe. Type no. 347 is a steel in this category.

Nonferrous Metals

Those engineering metals that contain no appreciable amounts of iron in their composition are classified as nonferrous metals. Obviously, this classification is extremely broad. It includes the alloys of such well-known metals as copper, aluminum, zinc, magnesium, nickel, tin, and lead. All of these are processed similarly to the ferrous metals. Further, there have been many metallic materials added to the nonferrous group by powder metallurgy, a process wherein metallic powder is die-pressed into the desired shape and the resulting product is then subjected to a sintering operation.

The cemented or sintered carbides are best known for their excellent properties in connection with the machining of metals as well as non-metals. Their first use, however, was for wire-drawing dies in which the chief composition component was tungsten carbide.

Heat-resistant Alloys. The heat-resistant casting alloys of cobalt base were introduced for the highly stressed gas-turbine blading in 1941, and developments and modifications have been rapid since then. Some of these alloys, especially those of the Stellite group, had been used in other applications, such as tool-bit material and hard surfacing for abrasion resistance, for many years before that. These alloys are not confined to casting, since there are also wrought products of similar composition.

There are other alloys in the field of heat-resistant castings; prominent in this classification are many Ni-base alloys, especially of the Hastelloy group, whose compositions are primarily Ni, Mo with small percentages of Fe and, in some cases, Cr and W. Other nickel-base alloys that are more widely used are known under trade names such as Inconel, Monel, and "K" monel. These latter are especially noteworthy for resistance to corrosion both at normal and at elevated temperatures.

COPPER

There is general agreement on the fact that copper and its chief alloys, brass and bronze, are the oldest metals known to civilization. They remain as the standard material for a multitude of engineering applications in the face of competition from many directions. Some of this competition was fostered during wartime when copper was in short supply; in other instances the scarcity of copper in the national economy, as in Germany, gave rise to the use of competitive materials.

Copper and its alloys are available to industry in wrought as well as cast form. Within the two classifications, these materials are produced by every manufacturing method, with a wide range of products resulting. However, the high electrical conductivity of copper gives this metal its greatest field of application. Copper has also had wide application because of its inherent corrosion resistance.

The wrought alloys of copper are available in a complete range of physical forms. In addition to these end-products, there are also copper and copper-base alloy forging rods, bars, and shapes, as can be noted in ASTM designation B124-49. Forgings from the materials under this specification are used in valve bodies and similar equipment where the combination of strength, corrosion resistance, and pressure tightness dominate. Pressure regulators and cylinder valves used for oxyacetylene welding equipment are familiar examples of the application of copper-base alloy forgings.

Copper-base Casting Alloys. The tonnage of copper-base alloy castings produced annually reaches an imposing total. Producing sound castings requires exacting control throughout the molding and core departments as well as in the melt shop. In fact, the raw materials, such as molding sand, core sands and binders, fuel, ingots, and, especially, scrap metal, must be given the closest attention if casting defects are to be avoided.

Casting design is an important matter, especially when such alloys as aluminum and manganese bronze are to be cast. Both liquid and solidification shrinkage must be understood by the foundry in order that correct gating and feeding methods will be employed. The melt shop must understand the affinity that the various alloys, in the molten state, have for gas. Hydrogen is especially difficult to control, since there are several sources from which this gas can enter the melt. That careful attention is given to every level in the process is evidenced by the fact that satisfactory copper-base alloy castings in a wide range, from those weighing but a few ounces to large ships' propellers weighing as much as 25 tons, are in regular production.

Copper-base casting alloys are classified primarily as bronze and brass. In very general terms, bronze is an alloy of copper and tin and brass is an alloy of copper and zinc. The properties of both bronze and brass are modified by changing the ratio of the basic constituents and also by the addition of other metals such as lead. Consequently, there is an impressive number of bronze and brass compositions available. In order to standardize such a range, it is recommended that one of the several standard casting specifications available be used as reference. The leading specifications include ASTM, SAE, Federal Standard, and U.S. Navy Department.

The foundry shop, producing castings to specifications, can proceed in one of two ways: either it can make its own alloys by melting the constituents of the composition, or it can purchase specification metal in ingot form. Both of these methods are used; however, less alloy loss is experienced when prepared ingot is melted. This procedure is especially recommended for the smaller shops, since accurate alloying in a crucible requires extreme care both as to weights and in the technique of making the additions.

The designer should consistently use standard specifications as a guide rather than follow the loose practice of merely calling for brass or bronze for a given application; a better end product will result, and the manufacturing costs will be held to a minimum. A typical alloy is found in ASTM specification B145-49T, no. 4A, which is referred to as "85—three 5's." This alloy has high mechanical properties coupled with desirable characteristics for both the foundry and the machine shop.

ALUMINUM ALLOYS

Metallurgical language has no counterpart to the terms steel, bronze, and brass that can be applied to aluminum alloys. There is some com-

Fig. 2-6. Final rolling operation on cold mill for aluminum-alloy sheet coils. (*Courtesy of Kaiser Aluminum & Chemical Co., Spokane, Wash.*)

mercially pure aluminum used in the manufacturing industries, but by far the greatest field of application is for the aluminum alloys, which are available in both wrought (Fig. 2-6) and cast forms. Since that expression is cumbersome, it is becoming common practice to refer to *aluminum alloys* as "aluminum." There is so much interest in this branch of the light-metals field that too many applications are being made without the careful analysis that the introduction of any new material deserves.

Aluminum-alloy Properties. The development of aluminum and its alloys, and its increasing importance as an engineering material, is most impressive when it is realized that the first commercial metal was produced only sixty years ago. A major contributing factor was the invention of Duralumin by Dr. Wilm in Germany in 1909. This alloy is more familiarly known in America as 17S; it was the first of the heat-treatable aluminum alloys and also the first one to exhibit the property of natural age hardening.

The position of aluminum has been won through a combination of physical properties that is peculiar to this metal. An important one is that of low specific gravity, the range of the established alloys lying between 2.52 and 2.87. This property is important when the combination of weight and mechanical properties is considered in the light of strength/weight ratio.

Another physical property of aluminum and its alloys is their high electrical conductivity; EC-O shows a value of 62 per cent of the International annealed copper standard. When, however, this comparison is made with specific gravities considered, the EC-O alloy shows a mass conductivity of 201 per cent compared with copper. Thermal conductivity is high for the entire range of aluminum alloys; this fact is reflected in the use of these materials for food-processing equipment and for such parts as pistons and cylinder heads for internal-combustion engines.

The corrosion resistance of the aluminum alloys varies somewhat with their composition. Commercially pure aluminum 2S has a high resistance to corrosion. Those alloys containing copper in substantial amounts are more susceptible to corrosive action and this susceptibility is influenced by the heat treatment given them. The development of the clad sheet materials, which are, in effect, 3-ply composites wherein the two outer layers are usually commercially pure aluminum encasing an inner core of high-strength alloys, has proven to be an eminently satisfactory method of protecting the latter from corrosion. Other clad material is available wherein an aluminum alloy of a composition that is anodic to the core is used for the cladding or encasing material; alloys R301 and Alclad 75S are leading examples in this category.

It seems desirable before closing this discussion of the properties of aluminum alloys to call attention to the fact that as a class they actually show higher mechanical properties at subnormal than at normal temperatures. As more information is developed on this aspect of their properties, it seems reasonable to predict that these alloys will replace currently used materials which are susceptible to low-temperature embrittlement in certain applications. Such a possibility indicates a profound change in certain design categories.

Aluminum-alloy Designations. The designation of aluminum alloys is somewhat complex. The best-known system of designation is the one developed by the Aluminum Company of America. It is widely used in the shop and the designing room alike. The advent of other producers in the field has introduced further designations as exemplified by the "R" series of the Reynolds Metals Company. Kaiser Aluminum & Chemical Company has not, as yet, offered individual designations.

In the system developed by Alcoa, the wrought alloys are designated with a number followed by the letter S, for example, 17S. A modification of the base composition of an alloy is shown by the addition of a prefixing letter such as A. Thus A17S, the material widely used for aircraft rivets, is a modification of 17S. Casting alloys, on the other hand, are designated by a number only, for example, 108. Here, as with the wrought alloys, a prefixing letter denotes a modification of the base alloy; thus A108, a permanent mold-casting alloy, has been modified from the sand-casting alloy 108.

Wrought Aluminum Alloys. The wrought aluminum alloys are divided into two categories, the strain-hardening and the heat-treatable. In the former type, increased strengths accompanied by decreased ductility can only be obtained by cold-working. Heat treatment is of no avail for improving strength; however, strain-hardened alloys can be annealed. The strain-hardening alloys and their temper designations are shown in Table 2-2.

TABLE 2-2. STRAIN-HARDENING WROUGHT ALUMINUM ALLOYS

Alloy no.	Temper	Condition
2S, 3S	H12, H14, H16, H18	Strain hardened only ranging from $\frac{1}{4}$ hard to full hard
4S, 52S	H32, H34, H36, H38	Strain hardened and then stabilized
56S	H18	Full strain hardened
All of	"O"	Fully annealed

The heat-treatable alloys can be classified as those that age-harden naturally and the ones that require artificial aging. A further improvement in mechanical properties is possible through cold-working alloys that have previously been fully heat-treated; such processing is shown by a specific temper designation, viz., 24S-T36 as indicated in Table 2-3, an abbreviated listing of some of the more widely used wrought aluminum alloys.

Aluminum Casting Alloys.   Castings are made exclusively from aluminum alloys, since commercially pure aluminum is not specified in cast form.   The casting alloys are divided into two classifications, depending on the post-casting treatment.   One type, which includes those that are sometimes referred to as the common casting alloys, does not require any

TABLE 2-3.   TYPICAL TEMPER DESIGNATIONS FOR SOME WROUGHT ALUMINUM ALLOYS

Alloy no.	Temper	Condition
11S	T3 T8	Solution heat-treated Solution plus precipitation H.T. (full H.T.)
14S	T4 T6	Solution H.T. Solution plus precipitation H.T.
17S	T4	Solution H.T. and natural aging
18S	T61	Solution plus precipitation
24S	T4 T36	Solution plus natural aging T4 plus cold-working
25S	T6	Solution plus precipitation
32S	T6	Solution fully heat-treated
A51S	T6	Solution fully heat-treated
53S	T4 T6	Solution heat-treated Fully heat-treated
61S	T4 T6	Solution heat-treated Fully heat-treated
63S	F T6	As extruded Fully heat-treated
75S	T6	Fully heat-treated

heat treatment; rather, these are used in the as-cast condition.   The other classification refers to those alloys that are given some type of heat treatment prior to end-use application.   It should be strongly emphasized that a heat-treatable casting alloy should not be used unless a heat treatment is specified in conjunction with it.

Aluminum alloy castings are made by every casting process common to the foundry.   Sand castings, both green and dry, account for the bulk of casting production.   Sound castings demand foundry knowledge peculiar to these alloys. Correct gating, along with proper melting and pouring temperatures, requires most careful attention. Such fundamentals as directional solidification, exclusion of oxides, and proper feeding must be included in the foundry control program.

MAGNESIUM

There was little interest displayed in magnesium in the United States prior to World War I; the industry had its beginning here in 1915. The three distinguishing properties that are combined in magnesium are low specific gravity, a hexagonal lattice, and the fact that it is anodic to all the other common metals. This combination makes magnesium a unique metal and governs its processing and applications alike. There is scant use for pure magnesium in engineering industry; its commercial alloys are the metals of importance to engineering manufacture. Aluminum is the chief alloying element, followed by zinc and manganese.

Designation of the commercial magnesium alloys is not quite as involved as in the case of aluminum. The ASTM specifications cover these alloys, as do others, such as Federal and SAE. The trade name Dowmetal, established by the Dow Chemical Company, the first commercial producer, continues to be the most popular designation. They use a system of letters, or letters followed by hyphenated numbers, for identification. On the other hand, the American Magnesium Company uses a designation system in which the suffixed letter S indicates a wrought alloy. In addition this company uses the trade name Mazlo and prefixes all their designations with the letters AM. A study of Table 2-4 will show identifications and specifications of the most generally used commercial magnesium alloys.

Properties of Magnesium Alloys. The specific gravities of the magnesium alloys range from 1.76 to 1.87, which makes them the lightest engineering materials. The chief interest in applying magnesium alloys is in the direction of weight saving. Consequently, as was to be expected, the aircraft and transportation industries have been pioneering with these alloys to the greatest extent. Processing and production machinery possessing rapidly reciprocating or rotating members, for example, certain textile machines, have utilized magnesium alloys to good advantage. Hand tools and portable power tools like electric drills also feature them. The most recent applications of magnesium alloys—such innovations as the castings on portable chain saws, foundry flasks, and bottom boards and even falling and bucking wedges used in logging—are directed toward the elimination of human fatigue in handling and lifting.

Physical Forms of Magnesium Alloys. Magnesium alloys are available in all of the physical forms common to the nonferrous field, impact extrusions being the exception. The classification of wrought and cast alloy forms is shown in Table 2-4. One important point to note about magnesium alloys is that they cannot as yet be rolled into sheets in as wide a range of sizes as can the aluminum alloys.

Wrought Magnesium Alloys. The use of magnesium alloy sheet must contend with the fact that drawing operations have to be done at elevated temperatures. Generally both the blank and the dies are heated; the latter are rigged with either gas or electric heating devices so arranged as

TABLE 2-4. MAGNESIUM ALLOYS: SPECIFICATIONS, FORMS, AND APPLICATIONS

ASTM specification	Alloy	Federal	Dow	American Magnesium	Product form	Application
B90-49T	A231A	AN-M-29	FS-1	AM-C52S	Sheet and strip	Cold forming
	MIA	AN-M-30	M	AM-3S		Deep drawing, low cost, weldable
B107-49T	A261A	AN-M-24	J-1	AM-C57S	Extruded bar rod and shapes	General purpose
	A280A	AN-M-25	O-1	AM-C58S		Highest strength
	MIA	AN-M-26	M	AM-3S		Light stresses, weldable
	A231B	AN-M-27	FS-1	AM-C52S		Cold forming
B91-49T	A261A	AN-M-20	J-1	AM-C57S		Press forgings
	A280A	AN-M-21	O-1	AM-C58S	Forgings	High strength, difficult to forge
	A231B		FS-1	AM-C52S		Forges readily
B80-49T	A263A	A	H	AM-265		General purpose
	MIB	AN-QQ-M-B	M	AM-403	Sand castings	Weldable
	A292A	C	C	AM-260		Pressure-tight
B199-49T	A292A		C	AM-260	Permanent mold castings	Strong, corrosion resistant
	AM100A		G	AM-240		Casts readily, poor corrosion resistance
B94-49T	A291A	AN-M-16	R	AM-263	Die castings	Small castings

to maintain the required temperature. The depth of the draw as well as the alloy used determines the requisite temperature, which ranges from 100°F to as high as 600°F. However when proper temperatures and drawing speeds have been established, magnesium alloys are capable of very deep draws.

Magnesium Alloy Castings. Magnesium alloy castings offer the widest field of application for this structural material, since green sand, permanent mold, and die-casting processes are all practical. Castings of a wide range of sizes and of intricate shapes are in production. Gating and risering as well as the placement of chills demand careful attention. The low specific gravity of these alloys must be considered when gating and risering, since the head pressures of ferrous castings are not obtainable.   Risers must be larger and more numerous if sound castings are to be produced (Fig. 2-7).

Magnesium alloys can be melted in steel pots that have been given an aluminum coating.   The use of flux to protect the molten metal is a requirement of profound importance.   The molten metal should be stirred with a steel rod to free impurities, which unite with the flux thereby cleansing the metal.   Following the melting operation, the metal is transferred to a superheating furnace where temperatures of 1650°F to

Fig. 2-7.   Pouring magnesium-alloy castings.   Note gating on castings in foreground.   (*Courtesy of Major Magnesium Products, Ltd., Vancouver, B.C.*)

1700°F are used for about 10 min in order to promote a fine grain size in the metal casting, which, in turn, improves the mechanical properties of the casting.

The flux is skimmed from the molten metal and the latter is then dusted with a protecting agent prior to pouring.   The mold should always be made with a pouring basin wherein the metal and oxides can separate. This is necessary because the specific gravity of the oxide and of the metal are so close together that the mechanical separation afforded by a properly designed pouring basin is the only solution for obtaining clean metal.   Pouring temperatures average around 1500°F depending on the type of alloy as well as the casting section.   Freshly poured castings should remain undisturbed for an appreciable period because of the hot-short character of the magnesium alloys.

Magnesium Alloy Casting Heat Treatment.   Depending on the choice of the alloy, magnesium castings produced from either sand or permanent molds are generally given a heat treatment.   Solution heat-treatment is used for the purpose of increasing tensile strength, ductility, and toughness but it does not change the yield strength.   For the highest values of tensile and yield strength, a solution heat-treatment followed by aging is recommended, although this treatment causes some deterioration in ductility.   It is common practice to heat-treat castings prior to machining because of the fact that they are not subject to dimensional change following the heat-treat operation.

Machining Magnesium Alloys.   The machinability of magnesium alloys is outstanding among the engineering metals.   Actual operations using carbide-tipped tools have been performed at cutting speeds in excess of 2,000 fpm.   Milling operations have been reported in which as much as 340 cu in./min have been removed.

In machining magnesium alloys, several precautions are necessary. Accurate clamping and chucking must be used in order to prevent distortion due to their lower modulus of elasticity.   Further, because of that characteristic, the alloys cut closer to size, indicating that slightly oversize drills, taps, and reamers should be used.   Most important in machining these alloys is the necessity for sharp, polished tools.

Corrosion Prevention.   It is a fact that these alloys have not been readily accepted because when they were introduced their resistance to corrosion was considered low; however, development work in purification and alloying has made possible alloys of good resistance to corrosion.

Along with improved composition, surface treatments have also undergone development.   Magnesium alloy products are distinctive in appearance because of surface treatment.   The resulting colors broadly range from yellow, brown, black, gray to iridescent blends of red to yellow. These surface treatments include chromate pickle and dichromate dip among others.   There are, in fact, specifications governing the different surface treatments, and the purpose of each is to prevent tarnishing and to form a base for paint or for decoration, as through dyeing.

ZINC

Zinc and its alloys are important to engineering manufacture in varied applications.   Zinc coatings are a well-known means of protecting ferrous metals from corrosion.   Galvanizing is the best-known coating method.   It is processed either as a hot dip or electrolytically, depending on the nature and the volume of the work.   Modifications such as adding small amounts of tin to control spangle are commonly practiced, as is the addition of aluminum for brightness of finish.

Zinc impregnation, or sherardizing, is a further method of applying coatings for corrosion resistance. Powdered zinc is used in this process, which is accomplished in heated drums, where the powder and the work-piece come in contact in the course of the rotation of the equipment.

Zinc anodes are used for cathodic protection where applications are practical; a typical example is their use in steel pipelines placed underground. Components such as boiler and hull plates have also been successfully given cathodic protection.

Zinc Alloy Castings. Zinc-base die castings are applied in many industries. In the automotive industry, a leading example, they are used for radiator grills, hub caps, body trim, door hardware, instrument panel trim, as well as motor parts such as carburetors, gas pumps, and others. Other industrial applications are tool parts, building hardware, outboard motors, electric and gas motor components, household appliances, to make a partial listing.

The popularity of zinc alloys for die casting is due to the fact that they take an excellent finish and are simple to make, since submerged-plunger die-casting machines are applicable (Chap. 7). The die castings have close dimensional limits. They can be chromium plated for pleasing appearance and lasting beauty. Other finishes such as electroplating with most metals, organic finishes, plastic and chemical treatment are also used. Zinc alloy castings tarnish unless they are given some surface treatment.

Sand casting is largely restricted to drop-hammer dies for fabricating aluminum, magnesium, stainless steel, and other sheet metal types. Detailed information on drop-hammer operation is given in Chap. 10. Dies of this type are readily machined and are economical especially where limited production runs obtain. Permanent mold castings and slush castings are also produced from zinc alloys.

Zinc-base casting alloys contain aluminum as the major alloying element. Copper and magnesium are present in some alloys, in considerably lesser amounts than aluminum. There are relatively few zinc-base casting alloys in comparison with those of such other nonferrous metals as copper and aluminum.

TITANIUM

In the continuing program of the development of new engineering materials, titanium and its alloys are now receiving attention. The work that has so far been done is not sufficient to form the basis of a definite evaluation of the potentialities of titanium alloys. Some of the properties of these alloys are known. They lie about midway between aluminum alloys and steel so far as specific gravity is concerned. They offer unusual ductility and excellent corrosion resistance, especially in marine atmospheres, as well as good fatigue resistance.   A high degree of surface hardness can be obtained.

Some of the titanium alloys are heat-treatable; all can be advantageously cold-worked.   There have been a host of alloys developed experimentally, and several producers are in the field.   What can be expected in the way of mechanical properties is impossible to estimate accurately, but it can be said that these alloys will compare very favorably with and exceed most engineering metals on the basis of weight/strength ratio.

At the present stage of development, their cost is so great as to preclude their general use.   New methods of winning titanium from its ores must be found if costs are to be substantially reduced.   There is no question about availability, since titanium is one of the most abundant elements. In its favor, too, is the fact that titanium alloys can be shaped by most methods common to other engineering metals.   They are now offered as sheet, strip, plate, bars, rods, wire, forgings, and tubing.   From present indications, it would appear as though titanium alloys will find their broadest applications in aircraft and similar directions where favorable weight/strength ratios are critical.

Plastics

ASTM designation D883-49T[1] carries the following definition: "A plastic is a material which contains as an essential ingredient an organic substance of large molecular weight, is solid in its finished state, and at some stage in its manufacture or in its processing into finished articles can be shaped by flow."   In general it can be stated that plastics are synthetic organic materials in which the binders are synthetic or natural resins, protein substances, or cellulose derivatives.   Plastics can be formed by molding, casting, and extruding; another application for these materials is their use as coatings.   They are also used as bonding agents in a variety of processes and products.   The importance of plastics is evident from the ASTM Standards, 1949, which carry a total of 109 specifications, recommended practices, methods of tests, and other related information.

The most generally used classification for plastics is the one based on their thermal setting properties.   Plastics which can be repeatedly softened by heating and hardened by cooling are known as *thermoplastics*, or cold-set plastics.   Since there is no chemical change involved in heating, it would be expected that this process could be repeated without limit; however, the heating temperatures must remain low, and for this reason thermoplastic materials are restricted in their applications.   This group of plastic materials includes:

[1] "ASTM Standards," American Society of Testing Materials, Philadelphia, 1949.

Cellulose acetate   Polystyrene
Cellulose nitrate   Polyamide
Ethyl cellulose   Vinylidene chloride
Methyl methacrylate   Vinyl copolymers

Thermosetting plastics, on the other hand, undergo a chemical change during heating and assume a final shape that is retained on cooling. They are therefore designated as the hot-set plastics. They will not soften, by reheating, once they have been processed; when subjected to temperatures of 400°F they will char or burn. Representative materials in this classification include:

Allyl alcohols   Phenol formaldehyde
Furfural formaldehyde   Polyesters
Melamine formaldehyde   Urea formaldehyde

Plastic Molding Compounds. The powders used for plastic molding are composed of a number of ingredients; of these, the binders exert the greatest influence on the end product. Next to the binders, filling materials are given the most attention. As in other products, fillers are used as a replacement for more costly materials. The choice of filler is also governed by the modification that it will exert on the final properties of the plastic compound. Wood flour, made from soft wood, is a commonly used filler of considerable strength. Fillers also aid in promoting machinability. Other filler materials are fabrics, Fiberglas, wood pulp, mica, and asbestos; the last two impart heat resistance to the plastic. Where hardness is more desirable than strength, inorganic binders such as China clay, infusorial earths, and gypsum are used.

To control the plastic mixture during and after processing, several other ingredients are added. These include such items as plasticizers, lubricants, catalysts, hardeners, solvents, and coloring materials; in each case the ones used are, necessarily, those most compatible with the basic mixture and best calculated to develop the desired properties in the end product.

The function of the plasticizers is to increase the plasticity of the batch so that it will flow properly during processing.

In some cases lubricants are ingredients of the plastic formula, while in others they are applied directly to the mold surfaces by spraying or brushing. In either case the lubricants are present in order to prevent the plastic pieces from sticking in the molds. Experience with lubricants indicates that the choice is highly important; a given lubricant will prove successful with a given plastic when used in one mold but will prove unsuccessful in a different mold. Recognized lubricants are such materials as grease, fats, wax, oils, and various soaps.

The use of catalysts has the same function in connection with plastics as in other chemical processes. A catalyst is used to initiate or to alter the rate of a chemical reaction without becoming a part thereof. Under certain conditions, where the formulation products are complex, the catalytic agents do exert profound influence on the nature of the final product. Catalysts are also referred to as accelerators and, under some circumstances, as hardeners.

The fact that plastic products can be produced in pleasing and even brilliant colors, or color combinations, is one of the chief reasons for their

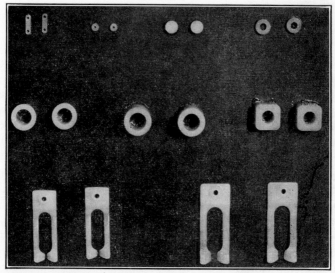

Fig. 2-8. Components molded from nylon. Those in center row are bearings; lower row shows textile machinery parts.

increasing popularity in manufactured items. Coloring of plastic end products is accomplished either by dissolving coloring matter in the plastic mixture at some stage of the processing or by applying dyestuffs to the finished product. Successful coloring requires the same careful attention to detail that characterizes the other features of the plastic-making process.

The majority of plastic parts are formed by molding (Fig. 2-8). The selection of the molding method is governed primarily by the basic type of plastic to be processed. The term molding as applied to plastics manufacture refers to the use of dies, heat, and pressure in combination.

FABRICATION METHODS FOR PLASTICS

Hot Compression Molding. In hot compression molding the material is loaded directly into the mold cavity either as powder or as a pre-form pellet; heat and pressure are then applied to complete the molding cycle. This method is used mainly for forming the hot-set materials. Mold design is important because time saved in loading the mold results in lowered production cost. Care must be exercised to prevent contamination of the powder. Heat is applied to the mold as well as the material. Actually the heat in the material is the key to success. Too frequently, mold or platen temperatures are carefully maintained while no attention is given to the temperature within the mixture being processed. Emphasis on temperature control is necessary because in the molding of the hot-set materials heat performs the dual function of providing for plasticization and for setting or polymerization of the material. A molding compound containing controlled amounts of accelerator can be molded without heat application.

Cold-set Molding. Molding thermoplastic, or cold-set, material requires a different technique because of the inherent nature of the molding materials. Compression molding, when used for the cold-set materials, is usually confined to large parts. For regular production, compression molding requires a long cycle, since the mold must first be heated to give plasticity to the material and then a subsequent cooling period is needed to harden the molded part. This alternate heating and cooling is a time-consuming and therefore a costly method of molding.

Pressure is used in compression molding to compact the material in the die. In the case of large surfaces such as radio cabinets, pressure causes the material to flow within the die. Obviously pressures vary in intensity with different die designs and different molding materials.

Transfer Molding. A modification of the compression method known as transfer molding is used chiefly for hot-set materials. In effect, transfer molding breaks down compression molding into two operations. The molding material is heated to plasticity in an external chamber from which it is forced through an orifice into the heated molding die proper, where it undergoes polymerization. The advantage of transfer molding lies in the fact that flow within the die is accomplished more easily; this allows greater latitude in product design. There is no pressure exerted until the die is filled, which means that more intricate or fragile die parts are not subjected to pressure variations that could cause damage; rather, fluid pressure applies equally throughout all parts of the die.

Injection Molding. The standard method for forming the thermoplastic materials is termed injection molding (Fig. 2-9). This method can be compared to die casting of nonferrous metals in its operating cycle. The material to be molded is heated to plasticity in an external chamber; when in this state, it is forced through a sprue into a cold die for the cooling necessary to its hardening, or setting. This operation cycle has been built into automatic presses whose mechanical details vary

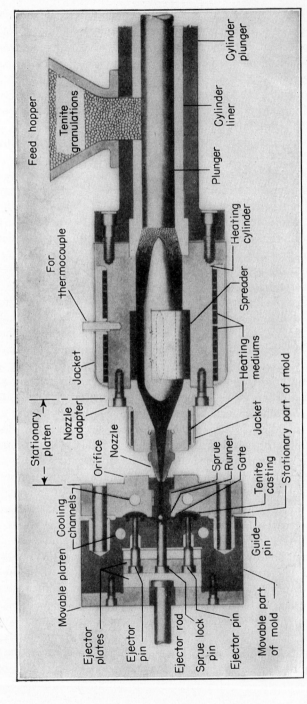

Fig. 2-9. Sectional view illustrating general method of injection molding. (Courtesy of Tennessee Eastman Corp., Kingsport, Tenn.)

somewhat; in general their operation follows the principle of a single piston forcing the cold material into the heating chamber and, by further movement, into the cold mold. Molding cycles as short as 20 sec. are achieved by injection molding.

Extrusion. When plastic parts of a constant cross section and of any length are required the cold-set materials can be processed by extrusion. The mechanical details of this process are quite simple. The plastic powder is fed from a hopper through a plasticizing chamber by means of an enclosed conveyor screw. The material, having been heated to flowability on its forward movement, is forced through a die the cross section of whose aperture is of the contour desired in the molding. Upon passing through the die, the molded extrusion is picked up on an endless belt conveyor which carries it under air cooling jets. The latter are adjusted as to temperature, air velocity, and volume in order to solidify the molding to the desired shape, it being possible to modify the cross section of the molding from a given extrusion die by stretching the molding on the conveyor as it is hardening. Production speeds are subject to variation, yet a molding 1 by $\frac{1}{8}$ in. in cross section can be extruded at a speed of approximately 750 ft/hr. Tubing made by the extrusion process is becoming more and more widely used in industry.

Dies for Plastics. Dies used for the various methods of molding plastics are made from steel almost exclusively. The choice of die steels lies between the carburizing grades and the direct hardening types. Venting of the die must be provided in both transfer and injection molding. The shrinkage potential of the plastic material being molded must be considered in establishing correct die dimensions. This shrinkage allowance is not a fixed value; it varies with the temperature as well as the pressure used in a given mold. As an example, a general-purpose phenolic with organic filler will show a shrinkage in the range of 0.007 to 0.009 in./in.

Casting Plastics. All the methods for molding plastics mentioned above employ a combination of heat and pressure. There is another important production method known as casting that does not require the use of applied pressure; it is used with liquid casting resins of the phenolic, methacrylate, and styrene types. The method consists of pouring the liquid plastic into lead molds and then placing the poured mold into an oven for final hardening. The resulting castings do not possess the high finish obtained in die molding, but because of the facility with which castings can be made this is an important method of plastic fabrication. Castings are produced as nearly as possible to size in the case of such objects as pipe stems, brush backs and knife handles. Sheet and large panels and rather complicated shapes are likewise produced as castings. In such items as radio housings, the tooling for mold production grows complex. Simple cylinders are cast in lead molds produced by dipping a steel arbor into a lead bath. The adhering lead solidifies into a tube that can readily be stripped from the slightly tapered arbor. After the casting has been cured in the oven, the mold is removed by mechanical means without difficulty.

Laminated Products. Laminated products are classified as plastics, since their composition and processing follow, in modified form, those familiar to molded plastics. They are of interest to engineering manufacture because they offer a combination of mechanical properties of a higher order than the general run of molded plastics. The laminates are used in such mechanical components as gears, cams, bushings, housings, and washers. Laminated plastics are made from liquid binders and a filler in sheet form. The grading of the end product is based on the type of filler rather than on the resin binder used. The fillers are paper base of various types, fabric base, asbestos-paper base, asbestos-fabric base and glass-fabric base; each of these bases modifies the finished product.

The processing of the laminates is relatively simple. The filler sheet is dipped into a plastic solution whose viscosity has been regulated by a previously added solvent. The sheet is then fed through squeeze rolls, much in the manner of hot-dipped tin-plate manufacture, and from the rolls through a drying oven for the purpose of curing. Following this operation, the sheet is rolled into coils or bolts for further processing. When laminated sheet is to be made, the previously processed material is cut into desired lengths of sheet and stacked between plates on the platens of a press. The surface of the plates is treated to the finish desired on the completed laminated sheet. The pressing operation combines a temperature of approximately 300°F with an operating pressure around 1,500 psi, which results in uniting the individual sheets and effecting the final set in the resin.

The single impregnated sheet is also used for producing laminated tubes and rods. In the former, the sheet is wound on a mandrel whose diameter corresponds to the internal diameter of the tube. After the tube wall has been built up to the requisite thickness, the tube can either be placed in an oven for setting or, for a stronger product, placed between split, heated dies for compacting and setting. The manufacture of rod stock of laminated material follows the same general scheme excepting for the fact that a small-diameter mandrel is used and is withdrawn prior to the final pressing operation. Laminated plastics are the basis of a limited number of molded parts—ignition distributor housings and shop safety helmets, among others.

Resin-bonded Plywood. The manufacture of resin-bonded plywood is a major industry. Wood sheets are used in place of the previously mentioned paper and fabric sheets in this product. An interesting development has been the use of high-frequency induction heating for curing plywood. There has also been a considerable amount of work done on molding plywood to specific shapes. The most noteworthy results have been achieved in connection with airplane fuselages and small boat hulls. Plywood is not usually classified under the heading of plastics; however, its properties offer alluring possibilities to engineering designers.

Machining Plastics. Plastics in the form of rod, sheet, extrusions, and molded and cast parts are not strangers to the production or machine shops. These products machine fairly well, although fillers of the abrasive type cause cutting tools to dull readily or even burn when improper feeds and speeds are used. Carbide-tipped tools are recommended because their operating characteristics are in line with the demands peculiar to machining plastics. Tool angles should be modified from those used in machining metals. An important consideration is that plastics are poor heat conductors. This property must be closely watched when machining the cold-set plastic materials to avoid difficulties resulting from softening. Most machining is done dry, although air and coolants may be necessary for certain jobs. Machining speeds are generally high; it is impossible to give exact values because of the wide variety of plastic materials. Tools must be kept very sharp in every phase of machining plastics. Milling operations are performed best with large-diameter cutters of many teeth and running at high speeds with small feed and depth of cut.

Fastening and Joining. Since the mechanical properties of the general run of plastics are too low to justify their use in structural members of an engineering design, the problem of joining them resolves itself primarily into a matter of fastening. The accepted types of fasteners such as rivets, bolts, and screws are used. The use of washers is strongly recommended under heads and nuts in order to distribute the compression load over a wider area and to prevent pulling through that may tend to occur under certain conditions of loading.

The problem of joining is frequently solved by using cements; they are especially effective when used with the thermosetting materials. There are several types of cements available, the choice being dependent upon the basic plastic material. Solvents are successfully used without any additive material; however, the parts to be joined should be shielded with a heavy masking tape in order to prevent diffusion beyond the desired joint area.

Plastics in Industry. The widest application of plastics in industry is found in nonstructural parts. One development for the machine shop is that of the resin-bonded grinding wheel. These abrasive wheels have extended the scope of grinding because they possess mechanical strength superior to the better-known vitrified types. However, plastic products in themselves have received the best reception from the automotive and aircraft industries in the mechanical field. Plastic products are standard for many applications in electrical machines and equipment. In fact many major developments have come in the plastics as an answer to the demands of the electrical industry.

Products made from plastics are generally of small dimensions. A noteworthy departure from this concept is the making of all-plastic boat hulls. Hulls currently in production are for small boats, although no maximum size limitations are apparent. Undoubtedly this hull development will result in additional large products being made from plastics.

Survey Questions

2-1. In what manner is the selection of engineering materials correlated with manufacturing methods?

2-2. List the important ferrous metals that are widely used in engineering manufacture.

2-3. Is foundry iron produced to more than one specification?

2-4. Explain the meaning of "gray cast iron class 30."

2-5. What is the method used for chilling cast iron?

2-6. Give some applications of chilled iron castings.

2-7. How does the silicon content influence the machinability of gray cast iron?

2-8. Nodular cast iron is also termed "ductile cast iron." Explain this terminology.

2-9. Where should malleable cast iron be specified to best advantage?

2-10. By what methods is wrought iron shaped to end-product usage?

2-11. Does the crucible process produce constructional steels?

2-12. Which one of the steel-making processes accounts for the greatest production tonnage?

2-13. Wherein do AISI and SAE steel specifications differ?

2-14. Suggest at least three applications for the low-alloy, high-strength constructional steels.

2-15. List the prominent alloying elements incorporated in alloy steels.

2-16. Are all types of stainless steels nonmagnetic?

2-17. Can any of the stainless steels be heat-treated?

2-18. Do cemented carbides belong to the ferrous or the nonferrous metal classification?

2-19. Where are heat-resistant alloys employed in jet engines?

2-20. Of what widely used alloys does copper form the base?

2-21. By what methods are copper base alloys processed?

2-22. Is brass a metal or an alloy?

2-23. What is Duralumin?

2-24. Is there any variation in the corrosion resistance of the different aluminum alloys?

2-25. How are wrought aluminum alloys designated?

2-26. Explain the designation "H16." Where is it applied?

2-27. Are aluminum casting alloys heat-treatable?

2-28. Give an application for an aluminum common casting alloy.

2-29. Give the leading trade names for magnesium alloys.

2-30. Describe melting equipment used in magnesium foundries?

2-31. Considering the metallic alloys generally used in manufacturing, which group has the highest machinability?

2-32. Explain the term "galvanizing."

2-33. What metal is the basis of most automobile-body hardware?

2-34. Why is titanium of interest as an engineering material?

2-35. Define the term "plastic."

2-36. List the usual methods for shaping plastics.

2-37. Give another designation for cold-setting plastics.

2-38. When can the extrusion method of shaping plastics be used?

2-39. Explain the difference between thermosetting plastics and thermoplastics. Give a specific application for each type.

2-40. How is the final color of a plastic obtained?

2-41. Is resin-bonded plywood regarded as a laminated plastic product?

REFERENCES

"Alcoa Aluminum and Its Alloys," Aluminum Company of America, Pittsburgh, 1950.

"Alloy Cast Iron," American Foundrymen's Association, Chicago, 1939.

"Aluminum Alloys and Mill Products," Reynolds Metals Co., Inc., Louisville, 1949.

"American Malleable Iron: A Handbook," Malleable Founders' Society, Cleveland, 1944.

"ASTM Standards," American Society of Testing Materials, Philadelphia, 1949.

Aston, James, and E. B. Story: "Wrought Iron," 2d ed., A. M. Byers Co., Pittsburgh, 1941.

"The Cast Metals Handbook," 3d ed., American Foundrymen's Association, Chicago, 1944.

Francis, C. B.: "The Making, Shaping, and Treating of Steel," 5th ed., Carnegie-Illinois Steel Co., Pittsburgh, 1941.

Hughes, Thomas P.: "Metals and Plastics," Irwin-Farnham Publishing Co., Chicago, 1947.

"Metals Handbook," American Society for Metals, Cleveland, 1948.

Samans, Carl H.: "Engineering Metals and Their Alloys," The Macmillan Company, New York, 1949.

Sasso, John: "Plastics Handbook for Product Engineers," McGraw-Hill Book Company, Inc., New York, 1946.

Simonds, H. R., and Carleton Ellis: "Handbook of Plastics," D. Van Nostrand Company, Inc., 1943.

von Zeerleder, Alfred: "The Technology of Aluminum and Its Light Alloys," Nordemann Publishing Co., Amsterdam, 1936.

Young, James F.: "Materials and Processes," John Wiley & Sons, Inc., New York, 1944.

CHAPTER 3

PATTERNS FOR METAL CASTINGS

Engineering metals are, for the most part, readily formed by casting, a manufacturing method of great antiquity. Foundry patterns are designed to produce satisfactory castings when a sand mold is to be used. Yet, since castings generally require some machining, such matters as machinability must also be kept in mind. The patternmaker is given a drawing of the finished part, in more or less detail; from this he is expected to make a pattern that will prove satisfactory in all subsequent processing and in the finished product. The responsibility that is thus placed upon the patternmaker is out of line with his subordinate position in the manufacturing organization. He is called upon to make decisions that more properly belong to the designer. The problem can be solved if designer and patternmaker combine their knowledge and efforts. This chapter is not intended to cover machine design. It is intended, however, to develop certain facts and practices of design that are fundamental to the patternmaker and the foundry alike.

Pattern Details

Importance of Pattern Ribs. When a drawing reaches the pattern shop it is analyzed there with a view to the problems which will arise in the foundry when the part is cast. If the designer has failed to provide supplemental information such as the direction of stress application, the patternmaker will be in ignorance on this important matter and it will not be given consideration in the making of the pattern. An example of this is the location of ribs on a pattern. The direction of load application will develop a major fiber stress normal to that direction. In consequence the pattern should be made with the major metal volume in such a position as to resist the force of load application; this will result in the lowest possible unit stress. Such a solution for lowered unit stress is found, for example, in rolled steel and extruded aluminum-alloy sections of bulb design. Bulbed sections of aluminum alloys are prominent in aircraft construction; similarly, steel bulbed sections are used for certain critically stressed members in shipbuilding. Examples of such sections are shown in Fig. 3-1.

In the matter of rib location in the construction of a pattern, where circumstances permit, the practice should be followed of placing the ribs in such a position that they will be in compression and the flat surface in tension, rather than the reverse. Ribs placed in tension will be more susceptible to cracking owing to the condition of loading. It can readily be seen in design B, Fig. 3-2, that the stress is distributed over a large area. This construction is referred to in the shop as "ribs in compression

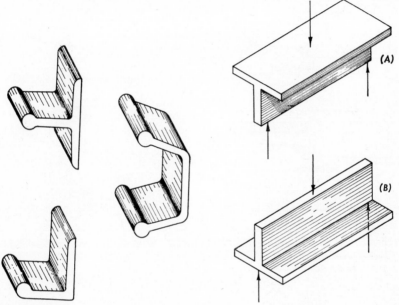

Fig. 3-1. Sketches of rolled and extruded bulbed sections.

Fig. 3-2. A, rib in tension. B, rib in compression, flat surface in tension—preferred design.

and flat surfaces in tension." Obviously the rib strength can be further improved by bulbing or beading (Fig. 3-1). However the use of a bead, whether on a rib or as a reinforcement on a thin section, should be held within the limits of practicality from the molding standpoint. A bead split along the parting line presents no molding difficulty, nor does one placed on a horizontal surface of a pattern made with vertical draft. When, however, beads are placed on vertical surfaces of patterns where they project in a way that will interfere with drawing the pattern from the mold, a complicated core job results.

Locating Machined Surfaces. It is axiomatic that a pattern should be made in such a way as to place the major machined surfaces on the bottom, or drag, side of the casting as it is molded. This practice is followed wherever possible in order to take advantage of the fact that the metal at the bottom of the casting is sound, since slag and loose sand tend to float and will come to rest against the upper, or cope, side of the casting, so that any unsound metal will be in that area.

Filleting.   A very common error made by the draftsman in the designing department is neglecting the proper use of fillets on a pattern.   This drafting room error is frequently corrected by the patternmaker; he is, however, limited in his choice, since placing an inside fillet and disregarding the outside corner may result in a mass concentration making the

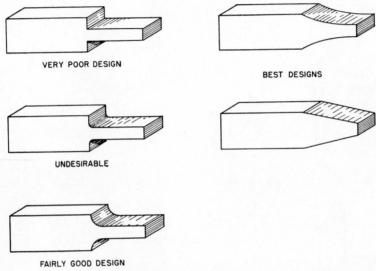

VERY POOR DESIGN

BEST DESIGNS

UNDESIRABLE

FAIRLY GOOD DESIGN

Fig. 3-3.   Schematic drawing of section changes in casting design.

casting unsound at that location.   The omission of the fillet, on the other hand, will result in undesirable stresses from cooling and may form the basis for a crack.   The extent of such defects will vary with the type of metal being cast; those of high hot-short characteristics prove especially troublesome.

Filleting is important at the junction of section changes.   An even better solution, however, is a gradual taper.   The available methods of designing junctions of section changes are shown in Fig. 3-3, with appropriate notations.

Pattern Draft.   Draft on a pattern facilitates its molding since, once the pattern is loosened in the mold, it can be readily withdrawn; the draft provides for a clean and easy lift.   The amount of draft, sometimes spoken of as taper, is actually a variable quantity although it is usually taken to mean one degree.   The designer should consider the amount of permissible draft when he is establishing design dimensions in order to avoid scant sections and surfaces at critical points on the casting.

Careful attention should be given to the possibility of avoiding undercutting, which is in reality reverse draft, or back-draft. There are complicated designs in which this undesirable condition cannot be avoided; where back-draft does occur, molding the pattern becomes complicated and necessitates the use of cheeks or cores or both.

Pattern Parting Line. It is frequently possible to design patterns in such a way that they can be made in one piece and molded entirely in the drag flask. In such instances the draft is in one direction from the pattern face and there is no problem of locating the parting line on the pattern. When a more complicated pattern shape is encountered the pattern must be made in sections or parts—the "split" pattern. The junction line is referred to as the *parting line*, and since the pattern will then be molded in both the cope and the drag flask, the pattern draft will be divergent from the parting line. The location of the parting line calls for consideration of previously mentioned factors such as location of ribs and machined surfaces as well as of the problem of molding the pattern. It is sometimes possible to locate a parting line or split the pattern in such a

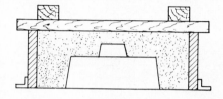

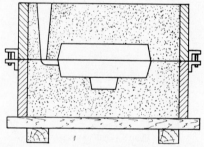

Fig. 3-4. Example of a single-piece pattern (top) and a split pattern for the same casting (bottom). Draft is exaggerated in both patterns.

way as to overcome back-draft. There is no single feature of pattern-making that requires more exacting study than does the location of the parting line (Fig. 3-4).

It is not always possible to develop a straight parting line because of the inherent shape of the casting. Every effort should be made to achieve a straight parting surface up to and including redesign, since an irregular parting line requires more molding time or additional pattern rigging. The principle of redesign from an irregular to a straight parting line is sketched in Fig. 3-5. The discussion here has been based on the idea of a single pattern. When production attains a considerable volume regularity of parting lines is not so important because more elaborate pattern equipment can be justified.

Follow-boards. One standard method for simplifying the molding of a pattern with an irregular parting line is the use of the follow-board. The follow-board is made to the contour of the pattern parting line. It is built up from wood which is recessed to receive the pattern to its parting line. Another method of making a follow-board, or "match,"

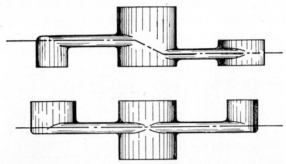

Fig. 3-5. Example of a pattern redesigned for production. Top, irregular parting line; bottom, redesign permits a straight parting line.

Fig. 3-6. Follow-board shown at left is for one-piece pattern of steering wheel at right.

is to pour a plaster of Paris mixture to the desired shape; a mixture of sharp sand, binder, and hardener can be used in the same way. Patterns of irregular parting line are on occasion molded with a follow-block or fill-in piece for economy in pattern equipment.

Follow-boards are not used exclusively as a device for simplifying the molding of irregular parting lines; they also serve to facilitate the molding of patterns of thin section where splitting on the parting line would result in a fragile pattern section. Such sections are likely to warp and at best are subject to damage and breakage in routine molding practice. Figure 3-6 illustrates a steering-wheel pattern with its accompanying follow-board.

In this design the rim section is I-shaped, with a web thickness of $\frac{1}{8}$ in.; obviously if this pattern were to be split through the web it would be too fragile for foundry use.

Match Plates and Mounted Patterns. The accepted method for the production molding of irregular-parting-line patterns is to mount them on "match plates"; regular-parting-line patterns are given like treatment. The manner of constructing the match plate is determined by

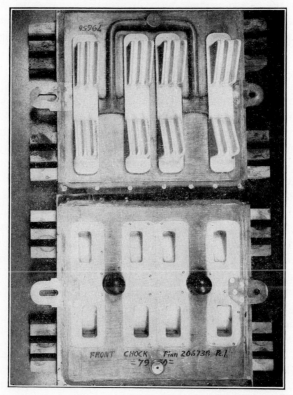

Fig. 3-7. A mounted pattern using different patterns. Note gating on drag side.

the amount of production to be obtained from the patterns. Where production runs are to be extensive it is common practice to cast the pattern parts and the plate as an integral unit; the casting is generally some type of aluminum alloy. The match plates for regular-parting-line patterns are frequently built up by mounting the mating pattern parts on opposite sides of a hardwood board or metal pattern plate. Obviously the term match plate is derived from the fact that the pattern parts mounted on each side of the plate will match perfectly. The term mounted pattern refers to one or more patterns that have been fastened to a plate or board, usually a series of patterns on a single board (Fig. 3-7).

This series may consist of duplicates or of different parts with a similarity in volume and section. Patterns so mounted are provided with necessary runners and ingates arranged so that the entire group can be poured at the same time.

In the foundry the mounting of patterns is comparable in importance to tooling in the machine shop; consequently, imagination and understanding of the casting process and foundry equipment are required of the patternmaker. It is customary in production work to mount every pattern that can possibly be adapted to this form of treatment. Such complex castings as V-type motor blocks are in production using mounted patterns.

Solidification Behavior of Castings

Solidification Phenomena. The design of a sound casting requires a knowledge of the behavior of cast metal from pouring to cooling at room temperature. As the mold fills with molten metal a temperature gradient is established between the mold interface and the casting. Obviously the influence of the mold temperature will be exerted first on the metal which lies in contact with the mold face and a cooling action will be started there. A given casting section then will be solidifying from all bounding surfaces toward the center. If the casting has been designed with a uniform section throughout, its solidification rate will be uniform. However, when sections of varying thickness are present in a casting, differential solidification rates will develop within the casting. This condition is a major cause of unsound castings. In the process known as slush casting, the mold is inverted immediately after pouring in order to drain the still liquid metal from the casting interior; thereby a casting is left that is merely a shell of metal. Such castings are used for making small metal toys and some types of plumbing fixtures.

The first metal to solidify is actually chilled, since the mold surface has not had sufficient time to become heated. The casting will exhibit a fine, close-grained structure at this surface but a coarser texture toward the center of the section. However, actual porosity—or what is even worse, a cavity—will not occur if provision is made for a continuing supply of liquid metal through some feeding device. This "feeding" is necessitated by the behavior of the solidifying mass, which draws upon the liquid portion of the casting, or melt, until solidification is complete. An understanding of the phenomena of solidification is necessary if the designer is to obtain maximum strength from a cast section. The thinner the casting section within practical limits, the greater will be its strength per unit area. The graphs in Fig. 3-8 applying to Alcoa alloy 195-T6 show the effect of section thickness.

To insure the production of a casting free of porosity the casting must be designed, or the pattern made, in such a way as to avoid large concentrations of metal. The design must be studied from the viewpoint of the actual solidification behavior of the liquid metal within the mold. It is obvious that the last part filled will be the hottest and that it will be in a liquid state while the part of the mold filled first is solidifying. When the problem of *directional solidification* has been solved—*i.e.*, the progressive feeding of molten metal in the direction of solidification has

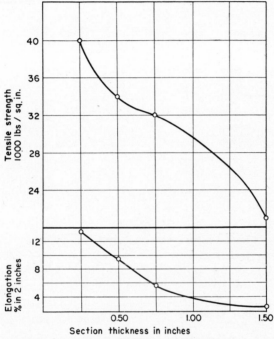

Fig. 3-8. Effect of section thickness on tensile strength and elongation for aluminum alloy casting 195-T6. (*Courtesy of Aluminum Company of America, Pittsburgh.*)

been attained—castings will be satisfactory. The final part of the casting to cool will receive molten metal from the sprue, or riser, to compensate for any solidification shrinkage that might tend to develop there.

Unsound sections in castings can frequently be attributed to the fact that "hot spots," or metal concentrations, occur at locations where they cannot receive adequate liquid metal to compensate for solidification shrinkage. Typical examples of such difficulties are shown in Fig. 3-9 together with suggested corrective measures. It is impossible to overemphasize this very basic factor of casting design. Traditionally, castings have always been of great bulk or mass; close analysis of the phenomena of solidification, however, indicates that mass in itself does not

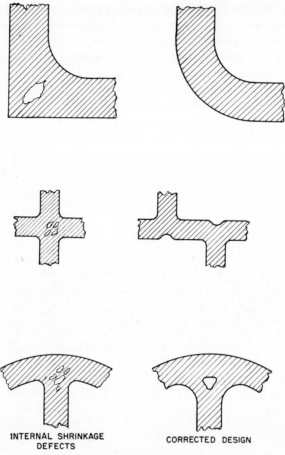

INTERNAL SHRINKAGE
DEFECTS   CORRECTED DESIGN

Fig. 3-9.   Effect of improper design, together with corrective design.

mean much from the viewpoint of strength.   Limitation on minimum
section thickness must be observed if mis-runs are to be avoided in the
casting.   The data in Table 3-1 are recommended by the American
Foundrymen's Society.   The use of these values must be tempered by

TABLE 3-1

Casting alloys	Recommended min. section thickness, in.
Aluminum	$\frac{1}{8}$
Brass and bronze	$\frac{3}{32}$
Gray cast iron (soft)	$\frac{1}{8}$
Magnesium	$\frac{5}{32}$
Malleable cast iron	$\frac{3}{32}$
Steel	$\frac{3}{16}$
White cast iron	$\frac{1}{8}$

the judgment of the patternmaker, who will take into account the fact that small surface areas are more readily poured, or run, than large ones.

Contraction and Shrinkage. Castings permitted to remain in a sand mold will cool slowly because of the insulating nature of the sand. When metal molds are used, as in die or permanent-mold casting, the cooling rate is accelerated. During the cooling period the casting is contracting in size. If, then, the pattern is made exactly to design dimensions, the resulting casting will be too small by the amount of its contraction. Each classification of the cast metals has a different set of values in this regard. Further, the same metal yields varying results in accordance with the size and shape of the casting as well as the position in which it is molded. In order to compensate for normal contraction, or shrinkage,

TABLE 3-2

Casting alloy	Contraction, in./ft
Aluminum	$\frac{1}{8} -\frac{5}{32}$
Brass	$\frac{3}{16}$
Bronze	$\frac{1}{8} -\frac{1}{4}$
Gray cast iron	$\frac{1}{10}-\frac{1}{8}$
Magnesium	$\frac{1}{8} -\frac{5}{32}$
Malleable cast iron	$\frac{1}{8} -\frac{3}{16}$
Steel	$\frac{3}{16}-\frac{1}{4}$

to use a shop term, pattern dimensions are increased. This is accomplished by using a shrinkage rule graduated so as to increase dimensions in the amount of the contraction characteristics of the metal in question. Shrinkage rules are available for all cast metals; a notation of shrinkage value is marked on them. The data in Table 3-2 are offered as a general guide for contraction allowances.

Distortion in Castings. Slight distortion of a finished casting may be traceable to any one of several causes; an unyielding mold or carelessness in handling immediately after solidification may be responsible. However, a more serious distortion is traceable to the casting shape (Fig. 3-10). An expedient used to overcome such distortion is that of "faking" the pattern in a direction opposite to the one in

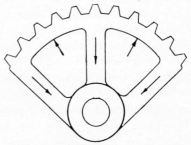

Fig. 3-10. Diagrammatic sketch of forces acting on a casting during cooling period owing to heavy metal concentration at the hub.

which the casting will distort. It will shed some light on the behavior of a casting during cooling to observe that a bushing stock casting will contract diametrically, whereas a half bushing casting will contract along its arc.

Effect of Design on Machining. Consideration given to machining problems by a designer will be helpful in subsequent processing. Locating points should be shown on the drawing; they are useful for checking both the pattern and the resultant casting. The locating points are preferably placed on a part of the casting that is not subject to such variations as those caused by parting-line shifts. It is always necessary to remember that layout for machining a casting must be done from some base point or points.

Coring Considerations

The core work on a casting is another essential that calls for careful analysis when the pattern is being made. Cores are used to form desired depressions, recesses, or contours in the casting. The largest single use of cores is for forming cast holes of a desired size, shape, and location. Cores are broadly classified as green-sand or dry-sand, depending on their method of manufacture. Green-sand cores are made from the same molding sand as that used in the molds; in most instances they are an integral part of the mold. There are jobs, such as soil pipe, where the green-sand cores are made separately and then placed in the mold. Green-sand cores are the most economical to use, since they require no additional materials or processing and since they are returned to the system sand in the same way as molding sand from the molds.

Dry-sand Cores. Dry-sand cores are made from materials and by processes different from those involved in the mold in which they are used. An exception occurs in some complicated jobs where the entire mold is made up of a series of dry-sand cores, for example, the cast-aluminum cylinder heads for air-cooled radial aircraft motors. A dry-sand core is composed of some type or types of sharp sand mixed with a binding material selected on the basis of its imparting desirable mechanical properties to the core. The core mix is molded in a core box; there may be several of these for a single casting. A simple method is one where the core mix is rammed into the core box manually; a plate of metal or heat-resisting material is placed as a cover of the open side of the box and the assembly is then inverted so that the core rests on the plate. When the surface of the core is irregular, a casting, known as a core dryer, made to fit the contour of the core, replaces the flat type of core plate.

The next operation consists of placing the core plate, supporting the newly made core, into a core oven for baking. Ovens are of various designs as to means of heating as well as to internal shelving arrangements. Large production is baked in ovens with conveyor-type shelving so arranged that the core is sufficiently cool for hand handling when it emerges from the oven. Smaller core ovens have drawers or even cars

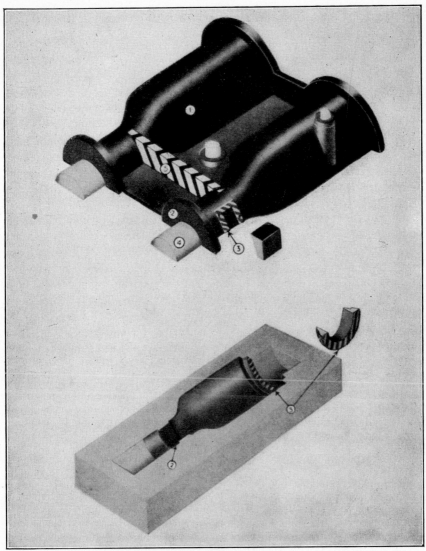

Fig. 3-11. Standard pattern colors. Pattern shown at top and core box below.

1. Surfaces to be left unfinished are painted black.

2. Surfaces to be machined are painted red.

3. Seats of and for loose pieces are to be marked by red stripes on a yellow background.

4. Core prints and seats for loose core prints are to be painted yellow.

5. Stop-offs are to be shown by diagonal black stripes on a yellow background.

that can be pulled from the ovens for both loading and unloading the cores.

Dry-sand cores require a means of anchoring them into position in the mold to prevent shifting during the casting operation. The usual method is that of adding core prints to the pattern. A core print forms an imprint or depression in the sand mold of a shape and size corresponding to the print on the core. Size and location of core prints are usually left to the patternmaker's judgment. Core prints serve the dual purpose of providing core support and vents for gas escapement. When a core extends through the casting, a core print can be placed at its ends. There are situations, though, in which the core is almost entirely surrounded by metal and there is a total lack of openings in the casting, where core prints could be placed.

The patternmaker has to choose between two alternatives in solving this problem; he can arbitrarily place a core print or prints at desired locations, or he can use available core print locations and metal core supports, known as core chaplets. A false core print is one used at some point other than a designed opening in the casting. The cored hole resulting must then be closed with a threaded plug or by pressing in a metal stamping, depending on the design requirements. Core chaplets are obtainable in about every conceivable shape and size. They are made of steel stampings that have been tinned to aid in fusing into the casting and prevent their rusting in storage or the mold.

Cores frequently require the use of metal rods, arbors, or wires as reinforcement to give the necessary strength to withstand the pressures developed by the metal filling the mold. These metal pieces are withdrawn from the casting at the time the cores are removed. This is another reason for having cored holes situated to permit easy removal.

Core boxes are made concurrently with the pattern. In many cases there is the necessity for making several core boxes to accommodate a single pattern. This work can be reduced, sometimes, by fitting loose stop-offs, or removable pieces, into a core box in an arrangement that will permit one core box to be used for making several different cores. Core boxes are often built to produce a segment of a core; these segments are fitted and pasted together to form the large final core.

Pattern and Core Box Colors. Standardization of the painting of wooden patterns and core boxes has been adopted to aid the foundry in understanding the various features of this equipment. This color code has been approved as American Recommended Practice B45.1—1932 under the Procedure of the American Standards Association. Figure 3-11 shows the standardized color scheme applied to a wooden pattern and its core box. The numbers shown in the figure have the following meaning:

1. All surfaces that are to be left unfinished are painted black.

2. Surfaces that are to be machined are painted red.

3. Seats for loose pieces are painted with red stripes on a yellow background.

4. Core prints and their seats are painted yellow.

5. Stop-offs are shown by diagonal black stripes painted on a yellow base.

Pattern Construction

Materials for Patterns. The selection of a satisfactory species of wood for the pattern is determined by the service expected of the pattern and also by the amount of shaping needed to make the pattern. Such soft woods as white pine, sugar pine, and western cedar are most popular, since they are relatively light in weight and can be fashioned easily. Philippine mahogany is common for patterns that are to have a long service life in the foundry. Patterns for extended production runs are made from metal. Aluminum alloys are most useful because of favorable weight and ease of finishing. Metal patterns are cast from a master pattern that, in turn, is made with double shrinkage allowance. In order to gain a fuller appreciation of the many problems facing the pattern-maker and his solutions for them, it is suggested that a modern treatise on patternmaking be consulted. An outstanding text is "The Pattern Maker's Manual," by McAfee and Wagner.[1]

Plaster in Patternmaking. Among several procedures for the use of plaster, perhaps the best-known one is that of starting with a wooden counterpart of the core. This is mounted inside an open-top knockdown wood box of a size which will give the desired wall thickness for the plaster core box that it is intended to produce. That part of the box which will be in contact with the plaster mix must be treated with a parting compound such as petroleum jelly or grease.

The batch is prepared by sifting the plaster into water. Large volumes of plaster must not be added or lumps will develop in the mix. Two volumes of water to three of plaster of Paris is regarded as a satisfactory ratio. The acceptable viscosity is one approaching that of thick cream. The chief source of trouble in casting plaster arises from the inclusion of air bubbles which produce porosity or voids in the cast.

As the cast sets, it will begin to develop temperature, accompanied by expansion; all wood parts must be withdrawn immediately when there is evidence of heating. The cast can then be set aside for a day, during which time it will develop hardness and strength. The working surfaces are given several coats of shellac prior to the use of the cast in the foundry.

The above operation will produce the core box, since the cast was made

[1] An official publication of the Pattern Makers' League of North America, 1947.

against a wood replica of the desired core.   The wood replica is then used as the foundation for the pattern.   It need only be built up for the requisite metal thicknesses; flanges or bosses may be added by applying some material, such as sheet wax, which forms easily.   When this building-up process is completed, the newly finished piece can, in its turn, be used as a pattern for a plaster cast.   Upon completion, these two casts will provide pattern and core box for several castings.

Gypsum Cement Patterns.   Gypsum cement is another material of interest for the patternmaker.   It is not cast by the method described for

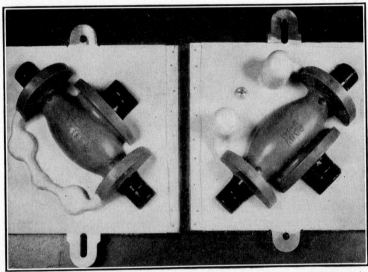

Fig. 3-12.   Plastic globe valve pattern mounted on a board.   Note gating and risering.   (*Courtesy of Puget Sound Naval Shipyard, Bremerton, Wash.*)

plaster of Paris, which is poured in liquid form.   Gypsum cement is mixed with water to form a liquid that soon reaches a stage of plasticity. When in this condition, it is "skreeded," or worked to contour, by means of a metal template.

Patterns from Plastics.   Plastic patterns can be made economically, since they are cast into shape from a liquid mix that is poured into a mold. Their smooth, glosslike surface makes them easy to draw from the mold and gives the latter an excellent surface finish.   A further advantage of plastic patterns is the fact that they can be left in a sand mold for an indefinite period without suffering deterioration of any kind.   They require no surface coating or painting protection.

The actual making of a plastic pattern is similar to that described for plaster of Paris.   The chief difference is that in the case of the plastics the mold with its newly poured plastic needs to be treated at a curing temperature of approximately 140°F, since a thermosetting type of plastic is used.

Plaster molds have proven satisfactory for this work. The mold is coated with Tygon paint that acts as a parting for the cast plastic. Improved finish for the plastic is obtained by using a polishing wax over the paint. After the plastic mix has been poured into the mold, it is left at room temperature for several hours; this period, during which it becomes opaque, is followed by oven curing. Figures 3-12 and 3-13 show a plastic pattern for a globe valve and its core box.

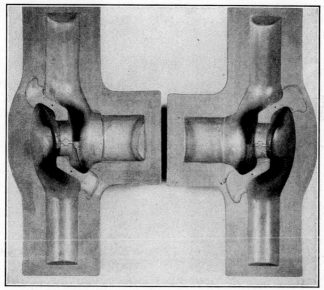

Fig. 3-13. Two halves of plastic core box for globe valve pattern. (*Courtesy of Puget Sound Naval Shipyard, Bremerton, Wash.*)

Match plates cast in their entirety from plastics have not come into wide use because there is some question about their ability to withstand the shock imposed by the foundry molding process. Some match plates using a metal reinforcing frame have been introduced, despite the objectionable feature that the metal adds considerable weight. Another approach to the problem is that of using a metal plate and casting the plastic pattern directly to it.

Survey Questions

3-1. Wherein does a pattern drawing differ from a machine design drawing?
3-2. When is it desirable to employ a bulbed section?
3-3. How is it possible to weaken a casting by using ribs?
3-4. Distinguish between the terms "split pattern" and "solid pattern."
3-5. Why is the placement of fillets important?

3-6. Give some reasons for locating machined surfaces from the viewpoint of casting.

3-7. Why is pattern draft of importance?

3-8. Are follow-boards used with match plates? Why or why not?

3-9. Is there a distinction between gated patterns and match plates?

3-10. Are loose patterns used in production foundries?

3-11. Explain the influence of section thickness on unit strength of a casting.

3-12. Why is directional solidification important?

3-13. What casting defects result from hot spots?

3-14. List the important causes of casting distortion.

3-15. Would a patternmaker use the same shrink rule for all ferrous castings?

3-16. Are shrink-rule graduations the same as those on a standard rule?

3-17. Into what two broad categories are cores classified?

3-18. Which of these is more economical? Why?

3-19. Is there any distinction between core plates and core driers?

3-20. Do core prints and core chaplets serve identical purposes?

3-21. What materials are general for making patterns?

3-22. How is a pattern marked to show surfaces to be machined?

3-23. Are foundry patterns made of materials other than wood or metal?

3-24. Mention some of the advantages that are realized from the use of plastic foundry patterns.

REFERENCES

"American Malleable Iron: A Handbook," Malleable Founders' Society, Cleveland, 1944.

"Analysis of Casting Defects," American Foundrymen's Association, Chicago, 1947.

"The Cast Metals Handbook," 3d ed., American Foundrymen's Association, Chicago, 1944.

"Designing with Magnesium," American Magnesium Corporation, Pittsburgh, 1945.

McAfee, E. J., and R. G. Wagner: "The Pattern Maker's Manual," Pattern Makers' League of North America, 1947.

"Steel Castings Handbook," 2d ed., Steel Founders' Society of America, Cleveland, 1950.

CHAPTER 4

SANDS FOR THE FOUNDRY

Sand is the basic foundry material.   It is used, in some form, in every major foundry activity, from molding to the cleaning room and melt shop. These diverse applications require a variety of physical as well as mechanical properties.   Foundry sands include such materials as pit sand, beach sand, bank sand, sharp sand, and blended sand, to mention some of the more common types.

Molding sand is the most important one since it is the investment material used for sand castings.   The phrase "naturally bonded molding sands" has become the accepted term for molding sands that are used in the foundry in the condition in which they are mined.   They are tempered by water additions until their properties are satisfactory for molding use.   As the demands of the foundry became more diversified, it developed that naturally bonded sands could not meet all necessary molding and casting requirements.   Research uncovered the shortcomings of these sands and led to investigations that have resulted in the development of "synthetic sands."   Synthetic molding sands are compounded of refractory grains and bonding agents, together with tempering water.   These sands were formerly peculiar to steel foundries but are now used throughout the foundry industry.

Natural Molding Sand.   Naturally bonded molding sand is composed of grains of refractory material held together by a bonding agent that is primarily a clay; impurities may be present, in varying amounts.   Sand deposits are found in many parts of the country, and it is the accepted practice to name a sand for the region of its origin; thus Albany sand comes from the vicinity of Albany, N.Y.   The cost of transporting molding sand is critical to the foundry and accounts for the effort to use local sand, with its attendant difficulties.   The geological nature of a deposit can be such that a considerable variation in the sand will occur.   This situation is met by suppliers of molding sand through the use of blending or mixing equipment which ensures a degree of uniformity in the final product.

The lack of uniformity of performance by molding sands has been the subject of scientific investigations going back to the beginning of this

century.   Among the pioneering efforts in this direction was the work of
Dr. H. Ries, professor of geology at Cornell University, in testing some
Michigan and Wisconsin sands prior to and during 1904.[1]   Dr. Richard
Moldenke was another early student of molding sand.[2]   These researches
in molding sand are being continued by many investigators, notably
Dietert and Dunbeck.   Research work on foundry sands has lead to the
establishment of both adopted and tentative standards that now form
the basis of sand control.   Methods of testing are published in the
"Foundry Sand Testing Handbook" issued by the American Foundrymen's Society.

Synthetic Molding Sands.   The synthetic molding sands mentioned
above are compounded to meet specific requirements within a foundry.
Where a wide range of casting requirements must be met, several different
types of synthetic sand will be used by a foundry in order to obtain the
best results.

Silica sand, SiO_2, is the one used principally as a synthetic base sand.
It has become established over the years as a satisfactory material
capable of meeting the requirements imposed by every type of casting.
There are some other geological materials that are satisfactory for use as
base sands but they have not attained commercial importance.

Olivine, a natural combination of forsterite ($2MgO \cdot SiO_2$) and fayalite
($2FeO \cdot SiO_2$), is a satisfactory base sand.   Its expansion characteristics
are more favorable than those of silica: expansion is less and remains
constant throughout the casting temperature range.   Olivine composed
of 90 per cent forsterite and 10 per cent fayalite has a fusion temperature
in the range of 3100°F.   Olivine is being used in Norwegian foundries
with conspicuous success, since, among other advantages, it has less
tendency to cause silicosis than does silica sand.

Molding Sand Control Tests

Molding Sand Grains.   Grain shape, size, composition, and distribution, determine the suitability of a given molding sand for a particular
use.   Grain shape is observed by microscopic examination.   Grains are
classified as rounded, subangular, angular, and compound.   Compound
grains consist of two or more grains so firmly joined that the standard
AFS clay and fineness tests fail to separate them.   The four AFS grain-
shape standards appear in Fig. 4-1.

Grain size is determined by a standard AFS test.   This test procedure
is applied to new sands, which fall into three main types:

[1] The Laboratory Examination of Molding Sand, *Trans. AFA*, Vol. 15, pp. 63–79,
1906.
[2] Molding Sand Tests, *Trans. AFA*, Vol. 21, pp. 17–126, 1912.

1. Sands containing appreciable clay percentages as mined, termed naturally bonded sands.

2. Sands containing 2 to 3 per cent of clay bond as mined, known as crude silica sands.

3. Sands free of clay bonding material, known as washed sands.

The standard fineness test can be applied to all three classifications. In the case of the first two, however, the clay or bonding agent must be removed by a standardized washing procedure.

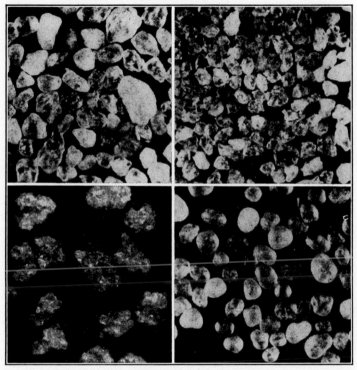

Fig. 4-1. Standard sand grain shape classifications.

Grain-fineness Test. The apparatus for the fineness test consists of a set of eleven nesting sieves 8 in. in diameter, mounted in a mechanical shaker device, together with a top lid and bottom pan. Sieve openings used are the U.S. Series equivalent nos. 6, 12, 20, 30, 40, 50, 70, 100, 140, 200, and 270.

The test is made with a 50-gram dried sample. The sample is placed in the upper sieve, the lid is put in place, and the sample is shaken for 15 min. The weight of sand grains retained by each sieve after this shaking is multiplied by 2. This product will express the weight of grains of the various sizes as percentages of the original 50-gram sample and will also show the percentage distribution of the various sizes of grains in the sample.

The grain-fineness number is calculated by multiplying the above percentage figures by a factor termed a multiplier. The products of this multiplication are added to obtain a total product.

The AFS grain-fineness number is then calculated from the formula

$$\frac{\text{Total product}}{\text{Total \% retained on screen}}$$

A typical calculation is given in Table 4-1.

TABLE 4-1. TYPICAL CALCULATION OF AFS GRAIN-FINENESS NUMBER*
(Cedar Mountain, Washington, sand.   Size of sample: 50 grams.   AFS clay content: 17.4 grams or 34.8%.   Sand grains: 32.6 grams or 65.2%.)

U.S. Series equivalent no.	Amount of 50-gram sample retained on each sieve		Multiplier	Product
	Grams	Per cent		
6	None		3	0
12	0.2	0.4	5	2
20	0.2	0.4	10	4
30	0.2	0.4	20	8
40	0.3	0.6	30	18
50	0.7	1.4	40	56
70	1.7	3.4	50	170
100	7.4	14.8	70	1,036
140	8.8	17.6	100	1,760
200	5.3	10.6	140	1,484
270	1.9	3.8	200	760
Pan	5.9	11.8	300	3,540
	32.6	65.2		8,838

$$\text{AFS grain-fineness number} = \frac{\text{total product}}{\text{total \% retained on screen}} = \frac{8{,}838}{65.2} = 136$$

* Analysis made in Foundry Sand Control Laboratory, Department of Mechanical Engineering, University of Washington.

Permeability Test. The venting property of molding sand is determined by the particular combination of grain size, shape, and distribution, plus the type and amount of binders included. This characteristic is termed permeability; it is defined as that physical property of the molded mass of sand which allows gas to pass through it. For molding-sand control purposes, green permeability is determined, since the tempered molding sand as used in the foundry sand system is under test. The unit for expressing permeability is an arbitrary one that is referred to as the permeability number. It is calculated from the formula

$$P = \frac{vh}{pat}$$

where P = permeability number
v = volume of air passing through standard specimen, cc
h = height of standard specimen, cm
p = pressure of air, gram/sq cm
a = cross-sectional area of standard specimen, sq cm
t = time, min

Instruments are available for making direct permeability readings (Fig. 4-2).

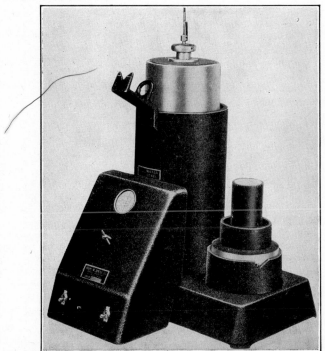

Fig. 4-2. Permeability meter for making standard AFS permeability test. (*Courtesy of Harry W. Dietert Co., Detroit.*)

The permeability of tempered molding sand is chiefly dependent on grain size, the larger sizes generally yielding higher permeability values; grain distribution is also important. Table 4-2 gives typical test values that have been taken from actual production foundries.

Green Compression Strength. Green compression strength is another quality of tempered molding sand that is regularly determined in the sand control laboratory. It is measured in pounds per square inch (psi) and is determined by the load a standard rammed specimen can sustain before fracture. This property is dependent upon the amount and type of bond present in the molding sand as well as grain shape, size, and distribution. Moisture content in the form of tempering water also exerts an influence on green compression strength.

TABLE 4-2. MOLDING SAND SPECIFICATIONS*

Kind of casting	Type of ramming	Per cent moisture, approx.	Shear strength		Compression strength		Permea-bility
			Green	Dry	Green	Dry	
Stove plate.....	Squeeze	7.5–8.5	1.3	6.0	7.0	19	9
8-lb plate.......	Jolt squeeze	7.0–7.0	1.4	6.0	7.0	33	15
15-lb plate......	Jolt squeeze	6.0–8.7	1.4	6.5	7.0	40	25
20-lb jobbing....	Hand	7 –8	1.8	7.0	8.0	40	35
Radiators.......	Hand	6 –7	1.2	7.0	6.5	52	35
Radiators.......	Machine	6 –7	1.4	7.0	7.0	52	35
Bath tubs.......	Sand slinger	5.0–6.0	1.1	7.0	6.0	46	70
Cylinder blocks..	Sand slinger	5.5–6.5	1.5	7.0	7.5	42	80
Cylinder blocks..	Jolt	6 –7	1.5	7.0	8.5	44	80
Car wheels......	Jolt	7.5–8.5	1.4	7.0	6.2	40	130
Boiler sections...	Jolt	6 –7	1.3	7.0	7.0	40	80
Boiler sections...	Sand slinger	5.5–6.5	1.2	7.0	6.5	40	80
Pipe...........	Jolt	8 –9	1.3	8.0	7.0	48	300
Pipe..........	Pneumatic	6 –7	1.3	8.0	7.0	48	300
Plow..........	Jolt	6 –7	1.4	8.0	7.5	47	30
Steel..........	Jolt	3.0–4.0	1.5	10.0	7.5	52	160
Steel plate......	Jolt squeeze	3.0–4.0	1.5	10.0	7.5	50	110
Flywheels.......	Jolt	6.3–7.3	1.3	7.0	7.5	40	90
Flywheels.......	Sand slinger	6.0–7.0	1.2	7.0	7.0	40	100
Bronze bushings.	Jolt	6.0–7.0	1.2	6.0	7.5	39	35
Aluminum plate.	Jolt squeeze	6.0–7.0	1.2	6.0	7.0	20	20
Aluminum large.	Jolt	6.0–7.0	1.2	6.0	7.5	32	37
Brass..........	Jolt squeeze	7.5–8.5	1.4	6.0	7.5	30	13
Malleable.......	Jolt squeeze	6.0–7.0	1.4	8.0	7.5	40	45
Magnesium.....	Hand or machine	3.8–4.2			6.5		60–75

* Data from Dietert and American Foundrymen's Society sources.

Sand Conditioning

Tempering Molding Sand. Moisture is an important factor in the control of molding sand. Its primary function is that of coating, or wetting, each sand particle. The amount of water necessary for this purpose is in direct relation to the extent of surface areas. Since synthetic sands are usually compounded from silica grains and a bonding clay, they do not require the high moisture content of the naturally bonded molding sands. The latter frequently are burdened with large amounts of silt in the clay bond and as a result require high moisture content for acceptable temper. When moisture is too high, excessive volumes of steam may be forced into the casting, causing blows and other defects such as rough surfaces and porosity. Too low a moisture content results in improper dry bond strength, which may cause cuts, washes, and dirty castings.

Bonding Agents. There are two types of materials that impart bond to sand. Clay minerals are most prevalent, since they are a constituent part of the naturally bonded molding sands. However, they vary in nature and may be of complex composition. When sand undergoes the casting cycle, some part of the bond may be affected adversely by high temperatures; it may be vitrified or burned so that it can no longer function as a bonding material. This condition is counteracted by the addition of new naturally bonded sand, where the base sand is of that type, or, as is the practice in some foundries, bonding clay is used to revive the sand.

The choice of bonding clays and their behavior have been the subject of considerable study. These investigations indicate that desirable results can be gained only through careful analysis of the requirements for a given casting sand. Bonding clays for molding sand are divided into four categories.

Class I. Montmorillinite clays, which are more familiarly known as bentonites. Chemical composition $(OH)_4 \cdot Al_4 \cdot Si_8 \cdot O_{20}NH_2O$
Class IA. Western bentonites
Class IB. Southern bentonites
Class II. Halloysite clays. $(OH)_8 \cdot Al_4 \cdot Si_4 \cdot O_{10}$ and $(OH)_{16} \cdot Al_4 \cdot Si_4 \cdot O_6$
White clays from Eureka district, Utah
Class III. Illite bonding clays. $(OH)_4 \cdot K_y(Al_4 \cdot Fe_4 \cdot Mg_4 \cdot Mg_6)(Si_{8-y} \cdot Al_y)O_{20}$
"Grundite" from Grundy County, Illinois
Class IV. Kaolinite bonding clays. $(OH)_8 \cdot Al_4 \cdot Si_4 \cdot O_{10}$
Ohio and Illinois fire clays

Actual foundry application of bonding clays has pointed to the bentonites as being of greatest interest. The general practice is to use Western bentonite for high dry strength and Southern bentonite for high green strength. A mixture in which these are both used is, theoretically, an ideal sand.

Bond strength is improved also by additives other than clays. In fact the use of cereal binders, such as corn flour, is routine in many foundries. It air-dries rapidly and also increases the dry strength of the sand. Cement is sometimes used for bond in large molds.

The addition of silica flour to steel foundry sands is another practice aimed at improving the functioning of these sands. Such additions exert a profound effect by increasing the hot strength of the sand, at the same time making the sand more workable. The drawback is lowered permeability—a condition that can affect the quality of the castings adversely.

Facing Sand. Facing sand, the sand used against the pattern, is specially prepared in order to ensure a clean, smooth surface on the casting. Sea coal has, over the years, been the accepted additive material for facing sand. Opinion is divided on the subject of the effect of sea coal on molding-sand properties. Residual sea coal and resulting ash have the effect of increasing the fines in the sand, thereby necessitating a higher moisture content if the sand is to be workable. The functioning of sea coal is explained by the reducing-type gas that it generates when affected by casting temperatures.

Tempering water has not escaped the attention of the advocates of higher sand strengths. There have been recommendations pointing to molasses, dextrin, and lignins as beneficial additions to tempering water for molding sand. There are some instances where tempering water has been replaced either wholly or in part by light fuel oils. This practice is confined, primarily, to those areas where climatic conditions are such as to cause rapid evaporation of the moisture in tempered molding sand.

System Sand. Prepared molding sand is used directly on the pattern in some foundries to eliminate the labor involved in the placement of facing sand. Where facing sand is used, backing sand is required to fill the remainder of the flask. System sand may consist solely of backing sand, depending on the operation routine. Backing sand does not require the degree of control necessary for facing sand.

Molding Sand Preparation. The preparation of molding sand for foundry use is of more than routine importance. Methods employed for this purpose run the gamut from hand shoveling, termed "cutting," to elaborate installations including washers, dryers, and completely mechanized mulling and handling equipment. In the smaller jobbing shops, where sand is "heaped," either hand shoveling or a mechanical sand cutter is used. The sand cutter travels over the shaken-out molding sand, from which the castings and tramp metal have been removed, and over which water and new bonding material have been spread, stirring and turning the sand by its reel-like action (Fig. 4-3).

The larger jobbing and production foundries have muller installations for their sand-conditioning equipment. Some of these installations are quite elaborate, since the volume of sand passing through them is enormous. Sand mullers vary in design, but the principal feature is that of wheel-like elements that are arranged to press and turn the sand passing under them (Fig. 4-4). Sand aeration devices are built into modern

Fig. 4-3. Mechanical sand cutter that is self-propelled and travels over the floor sand for purposes of tempering and aeration. (*Courtesy of Sather Foundry Co., Everett, Wash.*)

Fig. 4-4. Sand muller equipped with hard iron mulling elements and stationary pan. (*Courtesy of National Engineering Co., Chicago.*)

mulling equipment as a further means of improving the quality of molding sand. The mulling time, or cycle, is dependent upon the type of bonding clay in the system sand. Bonds of the fire-clay type require longer mulling time to develop their properties than the bentonites.

Control of Molding Sand Quality. Any program of quality control, in the foundry, should begin with the molding sand. Sand control laboratories are becoming more numerous in foundries of all categories.   Their rate of growth has been sensational and is in direct proportion to the appreciation of the fundamental importance of properly prepared sand in the production of salable castings.   A typical test record sheet used in

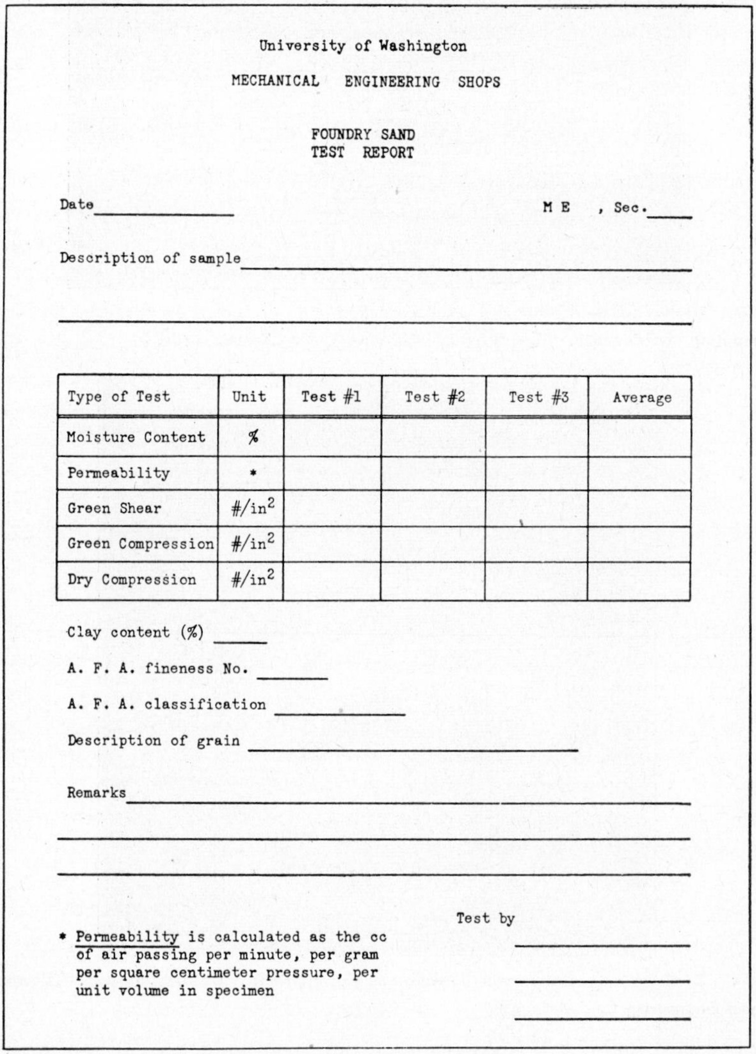

University of Washington

MECHANICAL   ENGINEERING   SHOPS

FOUNDRY SAND
TEST   REPORT

Date_____   M E   , Sec._____

Description of sample_____

_____

Type of Test	Unit	Test #1	Test #2	Test #3	Average
Moisture Content	%				
Permeability	*				
Green Shear	$\#/in^2$				
Green Compression	$\#/in^2$				
Dry Compression	$\#/in^2$				

Clay content (%) _____

A. F. A. fineness No. _____

A. F. A. classification _____

Description of grain _____

Remarks_____

_____

_____

                                                    Test by

* Permeability is calculated as the cc   _____
  of air passing per minute, per gram
  per square centimeter pressure, per   _____
  unit volume in specimen
                                                  _____

                                                  _____

Fig. 4-5. Foundry sand test report.

a sand laboratory is reproduced in Fig. 4-5.   The properties listed in the box form the basis for testing each batch of newly conditioned sand; such tests as those to determine AFS fineness numbers are made at less frequent intervals.   The mechanical properties listed in the specimen test sheet are not the only ones of interest to the control program, but they are the fundamental ones. Flowability, deformation, durability, and collapsibility are other properties of molding sand that affect the molding and casting process. Correctly conditioned molding sand is the major factor in any program pointed toward the elimination of defective castings. Information on this subject can be found in "Analysis of Casting Defects,"[1] in which case studies are discussed and remedial suggestions given.

The Core Room

Foundry Cores. Core sands do not have the wide geographical distribution of molding sands. Local deposits are tapped for this material, although silica sand from the Ottawa, Ill., district is widely accepted as the standard sand for cores. Olivine has also proved its suitability as a dry-sand core material.

Foundry cores are classified, as was mentioned in Chap. 3, as greensand and dry-sand cores. Dry-sand cores are made from sand that is usually free of, or low in, natural bond. It is mixed with a binder; the resultant batch is rammed into a core box for shaping and then placed on a core plate or dryer for baking in a core oven.

Dry-sand Core Binders. There are certain essential requirements for a satisfactory core binder. It should (a) hold core to shape while green, (b) impart sufficient mechanical strength to withstand casting conditions, (c) generate little or no gas during casting, (d) cause the baked core to be nonhygroscopic, (e) offer sufficient strength to withstand necessary handling, (f) burn out for easy removal from the casting, (g) be economical to use.

The core binders of widest application are those which depend upon baking to develop the necessary characteristics of the core. In this category the core oils are important. The bases for core oils are derived either from vegetable oils, such as linseed, or from mineral oils. Linseed oil has been a standby over the years for core making.

Polymerized mineral oils have been developed to the point where they are core binders of proved value. Here, as with the vegetable-oil binders, there is a wide choice of properties available to the prospective user. Core oils may be used separately or in combination with other binders, depending on the type, shape, and size of core to be made.

Core binders are broadly classified as liquid or dry. Sulfite liquor, molasses, and water, together with the core oils, are classified as liquid binders. Dry binders include such materials as proteins, pitch, resins, and a broad list of cereals. Cereals are distinctive for their ability to impart high green strength to the newly made core. Another favorable

[1] American Foundrymen's Association, Chicago, 1947.

aspect is that cereal binders burn out completely, thereby lessening residuals in the system sand.

A production foundry rarely finds it satisfactory to use but one formula for all its core requirements.   The danger of the substitution of one mix for another can be avoided by adding dyes of distinctive colors to the batches as they are mixed.   Preparation of core-sand mixes is performed by mulling equipment of the same type as that used for molding sand.

Fig. 4-6.   Core blowing machine.   (Courtesy of William Demmler & Bros., Kewanee, Ill.)

Dry-sand Core Making.   Making cores for limited production is largely a manual operation.   Adaptations of various molding machines for ramming, rolling over, and drawing the core boxes is common practice. There are, in addition, stock core machines used for making cores of uniform cross section and lengths up to 24 in.   The cross section of the core is determined by a die through which the core mix is forced by a screw feed device.   The latter is equipped with a spindle end that forms a vent on the axis of the core.

The one machine that is peculiar to core making is the core blower (Fig. 4-6).   The core-blowing machine fills and rams the core simultaneously. Core box equipment must be specially designed for core blowing, since filling and venting the core box introduces a novel requirement. The reservoir of the blower is filled with the core-sand mix, and air pressure approximating 100 lb is applied to cause the mix to flow at a high velocity through the openings in the blow plate into the core box. Core blowing is confined to small and medium-sized cores.

Fig. 4-7.   Dielectric sand core dryer.   (Courtesy of Allis-Chalmers Mfg. Co., Milwaukee.)

Core Baking.   Cores are baked at varying temperatures, depending upon core binders and core sizes.   Core ovens employing all the common fuels, as well as electricity, are in use.   The newest development in core drying is the introduction of electronics; Fig. 4-7 shows a dielectric oven equipped with generator and centralized controls and having an hourly capacity of 250 lb of sand at 3 per cent moisture.   The larger ovens feature circulation of forced air from an external heat source.   Conveyors are common in ovens where large production is demanded; many ovens are built with conveyors traveling vertically as a means of saving floor space.

The baked cores may be given a coating or wash by spraying, dipping, or painting; this is done to improve casting finish by eliminating burnt-on sand.   Core wash is selected on the basis of the casting temperatures and metal specification.

Survey Questions

4-1. Give at least four usages for sand in foundry operation.
4-2. How are natural molding sands identified?

4-3. Name two early researchers in molding sand.

4-4. Of what materials is synthetic molding sand composed?

4-5. Where is Olivine superior to silica as a molding-sand aggregate?

4-6. How is sand-grain size determined?

4-7. How many standard sand-grain shapes have been classified?

4-8. How does grain fineness affect casting quality?

4-9. Is the permeability of a molding sand a calculated or arbitrary value?

4-10. Explain temper of molding sand.

4-11. Give another term for bentonite.

4-12. Do Western and Southern bentonites give the same results when used as bonding agencies?

4-13. Differentiate between facing sand and system sand.

4-14. Is a muller the only type of sand-preparation equipment?

4-15. List the important properties of molding sand that should be tested for quality-control purposes.

4-16. Do molding-sand bond and core binders function similarly?

4-17. Classify core binders as to type, and list three in each classification.

4-18. To what does "blown cores" refer?

4-19. How are baked cores processed prior to placement in a mold?

4-20. What are the various methods employed for baking dry-sand cores?

REFERENCES

"Analysis of Casting Defects," American Foundrymen's Association, Chicago, 1947.

Dietert, Harry W.: "Modern Core Practices and Theories," American Foundrymen's Association, Chicago, 1942.

"Foundry Sand Testing Handbook," 5th ed., American Foundrymen's Association, Chicago, 1944.

"Testing and Grading Foundry Sands and Clays," 4th ed., American Foundrymen's Association, Chicago, 1938.

CHAPTER 5

GATING AND RISERING METAL CASTINGS

The gating system on a casting is the means of channeling molten metal from the ladle into the mold cavity. Obviously there are many different ways of arranging the gating. Further, functions other than merely providing a passage for the molten metal are included in the gating system. The type of metal being poured has a marked influence on the gating details, since the light metals are more susceptible to oxidation and are not capable of the head pressures that the ferrous ones exert. The gating system also requires correlation with the design of the casting which it is to serve from the viewpoint of metal distribution as well as of solidification. A summation of these demands on the gating system shows the critical role that gating plays in producing sound castings.

Gating Terminology. The absence of standardization in gating systems carries over into their terminology, and there is no assurance that the terms employed here are accorded general acceptance. The basis for this apparent disagreement seems to be traditional or, in some cases, provincial, since molding is a process dating from antiquity and its development has been shared by many nations.

The simplest gating system is the one in which metal is poured through a vertical opening that leads directly to the mold cavity; the opening is known either as a sprue or as a riser, depending upon the details of its functioning and, again, upon local terminology. The more generally used gating system is designed to lead the metal into the side rather than the top of the mold cavity. For some types of castings—especially where side surfaces must be preserved, as in a cast gear, for example—the metal is introduced into the mold cavity at the bottom, the openings being known as gates or ingates. A typical gating system is sketched in Fig. 5-1. In this example a sprue circular in cross section is shown, since that shape is most general; however, square, oblong, and oval sprues have also been used successfully. The use of a square-cross-sectioned sprue is popular for casting light metals; this contour is believed to cause less turbulence in the molten metal, thereby eliminating one source of the inclusion of oxides in the metal stream.

Control of Metal Velocity.   It is necessary to make the cross-sectional area of the sprue proportional with that of the runner and, in turn, with that of the gates, as a means of controlling the metal stream entering the mold cavity.   Control, as used here, refers to the velocity of the entering metal; it also is aimed at arresting the flow of oxides and inclusions into the mold cavity.   A high entering velocity gives the same effect as a nozzle does to the flow of water through a hose.   The jets of metal will have a tendency to impinge against the surface of the mold cavity with a force that will cause washing at those points, resulting in sand inclusions in the casting.   Another difficulty arising from high-velocity metal streams is the turbulence that results in the mold cavity, which is filled

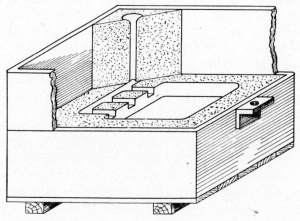

Fig. 5-1.   One arrangement of sprues, runners, and gates.

with air that must be forced out through the sand by the oncoming metal; however, air remaining above the metal will cause oxidation under the condition of extreme turbulence.

Design of gating systems is under continuing scrutiny because of the known effect gating can have on the quality of the casting.   Reduction in metal turbulence is of prime importance.   Turbulence can be reduced to the vanishing point by regulating the flow of the metal stream.   Sharp corners are especially troublesome.   They should be replaced by gradual curves—a change which amounts to a streamlining of the runner system. The sprue should also be given its deserved attention.   When metal is flowing down the sprue, proper pressure conditions must be maintained within that sprue; otherwise an aspirating action can develop.   This is especially true when the sprue takes the shape of an inverted truncated cone.   A similar condition occurs, but to a lesser degree, when the sprue is a cylinder.   The best condition results from a tapering sprue with the large diameter at the top and the small diameter at the bottom where the sprue joins the runner. It has been proven experimentally that the latter type of sprue is not subject to aspiration troubles.

The gating system is not open to theoretical solutions. The type of metal being poured, the volume of the mold cavity, as well as its area, all offer variables to the gating system design. In some instances it is desirable to introduce chokes in the runners, both for slag entrapment and to regulate flow velocity. Directional solidification of the casting is another matter of decided importance. There still remains a great amount of trial and error to be gone through in developing a properly functioning gating system for a given casting. Much experimentation can be eliminated through an understanding of gating fundamentals; yet this does not remove the necessity for the individual attention required by a particular mold.

Gating Nonferrous Castings. Among the cast metals, nonferrous alloys present the most difficult gating problems. They always require attention because of the necessity of restraining dross and oxides from entering the mold cavity. The general plan of attack for solving this problem includes either a skimming or a choking technique. Skimming refers to holding back the dross, which being lighter, floats on the surface of the molten metal. Strainer cores are placed in the sprue to act as a filter. Magnesium alloy castings are frequently gated with a pad of steel wool placed at the top or the bottom of the sprue in such a position as to strain the molten metal that passes through on its path into the mold cavity.

Skim Gate Types. Another method of separating slag and oxides from the molten metal makes use of a runner box, which is a reservoir on top of the mold. The sprue connects with one end of the runner box cavity; however, the sprue opening is covered with a small metal disk whose thickness is such that by the time the runner box is full of molten metal with its slag afloat, the disk will have melted, permitting the metal to enter the sprue. Pouring must continue at such a rate that the runner box is kept filled with metal in order to prevent the floating slag from entering the sprue. A stopper rod is used in place of the disk in some gating systems. The rod is removed the instant the runner box is sufficiently filled with molten metal.

The use of runner boxes is confined to relatively large castings. Smaller molds are poured directly into the sprue; or, on occasion, a cup acting similarly to a funnel, is placed on the sprue. In this gating method the cleansing of the metal is done at some point between the bottom of the sprue and the gate. There are, broadly speaking, two devices employed to accomplish the skimming action, one known as a choke gate and the other as a whirl gate. A choke gate is one in which either the runner or the gate is constricted at some point. The constriction acts to hold back the upper portion of the metal stream so that the clean metal from the bottom portion can flow into the mold cavity. The arbitration test bar casting in Fig. 5-2 illustrates the use of choke gates.

Whirl gates are not very commonly used although they have proven successful with some types of castings. They are designed to function by imparting a whirling action to the metal in the runner. Centripetal

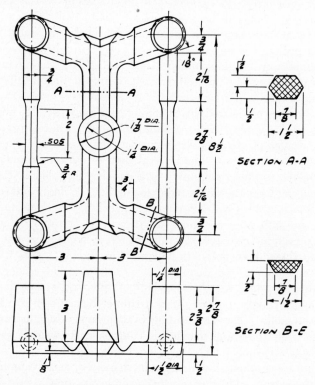

Fig. 5-2. Drawing of pattern equipment for casting arbitration test bar. Note choke gates at each end of bar.

action on the molten metal forces the lighter slag to the center of a vertical cylindrical opening. Solid metal at the periphery of the whirl-gate cylinder is gated into the mold cavity.

Pouring Rate. In a setup in which the gating system is designed to restrain slag from entering the mold the rate of pouring is extremely critical. When pouring is too slow, none of the slag-restraining measures described above will function as intended. It is considered good practice always to keep the sprue filled while pouring a mold. One resulting drawback is the likelihood of spilling metal over the top of the mold through failure to stop pouring at the instant the mold is filled. Experience in pouring and accurate timing are safeguards against this difficulty. Failure to keep a full stream in the sprue causes an injector action on the part of the flowing metal that results in drawing air down into the mold, thereby setting up additional oxidation difficulties. Pouring a mold correctly requires skill and judgment.

Improper shape, size, or location of the gates will cause turbulence of the metal in the mold cavity. Molten metal should fill the mold with-

out undue agitation: in foundry par-lance, "The metal should lie quietly." If the mold cavity is of some depth and is gated from the side cascading and splash-ing of the metal will result—a condition that will promote dirty castings. On molds of considerable depth, the practice of using step gates is usual (Fig. 5-3); there are several modifications, such as stagger-ing, gating horizontally, and gating at an upward inclination from the sprue. John-son and Baker have concluded that only the type of step gate in which the bottom step inclines upward at an angle of 60° and the remaining steps are horizontal will actually feed the casting in the desired sequence. Another conclusion of these investigators is that no gating system will prevent turbulence.[1]

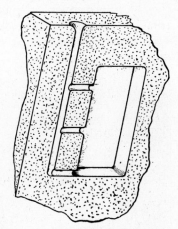

Fig. 5-3. Step gate.

Solidification. Solidification characteristics of cast metal tend to cause cavities or porosity in the casting (Chap. 3). Some relief can be expected from proper casting design; yet despite corrective measures the foundry must be prepared to meet the shrinkage[2] problem that is present with any heavy metal section. Two devices, viz., the use of risers and the use of chills—or both in combination—are the foundryman's methods of com-bating shrinkage. Reversing the idea of chills is done sometimes on thin sections by ramming anti-chiller pads, which retard the solidification rate by acting as insulators, against such sections. Since chills are of doubtful utility on heavy masses of metal, they find little favor except in the casting of light metals, since these rarely have heavy sections. Risering or heading a casting to compensate for shrinkage is accepted practice where heavy sections exist.

Theory of Riser Behavior. Concepts of the functioning of risers have lately undergone revision as the result of research into their behavior.

[1] Johnson, W. H. and W. O. Baker: Gating Systems for Metal Castings. *The Foundry*, Vol. 76, No. 10, pp. 68–73, 252, October, 1948.
[2] The generic term used for describing solidification defects.

Until rather recently it was generally believed that a riser should be a large reservoir of metal, open to the air, placed above the section that was showing shrinkage defects. It was presumed that this weight of metal would cause the solidifying section to be fed by the pressure it would exert. As a result of this concept, the feeling grew that the bigger the riser, the better the result. Risers of fantastic proportions came to be used; their weight was so imposing that the ratio of casting to riser was disproportionate. Surprisingly, though, larger risers did not solve the shrinkage trouble; frequently the defects increased in direct proportion to the riser size. Analysis uncovered the fact that reverse feeding was causing the

Fig. 5-4. Propellor blade casting, showing risers and gating. (*Courtesy of Puget Sound Naval Shipyard, Bremerton, Wash.*)

trouble; the riser was solidifying at a rate that caused it to draw molten metal from the adjacent casting area.

Risers function as expected so long as they remain open—*i.e.*, do not freeze across their top surface; several ideas are used to bring about the desired result. Unique among these is the device used by some foundries in Germany of placing electrodes over the risers on steel castings and striking an arc; in effect the functioning is the same as that of an electric arc furnace. The use of proprietary compounds that are placed over the riser surface is accepted practice in American foundries. Some of these are compositions designed to develop an exothermic reaction when in contact with the molten metal, thereby increasing its temperature and prolonging its period of fluidity. Other compounds are used on the surface of risers as insulators against early freezing. Charcoal has been used for this purpose over the years, as has asbestos. These devices have been of some value, but they have all fallen short of keeping the metal in the riser molten until after the casting has solidified.

Insulating Risers. Experimental work on insulating risers has been in progress at the Puget Sound Naval Shipyard under the supervision of Master Molder E. D. Boyle. He has used diatomaceous earth as well as Perlite for the basic insulating material in this work. The proprietary material Sil-O-Cel, which is sintered diatomaceous earth, is ground in a muller to a fineness that will enable it to pass through a no. 8 sieve. The ground material is then used in powdered form to cover the top of a riser. For other applications the ground material is mixed with such bonding agents as bentonite, synthetic resins, and water, forming a plastic mass that can be shaped for neck-down riser collars, contour anti-chiller pads, blind riser hoods and other similar devices. These shaped parts are dried at 400°F for a period of from 1 to 4 hr prior to setting in the mold.

Fig. 5-5. A pump body casting with both insulated risers and riser pads. (Courtesy of Puget Sound Naval Shipyard, Bremerton, Wash.)

Results obtained from using this insulating material when casting stainless steel, copper-nickel alloys, manganese and other bronzes, steel, cast iron, and aluminum have been very gratifying. An indication of the potential saving possible in metal when such insulated risers are used can be seen from the data obtained from a manganese bronze propeller blade casting (Fig. 5-4):

	Pounds
Gross weight as cast.............	12,800
Weight of risers..................	1,500
Net weight of casting...........	11,300

On this job the ratio of risers to casting weight is but 13.3 per cent. Figure 5-5 shows insulated risers on a high-test gray cast-iron pump body.

Blind Risers. Open risers are easily placed and do not substantially increase molding labor. Risers which do not open to the top of the mold, termed blind risers, are also used. Blind risers are placed in the runner with a very short gate leading to the mold cavity. A modification of the blind riser known as the shrink-bob is frequently used in the malleable foundry.

Blind risers are incapable of doing much feeding, since the gate or the riser freezes prior to complete casting solidification. Investigation of the action of such risers has led to a new theory on the mechanics of riser

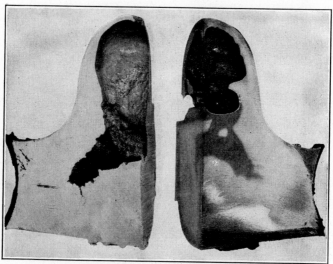

Fig. 5-6. Cross section of a riser in which a graphite rod was inserted. Note shape of shrinkage cavity. (Courtesy of National Carbon Co. Inc., Carbon Products Division, Cleveland.)

behavior. It is now understood that as the molten metal leaves the riser it creates a vacuum therein which precludes further metal flow. By inserting a dry-sand core that extends from the riser cavity into the molding sand backing, atmospheric pressure is exerted on the molten metal within the riser, causing the metal to flow and thus feeding the casting. Graphite or carbon rods have been used in place of a dry-sand core with good results on the feeding characteristics of the riser.

A series of experiments with graphite and carbon rods inserted in semi-blind risers was conducted at the Lebanon Steel Foundry and reported by Vosburgh and Larson of the National Carbon Co., who were connected with this study.[1] Results indicate that a graphite rod inserted in a riser is consumed by the contacting molten metal. This action in turn has a

[1] Vosburgh, F. J., and H. L. Larson: Tests Graphite Rods in Producing Steel, *The Foundry*, Part 1, pp. 108–111, 194, January, 1944; Part 2, pp. 128–129, 187–188, February, 1944.

dual effect on the metal in the riser, since the absorbed carbon lowers the melting point and the combustion of some of the carbon tends to increase the metal temperature. Both these factors have a favorable action on the fluidity of the metal in the riser. The shrink cavity in such a riser (Fig. 5-6) tends toward flatness across its bottom, in contrast to the piping-type cavity of the usual riser; this permits the use of shorter risers, with an attendant saving of metal.

The success gained by the use of graphite rods in semiblind risers was followed by experimental work with these rods in open risers. Early tests with this method of causing risers to feed was done at the Farrell-Cheek Steel Co., Sandusky, Ohio. Conclusions reached there indicate that the end shaping of the rods, together with their size, is a critical consideration for optimum results.

Survey Questions

5-1. Why is the gating system for a casting of importance?

5-2. Are runners and gates the same thing?

5-3. How can the velocity of molten metal entering the mold cavity be controlled?

5-4. Why are strainer cores used?

5-5. When is the use of runner boxes desirable?

5-6. How do whirl gates function to improve casting quality?

5-7. Is the rate of pouring a casting of importance?

5-8. Does the specific gravity of the casting metal influence the gating system used?

5-9. State two methods employed for combating shrinkage during metal solidification.

5-10. Is a casting generally poured through a riser or a sprue?

5-11. By what methods can risers be made to feed satisfactorily?

5-12. On what class of castings are blind risers commonly used?

5-13. Wherein does an insulating riser differ from a conventional type?

5-14. What insulating materials have been used to improve riser action?

5-15. How can the functioning of blind risers be improved?

5-16. Which metal, among those widely used for casting, requires the most risers?

REFERENCES

"American Malleable Iron: A Handbook," Malleable Founders' Society, Cleveland, 1944.

"The Cast Metals Handbook," 3d ed., American Foundrymen's Association, Chicago, 1944.

Dwyer, Pat: "Gates and Risers for Castings," Penton Publishing Company, Cleveland, 1935.

"Steel Castings Handbook," 2d ed., Steel Founders' Society of America, Cleveland, 1950.

CHAPTER 6

SAND CASTING

Metal castings are produced from sand molds predominantly because of the versatility and economy of this method. There is no other method for shaping metal that offers as much latitude and freedom of expression to the designer. Other methods of producing castings are explained in Chap. 7; these are largely confined to small or intermediate sizes. Casting tonnage is produced chiefly by gray iron, steel, and malleable iron foundries, which, with but minor exceptions, cast in sand molds.

Hand Molding. Hand molding is divided into bench and floor types. The former is restricted to small work where flask sizes are such that the molder can care for the entire routine. Molding is done on a bench designed to facilitate the work and conserve the molder's energy. All molding operations are performed manually in bench molding, the exception being the occasional use of a bench-type air rammer. It is customary for the molder to pour off his own work. However, this practice is not invariably followed; in some foundries pouring crews are employed.

Snap Molding. The pattern equipment and rigging used for bench molding is designed for production. Match plates and gated patterns are much in evidence, although loose patterns are common where small lots are scheduled. Although pattern equipment is of a diversified nature, flask equipment for bench molding is generally of the snap-flask type. Snap flasks, of either metal or wooden construction, are built to be removed from the finished mold for continuing re-use. The construction either has a lock on one corner with hinges on the opposite corner so the flask can be opened for removal (Fig. 6-1) or there is a metal sand strip, located at the parting, which can be withdrawn to permit the flask to be lifted upward from the finished mold.

Snap molds are strengthened to withstand casting pressure by a tight fitting jacket that is pushed onto them prior to pouring. Tapered snaps have the advantage of tight-fitting jackets, since the latter are brought to tightness by pressing them downward. Snap molds are weighted to prevent the pouring pressure from floating the copes.

Floor and Pit Molding. Floor molding is the term applied to the large work that is rammed up in flasks on the foundry floor. Exceptionally large castings of substantial tonnage are molded in a pit. The molding pit is bounded by strong concrete walls designed to resist the pressures generated during pouring. Castings weighing hundreds of tons have been molded in pits.

There is little difference between bench molding and floor molding insofar as the fundamental molding operations are concerned. The

Fig. 6-1. Closing a snap mold made in a tapered snap flask. (*Courtesy of The Hines Flask Co., Cleveland.*)

latter is done on a larger scale, with larger patterns and flasks and greater volumes of sand. Flask equipment is generally made of pressed steel or cast iron, since wooden flasks lack stiffness and are inflammable. Complicated patterns frequently require molding to be done in multiple-part flasks where, in addition to the cope and drag, intermediate flask parts known as cheeks are necessary. Cheeks are designated by number; for example, a four-part mold would be built up of a drag, a no. 1 cheek, a no. 2 cheek, and a cope. Floor molds are clamped prior to the pouring, and on occasion clamping is supplemented by weights for further security. The floor molder may use an air rammer but otherwise his work is chiefly manual. On large flasks he may call the crane for roll-over and lifting; too, some help in filling the mold with sand may be available from the

Fig. 6-2.   Steps in manufacture of 1½-in. bronze high-pressure globe valve (front row, left).   Plastic core-box halves, core rods, finished core, and cope and drag pattern boards (back row, left to right). Front row shows valve casting and cope and drag sections of sand mold.   (*Courtesy of Puget Sound Naval Shipyard, Bremerton, Wash.*)

crane.   Figure 6-2 shows the complete pattern, core, and mold for casting a 1½-in. high-pressure bronze globe valve.

Molding Machines

Plain Squeezer.   The operating principle of a squeezer is simple.   A flask is placed on the pattern board and filled with sand; the operator then tucks the sand around the edges.   A squeezer board, of a size to fit exactly inside the flask, is placed on the leveled sand and air pressure brings the flask assembly against the stationary head of the machine.   Continued upward travel of the mold against the head causes the squeezer board to be pressed into the sand, thereby firming it.   Mold hardness is controlled by regulating air pressure.   A regulating, or unloading, valve in the air line is adjustable to desired pressure settings.   The operating cycle is completed when the cylinder has exhausted its operating air and the table of the machine has returned to the starting position.

The squeezer is limited in its function to ramming; all other operations necessary to making a mold remain to be done manually.   Limitations as to size and shape of pattern that can be successfully molded on a squeezer confine its use to small, uniform-sectioned castings.   A flat pattern is ideal for the squeezer.   If, on the other hand, a pattern has pronounced projections, there will be but a shallow layer of sand above these, and, by the nature of the squeezing operation, that volume of sand will be firmed more than the balance of the mold, resulting in nonuniform hardness.

Plain Jolter.   A second basic design for ramming a mold is termed a jolter or, less frequently, a jarrer or bumper.   Molding machines embodying this design ram the sand in the mold by a combination of inertia and impact. The jolter table is fixed to a piston that travels vertically in an air cylinder (Fig. 6-3). The pattern board is mounted on the jolter table and the flask clamped into position. As the flask is being filled with sand, air is turned into the cylinder, causing the table to move upward; the valve arrangement on the cylinder cuts off the air at the end of the upward stroke, allowing the table assembly to drop. The downward motion is stopped abruptly when the table strikes a stationary bumping pad. This sudden jar causes the sand to be packed.

Fig. 6-3. Plain-type jolt molding machine. (Courtesy of SPO Incorporated, Cleveland.)

The top layer of sand in the mold is not completely rammed, which means that a hand ramming operation, generally called butting-off, must be done. There are few limitations to the size of the molds that can be jolt-rammed. Portable machines as well as some mounted with the table at floor level are used.

Jolt-squeeze Machines. The plain squeezer as well as the plain jolter require some degree of hand ramming to complete the mold. In order to eliminate hand ramming entirely the squeezer and jolter principles are combined into one machine, appropriately termed the jolt-squeeze. Machines of this design are capable of a broader range of work than can be done on the plain squeezer; however, they do not reach the capacity of the plain jolter. Jolt-squeezers are built in both portable and stationary models; a portable type is shown in Fig. 6-4.

Drawing a Loose Pattern from Its Mold. The molder of a loose pattern precedes the pattern-drawing operation by swabbing around the edges of the pattern, reinforcing the sand to prevent its crumbling. However, this operation is superfluous in machine molding, especially where proper sand control is observed. A draw spike is next driven into the pattern, if it is made of wood, or a draw screw is threaded into a metal drawplate attached to the pattern. Sometimes a rapping plate is present so that a rapping pin can be inserted therein. The molder strikes the rapping pin with sharp blows in order to loosen the pattern in the mold. It is also common practice to use a rubber mallet for rapping directly against the pattern. In either event, the pattern is rapped in all direc-

Fig. 6-4.   Placing flask over pattern board on a portable jolt-squeeze molding machine.   (*Courtesy of The Osborn Mfg. Co., Cleveland.*)

tions until it is free in the mold. An air or electric vibrator fastened to the pattern plate replaces this routine for machine molding. The vibrator is built into the table in some designs of molding machines.

Mechanical Pattern Draw. There are but two methods of removing a pattern from the mold, viz., (1) drawing the pattern from the mold and (2) drawing the mold from the pattern. Drawing the pattern from the mold can be done by the stripper principle. Stripper machines are built with a metal stripper plate that is cut out to fit the exact contour of the pattern at its parting line. The pattern is mounted so that it can be raised through the stripper plate until its parting line is on a plane with the plate. It is only necessary to move a lever in order to strip the pattern downward through the stripper plate. The mold is supported by the plate, so there is no likelihood of a cracked mold resulting from drawing the pattern. Stripper machines are available with mechanical ramming; the machine with this added feature is known as a jolt-squeeze stripper. A modification of the stripper principle is the pin-lift in which stationary pins contact the pattern plate as the completed mold moves vertically.

Roll-over Draw Molding Machines. Adding the roll-over feature to a jolt-squeeze machine provides for mechanical pattern removal and, thereby, fully automatic molding. The molding machine shown in Fig. 6-5 is equipped with a single set of controls by means of which one

Fig. 6-5. Jarless jolt roll-over pattern draw machine, showing pattern board that serves for molding both cope and drag. (*University of Washington Foundry Laboratory.*)

man performs the entire molding operation. The attendant jobs of placing the flask and bottom board and filling the flask with sand are considered here as being extraneous to mechanical molding proper.

Sand Slinger. The sand slinger embodies one of the oldest principles in molding in that it impels or throws parcels of molding sand into the mold. These parcels travel at a high rate of speed and follow each other in rapid succession. Their velocity is arrested upon contact with the pattern and pattern board; this results in a compacting action that imparts a rammed finish to the mold. Ramming effects develop in directions both normal and transverse to the path of the impelled sand. It will clarify this result to note how a snowball, thrown against any solid surface, behaves on impact with that surface.

The sand slinger fills and rams the mold but performs no other molding function.   Sand slingers are preferred for installation where molds are larger than bench size and especially where volumes of sand are needed for a single mold.   Sand slingers are used in both jobbing and production-type foundries.   Production foundries combine some type of pattern-drawing equipment with the sand slinger in order to eliminate manual molding operations entirely.   There are many different types of installations of this combined equipment.

Fig. 6-6. Sand-slinger installation with a turntable unit at Lynchburg Foundry Co. (Courtesy of Beardsley and Piper Div. of Pettibone Mulliken Corp., Chicago.)

The head of the sand slinger, from which the molding sand is impelled, must be guided over the flask area for uniform sand distribution and ramming.   Several designs have been developed in order to meet differing requirements.   Hand-guided head designs were followed, on large models, by a single control lever in the hands of the operator who was seated above the head.   A design intended for repetitive work has automatic operational control to the point of eliminating the operator. Other design modifications of the sand slinger center around the method of handling the molding sand.   Figure 6-6 (left) shows a sand slinger that is installed with a turntable unit.   The patterns are mounted on strippers which are, in turn, located on a revolving table that brings each molding machine under the slinger head for filling and ramming.   Following this operation, the pattern is stripped and the mold set off on a conveyor. It is usual to have the drag machine followed by the cope unit. Rigging of this general type is popular for agricultural implements as well as automotive castings.

Plastic Resin Sand Casting

Molding sand compounded from a base sand with the addition of a resin-type binder has been introduced for producing sand castings. There is no noteworthy change in molding routine prerequisite to its use in the foundry. Sand preparation requires specialized treatment that is, for the most part, governed by patents. Claims for improved casting results have been advanced in behalf of this material; yet widespread adoption has not come about.

Croning Process. In contrast to molding with a resin-bonded synthetic sand, the Croning Process introduces a new concept. Especially developed equipment and techniques are necessary for this molding method. Investment material is compounded from a fine-grained base sand and a resin-type bond. Metal pattern equipment suitably mounted with requisite gating is heated to approximately 400°F. The sand mix is spread over the pattern assembly, whose temperature causes the resin to melt and the molding material to flow around the pattern. Excess material is then poured off the pattern and the pattern assembly with its sand coating is baked until the resin bond has been plasticized, approximately 5 min. Upon removal from the oven, the plastic-sand shell is stripped from the pattern. The shell, which is a half mold, is about ⅛ in. in thickness. The halves are assembled for casting by placing them in a container and backing them with shot for the necessary strength.

Castings of close dimensional tolerance can be made by the generally cast metals. Quality is high because of the absence of any of the difficulties attributed to molding sand, such as loose sand, steam, and others. The process, also known as shell molding and the "C" process, has, thus far, been confined to the production of small to medium-sized castings.

Frozen Molds. Research on the possibility of casting metal in frozen green-sand molds was undertaken by the author in 1939. Additional work has been done by Prof. W. A. Snyder. In these investigations, green-sand molds were poured at temperatures as low as −20°F. It developed that permeability increased with freezing, along with mold strength. Such molds withstand rough handling and do not require strengthening against casting pressures. Cores need no rodding. Since steam is not generated at the beginning of pouring, gas inclusions are at a minimum. Excellent surface finish is obtained on the castings.

Our investigations were conducted primarily with aluminum alloys, although some gray-iron castings were also produced successfully. Close-grained castings were obtained because of the chilling action of the mold. It appears that this method of sand casting has considerable merit. A case in point is an aircraft radial-engine cylinder head that is cast in dry-sand cores. Cores of this type require much reinforcing and this involves considerable time-consuming labor.

Survey Questions

6-1. What is regarded as the most versatile method for shaping metal?

6-2. Is hand molding considered to be a mass-production method?

6-3. What is the meaning of "snap work" in a foundry?

6-4. Would a steel foundry or an aluminum foundry, making general castings, have the greater amount of floor molding? Why?

6-5. When are cheeks used in sand molding?

6-6. Are molding pits and foundry flasks used interchangeably?

6-7. Of what materials are foundry flasks made?

6-8. Name the top as well as the bottom parts of a sand mold.

6-9. List some advantages of machine molding over hand molding.

6-10. What type of casting is molded by squeezers?

6-11. Is a squeezer capable of uniform ramming?

6-12. Are there other names for jolters?

6-13. A plain jolter is capable of what molding function?

6-14. On what class of work is a jolt-squeezer preferable?

6-15. To what operation does "drawing a pattern" refer?

6-16. List the methods used for removing a pattern from a sand mold mechanically.

6-17. Is a sand slinger a complete molding unit?

6-18. On what basis should a choice between molding-machine types be made?

6-19. What are some of the pronounced advantages of the Croning molding process?

6-20. Is the sand aggregate for shell molds the same as for foundry sand molds?

6-21. How does the binder function in shell molding?

CHAPTER 7

SANDLESS CASTING METHODS

The concept of making castings by pouring molten metal into molds of a composition other than sand has its roots in antiquity. Sand molds are, except in extremely rare cases, capable of but one casting operation. Pouring the mold destroys it—the only salvage is the recovered molding sand. The important cost item of molding labor cannot be salvaged.

Despite the fact that sand molds, and their resulting castings, are being produced at favorable cost rates, they are encountering increasing competition from other casting methods. The supplier of castings must be alert to merchandizing his product, since his industry has passed the day when the customer was tractable. Specifications extend beyond purely metallurgical considerations and include such other items as dimensional accuracy, trueness to pattern, and, especially, surface finish.

Sandless Castings. There are several casting methods available to industry in which molding sand plays no part. Each of these offers some distinguishing property; at the same time, all are hampered by limitations insofar as versatility is concerned. Sandless castings are credited with the following advantages over sand castings:

1. Better surface finish
2. Closer dimensional accuracy
3. Greater possible speed of production
4. Reduction of scrap losses
5. Conservation of raw material
6. Lower machining costs
7. Lower finishing costs
8. Better mechanical properties in the casting

Centrifugal Castings

Castings of cylindrical shape lend themselves admirably to the centrifugal process (Fig. 7-1). There are modifications attendant upon the centrifugal casting process. The distinction between centrifugal castings and centrifuged castings should be understood. Centrifuged castings are produced in sand molds which are arranged in such a position on the casting machine that they can be rotated about a central axis. The sprue is located concentrically with the axis in order that pouring can be done while the molds are rotated about the sprue.

Centrifugal castings, on the other hand, are produced in molds rotating about their own axis. The mold axis may be horizontal, vertical, or inclined, depending on the dimensions of the casting, or, as in the case of the inclined axis, the internal shape desired in the casting. External shape is generated by the internal mold surface. Hollow cylinders are the most common forms of centrifugal castings, but fluted and hexagonal exteriors are also cast.

Fig. 7-1.   A group of typical centrifugal castings.   (Courtesy of Campbell-Wyant & Cannon Foundry Co., Muskegon, Mich.)

Metal molds are general for centrifugal castings. Other designs include such innovations as carbon molds, baked sand molds, and clay-lined molds. A development used in German foundries for casting steel gun tubes during World War II consisted of sprinkling the bore of the metal mold with refractory sand. Centrifugal force caused this sand to cling to the mold wall so satisfactorily that no binder was needed with the sand; the lining was renewed for each casting.

Heat generated in the mold during the casting process must be considered, since a relation exists between mold temperature and required speed of mold rotation.   D. S. deLauvaud, a Brazilian engineer, invented the method of centrifugally casting pipe in metal molds.   This method was introduced and developed in American by the U.S. Cast Iron Pipe and Foundry Company about 1925.

Centrifugal casting can be traced to the beginning of the nineteenth century in the patent office. Superiority is claimed for centrifugal castings because the casting action assures sound metal and fine-grained structure, with any slag or inclusions appearing at the inside of the casting where they can be removed by a subsequent machining operation. Gun tubes, liners, brake drums, bushing stock, and gear blanks, together with cast-iron pipe, constitute the bulk of the castings produced by the centrifugal method.

Permanent-mold Castings

Permanent-mold castings are also termed gravity die castings because they are produced in metal molds that are poured directly from the ladle. A distinction exists in this casting method between *permanent molds*, where mold and components are made of metal, and *semipermanent molds*, in which dry-sand cores are used in conjunction with metal molds. Permanent molds are used for casting both ferrous and nonferrous metals, the greater part of production being in the latter classification.

Permanent-mold castings have a finer-grained structure and in consequence are of higher strength than sand castings of the same metal. They have good surface finish, since they are cast against a machined surface. All the usual metals are satisfactorily cast in permanent molds, but the aluminum alloys predominate. Automotive pistons are largely cast by this method. There are many other applications, including vacuum cleaner housings, valve bodies, and gear laps. This method is economical for production runs of a wide range.

A permanent mold is made from a fine-grained cast iron. The mold can be cast to approximate shape, requiring only a finishing operation, or the mold is machined from a solid block of cast iron. Larger molds are built up, as are molds of complicated shape, for economy in manufacturing cost.

While production-type molds are built from cast iron, other mold materials have proved satisfactory. The author has used a permanent mold of aluminum alloy no. 43 for casting lead ducks used in the drafting room since 1937. This mold has produced several hundred castings and has shown no deterioration other than the normal wear resulting from handling. Some other permanent molds made from no. 43 have been used in the University of Washington foundry laboratory on an experimental basis.

A recent development in England known as the Parlanti Casting Process[1] features permanent molds made from aluminum-alloy castings. They use the British alloy L33 primarily. The process is a patented one and includes such developments as an anodized mold face which is

[1] Developments in the Parlanti Casting Process, *Machinery* (London), Vol. 78, No. 1990, pp. 3–8, Jan. 4, 1951.

sprayed with sillimanite for a refractory coating. Ferrous metals such as cast iron, steel, and heat-resisting steels have been poured successfully. A cast ring 5 ft in diameter, weighing 450 lb, is cast successfully from aluminum alloys by Parlanti.

Another innovation in permanent-mold construction made by the author is that of using steel-reinforced cement-bonded silica-sand molds. These cement molds are poured from a mixture of cement, silica sand, and water. The mold face is given a graphite wash as the refractory coating. Our experience with these molds has been satisfactory for casting aluminum alloys. One such mold produced 25 consecutive castings in 30 min.

Parting lines on permanent molds are in a vertical plane, with sprue and risers located so that they are bisected by this plane, for ease of removal when the mold is opened. Parting-line locations require careful study, since the mold is rigid and does not yield to the casting, which is contracting as it cools.

Castings must be designed for suitability to the permanent-mold process. Such items as undercuts, drawbacks, and coring can be successfully cared for to a degree but the versatility of the sand mold is impossible to achieve. Permanent-mold castings are generally of thin section; mass concentrations are avoided since they cause difficulty in cooling, with subsequent slowing of production.

Permanent-mold Design and Operation. Mold design and gating systems require fundamental knowledge of the permanent-mold process. Mechanical details of mold operation vary from hinged molds to sliding types. Closing mechanisms are also varied as to design; most depend on a mechanical action, but pneumatic as well as hydraulic systems are used for this purpose. The latter are especially well suited to permanent-mold production machines. Where production requirements are sufficiently high, permanent molds can be installed on a continuous casting machine. Such an installation permits continuous pouring that results in a high output rate.

Two important requirements of permanent-mold operation for proper casting results are temperature control and venting. Temperature control includes both heating and cooling. Molds in a continuous pouring system are made with radiating fins so placed that a stream of air can be blown over them for controlled cooling. Individual molds are also made with cooling fins located opposite heavy, or slow-freezing, casting sections. Another device used for local chilling is that of a copper stud screwed into the mold just short of the mold face with a considerable part of the threaded stud protruding from the outer mold surface. Where casting sections are thin and premature cooling starts, the mold can be insulated with asbestos or other material.

The problem of venting the mold must also be solved, since the mold is impervious to air. An easy solution is at hand when the gating system is open to the top of the mold cavity. Slanting the mold while pouring is one expedient for venting. Using a sectional construction in a part of the mold in an arrangement whereby venting space is permitted between sections is another solution of the venting problem.

Metal cores are a featured part of permanent-mold construction. Cores are always given draft of about 1 per cent of their length. Suitable provisions must be made for pulling the cores, which is a critical item. Cores are sometimes made in sections so they can be removed. For

Fig. 7-2. Semipermanent mold, showing dry-sand cores in place. (*Courtesy of Eaton Mfg. Co., Detroit.*)

example, in aluminum-alloy pistons where a three-sectioned core is used, the center section is pulled first and then the remaining sections can be withdrawn by a combined sidewise and upward motion. Metal cores must be protected by a coating such as a graphite-water paint, chalk, or a rouge-graphite mixture.

A permanent mold is usually gated in such a way that the metal enters from the bottom in order to eliminate splashing and minimize turbulence. A helpful device used for checking gating and mold design is that of pouring the newly made mold by using successively colder metal. The resulting misrun castings will show the behavior of the metal as it filled the mold.

Semipermanent molds feature the use of dry-sand cores as a replacement for metal ones. Such design permits more intricate internal cavities (Fig. 7-2). The cores are set into the mold much as in sand casting

practice.   Dry sand being permeable, they aid in solving the mold venting problem.

Permanent molds must be coated with a refractory lining to prevent
castings from sticking to the mold and also as a protection against metal
erosion.   There may be a base lining that is given a subsequent wash, as
is common practice where gray iron is cast.   A simple method for
producing a uniform and effective coating is to smoke the mold with an
acetylene gas flame.

Slush casting is a modification of permanent-mold casting.   A mold is
filled with molten metal and after a crust has formed the remainder of
the molten metal is poured out of the casting.   The resultant casting has
a satisfactory exterior although the interior is rough.   Small toys are
frequently produced by this process, which eliminates the necessity for
using internal cores.

Die Casting

Die castings are produced in metal dies into which molten metal is
forced under pressure.   Die casting differs from permanent-mold casting
in several respects:

1. Metal is cast under pressure.
2. Steel dies are used.
3. Casting cycle is entirely mechanical.
4. Operating cycle is faster.
5. Greater dimensional accuracy is achieved.
6. Better surface finish.
7. Tooling cost is higher.

High volume demand is the justification for die casting, with its tremendous production potential.

Classification of Die Castings.   Die castings are produced from nonferrous alloys almost exclusively.   Nonferrous alloys, from the standpoint
of die castings, are grouped as the low- and the high-melting-point types.
Low-melting-point types, in this classification, are those which are cast
well below 1000°F.   From a volume standpoint, zinc alloys are of
greatest importance, although there are some die castings made from lead
as well as tin alloys.   Aluminum alloys lead in the field of high-melting-
point types on a production-volume basis; the copper-base alloys and
those of magnesium are also in the high-melting-point category.   It is
well to remember these distinctions, since a die casting machine is
designed for one or the other and not for both.   There are machines that
can be changed over by modifications on the casting end.

Cold-chamber Die Casting.   Die casting machines of the cold-
chamber type are used for the high-melting-point alloys.   Cold-chamber
machines require the use of an auxiliary melting furnace in which the

metal is melted for casting (Fig. 7-3). The operator transfers the molten metal to the cold chamber with a hand ladle for each casting cycle. The balance of the casting cycle proceeds automatically, including the ejection of the finished casting. Typical cold-chamber machines, die-casting aluminum alloys, are capable of delivering from 80 to 200 casting cycles per hour. The operating principles of the cold-chamber machine are shown in Fig. 7-3.

Submerged-plunger Machines. Submerged-plunger injection machines are used for die-casting the lower-melting-point alloys. The

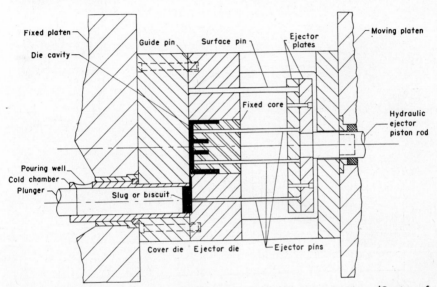

Fig. 7-3. Diagrammatic view of cold-chamber-type machine, showing die casting. (Courtesy of Hydraulic Press Mfg. Co., Mount Gilead, Ohio.)

operator of this type of die casting machine does not ladle molten metal, as is done in the case of the cold-chamber type. These machines are equipped with a hot-metal holding furnace in which molten metal is stored for feeding the injection system. A plunger works in a submerged cylinder that delivers a metered volume of molten metal to a gooseneck and its connecting die nozzle. There is some variation in the design of this metal feeding and pressure system as between different manufacturers. Operation is automatic in that the casting cycle is completed without interruption once the machine has been started on its operating cycle. Note that in the submerged-plunger machines all injection elements must be capable of withstanding the temperatures of the molten metal. Herein lies the reason for two design types; with the higher-melting-point alloys the problem of finding suitable metals for injection

elements has not been solved.   A typical die casting machine of the submerged-plunger type is shown in Fig. 7-4.

Dies and Die Operation.   Dies are made by sinking the desired die
impression into steel blocks or steel forgings.   A recent innovation in
die making is that of casting the dies by a precision casting method.
Dies consist of at least two parts, since they must open for removal of the
die casting.   Where the die casting is of intricate design, the die will need

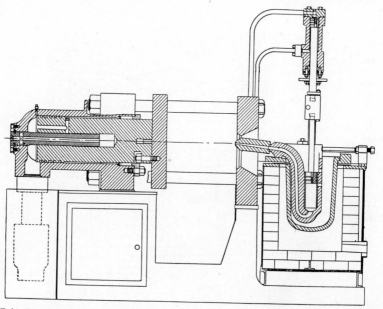

Fig. 7-4.   Diagrammatic view of submerged-plunger-type die casting machine. (Courtesy of
Hydraulic Press Mfg. Co., Mount Gilead, Ohio.)

additional parts to provide for undercutting and similar features on the
casting.

The part of the die through which the molten metal is injected is
fastened to the fixed platen of the machine.   The other part of the die is
fastened to the moving platen, which also carries the ejector plates.
Ejector pins move through this part of the die in such a way as to free the
casting from the die for removal.   These pins must function with correct
timing and must be so located that they do not indent the casting unduly
to the point of marring its surface by dimpling.

Some die casting designs require the use of cores.   Most cores are of the
movable type and are "pulled" from the casting mechanically.   Since
the cores are of metal and precision-machined, cored holes of extreme
accuracy are made in die castings.   Die inserts are placed in the die when

it is desirable to cast a part into the die casting. There are occasions when the insert takes the form of a die casting of a dissimilar metal.

Other die features include such items as venting and overflow wells. Most dies are water-cooled for temperature control under high-production operating cycles. Die life varies primarily with the type of metal cast. Zinc alloys are associated with long die life; production as high as 1 million shots has been recorded. Aluminum alloys tend to erode dies, and higher casting temperatures contribute to shortening useful die life to about one-quarter of this figure; with copper-

Fig. 7-5. Die-casting a spotlight shell on a universal-type die casting machine. (*Courtesy of Cleveland Automatic Machine Co., Cleveland.*)

base alloys, die life is even shorter. A die casting machine is shown in operation in Fig. 7-5.

It is difficult to give an exact production rate for die castings, since casting design and required metal volume are never alike in any two cases. However, an average maximum rate for low-melting-point alloys can be stated as 550 shots per hr with high-melting-point alloys reaching somewhat less than half that rate.

Research and development continue to show new possibilities in the die casting method of production. An adaptation of the cold-chamber design has been used for producing die castings of steel. Innovations consist of using tungsten carbide for injection elements and silicone lubricants to prevent premature die burning.[1]   A large die casting of an aluminum alloy has recently been perfected (Fig. 7-6).

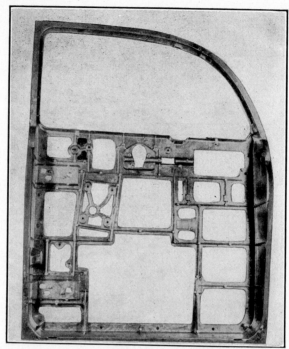

Fig. 7-6.   A die casting of an inner-door panel for an automobile body.   (Courtesy of Doehler-Jarvis Corp., New York.)

Precision Castings

Renewed interest in methods for producing castings of a degree of accuracy sufficient to eliminate the necessity for machining developed during World War II.   This trend in casting production has been so pronounced and its development so rapid that terminology has failed to keep pace.   The basic idea is not new; there is a record of precision casting in plaster by Benvenuto Cellini in the sixteenth century. Undoubtedly similar work had an even earlier beginning.

Terms employed for describing this general method include precision casting, precision refractory casting, plaster molding, precision investment casting, micro-casting, and lost wax casting.   All these terms do not refer to exactly the same thing, since a distinction is made between the method in which the pattern is expended with each molding operation and the one in which a permanent pattern is used.

[1] Stanton, R. B.: Steel Die-castings Produced Successfully, *American Machinist*, Vol. 93, No. 1, pp. 118–119, 1949.

Predominant interest attaches to the method using expendable patterns. Castings of a high degree of precision are made from a wide range of metal alloys and, in the case of some of the complex high-temperature-resistant alloys, this is the only economical manufacturing method available. Some examples of castings made by this method are shown in Fig. 7-7. While the castings shown are intricate, the method is not confined to small sizes; aluminum-alloy castings weighing approximately 24 lb are in production.

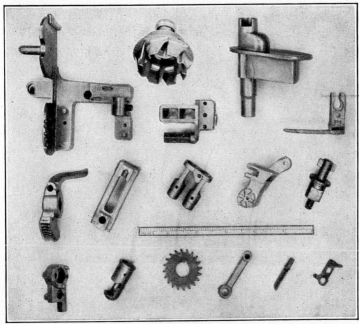

Fig. 7-7. A representative group of precision castings made by the expendable-pattern method. (*Courtesy of Precision Metalsmiths, Inc., Cleveland.*)

Precision Investment Castings. For the sake of uniformity the term precision investment castings will be employed here, since this usage is sponsored by the American Foundrymen's Society. Precision investment castings are made by casting metal into a mold from which an expendable pattern has been removed by melting, combustion, evaporation, or solution. For a more detailed description, it seems best to start with the pattern and follow the production sequences through to the final casting.

A master pattern is machined to a size that makes provision for process shrinkage to the finally desired dimensions of the casting. *It is here that the precision of the casting is established.* Extreme care must be exercised in making the master pattern because it in turn is used for making the die, or mold, in which the expendable patterns are produced.   No compromise with accuracy can be permitted in the making of the master pattern.

The molds in which the expendable patterns are produced are made from a variety of materials including soft metals, light metals, vulcanized rubber, carbon steels, plastics, and alloy steels.

Patterns in turn are made by injecting the expendable material into the mold.   Pattern material is generally selected from among beeswax, carnauba wax, petroleum wax, plastics, mercury, and fusible alloys. Molten wax is injected at pressures of 400 psi into water-cooled molds for some classes of patterns; in others, fusible alloys are poured into the mold under gravity.   A freshly filled mold is permitted to stand for a period of time sufficiently long to ensure solidification of the pattern.

Upon removal from the mold the pattern is checked for accuracy and any slight imperfections are corrected.   Patterns passing inspection are then mounted or clustered on requisite gating and sprue systems (these assemblies are frequently referred to as trees).   Wax patterns are readily joined by heating abutting surfaces until they flow together.   Careful handling is called for in placing patterns; they must be arranged in a manner that will facilitate their removal from the investment mold.

The completed pattern assembly is then invested as the next operation. Investment materials are of many kinds; included are such substances as silica flour, quartz, cristobalite, sillimanite, bauxite, gypsum, and plaster of Paris.   A point to remember in choosing the investment material is that it should be free of impurities; the possibility of its reacting with the casting metal at pouring temperatures must also be kept in mind.   Proprietary investment compounds, which simplify plant operations, are available.   Water is used as the vehicle, although chemical compounds are not uncommon for developing special properties in binding, rate of setting, and modifying mold permeability.

Investment procedures are varied; the choice depends primarily upon the casting finish desired.   For a very smooth casting surface the pattern is dipped into a silica-flour solution—a practice termed "coating".   When the first coat has set, the pattern may be dipped into a second solution of coarser material and then be placed in a flask for final investing.   It is more common practice, however, to place the pattern in the flask and pour in the investment without regard to a preliminary surface coating. Investing a pattern requires control; segregation in the investment material must be avoided and at the same time the patterns must be accurately covered.   Some investment techniques employ vibration, while in others the mold is slanted for desired results; tamping is also used. The major objective is to eliminate air bubbles from the solidifying investment.   A vacuum process of treating the freshly invested pattern has proved successful for eliminating air pockets (Fig. 7-8).

In some investing operations asbestos sheet is used to line the inside of the flask as an aid toward developing mold permeability. Vacuuming promotes mold permeability, since air bubbles are drawn along the path of least resistance, *i.e.*, away from the pattern and toward the outside of the mold. Evaporation of water in the investment while the mold is being processed is another source of mold permeability.

Upon completion of the investment operation the molds are permitted to harden for a period, the length of time depending upon the composition of the investment. Molds are then placed in a furnace, in an inverted

Fig. 7-8. Newly invested mold is treated in vacuum to remove air pockets. (*Courtesy of Precision Metalsmiths, Inc., Cleveland.*)

position, for the burnout operation. Temperature ranges are such that the pattern material will soften and flow out of the mold through the gating system; this may be done in one furnace or by a differential treatment using two furnaces. In the latter case the mold is brought to a relatively high temperature, approximately 1600°F for pouring heat-resistant alloys.

Most casting is done in a heated mold, but some casts are poured at room temperature. Conditions governing procedure are flowability of the casting metal, intricateness of casting design, and the need to prevent moisture accumulation within the mold cavity.

Molds are permitted to cool prior to breaking out the castings. No effort is made to salvage the used investment material; on the contrary, a disposal problem is created by this material. The final operation in precision investment casting is that of removing the gates. Grinding the gates is generally the only machine or mechanical work necessary on the castings.

PLASTER CASTING

A formidable number of castings are produced using plaster of Paris as the investment material. This method, as described here, differs from the previously presented precision investment casting technique in that *a metal pattern is used*. To be sure, various plasters and compounds are used for investment material. Investment material is mixed dry and introduced into the flask with water as a vehicle. The molding opera-

Fig. 7-9. Frozen-mercury precision patterns are dipped in cold refractory mix and hung up to dry in icebox at −60°C (−76°F). (*Courtesy of Sperry Gyroscope Co., Great Neck, N.Y.*)

tion is similar to sand practice, since the mold is jolted and, after the plaster has started to harden, is drawn off the pattern.

Molds are immediately placed in a conveyor-type furnace, where both free water and water of hydration are driven off with temperatures reaching 1650°F. Cooling of the mold follows in the same furnace. Any necessary cores are made of the same material as the investment. These are processed and placed in the molds just prior to pouring. Pouring is done over the lip and generally through an asbestos paper tube that is inserted into the sprue. Tube height aids in developing hydrostatic pressure within the mold cavity.

Mercury-pattern Precision Castings. A recent development in precision casting introduces the novel idea of making the expendable patterns of mercury, which is poured into the master mold and then frozen.

Following this operation, the frozen-mercury pattern is invested at sub-normal temperatures (Fig. 7-9). Upon reaching room temperature, the now fluid mercury is poured from the mold for re-use. Salvaging the pattern material is an economical aspect of the process, which is one capable of producing extremely accurate castings.

Survey Questions

7-1. Are foundry sand molds capable of re-use?

7-2. Are sandless castings confined to any particular type or kind of metal?

7-3. How are centrifuged castings poured?

7-4. Is centrifugal casting confined to the use of metal molds?

7-5. Name the product responsible for the greatest tonnage of centrifugal castings.

7-6. With what term is "gravity die casting" synonymous?

7-7. Are the mechanical properties of permanent-mold castings inferior or superior to sand types of the same composition?

7-8. Explain the Parlanti permanent-mold development.

7-9. Of what materials are permanent molds made?

7-10. Wherein do semipermanent molds differ from permanent molds?

7-11. State any shortcomings of the permanent-mold casting method.

7-12. How is coring cared for in permanent molds?

7-13. What type of castings is produced by the slush-casting method?

7-14. Are die castings and permanent-mold castings the same thing?

7-15. Are the ferrous metals produced as die castings?

7-16. Of what metal is the majority of automobile body hardware die-cast?

7-17. What type of machines is used for producing aluminum-alloy die castings?

7-18. How is the molten metal introduced into the die cavity of a submerged plunger-type die casting machine?

7-19. How are the die castings removed from their die?

7-20. Of what material are casting dies made?

7-21. Can inserts, such as studs, be cast into die castings?

7-22. Is the development of precision castings of recent origin?

7-23. What are master patterns?

7-24. Name the investment materials used most generally.

7-25. Where is mercury used in precision casting?

REFERENCES

Cady, Edwin L.: "Precision Investment Casting," Reinhold Publishing Corporation, New York, 1948.

Chase, Herbert: "Die Castings," John Wiley & Sons, Inc., New York, 1934.

"Metals Handbook," American Society for Metals, Cleveland, 1948.

Stern, Marc: "Die-casting Practice," McGraw-Hill Book Company, Inc., New York, 1930.

"Tool Engineers' Handbook," McGraw-Hill Book Company, Inc., New York, 1949.

CHAPTER 8

THE MELT SHOP

Molten metal is required for the production of castings. The function of the melt shop is to produce the necessary molten metal in a suitable condition and quality. The melting range of an alloy is the spread of temperature in which complete fusion occurs. In general, the melting points of the ferrous alloys are higher than those of the nonferrous ones, but the melting range in both classifications is dependent upon the specific composition of the alloy. Cast iron cannot be said to have a definite melting point because of the varied compositions and structural components included in this category. When a gray cast iron contains the phosphorus-rich component Steadite, it will start to melt near 1750°F, whereas ordinary gray cast irons melt in the range of 2000 to 2400°F. Aluminum alloy AN-A-33 (10 per cent mg) has a solidus temperature of 840°F and its liquidus is 1150°F, which gives a melting range of 310°F. These examples serve to show that the spread in melting range is similar in ferrous and nonferrous alloys.

The function of the melt shop is that of remelting, in contradistinction to smelting or refining, the metal charge. The chief exception occurs in the case of duplexing in the steel foundry, where the furnace is given a molten charge. Many melting operations include some type of alloying for analysis adjustment, but here again the furnace is operating on the remelting principle. Variations of the procedures in the melt shop include such innovations as ladle treatment of the melt as well as duplexing and even triplexing, wherein several furnaces are used in a supplementary routine to produce the requisite metal.

Furnaces and Fuels. The cost of melting a pound of metal is the leading consideration, while the chemistry of the melting process, as it affects a given metal, acts to limit the choice of melting equipment in any given case. The first cost of the melting equipment and installation charges also serve as modifying factors. There have been instances where such items as hazards and zoning ordinances have dictated the choice of melting equipment.

Regardless of type of furnace or fuel used, the fundamental of converting the potential energy of the fuel into heat units effective for melting the charge should receive first consideration. Transferring heat units into metal in order to bring about its fusion is the basis of foundry melting furnace design.

Fuels most generally used in foundry melting furnaces together with their calorific values in Btu are shown in Table 8-1.

TABLE 8-1

Fuel	Average gross calorific value, Btu	Unit
Coke................	13,000	lb
Natural gas..........	950	cu ft
Coal gas............	500	cu ft
Fuel oil.............	140,000	gal
Electricity...........	3,415	kwhr

Costs of the fuels listed vary widely with geography—coke showing a low price in the Midwest while electricity is cheapest in the Pacific Northwest, natural gas and fuel oil in the Southwest and other oil-producing areas. The point to note here is that fuel costs and availability must be studied for each locality in order to reach an intelligent decision on a given projected installation.

Furnace Heat Losses. Heat losses vary considerably with different furnace types. The crucible furnace has an over-all efficiency of 5 per cent maximum, whereas the coke-fired cupola will use up to 35 per cent of the total heat potential. Open-hearth practice indicates about 20 per cent of the heat used for molten steel with an additional increment being consumed by the slag. Electric arc furnaces show a 10 to 15 per cent over-all efficiency, the variation being accounted for largely in design and operation.

Waste gases account for the major part of the heat loss. There are installations, such as checkers on open-hearths, waste heat boilers on large reverberatory furnaces, and hot stoves on blast furnaces, that improve the over-all operating efficiency. The only major attempt at salvaging heat from furnace gases in the melt shop is the installation of the hot blast cupola.

Radiation heat losses also cut down the efficiency of the melting furnace. It is not always desirable to insulate a furnace against radiation losses since such insulation may have adverse effects on the life of the furnace lining.

The selection of the type of melting furnace is rather clearly defined as between ferrous and nonferrous metals. Since the former run to tonnage capacities, they are melted in furnaces of the direct-flame type for the most part. Nonferrous metals are poured in smaller-volume castings, with the result that their melting equipment is generally of the indirect-flame type. Exceptions are found in the case of the copper-base alloys, which are melted in such a wide variety of furnaces as the crucible, the indirect-arc, the direct-flame and, on occasion, the cupola furnace. The most versatile piece of melting equipment is the induction furnace, which is used for melting all foundry metals.

Cupola Furnace. The cupola furnace, or cupola, as it is termed in the industry, derives its name from the old Germanic word *Kuppel*, meaning stack (Fig. 8-1). The construction of the cupola is simple; it consists of

Fig. 8-1. A battery of four 66-in. cupolas. Metal from two cupolas being tapped into 6,000-lb U-shaped reservoir ladles. (*Courtesy of Whiting Corporation, Harvey, Ill.*)

a cylindrical steel shell open at the top, equipped with hinged doors at the bottom which can be swung into position for closing the bottom of the shell.

An opening in the shell just above the mantle is the location for the breast; here the tap hole is located, being built in with a clay-base mixture. Opposite to the breast and at a somewhat higher level is another opening through the shell, which is used for the slag notch. Circumscribing the shell at its lower end is the wind box; it is connected to the blower through suitable blast piping. Openings between the wind box and the furnace are known as tuyères; these may be a single row situated in a radial plane or there may be more than one row arranged in echelon. There is an opening equipped with a hinged door located several feet above the slag notch, through which the charges enter the furnace.

Cupolas are usually lined with fire-clay brick. However, cupola blocks are available and when these are used, there are fewer lining joints, which are points of weakness and the location for the start of lining failures. Plastic refractory compounds are available from which monolithic linings can be rammed, thereby entirely eliminating brick or blocks. When being prepared for operation, the cupola lining is given a protective coating of daubing made up of fire sand and refractory clay moistened to the consistency of stiff mud. After each heat, the daubing and its adhering slag are chipped off preparatory to the next daubing treatment.

Metallurgical coke is universally used for fueling the cupola. When charging the cupola, coke is placed on the bottom sand, which has previously been rammed over the bottom doors to protect them and also to direct the molten metal so that it will drain toward the tap hole. Coke is ignited by a torch flame impinging through the breast or by dry kindling placed ahead of the coke. As the first coke becomes fully ignited, additional coke is added, until the desired depth of coke bed has been laid. Bed height is an important consideration for achieving proper melting results.

When the bed charge has been fully ignited, the first metal charge is placed, with heavy material preceding the smaller pieces. The metal charge is followed by a coke charge, or split, until the cupola is filled to the level of the charging door. The metal charges and coke splits are held to a constant weight, in a range from 7:1 to as high as 12:1. These so-termed melting ratios refer to the number of pounds of metal that can be melted with 1 lb of coke in the split charges. If, then, the coke split weighs 40 lb, the metal charge will weigh 400 lb when a 1:10 melting ratio is being used. For sustained melting, flux—such as limestone, marble chips, or other calcium material—is charged on the coke layer to slag off coke ash and impurities introduced with the metal charge.

The cupola is tapped intermittently in the smaller operations; in the case of furnaces of larger capacity it may deliver molten metal continuously. At the conclusion of the heat, the prop holding the bottom doors in place is knocked out, thereby releasing the remaining coke and slag through the bottom—a spectacular display results.

Innovations in cupola design are frequent. A noteworthy example is that of using the heat of the escaping gases for heating the incoming blast in order to improve operation and increase the melting ratio efficiency. Installations in which blast is dried by freezing to eliminate moisture in the blast are an important feature in controlling cupola melting. Cupola operation is not a simple matter if quality metal of correct temperature is to be produced.[1]

Cast irons constitute the bulk of the metals melted in the cupola furnace. Gray cast iron, alloyed cast iron and white cast iron are melted

[1] For detailed information see "Cupola Operations Handbook," American Foundrymen's Association, Chicago, 1944.

in the cupola.   Copper is on occasion melted in the cupola, with ladle additions for making copper-base alloys.

Converter. The side-blow converter, also known as the Tropenas, is a modification of the better known bottom-blow Bessemer type.   Side-blow converters are employed for making foundry steel by a duplexing process (Fig. 8-2).   The converter metal is melted in a cupola and is then charged into the converter for refining into steel.   This method of

Fig. 8-2.   One of a battery of four 6-ton side-blow converters in operation.   (*Courtesy of Whiting Corporation, Harvey, Ill.*)

duplexing played an important role during World War II as a rapid means of producing steel for castings.

A shallow bath of molten metal is used for the converter charge.   Air blast approximating 4 lb in pressure is turned onto the molten bath.   The converter steelmaking process is one of oxidation.   The reaction of the oxygen in the blast with the oxidizable elements of the charge is an exothermic one that supplies all necessary heat for steelmaking.   The reactions within the converter are gauged by both the appearance and the volume of the flame issuing from the mouth of the converter.   Formerly the operator depended upon visual observation entirely; however, accurate operation is now obtained through electronic control equipment developed by the Jones and Laughlin Steel Company.

After the "blow," which is of 15 to 20 min duration, the steel is recarburized in the vessel; the converter is then turned down and its contents are discharged into a ladle containing any necessary deoxidizers. Low sulfur and phosphorous pig iron must be charged into the cupola for producing converter metal, although sulfur can be reduced by a soda-ash treatment in the cupola receiving ladle. Low equipment and installation costs, economy in melting and refining, coupled with rapid processing time, form a combination that makes the converter a competitor of any melting equipment installation in the steel melt shop.

Fig. 8-3. Tapping duplexed malleable iron from pulverized coal-fired air furnace. (*Courtesy of Whiting Corporation, Harvey, III.*)

Air Furnace. In the malleable iron foundry the melt shop is equipped for air-furnace operation where tonnage is required. Metal for malleable cast iron in smaller quantities is produced in the cupola or the electric arc furnace. There are some large-tonnage installations where duplexing is practiced—cupola melted metal is charged into the air furnace for subsequent refining.

An air furnace is large, with a long narrow hearth that has a firing area at one end and a stack at the opposite end (Fig. 8-3). Construction is primarily of fire-clay brick with a steel framework that provides the requisite stability for hearth, side walls, and roof. The hearth is built of fire-clay brick or silica sand or both. Roof sections of an arch shape, known as bungs, are designed to reflect heat downward upon the metal charge. This contoured roof design, resulting in reflected heat, gives rise to the application of the term *reverberatory* to the air furnace.

An air furnace is usually charged through the roof after removal of some of the bungs. Heat for melting and refining is generated by powdered coal or oil firing. The combustion gases flow over the charge to the stack, thereby heating both the furnace lining and the charged metal. Melting results from the action of the hot gases in combination with reflected heat from the furnace lining. In a furnace with a 25-ton charge the melting time will approximate 6 hr. Increased efficiency results from using preheated air obtained through a recuperator that is a part of the furnace installation. Direct-flame action, or contact between the fuel and the charge, does not occur in the air furnace.

Fig. 8-4. General view of a 5-ton Brackelsberg furnace in a malleable iron foundry. (*Courtesy of Whiting Corporation, Harvey, Ill.*)

When the charge is completely melted, it has become covered with slag formed from bottom material and adhering sand on the charged scrap. Refining action is accomplished after slag removal by maintaining an oxidizing flame above the molten bath on the hearth. Since the refining time is of some duration, it is possible to take samples and thereby to adjust the composition of the bath to desired specifications.

Air furnaces offer the favorable combination of quality metal in large quantities at an attractive cost. Large-sized scrap can be charged without difficulty where mechanical handling is used. Air furnaces are exclusive to the melt shop of the malleable iron foundry.

Brackelsberg Furnace. There are a few installations of a furnace constructed of a cylindrical steel shell lined with silica brick and fired with powdered coal through one end; this is known as the Brackelsberg furnace. This furnace rotates about its major axis, which is in a horizontal plane (Fig. 8-4). Melting is rapid and of low cost, owing to the use of powdered coal.   Capacities range from 4 to 8 tons per charge.   Melting efficiency is highest with continuous operation because of the heated lining; in consequence the Brackelsberg furnace is best adapted to round-the-clock operation.   Iron of gray as well as of white composition is melted in this type of furnace.

Crucible Furnace.   A crucible furnace has a cylindrical steel shell built with a rammed or bricked lining.   It has a cover that is either tilted, lifted, or swung clear to afford access to the crucible.   Heat is supplied through burners from either oil or gas as fuel; solid fuel is obsolete in cur-

Fig. 8-5.   Twin-fired crucible furnace.   (*Courtesy of Randall Foundry Equipment Corp., Cleveland.*)

rent furnace designs.   Furnaces are built for tilting on trunnions or they may be stationary, in which case the crucible must be lifted out of the furnace.

Crucibles are refractory containers, more or less barrel-shaped, open at the top where the pouring lip is located.   They are made of a mixture of fire clay and graphite that has been mixed into a stiff mud and is then shaped on a potter's dolly.   After forming, crucibles are baked and finally treated at a temperature sufficiently high to drive off the water of hydration.   Since the firing is not sufficiently intense to vitrify the clay, crucibles are susceptible to moisture pickup; consequently, crucibles should be heated to drive off absorbed moisture prior to installation in the furnace.   Crucibles are made from a variety of refractory materials; among them magnesia, silica, and silicon carbide are prominent.

There are many modifications of crucible furnaces; a novel design, with two furnaces operating in series, is shown in Fig. 8-5. These furnaces are of the crucible lift-out type, with burners located in the cover of one furnace. The crucible under the fired cover contains the metal to be melted. The combustion gases are channeled from this furnace into the second chamber, where they preheat its crucible. After the first crucible is drawn, the covers are reversed to bring the preheated crucible into the melting position, and a fresh one is charged into the previously emptied chamber.

Fig. 8-6.   Fisher oil-fired melting furnace remelting scrap brass.   (*Courtesy of Lindberg Engineering Co., Chicago.*)

The so-named pot furnace, in which a cast-iron pot replaces the ceramic crucible, is popular for remelting aluminum alloys. Similar furnaces are used for remelting and superheating magnesium alloys, although here pots fabricated from steel plate are used in place of cast-iron ones. This difference in melting containers, as between aluminum and magnesium alloys, is a vital requirement.

Open-flame Furnace. Where large melting capacities are necessary for copper-base alloys, a tilting furnace somewhat similar to the crucible type is used (Fig. 8-6). In this furnace, however, there is no crucible; instead the metal is charged directly into the furnace, where it is subjected to direct flame action. The melting operations of the open-flame furnace can be controlled to provide specification metal, as is evidenced by such castings as large ship propellers, among others (Fig. 5-4).

Electric Arc Melting Furnace. The general appearance of an electric arc melting furnace with top electrodes can be seen in Fig. 8-7. There is a cylindrical steel shell that is integral with a concave bottom. The top is separate and is constructed so as to open for charging or to be removed for repair; in either event, the top consists of a ring into which silica bricks are fitted. Suitable openings for electrode passage are provided by water-cooled castings. There is a charging door in one side of the furnace shell with the tap hole located directly opposite. Trunnions are provided for tilting the furnace when tapping the molten metal or as an aid in charging through the furnace door.

Fig. 8-7. Lectomelt three-phase arc melting furnace installation of 10-12T heat capacity. (*Courtesy of Pittsburgh Lectromelt Furnace Corp., Pittsburgh.*)

Furnace linings require careful attention since they have a short life at best. Linings follow one of two types, depending on whether basic or acid operation is used. In the basic-lined arc furnace the bottom courses are laid with fire-clay bricks. Magnesite bricks are placed on these and up the side walls to a distance above the slag line. The remainder of the lining, as well as the roof, is of silica brick. Magnesite is rammed in to complete the bottom. Bricks are laid dry with allowance for expansion to prevent bulging and lining failure. Numerous designs for water-cooling the lining, above the hearth, are installed to increase its life. Acid-lined furnaces are lined throughout with silica brick, the bottom being made by sintering ganister and silica sand.

There are some single-phase arc furnace installations; however, the great majority are three-phase for reasons of both power-line load and melting speed. Single-phase design has a bottom electrode and conducting bath, the charge forming a part of the electrical circuit. Three-phase arc furnaces have three electrodes in triangular arrangement entering through the roof. The charge is melted and refined by heat radiated from the arcs between the electrodes as well as resistance due to current flow through the bath. The bath is not a part of the circuit but it carries current because its resistance to current flow is lower than the air path between the electrodes.

Rocking-type arc furnaces are designed with the electrodes entering the ends of the furnace. This design prevents arc impingement on the charge, thereby providing means for melting in which there will be no carbon pickup from the electrodes. A second distinctive feature is that the rocking action of the furnace continually stirs the bath, thereby promoting homogeneity. The rocking action is controlled automatically. These furnaces are employed for melting copper-base alloys, nickel alloys, gray and white cast iron, stainless and alloy steels in a capacity range from 10 lb to 2 tons per charge.

Induction Furnace.   The induction furnace is in effect a transformer in which the charge forms the secondary. The primary coil is copper tubing with circulating water acting as a coolant. The charge to be melted is held in a crucible that is placed within the primary coil. The heating energy is transferred by electromagnetic induction from the cold exterior portion of the furnace into the charge. When high-frequency current is applied to the terminals of the primary coil, all the space within the coil is subjected to a rapidly alternating electromagnetic field. Any electrical conductor within this field has currents induced in it; these currents cause rapid heating. Figure 8-8 is a diagrammatic sketch of an induction furnace.

The choice of electrical equipment for providing the necessary high-frequency current is governed by the capacity of the furnace. For use where input requirements do not exceed 40 kw, there is a spark gap converter available. This equipment, which uses single-phase, 220- or 440-v, 60-cycle current, consists of a high-reactance transformer, a discharge gap composed of a mercury pool and two copper electrodes operating in an atmosphere of hydrogen, and a bank of capacitors connected to the furnace primary. Frequencies available from this equipment vary between 20,000 and 40,000 cycles, depending on the furnace size and requirements.

On larger furnaces, a motor-generator set is used for producing currents with frequencies that fall in the range of from 1,000 to 3,000 cycles. These are not fixed values, since melting requirements dictate the choice of current frequencies. There is also mercury arc frequency-changing equipment built that converts three-phase arc power into single-phase power at a frequency of about 1,000 cycles.

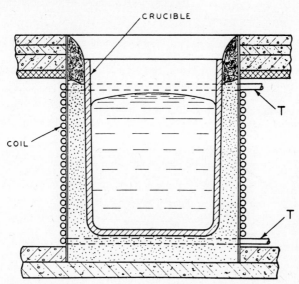

Fig. 8-8. Diagrammatic sketch of a high-frequency induction melting furnace. (*Courtesy of Ajax Electrothermic Corp., Trenton, N.J.*)

The advantage of induction melting is that the charge can be melted entirely free of contamination.   There is no fuel burned and no flame impingement or gas contamination.   Induction melting can be carried on in vacuum or under controlled atmospheric conditions.   Molten metal can be produced under exact control in the induction furnace, hence this is regarded as the best method for melting quality metal.

Survey Questions

8-1. Does gray cast iron have a fixed melting point?
8-2. Do foundry furnaces function as smelting or as melting equipment?
8-3. Explain duplexing as applied to the melt shop.
8-4. Where, in general, are electric melting costs at a minimum?
8-5. List the major sources of heat loss associated with melting furnaces.
8-6. In what type of foundries are cupola furnaces used?
8-7. How and with what materials are cupolas lined?
8-8. Why is a cupola lining daubed?
8-9. What is meant by a 12:1 melting ratio?
8-10. From what sources is cupola blast obtained?
8-11. Describe a typical cupola charge as to composition.
8-12. Is steel melted in a cupola?   Explain.
8-13. In what type of foundries are converters installed?
8-14. Do side-blow and Bessemer converters operate in the same manner?
8-15. Are converters melting furnaces?

8-16. How are air furnaces fueled?

8-17. Are air furnaces charged continuously, as are cupolas?

8-18. Describe the shape of a Brackelsberg furnace. Does it occupy a greater or lesser floor area than a cupola?

8-19. How are crucibles made?

8-20. Where crucible melting is used, how is the molten metal withdrawn from the furnace?

8-21. List the general types of metal that are melted in crucible furnaces.

8-22. Are open-flame furnaces equipped with crucibles?

8-23. Where are electric arc furnaces most generally used?

8-24. Wherein do acid furnaces differ from basic ones?

8-25. Does the metal bath act as a part of the electrical circuit in electric arc furnaces?

8-26. Are nonferrous metals melted in arc furnaces?

8-27. Describe the operating principle of an induction furnace.

8-28. Is there any difference in the electrical circuits in an arc furnace and in an induction furnace?

8-29. What are the chief advantages of induction melting?

REFERENCES

"The Cast Metals Handbook," American Foundrymen's Association, Chicago, 1944.

"Cupola Operations Handbook," American Foundrymen's Association, Chicago, 1944.

Francis, C. B., "The Making, Shaping, and Treating of Steel," 5th ed., Carnegie-Illinois Steel Co., Pittsburgh, 1941.

Hurst, James E.: "Melting Iron in the Cupola," Penton Publishing Company, Cleveland, 1929.

"Metals Handbook," American Society for Metals, Cleveland, 1948.

"Steel Castings Handbook," 2d ed., Steel Founders' Society of America, Cleveland, 1950.

CHAPTER 9

METHODS OF CLEANING CASTINGS

Castings are routed from the pouring floor through the cleaning room for process finishing. The amount of cleaning required, as well as the method employed, is a function of the casting process. Sand castings require more processing than do those produced from permanent molds. There are additional factors that require consideration before a casting cleaning program can be established. Among these are the composition of the casting, the end use, and the type or class of finish desired.

After the casting has been poured, an interval sufficiently long to permit necessary solidification elapses prior to the removal of the casting from the sand mold. "Shaking out" is the generic term applied to this foundry operation. In small foundries, shaking out is a tedious and rather unpleasant manual operation. Production foundries shake out with mechanical devices so designed that the molding sand and flasks are separated from the casting—the former two are recycled into their respective systems and the casting is conveyed to the cleaning operation (Fig. 9-1).

Removal of Gates and Risers. Gates and risers are removed from iron castings by a sharp blow with a hammer. In order to prevent breakage or having the gate break into the casting, the hammer blow should be struck against the sprue in a direction toward the casting. Gates should be lightened at the junction with the casting in order to give a clean break at that point.

Steel castings pose a more difficult problem of gate and riser removal. Some risers can be knocked off, but the majority cannot, because of the nature of the material and also because of the fact that they are generally of large cross section. Torch cutting of risers is the universally accepted practice in the steel foundry.

A sprue-cutting machine similar in design to a small power shear is used in brass and bronze foundries for sprue cutting. Other types of nonferrous castings are separated from gates and risers by band-sawing. Greatest economy results from using a band saw of correct tooth pitch for the metal being cut. Accurate sawing will save subsequent grinding time; care should be exercised to prevent sawing into the casting when removing gates and risers.

Tumbling Mills. Small and intermediate-sized ferrous castings are cleaned of adhering sand in tumbling mills. These mills, or rattlers, as they are known in the foundry, are hollow cylinders equipped with removable staves that form the outside wall. At the center of each end are placed trunnions on which the mill rotates. Castings that have had

Fig. 9-1.   25-ton mold shakeout machine, showing mold being lowered for shakeout. (*Courtesy of Allis-Chalmers Mfg. Co., Milwaukee.*)

their sprues removed are packed into the mill through the side opening created by the removal of adjacent staves. Care should be taken to avoid an admixture of heavy and light castings in a load as a precaution against breakage. Small pieces such as rattler stars, steel slugs, gate scrap, sprues, and risers are included with each load. Cleaning results when the mill is rotated, causing the castings to rub against each other and the smaller pieces to ride over casting surfaces.

Tumbled castings have a bright and clean surface finish. It is only in cases of severely fused sand that additional cleaning is necessary. Adhering sand that is removed in tumbling is carried from the mill by a connected exhaust system. Figure 9-2 shows tumbling mills equipped with exhaust systems.

Tilted mills, open at the top or small end, are used for cleaning some copper-base castings. Abrasives, sawdust, or cereal products are charged with the castings to impart a polish. Mills of this type are operated with either a wet or a dry load, depending on the surface finish desired on the work. Some horizontal mills are also operated with a wet load, but polishing rather than sand removal is the objective. Mills in which polished balls are charged with the load are used for burnishing.

Blast Cleaning. Impact cleaning, as originally practiced, consisted of directing a stream of sand of high velocity against the surface to be

Fig. 9-2. An installation of tumbling mills connected with an exhaust system. (*Courtesy of W. W. Sly Mfg. Co., Cleveland.*)

cleaned. The cleaned surface has a pleasing appearance, and adhering sand can be completely removed no matter how tenaciously it may cling to the casting. The use of sand for impact cleaning has all but disappeared because of the introduction of metal abrasives. Sand grains shatter rather easily, thereby losing their efficiency and at the same time creating a dust problem.

Metal abrasives have been developed that are now used as the material for blast cleaning. These are made from cupola melted metal by causing the fine metal streams leaving the cupola spout to be blown by an air stream or steam jet. The blowing action is such that the resulting metal globules are directed into a water quench which gives them a high degree of hardness. The globules, or shot, are then screened for sizing and grading in accordance with standard specifications.

Metal abrasive shot are spherical; consequently, when used for impact cleaning, they give the effect of peening with a multitude of miniature ball-peen hammers.   The resulting surface is not satisfactory for enameling, plating, or galvanizing; however, the process of shot peening is also useful for increasing fatigue resistance of stressed members.

Metal shot that fail to meet specifications are further processed by a crushing operation that shatters them into sharp-edged and -angled particles.   These particles, known as angular grit, are used in blast cleaning and produce a mat finish on the blasted surface.   The cleaning action of grit can be likened to the effect of using many minute chisels.   Surface imperfections are exposed by these sharp-edged cutting abrasives.   The choice of metal abrasives as between shot or grit is governed both by the nature of the surface to be cleaned and the type of surface finish desired. Blast cleaning as a method for surface preparation cannot be handled in a haphazard manner.

Air-blast abrasives, whether sand or metal, must strike with a high impact value if their action is to be effective.   Compressed air, as the vehicle for carrying abrasives, is well known.   In air blasting, the abrasive is stored in a container and is introduced into the air stream at a regulated rate.   Methods of accomplishing this are the direct pressure principle, the gravity feed system (where gravitational forces act only to introduce the abrasive into the air stream), and the suction system, in which the abrasive is lifted from its container by static vacuum developed in the blast gun.   An example of an air-blast cleaning room is shown in Fig. 9-3.

The air stream carrying the abrasive is directed against the surface through a nozzle.   The latter is subjected to a high degree of wear and must be renewed frequently if top performance is to be maintained. Nozzles are available in diverse designs and various materials, ranging from iron pipe to hard alloys.   Positioning the nozzle with respect to the work is another modifying factor in air-blast cleaning, since the cross-sectional area of the blast stream increases as it lengthens.   A larger pattern results when the nozzle is moved farther from the work, but at the same time abrasive velocities are slowed.

Water-blast Systems.   Water is used as the vehicle for carrying the abrasive in water-blast cleaning.   This design has been in successful operation for several years.   Stream velocities of 20,000 fpm are used with this equipment, which is capable of removing cores as well as adhering sand.   Water-blast systems are economical to use, since both water and sand can be reclaimed for re-use.   A water-blast room installation is pictured in Fig. 9-4.   All types of metal castings can be cleaned with water blast.

Fig. 9-3. Air-blast cleaning room with open floor for passing the abrasive. *(Courtesy of W. W. Sly Mfg. Co., Cleveland.)*

Fig. 9-4. Water-blast cleaning room in operation at the Philadelphia Naval Shipyard. This room is open at the top, since there is no dust problem. *(Courtesy of The Hydro-Blast Corp., Chicago.)*

Mud Blasting.   Mud blasting is a system in which a very fine abrasive is used for delicate cleaning operations.   Polishing discolored machined surfaces can also be done by mud blasting.   Mud-blast systems for polishing employ abrasives of widely differing character extending from extremely fine silica powder to cereals.   Equipment is not on the large scale that is characteristic of water blasting.

Airless Blast Methods.   The idea of propelling abrasives by centrifugal force rather than by air velocity is almost as old as blast cleaning itself. The development of suitable propelling wheels has resulted in three recognized systems, known respectively as (*a*) batter type, (*b*) slider type, and (*c*) valveless type wheels.   The principal differences between them stem from the method of introducing the abrasive to the wheel and, further, from the action of the abrasive while in contact with the wheel.

Design trends have been in this direction to the extent that modern production equipment is mainly of the centrifugal type.   Casting handling equipment has been built around the centrifugal unit to the point of eliminating a substantial amount of the labor formerly necessary to the casting cleaning operation.

In the case of smaller castings and in those instances where batch operation is satisfactory, cleaning is best done in equipment that combines the action of the tumbling mill (Fig. 9-2) with the centrifugal blast device. In fact, the tumbling mill design is modified somewhat in that a moving element within the mill causes the castings to roll in a manner that will bring all their surfaces into the abrasive stream.   One such design is shown in Fig. 9-5.   This equipment provides satisfactory low-cost cleaning for castings and other metal products such as forgings.   Surface finish is pleasing and of good quality.

Grinding and Chipping.   Castings whose surfaces have been cleaned by any of the previously mentioned methods require further processing for the removal of fins, gate stubs, riser bases, and casting imperfections. The amount of time needed is, as a general rule, directly proportional to the metal used in the casting.   Accordingly, steel castings require more grinding and chipping than is necessary for gray cast iron.

Chipping with an air hammer and chisel demands stamina on the part of the operator.   A solution to this problem will be a welcome innovation to the foundry cleaning room, since, for one thing, a source of nerve-shattering noise will be eliminated to the benefit of all foundry personnel.

Grinding requires attention to such matters as selection of correct abrasive wheels for the metal being ground.   Care in wheel selection, coupled with correct peripheral wheel speed, is the combination that will yield best results.   Casting grinding is performed by portable, swing, or stationary grinding machines (Fig. 9-6).   Proper protection of the worker

Fig. 9-5. Tumblast cleaning equipment installed at the Balmar Corp., Baltimore. (*Courtesy of American Wheelabrator & Equipment Corp., Mishawaka, Ind.*)

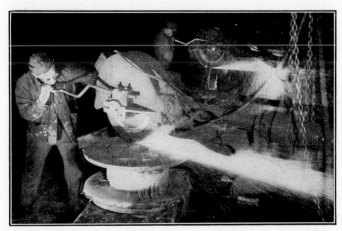

Fig. 9-6. Grinding a riser base on a steel casting with a swing-frame grinder. (*Courtesy of Norton Co., Worcester, Mass.*)

is necessary against such hazards as flying abrasive particles and wheel breakage. Eye protection in grinding as in chipping is of decided importance. Goggles and face shields equipped with shatterproof lenses are required equipment. Ventilation and good housekeeping are further items of importance to the modern foundry cleaning room.

Survey Questions

9-1. To what does "shake-out" refer in a foundry?

9-2. Is shake-out a manual or mechanical operation?

9-3. How are sprues removed from gray iron castings?

9-4. Are steel-casting risers knocked off by hammering?

9-5. What equipment is common for removing gates and risers from steel castings?

9-6. How does a tumbling mill function?

9-7. Wherein does grit blasting differ from sand blasting?

9-8. Is shot blasting employed for other than cleaning operations?

9-9. Of what materials are blast-cleaning nozzles made?

9-10. Is there any superiority of water-blast over air-blast cleaning?

9-11. On what class of work is mud blasting used?

9-12. Classify the airless blast methods.

9-13. How is the necessary velocity for abrasives obtained in the airless blast systems?

9-14. What is meant by "chipping a casting"?

9-15. Describe the usual tools used for chipping.

9-16. List the safety precautions to be observed in chipping and grinding.

9-17. Describe a swing-frame grinder.

9-18. Which type of metal castings requires the most time for chipping and grinding?

REFERENCES

Reams, C. A.: "Blast Cleaning and Ventilation," Penton Publishing Company, Cleveland, 1939.

"Recommended Practices for Metal Cleaning Sanitation," American Foundrymen's Association, Chicago, 1939.

Rosenberger, William A.: "Impact Cleaning," Penton Publishing Company, Cleveland, 1939.

CHAPTER 10

COLD SHAPING

The preceding chapters have been devoted to the various aspects of shaping metal by casting. The final structure of a casting depends upon the combination of factors operative during the molding, melting, casting, and shake-out periods. Except for powder metal products, the forming of metal starts with a casting process. The cast-iron series is not subject to subsequent mechanical processing such as can be applied to all other metals and alloys in both the ferrous and the nonferrous group.

"Wrought" is the word most commonly applied to mechanically worked metals. Some confusion results from its use, since wrought iron is a distinct ferrous metal. The term wrought is an established one in connection with mechanically worked aluminum alloys wherein manufacturers' specifications use the symbol S for its designation.

Cold shaping is performed on metal that has previously been mechanically worked. By far the major part of cold shaping uses sheet metal as its raw material, although there are other cold-shaped products, such as wire and cold-drawn tubing, for example, that are not formed from sheet material. Viewed from an engineering standpoint, cold shaping has the merit of changing the mechanical properties of the metal that is so processed. It is impossible to generalize on this point, since the nature of the material as well as the type and amount of cold shaping must be known if proper assessment of mechanical property changes is to be made.

Cold Working

Cold working and cold forming are the two chief methods employed for cold-shaping metal. Cold working, as a general rule, is a process of finishing previously hot-formed material. The objectives of the process are improved surface and dimensional finish, increased yield and tensile strengths, and, further, increased hardness, lowered ductility, increased endurance limit, and better machinability. By definition, cold working is "deforming a metal plastically at such a temperature and rate that strain hardening occurs. The upper limit of temperature for this process is the *recrystallization temperature*."[1] The two principal cold-working

[1] "Metals Handbook," p. 4, American Society for Metals, Cleveland, 1948.

methods are rolling and drawing, the former applying to flat products and some bars and shapes, the latter to tubular products, wire, and bars. Other cold-working processes include swaging, cold heading, roll threading, knurling, coining, and, for some nonferrous alloys, cold forging, extrusion, and pressing.

The effect of cold working on standard specification steels is shown in Table 10-1, where mechanical properties of some plain carbon steels are given. The values shown in the table are approximate; they simply represent the average of many tests.

TABLE 10-1. APPROXIMATE MECHANICAL PROPERTY VALUES FOR COLD-DRAWN AND HOT-ROLLED CARBON STEELS OF THE SAME ANALYSIS*

Mechanical properties	Grade of steel			
	AISI C1020 SAE 1020	AISI C1035 SAE 1035	AISI C1045 SAE 1045	AISI C1050 SAE 1050
Cold Drawn				
Tensile strength, psi	70,000–85,000	90,000–110,000	85,000–115,000	100,000–120,000
Yield, psi	60,000–70,000	75,000–90,000	80,000–100,000	85,000–100,000
Elongation, per cent in 2 in	15–25	10–20	10–15	10–15
Bhn	149–170	170–202	183–228	202–235
Hot Rolled (Turned and polished on precision shafting)				
Tensile strength, psi	50,000–70,000	70,000–90,000	80,000–100,000	90,000–110,000
Yield strength, psi	25,000–45,000	30,000–50,000	35,000–55,000	45,000–65,000
Elongation, per cent in 2 in	30–40	20–30	20–30	15–25
Bhn	110–140	143–182	156–202	179–223

* UDS "Steel Handbook No. 47," Republic Steel Corp., Union Drawn Steel Division.

Reference to the table shows the effect of cold working to be more pronounced on yield strength than on tensile strength; it also indicates that the improvement in these characteristics is more noticeable in the steels of lower carbon range. Steels are composed of definitely proportioned pearlite and ferrite grains, and the latter are susceptible to deformation or fragmentation under the influence of cold working. The lower the carbon in the steel, the greater the ferrite constituent and consequently the greater the degree of grain deformation. Actually, a piece tested immediately after grain deformation occurs will have no elastic limit, but after a period of rest some elasticity will be regained owing to a reorienta-

tion of the deformed ferrite.   The elastic limit, however, will be higher
than that of the material prior to cold working.

Cold Rolling.   Cold rolling is done on previously hot-rolled material
that has been subjected to a surface cleaning treatment for the removal

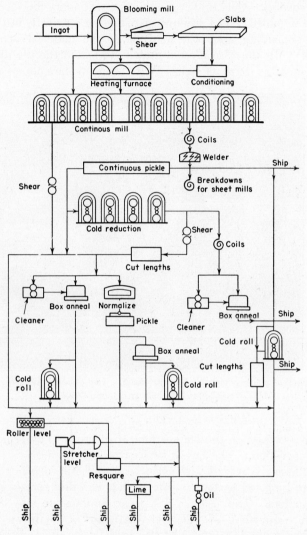

Fig. 10-1. Continuous mill flow chart. (*Courtesy of American Iron and Steel Institute, New York.*)

of adhering scale.   Pickling in a hot sulphuric acid solution is the usual
method for scale removal.   The material thus cleaned is passed through
roller dies for the cold-working operation.   The amount of reduction per
pass is slight, consequently the number of passes used is a function of the

surface finish desired as to both dimensional and smoothness characteristics.   The continuous mill has been developed as a means of meeting
the increasing requirements for steel sheet.   Figure 10-1 is a flow chart
for a continuous mill.   See also Fig. 2-5, page 15.

Cold Drawing.   Cold drawing employs a stationary die through which
the metal is pulled.   The amount of reduction, or draft, in the die is a
variable, depending upon the analysis of the material being worked
(Fig. 10-2).   In the case of cold-drawn steel bars the die draft ranges
from $\frac{1}{64}$ in. to as much as $\frac{1}{8}$ in.   Wire is one of the volume products of

Fig. 10-2. Measuring bar on multiple-bar drawbench in cold-drawing operation. (*Courtesy of Union Drawn Steel Division, Massillon Plant, Republic Steel Corp., Cleveland.*)

cold drawing.   Wire bars are cleaned of surface scale and pointed so that
they will pass through the die a sufficient distance to be gripped for the
drawing operation.   The bar is drawn through a succession of dies in
order to reduce it to final wire gage.   Dies for wire drawing are chiefly
made from tungsten carbide, although diamond dies remain popular for
small diameters.   The result of cold-work deformation may be so severe
as to require annealing or other heat treatments of the drawn wire.   The
micrographs in Figs. 10-3 and 10-4 clearly show the effect of cold drawing.
The distortion of grain in the direction of drawing is very pronounced at
this degree of cold reduction.

Coining.   The process of cold-working metal in a press-type die is
termed coining.   Common applications of coining are for making medals,
badges, coins, and similar embossed parts.   Heavy pressures are the rule

in coining, since plastic flow must be induced in the metal in order that die delineations can be faithfully reproduced. There are operations used on some castings whereby they are die-sized to produce pattern

Fig. 10-3. 4140 steel $\frac{7}{32}$-in. rod as annealed. Bhn 197. ×1,000. (Courtesy of Wyckoff Steel Co., Chicago.)

Fig. 10-4. 4140 steel $\frac{7}{32}$-in. rod annealed and cold-drawn to $\frac{1}{8}$-in. rod. 67 per cent reduction by cold work. ×1,000. (Courtesy of Wyckoff Steel Co., Chicago.)

fidelity; however, that is not a coining operation in the usually understood sense of the term.

Shot Peening. In the previous chapter the method of cleaning castings by air blasting was described. This technique has recently begun to be used as a method of cold working; however, when used for cold working

it is referred to as shot peening.   It consists of the impingement of fine
metal shot under high velocity against the metal surface to be peened.
The result of this shot impact is that the outer fibers of the metal flow
plastically in tension.   The effect is confined to a very narrow surface
band, with the result that the layers immediately beneath the surface,
which are not stretched, exert a force causing compression in the peened
surface.

These residual compressive stresses are of profound significance in
increasing fatigue resistance of the component so treated.   Since fatigue
failures generally result from tension stresses, it can be seen that a surface
in compression will have a longer life.   Shot peening of gear teeth has
been developed into a standard manufacturing procedure because it has
been found that gears thus treated exhibit longer operating life.

Cold Forming

Cold forming of metal is a fundamental method for manufacturing an
increasingly wide array of products.   Formerly, cold forming was associated exclusively with producing components for the engineering industries; however, the scope of application has broadened to include every
phase of domestic product as well.   This popularity has resulted from the
development of metals and alloys which fit themselves into the cold-
forming process both functionally and production-wise.   The wide
acceptance of cold-formed parts is demonstrated by the equipment of the
modern home, where examples include everything from appliances,
fixtures, and furniture to motorcars and components of the house itself.
The automotive and aircraft industries depend largely on cold forming
for the fabrication of component parts.

It is of special interest to note the trend toward using cold-formed parts
in prime movers.   Whereas steam and gas engines feature the use of
castings for their major components, the current development of gas
turbines and jet propulsion is based on the use of cold-formed metal parts.
This development is of such a fundamental nature that our engineering
manufacturing concept of power units is due for revision in the years
ahead.

Cold forming is the process of shaping sheet metal or plate by mechanical means at room temperature.   Fundamentally, two aspects are
included in cold forming: either the metal is stressed beyond its elastic
limit to the point of permanent deformation or it is worked beyond its
ultimate strength to the point where fracture or severance occurs.   In
any event, cold forming is applicable only to those metals that are plastic
at room temperature.

Plasticity is not a common term, since no unit value for measuring this
property of a metal has been devised.   Plasticity is a function of tem-

perature; further, it is dependent upon crystalline structure. Thus magnesium alloys, which have a hexagonal lattice, are difficult—in many instances even impossible—to shape by cold forming. Plastic behavior in metals is dependent upon deformation in the crystalline structure. In cold working, the deformation is considered to take place as a trans-crystalline action in the sense that movement occurs along numerous slip

Fig. 10-5. Cold-formed side rails. (*Courtesy of Clearing Machine Company, Chicago.*)

planes within the crystals. Obviously, then, factors limiting deformation (plasticity) are crystal orientation and crystal structure in combination with the binding forces between atoms in the crystal. Detailed information on the phenomenon of plasticity is found in the section of the "Metals Handbook" entitled The Crystal Structure of Metals and Alloys, by Kent R. Van Horn.[1]

Cold forming results in a loss of ductility in the metal due to strain hardening—a condition mentioned earlier in this chapter in connection with cold working. In some cold forming it is necessary to introduce an

[1] American Society for Metals, Cleveland, 1948.

annealing operation in the production sequence in order to restore plasticity for succeeding forming operations. An analogous situation is found in some cold-working processes; wire drawing offers an example.

Cold forming is applied principally to sheet metal, since such material lends itself well to high production rates. However, cold-forming equipment of greater capacities is being introduced in industry, widening the scope of components that can be produced. A press weighing

Fig. 10-6. Producing metal moldings on drawbench. (*Courtesy of Boeing Airplane Co., Seattle.*)

approximately 1,000,000 lb with a capacity for 398 in. between columns, as well as a side rail formed therein, is shown in Fig. 10-5. The type of equipment used for cold forming includes presses of all basic concepts, together with roll formers, stretchers, spinning lathes, and drawbenches for longitudinal contours and moldings.

Drawbench. Moldings or contoured strip, when required in modest amounts, is readily produced on a drawbench. This equipment consists of a housing, in which the dies are held, mounted on a bench wherein a continuous chain is located. A clamping mechanism, which grips the stock to be formed, is arranged so that it can be connected to the chain, thus applying the power and movement necessary for drawing the strip through the die (Fig. 10-6). The dies are made from hardwood, fiber, or steel, depending on the gage and kind of material to be formed. Although it is not generally realized, drawbenches offer an economical method for making moldings and, with slight modification of the die head, provide an excellent means of straightening extrusions and bars by straining along the major axis.

Fig. 10-7. Tishken cold-rolling machine. (Courtesy of Kawneer Mfg. Co., Niles, Mich.)

Roller Forming. Roller forming follows two general principles. Perhaps the best-known method is that of cold-shaping previously formed sections into circles or area. Another method of cold forming with roller dies is found in equipment that uses coiled strip as its raw material. Closed sections of innumerable cross-sectional designs are produced by cold forming in roller die machines. In the designing of roller dies ingenuity is required to hold the number of required roll passes to a minimum. Too, the amount of forming per roller die pair needs to be correctly calculated in order to prevent rupture of the section being formed.

Contoured flat sections, where quantity requirements warrant, are produced in roller die equipment (Fig. 10-7). Metal moldings of a wide variety of shapes are made on this equipment. This method competes with extrusion where shape imposes no limitations. Metal moldings can be produced economically on either drawbench or rolling equipment in those cases where wall or metal thickness is constant; when wall or metal thickness is a variable, extrusion is the indicated method of production.

Sheet and plate are formed into cylindrical shapes or sections having compound curves on equipment of the pyramid roll type (Fig. 10-8). Rolled cylinders are removed by swinging down the end housing and stripping off the formed cylinder. Where heavy plates are to be rolled, it is the general practice to form the edge of the plate to the desired radius in a press, in order to prevent flat edges in the finished cylinder. There is a modified design of pyramid rolls known as pinch rolls wherein the roll location is changed from the true triangular location to one in which two

Fig. 10-8. Cold-forming plate into a firebox in the boiler shop of The Baldwin Locomotive Works, Eddystone Division, Philadelphia.

rolls are in vertical tandem with a third roll located to their rear. It is said that pinch rolls eliminate the flat edge that occurs on plate rolled with the pyramid type. Pyramid rolls are used for forming ships' plates for both bow and stern contours. In ship-plate work the roll operator must employ ingenuity and a high degree of skill to develop the forming that the hull lines require.

Brakes. Cold forming of sheet and plate for longitudinal bends is generally done on brakes. Two general categories cover the field—leaf brakes and press brakes. Leaf brakes are for the most part manually operated and are regarded as basic equipment in the sheet-metal shop. A skilled operator can produce a remarkably wide variety of products with a leaf brake. Spring-back of the work after forming confronts the operator with the problem of making allowance for such behavior. The degree of spring-back is a variable depending upon the character and gage of the metal being formed as well as the amount of deformation.

Press brakes are larger and of greater capacity than leaf brakes. For a comparison of these two types of machines, see Fig. 10-9, where a hydraulic press brake is shown in operation and a leaf brake can be seen at the rear of the shop. Press brakes are designed mainly for hydraulic operation. Mechanically operated press brakes are also available.

Press brakes are built to accommodate dies for punching, blanking,

Fig. 10-9. Press brake in operation on metal shelving. (*Courtesy of Pacific Industrial Manufacturing Co., Oakland, Calif.*)

wiring, beading, shearing, seaming, and forming. In consequence these machines are extremely versatile and perform a variety of work in the jobbing shop; so much so that they can be substituted for many types of presses. Press brakes offer an interesting study in construction since they are for the most part composed of heavy steel plates joined by welding. Press-brake design exemplifies the possibilities offered by the combination of flame cutting and arc welding.

Stretch Forming. When production requirements are insufficient to justify elaborate press tooling, cold-formed parts can be shaped rather inexpensively by stretch forming. This method is applied principally to the cold forming of aluminum alloys for aircraft components. The requisite shaping is obtained from a die positioned on the platen of the metal-stretching press. Such dies are made from wood or Kirksite.

In the latter instance the dies are cast in plaster molds and only hand finishing is necessary.

In operation the stretching press utilizes a set of jaws, located parallel to the major axis of the platen, which grip the edges of the sheet to be formed. The jaws are constructed in a manner that permits their moving away from the platen. When the press is operated, the jaws travel horizontally while the platen, carrying the die, moves vertically; this combined action forms or stretches the sheet to the die shape. It will be seen from Fig. 10-10 that the ends of the sheet are not confined; only the sides are gripped in the press.

Fig. 10-10.   300-ton sheet stretch-forming press.   (*Courtesy of Boeing Airplane Company, Seattle.*)

Spinning. When a sheet-metal part is of such a shape that parallel planes through the part will be circular or oval, it can be formed by spinning. It is usually understood that spinning is the preferred cold-forming method where production is small. There are instances, though, where articles are spun in order to take advantage of the pleasing finish developed from the lines of the forming tool. Modifications of spinning such as bulging, trimming, necking, and wiring are important to cold forming.

Most types of sheet metal lend themselves to spinning. The chief precaution in selecting a material is to note its work-hardening properties, since materials that have this tendency to a marked degree will require annealing or continued heating during the spinning cycle. Magnesium alloys cannot be spun at room temperatures excepting in those cases where very small amounts of forming are involved. More extensive shapes can readily be produced by playing a torch on the magnesium blank while it is being spun.

Spinning lathes are designed for a range of spindle speeds (Fig. 10-11). The head stock spindle is threaded for mounting the chuck. The latter is made from cast iron, steel, or wood, the choice depending upon the job. Many shapes are not truly cylindrical, with the result that a solid chuck cannot be removed from the finished part; sectional chucks are used in such cases.

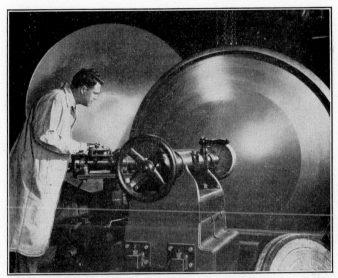

Fig. 10-11. Spinning lathe in operation. (Courtesy of A. Roland Teiner Co., Inc., Everett, Mass.)

Tools and chucks should be polished to a high degree of surface finish as a means of avoiding scratches on the work. Chromium plating of tool and chuck equipment is recommended for increased life and improved surfaces on the spun part. Forming rolls and tools made from tool steel are given a high polish prior to being placed in service.

Tool mounting depends on the type of lathe and the shape of the part. In many cases tools are mounted on the compound rest of the lathe and guided by the controls on the apron of the carriage. Other installations feature a work rest equipped with fulcrum pins that act as points of leverage for tools held by the operator. Lubricants must be used on the metal blank in contact with the spinning tools.

Drop-hammer Forming. The aircraft industry has developed the method of cold-forming sheet-metal parts under a drop hammer. The choice of this method is based on the fact that relatively inexpensive dies, cast from Kirksite, can be used for forming large parts of involved contour (Fig. 10-12). The force acting on the sheet to be formed is an impact one resulting from the kinetic energy developed by the falling of the upper die and holder. Aluminum alloys are most generally formed by the drop-hammer method, but stainless steel, magnesium, zinc, and other sheet stock have also been shaped in this manner.

Guerin Process. Hydraulic-press equipment was used by the Douglas Aircraft Company in 1935 in connection with an innovation in blanking as well as forming aluminum sheet. The success of this venture was so complete that the new method was patented as the Guerin Process. A

Fig. 10-12. Drop hammer, showing die and formed part. (*Courtesy of Boeing Airplane Company, Seattle.*)

live rubber pad acts as the medium for transmitting the force exerted by the press to the surface of the metal sheet that has been placed on the die block (Fig. 10-13).

The rubber pad is contained in a member that is fastened to the press moving platen. The sheet is placed on a die of such external dimensions that the pad holder will mate with it. The die is one-half of the orthodox die set, and it is made from a material such as wood, plastic, masonite, or plaster for forming. For blanking or cutting operations, the die is cut from tank or boiler plate in order that a cutting edge is available. Several different dies can be placed on the press bed simultaneously. A further speeding of production is obtained from the use of four tables that are loaded outside the press thereby increasing the time the press is in actual operation.

Deep Drawing. Some of the deep-drawn parts that are now accepted production parts are spectacular achievements resulting from teamwork between metallurgy, engineering, and manufacturing. There are many instances where a deep-drawn part is produced through a sequence of operations because of design requirements or material characteristics. Noteworthy examples of this method are found in ordnance, *e.g.*, shell cases. These components were universally made from copper-base alloys of high ductility. Shortages of that material caused specifications to be changed to ferrous materials. The windshields for large-caliber projectiles as well as rockets are other examples of ordnance components produced by deep drawing.

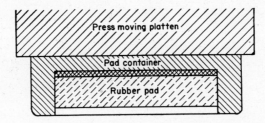

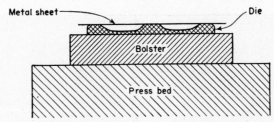

Fig. 10-13.   Schematic drawing of Guerin Process.

Heavy-gage Forming.   The production achievements in this area are found in the automobile field preponderantly; automobile bumpers and bumper guards are typical heavy-gage cold-formed parts. Wheels, axle housings, frame members, cover plates, and jack components also belong in this category. Freight cars are built largely from heavy-gage cold-formed parts.

Can Making.   The metal-container industry, especially the "tin can" phase, produces the largest number of cold-formed products in the entire field of cold shaping. This industry employs tin plate—a steel sheet coated on both sides with tin—as its principal raw material. The can lids are stamped out on standard-type presses. The can bodies are produced on bodymaking machines that are for the most part designed and manufactured by the can companies for their own manufacturing plants. These machines use a tin-plate sheet of precut size that is fed into the bodymaking machine automatically (Fig. 10-14). The body-maker produces a folded, soldered seam on the major axis of the can.

In some types of can bodies there is a spot weld at each end of the seam as a replacement for the fold in order that two rather than four thicknesses of metal exist where the body is flanged to make the joint with the lid. These operations are all done automatically within one body-

Fig. 10-14. Straight-line M.J.B. collar can machine.   (*Courtesy of Continental Can Co., Inc., New York.*)

Fig. 10-15. Impact extrusion of a collapsible tube from aluminum alloy. (*Courtesy of Aluminum Company of America, Pittsburgh.*)

making machine at a production rate of approximately 400 can bodies per minute. The exact production rate varies with body size and joint design and may total as high as 700 per minute.

Impact Extrusion. Collapsible tubes are produced from aluminum or lead alloys by impact extrusion. This method is classified as cold shaping although there are some instances where the metal blank is heated for increased ductility. A male and a female die are employed, with clearance between the two equal to the thickness desired in the tube walls.   A blank of the material to be extruded is placed in the female die; this is then struck by the descending punch, causing plastic flow.   Since the only escape area for the metal is that surrounding the punch, it flows upward, encompassing the punch, from which it is stripped at the conclusion of the operation (Fig. 10-15).

Press Forming

The press forming of metal sheet of all compositions and gages in a prodigious array of designs characterizes the rapidly expanding pressed-metal industry.   The range of possibilities open to the designer who contemplates using pressed-metal parts can be observed in the transportation, home appliance, and furniture industries.   The equipment used by the transportation industries, as exemplified by aircraft, motor cars and trucks, trolley coaches, busses, and streamlined trains, demonstrates the utility and economy of cold-forming metal in presses.   The development of press equipment continues to meet the demands for broader applications and lower cost of pressed-metal parts of stampings.

Fundamentally the two principles involved in the production of pressed-metal parts are: (1) cold-working the material below its ultimate strength and (2) working it beyond its ultimate strength to the point where severance occurs.   The former group includes bending, drawing, deep drawing, flanging, bulging, necking, curling, and impact extrusion.   All the processes in the latter group involve some form of severing the sheet or strip stock.   Shearing sheet metal in press operations takes such forms as blanking, slitting, parting, piercing, and perforating.

Metal stampings, then, are essentially the products resulting from cold-forming sheet metal in tension, bending, compression, or shear, or of their several combinations.[1]   The behavior of these forces on metal is familiar to those who have had experience in physical testing.   In every case the degree to which a given metal will flow plastically at room temperature is the determining factor in selecting the tooling.   Plastic flow varies with the differing compositions of one alloy as it does with alloys of different metals.   Plasticity can be gaged by noting both the ductility and the malleability of the metal under consideration.   It is well to remember that cold-rolled sheet has been strain-hardened during its manufacture, and the degree to which it has subsequently been annealed determines its ductility.   Selection of the correct temper for a piece to be cold-formed frequently spells the difference between success or failure.   Economy is greatest when the softest suitable temper is chosen, since there is a saving to be realized in the initial cost of the material.

[1] For detailed information on calculating the magnitude of these forces see "Computations for Sheet Metal Working Operations," E. W. Bliss Company, New York.

The grain of the sheet is an important consideration in tooling for stampings. Grain is considered as being in the direction of rolling (Fig. 10-4). Good design stipulates that no bends should be made in the direction of the grain, or that, if this condition cannot be met, dead-soft material should be specified. Material layouts for blanking overcome grain problems by using an angular pattern. This device may result in large amounts of scrap remaining from the original sheet or strip, but it

Fig. 10-16. Drawing and forming the solid-steel turret top of the Unisteel body by Fisher. (*Courtesy of Fisher Body, Div. of General Motors Corp., Detroit.*)

has the virtue of placing grain diagonally where its effect will be of least consequence. The use of generous radii on bends minimizes the adverse effect of grain. A case in point is the automobile body top stamping shown in Fig. 10-16.

PRESSES

The selection of the correct press for the production of a stamping offers a difficult problem, since there are a host of factors that require attention. It is a regrettable fact that in far too many instances press equipment is considered to belong in the ancient punch-press category rather than in the realm of modern machine tools. Pressed-metal parts are expected to fit as they come from the dies without any rework or restriking. These requirements can be and are being met by the proper combination of correct press equipment, press controls, die design and construction, and material selection.

Mechanical Presses. Presses are rated according to the pressure, in tons, that they are capable of exerting. The choice of a press becomes a

Fig. 10-17. Inclinable press performing a blanking operation. (*Courtesy of The Minster Machine Co., Minster, Ohio.*)

matter of selecting one that has sufficient capacity to deliver the indicated pressure necessary for the contemplated operation. Mechanical presses are used exclusively in the lower operating capacities. Consideration of equipment cost, plus the fact that the mechanical presses operate on a faster cycle than hydraulic presses, largely explains this preference. Mechanical presses cover a wide range of design as to both physical form and mechanical details. In addition to transfer types, presses are available with single-stroke operation as well as fully automatic cycling.

Inclinable Presses. Inclinable presses of open-back construction are among the most versatile of the mechanical types (Fig. 10-17). They are employed for stamping, forming, drawing, and perforating operations. For operations where punchings and blanked parts are to be dropped through the bed, these presses are operated with the frame in an upright position. When forming, or a similar operation which delivers the part on the top of the table, is desired, the frame is placed in the inclined position. As a result the pieces are delivered automatically through the opening in the back of the frame, eliminating the necessity for manual removal. The increased safety of this design is a further point of importance.

Horn Presses. Horn presses, because of their removable table feature, are capable of performing an extended variety of work. The frame of the horn press is bored to receive the "horn." The horn in turn is replaceable with others of differing end or face shapes; this increases the range of operations. The frame face below the horn is machined and equipped with T slots for attaching a table on which dies of various types are mounted.

The previously described power presses owe their classification to the design of the frame. Additional designs include open-end and column presses. The latter, in turn, are classified according to the mechanism used for power application, e.g., single-crank, single-action double-crank, double-action toggle, and triple-action.

The single-crank press is equipped with a single throw crankshaft which applies pressure to the ram at a single point only. It is the one that is generally used for the production of small and intermediate-sized stampings. When power is applied to the ram at two points by means of two connecting rods, the construction is known as a double-crank press (Fig. 10-18). On the larger stampings, where great pressures are required, power is delivered to the four corners of the ram by double crankshafts which have two connecting rods each.

Hydraulic Presses. Presses of the hydraulic type are usually built in capacities above 50 tons; the maximum size is being extended as requirements dictate.

Among the unique operating features of the hydraulic press are control over ram speed as well as pressures. These can be varied within the range of press capacity, as can the length of the stroke. The speed of the ram, whether high or low, is constant throughout the drawing stroke, an important consideration in deep drawing, since it permits the material being worked to respond to the operating pressure. Hydraulic-press design affords maximum protection against die breakage in cases where excessive stock thicknesses or excess pieces are inadvertently placed in the die, because ram pressures cannot exceed the maximum for the press. Inching the ram and the comparatively slow speed of entrance into the work are also characteristic of the hydraulic press.

Transfer-type Presses. Fully automatic press operation combined with inter-die transfer in one machine is the current solution for mass production. Such presses have one large, or master, slide on which the individual die station slides are mounted, with the result that all dies operate simultaneously. Each individual slide is arranged for separate adjustment, so that extreme flexibility in tooling is afforded. In addi-

Fig. 10-18. 135-ton double-crank straight-side press, with 60 in. between uprights, performing an operation on metal furniture. (*Courtesy of The Minster Machine Co., Minster, Ohio.*)

tion, this individual slide design permits the removal of any die or die set for sharpening or repair without interference with any of the other die stations.

These presses are equipped with automatic stock feed—roll feeds for coiled stock and stack feeds for prestamped blanks. The feed delivers the stock to the first die station, where the first of the operations of that sequence is performed. Following this, the partially formed part is mechanically transferred to station two for the second operation. This routine continues until the part has passed through all the required operations.

The number of stations is dependent upon the design of the stamping. In Fig. 10-19 a ten-station press is shown tooled for producing trimmings for electric-range heating elements. If all stations are not required for a given piece, any in excess are left open so far as dies are concerned; however, the mechanical transfer continues to operate and move the pieces forward.

Press Feeding. In order to take advantage of the operating speed of small mechanical presses it is necessary to feed stock into the die by some

Fig. 10-19. Close-up of die stations for producing trim rings. (Courtesy of Verson Allsteel Press Company, Chicago.)

mechanical means that synchronizes with the movement of the ram. There are several solutions to this problem, including gravity, suction, and air pressure, as well as mechanical devices such as grip, stack, table, and magazine feeds, but the roll type and dial-station design are common to all.

Where the stock is in coils, a receiving stand is used in conjunction with the feeding mechanism; in addition, a scrap cutter is used for rapid disposal of the stock scrap. Scrap disposal is always a problem in production work.

The use of a rotating fixture, placed on the bed or bolster which carries several dies, arranged so that with each stroke of the press the fixture indexes one die station, has several advantages. It is used principally for punching, peening, and flanging assembling operations. The operator can load the dies on the opposite station from the operating press stroke; this gives him freedom of movement and, more important, keeps his hands clear of possible injury. An example of a press equipped with a Littell ratchet feed is shown in Fig. 10-20; this also includes an air discharge.

Fig. 10-20. Geared press secured with eight dies; Littell ratchet feed and air discharge. (*Courtesy of Niagara Machine & Tool Works, Buffalo.*)

Every press must be provided with suitable safeguards against injury to the operator. A common solution is that of dual control, in single-stroke press operations, which causes both hands to be engaged while the press is in its operating cycle. Observation of a press department will show many interesting and ingenious safety devices on various press operations.

DIES

While press selection is an important consideration, presses must be equipped with the requisite dies in order to perform the work for which they are intended. Dies are the tools of power presses. Essentially, a die is composed of an upper, or male, component known as the punch, which mates with the lower, or female, component called the die.

This arrangement means that the punch moves and the die is stationary; in actual practice this order is sometimes reversed.

The die parts just described are mounted in a die set prior to installation in the press. Die sets can be secured from manufacturers of such equipment, or as is frequently done, the dies are constructed as a part of the die set. In either case a die set consists of a shank, a punch plate, and a punch holder, comprising the upper part, and a lower part made up of a die shoe equipped with clamping flanges and a die plate in which the die is mounted. To maintain alignment between the dies there are guideposts or leader pins fastened in the die shoe that have sliding contact through suitable bushings located in the punch holder. This is of importance, since it is essential to such operations as blanking and shearing in all its variations that the punch and die register correctly.

Blanking dies require a guide strip for the stock, stripper mechanisms, and stock stops to be built into the die set. The arrangement of these auxiliaries varies considerably. Blanking dies are made in many variations and combinations because, where design permits, the blanking operation is combined with such other features as piercing, edging, forming, and/or drawing.

A combination die is one in which more than one operation is performed. Careful evaluation is required in order to determine whether a combination die or a progressive die is indicated for a given job. In a progressive die one operation follows another at different stations in the die, whereas in a combination die the various operations follow each other while the part being worked remains in the same position in the die (Fig. 10-21). A further solution to this problem is to use two individual dies in the same press, with each press stroke operating both dies.

Diemaking. Diemaking denotes craftsmanship of the highest caliber. There has been an evolution occurring in this craft through the introduction of high-precision machine tool equipment such as jig borers, duplicators, and novel grinding equipment. However, the skill of the diemaker has not become obsolete; his ability continues in demand and is accorded the universal respect it deserves.

The selection of die materials is not an easy matter, since both cost and production demands must be considered. Die steels are broadly considered as either water-hardening, oil-hardening, or, in a few cases, air-hardening. Other materials such as cemented carbides are gaining recognition because of their high production potential.

In order to reduce die costs, it is well to consider the possibility of composite dies. These are built up from standard tool-steel shapes to conform to the desired die contour. The tool-steel shapes are resistance-welded to low-carbon-steel backing plates which either replace or complement the die set. Machining is easier, since the soft steel offers no

difficulty after the die has been heat-treated.   Another, similar device is
that of contouring the die parts from mild steel and then surfacing them
with hard facing or tool steel by means of electric arc welding.

Forming dies for large work are cast to shape from close-grained alloy
cast iron; there remains only the necessity of putting a finish on the die.
The forming dies for automobile body parts are primarily of this type.
Despite the apparent saving of cast-iron dies, the tooling cost is such
that a 200,000-model year is considered necessary to amortize die costs.

Fig. 10-21. Combination cutting, drawing, and corrugating die for producing garbage-can lids.
(*Courtesy of Niagara Machine & Tool Works, Buffalo.*)

Diemakers are confronted with the problem of spring-back of the workpiece.   Allowance for this behavior is built into the die, yet much trial-
and-error experimentation is required in almost every die in order to
arrive at the proper die compensation.

Lubrication of the die is commonly practiced with drawing operations.
The lubricant used for this purpose varies with the material and the
severity of the drawing operation.   Mineral oil and lard oil (and its
mixtures) have much to recommend them.   Solutions of graphite in
kerosene seem in greatest favor where heavy draws are made.   In addition to these, soluble oils of the machine-shop coolant type are perhaps
the widest used of all lubricants for drawing.   The method of applying
the lubricants varies from dipping the workpiece to automatic spraying.

Survey Questions

10-1. Is there any processing preceding cold shaping of metal?
10-2. How does cold shaping affect mechanical properties?
10-3. Explain the term "cold working."

10-4. What form of metal is commonly cold rolled?

10-5. Are cold rolling and cold drawing the same method?

10-6. Name some end products that are coined.

10-7. Why are gear teeth shot-peened?

10-8. Why is the property of plasticity of importance to cold forming?

10-9. Does cold forming have any effect on ductility?

10-10. For what type of product could a draw bench be used?

10-11. In what type of equipment are roller dies used?

10-12. How are metal moldings produced?

10-13. Give an application for pyramid rolls.

10-14. Are leaf brakes or press brakes the more common?

10-15. In what forming methods is spring-back encountered?

10-16. In what industry is stretcher forming of importance?

10-17. Give some examples of spun-metal parts.

10-18. Wherein do spinning lathes differ importantly from engine lathes?

10-19. How and from what material are drop-hammer dies for cold forming made?

10-20. Does press forming use impact as does the drop hammer?

10-21. At what temperature is the general run of press forming done?

10-22. How is the grain in a sheet of metal determined?

10-23. Is sheet metal considered to have temper?

10-24. When is restriking necessary?

10-25. In what production categories are mechanical presses most common?

10-26. Does an inclinable press have a distinctive appearance?

10-27. Give an example of horn-press production.

10-28. In what type of production are hydraulic presses dominant?

10-29. Wherein does stroke action differ as between mechanical and hydraulic presses?

10-30. Does the Guerin process show economies in its field of application?

10-31. To what operation does dial-station feeding refer?

10-32. Why does a rotating fixture increase production?

10-33. In what respect are transfer-type presses distinctive?

10-34. Name the component parts of a die set.

10-35. What is the function of a blanking die?

10-36. By what forming method are shell cases made?

10-37. List the important die materials.

10-38. Are can bodies produced on standard or special-purpose equipment?

10-39. Give an example of an impact-extruded part.

10-40. Are ferrous metals shaped by impact extrusion?

10-41. How are automobile bumpers produced?

10-42. Are heavy plates cold shaped? If so, give some examples of end products.

REFERENCES

Crane, E. V.: "Plastic Working in Presses," 3d ed., John Wiley & Sons, Inc., New York, 1944.

Francis, C. B.: "The Making, Shaping, and Treating of Steel," 5th ed., Carnegie-Illinois Steel Co., Pittsburgh, 1941.

"Metals Handbook," American Society for Metals, Cleveland, 1948.

Samans, Carl H.: "Engineering Metals and Their Alloys," The Macmillan Company, New York, 1949.

"Steel Products Manual," American Iron and Steel Institute, New York, 1949.

"Tool Engineers' Handbook," McGraw-Hill Book Company, Inc., New York, 1949.

CHAPTER 11

HOT SHAPING

Hot shaping is employed for forming all engineering metals with the exception of those that are produced as castings. Steel and wrought iron are best-known for their capacity to be hot-worked; however, as was mentioned in Chap. 2, the nonferrous metals are gaining popularity because of their hot-forming properties. There is an interesting departure from the generally held conception of hot working in the case of the light alloys: their temperature range for hot shaping is such that they do not change color.

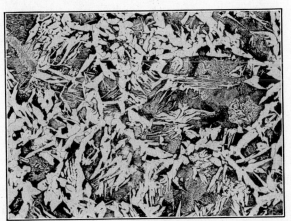

Fig. 11-1. As-cast condition, 0.24C steel. ×100 etched with a combination of Picral and Nital. (*Courtesy of Battelle Memorial Institute, Columbus, Ohio.*)

Hammering, either manual or mechanical, is one of the principal hot-shaping methods, although custom terms its end product a forging. When pressure is applied to a heated piece, instead of repeated blows, the resulting product is termed a pressing or a press forging, depending upon the equipment used. The greatest tonnage of hot-shaped products, however, is produced in rolling mills, where the material is passed successively through roller dies. The nonferrous alloys can be hot-shaped

into moldings, tubing, and shapes by forcing them through a die under
heavy pressures in a method known as extrusion; the end products are
termed extrusions.   There is a modification of extrusion whereby steel is
extruded in dies; this will be described in detail later in this chapter.
Spinning, piercing, and fluing are other methods of hot-shaping metal.
The change in structure of steel as a result of hot working is illustrated
in Figs. 11-1 and 11-2.

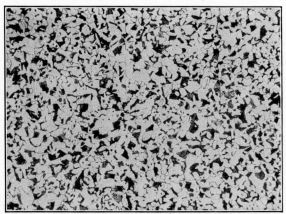

Fig. 11-2. Hot-worked condition, 0.24C steel.   ✕100 etched with a combination of Picral and
Nital. (*Courtesy of Battelle Memorial Institute, Columbus, Ohio.*)

Hot Rolling

Production requirements for large tonnages of bars, shapes, plates, and
sheets are met by hot rolling.   The limitations on hot rolling are section
contour and cross-sectional area.   Steel accounts for the bulk of the
annual output of the rolling mill, although the light metals as well as the
copper-base alloys are also produced in rolled form.

Ingots. Rolling starts with an ingot.   Ingots are produced from
furnace metal by teeming into metal molds.   Large ingot molds are top-
poured individually.   When smaller ingots are desired, the molds are
arranged for bottom pouring, several molds being connected by refractory
runners to a master mold.   The ladle, which is of the bottom-pour type,
is brought over the master mold and the ladle stopper is then raised,
permitting the steel to flow into the master mold, whence it enters the
ingot molds.   Ingots are of various shapes and sizes, depending upon the
products for which they are intended.   Square or rectangular ingot shapes
predominate, but fluted as well as flattened cross sections are also produced.   The design of an ingot is critical, since the amount of shrinkage
cavitation must be controlled for highest yield of sound steel.   The

shrinkage-affected portion is cropped from the upper part of the ingot prior to rolling in order to avoid seams and unsound areas in the rolled product.

Ingots are permitted to solidify in the molds. Solidification is accompanied by shrinkage and contraction, which tend to free the ingot from the mold. The ingot is not permitted to cool unduly; such practice would be wasteful in view of the fact that high rolling temperatures are necessary. The ingot is immediately placed in a soaking pit furnace, where it is stored at rolling temperature, approximately 2300°F, until needed. In cases where the ingots have been permitted to cool completely they are charged into reheating furnaces prior to rolling.

Blooming Mill. A blooming mill is the first mill used in reducing an ingot in the production sequence leading to the finished product. Blooming mills receive the heated ingot and reduce it in size and shape by passing it through a stand of rolls. These mills are built in three designs —reversing, continuous, and three-high types. The first two are of two-high design, *i.e.*, there are two rolls, one above the other. Both rolls may be power-driven. The rolls are located in massive roll housings and the drive is arranged on the outside of one housing.

Continuous mills make one reduction in each roll stand. The reduction in any rolling operation is known as a pass. Since several passes are required, a continuous mill is composed of several roll stands arranged in tandem so that the ingot passes along a continuous path. Mills are equipped with manipulators—mechanical devices for turning the ingot— in order that the various faces will be in the rolls and a more uniform structure developed in the bloom.

Reversing mills operate so that the direction of rotation of the rolls can be reversed. In operation the ingot passes through the rolls, which are then closed the amount of the next desired reduction, known as draft, and the direction of ingot travel as well as roll rotation is reversed. The ingot is thus subjected to repeated passes in a single roll stand. A reversing mill with the ingot entering the rolls is shown in Fig. 11-3. The rollers on the table in the immediate foreground are also reversible and govern the direction of travel of the ingot.

The three-high mill employs an additional roll located in line and above the two lower ones. This mill does not reverse; instead travel direction of the ingot is reversed. After going through the lower pass, the ingot lands on a lifting table which raises the ingot to the next pass between the intermediate roll and the top roll. Upon emerging from that pass, the ingot is taken by the lifting table on the opposite side of the roll stand and lowered to the level of the first pass.

Rolling Sequence. The function of the blooming mill is that of reducing an ingot to a bloom, which is the first intermediate product in the rolling sequence. Blooms are rolled to various shapes and sizes, depending upon their intended end use. The majority are square or rectangular in cross section, although some circular blooms are rolled for such items as projectiles, wheels, and circular shapes for tubing. Blooms are most frequently rolled into billets, which, in their turn, are semi-finished products that are further rolled into bars and small structural

Fig. 11-3. 44-in. two-high reversing mill at the Aliquippa Works. This mill is driven by a Camden compound steam engine delivering 10,200 hp at 70 rpm. (*Courtesy of Jones & Laughlin Steel Corp., Pittsburgh.*)

shapes. Large structurals are rolled directly from blooms. The flow sheet in Fig. 11-4 shows the various phases of the rolling sequence as applied to structurals.

Ingots destined for flat products such as plate, sheet, and strip are rolled into slabs. Slabs are much wider than they are thick. They are 16 sq in. or more in cross section and have a minimum thickness of $1\frac{1}{2}$ in.

Rolls. The design and manufacture of rolls constitute a critical aspect of the production of rolled steel. Roll designers arrive at the finish pass for a given section by different steps and use differing amounts of draft in various passes. The objective sought is to employ as few passes as possible from billet to end product.

Rolls are machined from castings for the most part, although there are some roll forgings used for special categories. Castings require much less machining, since grooves can be cast, as can the wobbler sections. Rolls are plain cast iron, alloy cast iron, plain carbon steel, and alloy steel. The cast-iron rolls are chill-cast where hard surfaces are necessary, as on the finishing passes, while sand-cast rolls are more popular for the rougher and intermediate passes.

Plate Rolling. Two broad classifications of mills are used for plate rolling. In the sheared-plate mill, both the width and the length of the plate are increased by rolling, whereas in a universal mill, side rolls are used to control the width of the plate as it is rolled and therefore length only is increased by rolling. Cross rolling is used in sheared-plate mills as a means of improving the structure on the rolled plate.

Plate rolling demands rigidity in the rolls to avoid deflection and thereby produce a plate of constant gage across its entire width. In order to accomplish this end, four-high mills are used for rolling plate. A four-high mill has two smooth rolls for the actual work of rolling; these rolls are in rolling contact with a second roll, known as the backing roll. In effect, then, there are two rolls above and two below the plate as it is rolled.

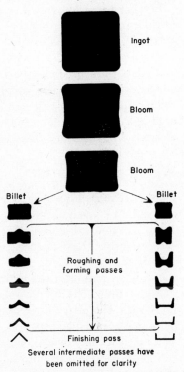

Fig. 11-4. Rolling sequence from ingot through structural shape. (*Courtesy of American Iron and Steel Institute, New York.*)

Clad Plates and Sheets. As a means of combating surface corrosion, in some of the process industries a clad plate which has a corrosion-resistant surface is used for fabricating tanks and similar equipment. Clad plates are rolled by placing the clad material—for example, nickel, inconel, or stainless steel—on a carbon steel plate; then there is another plate placed on the clad material, with parting compound between the latter two. This bundle is welded around its edges and heated to correct temperature prior rolling to gage. After rolling, they are sheared around the edge to remove the welded portion and the plates are separated;

because of the parting compound, the clad material will have become welded only on one side.

Aluminum clad sheets are produced by a rolling-welding combination. The core alloy is stacked between two corrosion-resistant alloy slabs. The stack is furnace-heated to welding temperature and then rolled to gage. All three components are machined prior to stacking in order to ensure correct thicknesses in the end product.

Copper-base Alloys. In copper-base alloys, cakes—similar to ingots in their function—supply the basic metal in the rolling sequence. Most of the copper-base alloys have satisfactory hot-rolling characteristics; the exceptions are those with a pronounced lead content. Rods, bars, and shapes are produced by hot rolling. The mill equipment used for copper-base alloys is similar to that for steel. Rolls are used cold, as in rolling aluminum alloys, and in some instances oil is used to prevent scaling the product being rolled. Rolling temperatures for copper-base alloys fall in the range from 1300 to 1650°F.

HOT-ROLLING LIGHT ALLOYS

Aluminum-alloy ingots are chill-cast by top pouring in water-cooled molds. The shell formed by rapid cooling is withdrawn from the mold at a uniform rate and further cooling is achieved by direct application of water. Ingots are sawed off to the desired length as the process proceeds continuously. Rapid cooling causes the ingot to contract in the mold so that it can be lowered. The objective of this system is to produce a sound ingot free from the piping effects.

Aluminum alloys are hot-rolled on equipment similar to that employed for steel. There are differences in rolling techniques; one is that the light metals require a lubricant. Soluble oil emulsion is used, which acts both as a lubricant and as a coolant on the rolls.

Rolling Magnesium Alloys. The slabs used for producing magnesium sheet and plate are extruded from cast ingots of circular contour. Heavy reduction is possible in hot rolling, with the result that sheet has but few cold finishing passes.

Frequently the rolls are maintained at a temperature range of 400 to 600°F during rolling. Magnesium alloys are not at present available in the large assortment of gages, widths, and lengths that can be had in the aluminum alloys. This condition is being remedied by the introduction of the continuous mill. New technical developments have solved the problem of rolling magnesium alloys in light gages and commercial sizes.

SEAMLESS TUBING

Seamless steel tubing is produced by a method akin to rolling in that two rolls are used at the start of the piercing process. These rolls are shaped like two truncated cones joined at their base. They are located directly above and at an angle to each other with a center spacing somewhat smaller than the billet diameter. The rolls revolve in the *same* direction. As a result the billet is alternately bulged and compressed; this causes cracking along its axis. Simultaneously with this action, the billet is forced over a pointed mandrel which serves both as a guide and as a means of producing a hole of nearly uniform diameter. The pierced billet then passes through further processing rolls where OD is controlled and the center enlarged by an eccentrically operating bar.

Forging

Forging methods are divided between hammer, press, and rolled types. The basic principle in forging is that of shaping metal by impact or pressure either on anvils, in open dies, or in closed dies. The choice of method is governed by size, design considerations, and production requirements. Forgings are produced at elevated temperatures. Forgings start from a previously rolled billet or bar in the majority of cases. Large forgings are made directly from the ingot. Production forging is based entirely on the use of rolled stock. Forgings show a fiberlike structure and flow lines that result in directional properties in the finished forging.

There are alloys in each group of the wrought engineering metals that can be forged. Not all the alloys in the nonferrous groups forge satisfactorily. Heating methods require consideration from the viewpoint of the scaling and, for some steels, of surface decarburization. Controlled furnace heating with reducing atmospheres is required when heating alloy steels for forging.

HAMMERED FORGINGS

When individual forgings are required, hammering is the indicated method of production. Such forgings are termed blacksmith, or hand, forgings when they are hammered out manually on an anvil. Hammered forgings are also termed flat die or miscellaneous forgings.

Blacksmith forgings are limited to small parts, principally repair work. Hammered forgings are most commonly produced with steam hammers similar to the one in Fig. 11-5. A typical forging crew consists of the blacksmith, hammer driver, and helper, or heater.

Steam Hammers. The two general types of steam hammers are known as the single-frame and the double-frame; they are also designed to operate on compressed air in some instances. Figure 11-5 shows a single-frame hammer that is steam-operated. Most single-frame hammers are built with the anvil separated from the frame; in a variation known as the self-contained hammer the anvil is integral with the frame. The latter type is preferred for contoured die forgings because better die alignment can be expected.

Large hammered forgings are produced in double-frame hammers, which are of more massive construction than the single-frame type; the designs of the two, except for the frame, are similar. The double-frame

Fig. 11-5. A typical steam-hammer forging operation. (*Courtesy of Chambersburg Engineering Co., Chambersburg, Pa.*)

hammer is of greatest importance in the production of heavy forgings. One special use for this hammer is that of reducing forging ingots into billets. This operation is termed cogging, and double-frame hammers are frequently designated as cogging hammers.

Pneumatic Hammers. Small hammered forgings are frequently produced on pneumatic hammers. These are not to be confused with air-operated hammers of steam-hammer design; the pneumatic hammer is a separate type. It is equipped with an electric motor that, through suitable drives, connects to an air compressor. The pneumatic hammer is a self-contained unit requiring only electrical service for its installation.

This equipment is of interest where neither steam nor compressed air is available; it offers flexibility for a diversity of small forgings.

Impact Die Forgings. Impact die forgings are also known as drop forgings. Both titles are descriptive: the first one indicates that the forging is made in a die by impact; the second refers to the fact that drop hammers are used for supplying the impact. Forgings of this type are produced in a tremendous variety of shapes and sizes from a diversified assortment of metals. Steel drop forgings are in the majority and

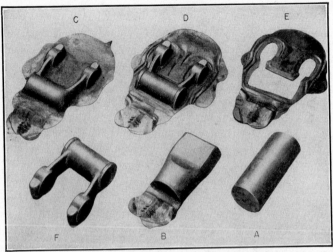

Fig. 11-6. Forging sequence for a steel truck shackle starting with round bar stock. (A) Bar stock is heated and tong hold drawn, (B) breakdown of stock to fill die cavity, (C) blocking, for metal distribution, (D) finishing forging except for trim, (E) flash that has been trimmed from forging, (F) finished and trimmed shackle forging. (*Courtesy of Drop Forging Assn., Cleveland.*)

are well known. Nonferrous die forgings are found in engineering construction.

Drop forgings are limited in both shape and size. Shape must permit their removal from the dies without undue sticking. Steel drop forgings tend to stick in the die, since they contract on cooling. Another cause for sticking is that the metal of the forging, being under plastic flow, will intermingle with the die surface, which, even though it is polished, remains sufficiently rough to offer anchor points for the forging metal. Oil and mixtures of graphite are sparingly sprayed or swabbed into the dies to overcome this difficulty.

The designer of die forgings must take into consideration the draft necessary for removal from the die. Draft is used on both external and internal surfaces. The latter is the larger because the internal surface when shrinking tends to lock in the die, while external surfaces behave in the opposite manner.   Circular or oval cross sections are ideal, since they are free of the draft requirement.   Further design considerations include location of parting line, flash trim line, directional grain flow, corner radii, and die wear.

Forging Sequence.   A typical sequence for a drop forging is exemplified by the truck shackle in Fig. 11-6, where the forging stock is a round bar.   All the necessary forging operations are performed in one die, which is of a size permitting the necessary impressions for the various steps in the sequence.   The flash is trimmed in a separate die mounted in a trimming press.   The forging die for the truck shackle is shown in Fig. 11-7, with both halves of the die on view.

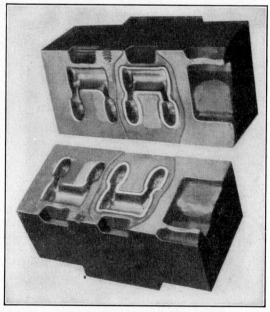

Fig. 11-7.   One set of closed impression dies designed to perform all the necessary **forging** operations to shape the truck shackle.   (*Courtesy of Drop Forging Assn., Cleveland.*)

Flash.   Note that in C, D, and E of Fig. 11-6 there is excess metal; this is termed flash from the fact that the extra metal not needed for the forging "flashes" out of the die cavity.   Flash originates from the variance in the original stock and also from the shape of the stock being such that it will not fill the die at all points unless excess develops at the lower volume die cavities.   The flash is removed from the forging in a trimming press in a separate operation.

Drop Hammers.   Impact die forgings are generally produced in drop hammers equipped with closed impression dies.   There are several types of drop hammers, including the board drop, the steam drop, and the gravity drop. The board drop hammer (Fig. 11-8) is designed for raising the upper die by means of boards attached to the die block. At the top of the frame, rollers are located on each side of the boards; the boards are raised by bringing the rollers, which are opposite in rotation, into contact with them. When the ram has reached its upper travel position, cams clamp the boards and hold them. The impact blow is delivered by releasing the holding cams; this permits the ram assembly to drop and strike the lower die, which is positioned on the anvil.

PRESS FORGINGS

The basic difference between press forging and hammer forging is that in the former, one stroke of the press is generally sufficient, whereas several blows are essential with hammer forgings. Press forging is employed for every type of forging operation, from open to closed die. Large forging ingots are worked in a forging press (Fig. 11-9). Manipulation of this 40T ingot is by an endless chain at each end which connects with an overhead crane;

Fig. 11-8. 2,000-lb motor-driven board drop hammer. (Courtesy of Erie Foundry Co., Erie, Pa.)

by these means the ingot can be rotated or translated as desired. The endless chain is driven by an air motor incorporated with the lifting hook sheave.

Tail-shaft forgings for ships are produced in forging presses. In fact symmetrical forgings of circular or tapering cross section and of substantial length are typical forging press products. Forging presses for such work are of large capacity and operate on the hydraulic principle. There are also mechanical presses for the manufacture of press forgings.

Closed Die Press Forgings. Closed die forgings from nonferrous metals and alloys are generally made in a forging press. These materials exhibit the high degree of plastic flow which is necessary to filling die cavities in one stroke of the press. A major advantage of press forging is that there is much less draft required in the dies—2 or 3°—in contrast to drop forgings, which need more than double that amount. This is important, since less machining will be necessary on vertical faces and, in some designs, no finish will be required because of the fact that the forged face is almost perpendicular to the trim line.

The answer to the question of the preferred method as between hammering and pressing die forgings can be reached through a study of

Fig. 11-9. A forging press engaged in forging a tail shaft. (*Courtesy of Isaacson Iron Works, Seattle.*)

material selection plus available equipment and forging volume. A successful press forging of a railroad car wheel is shown in Fig. 11-10; however, despite this type of achievement in press forging, there is a competing method of roll forging such car wheels from circular blanks.

Massive Forging Presses. A development program that will ultimately result in the production of forging presses of capacities reaching to 75,000 tons is now under way. The utility of extremely large presses was first demonstrated in the construction of German aircraft. Following World War II, several large presses were discovered in the manufacturing industries in Germany. The largest of these, a 33,000-ton forging press, built in 1943, ultimately went to Russia. A 16,500-ton press of German manufacture was captured by our forces and has been erected in this country. Designs are now being contemplated in this country for forge-pressing major structural components for aircraft. While the final capacity of these presses has not been determined, it is thought that it will be possible to have presses of sufficient capacity to forge such parts as wing spars and main beams, among others.[1] This development indicates that construction details on future aircraft will be profoundly influenced by the use of pressed forged parts.

Fig. 11-10. Forming a wheel blank: Baldwin forging press in the shops of Standard Steel Works Division, the Baldwin Locomotive Works.

ROLL FORGING

Circular-shaped products like gear blanks, brake drums, and various wheel types can be roll forged in a mill between vertical dies. The forging blank is pierced at its geometrical center for mounting on the die arbor. The mating die closes against the blank with the pressure of a forging press. Following the closing operation, both dies revolve, causing upsetting and plastic flow sufficient to fill the die cavity.

Roll-forging equipment takes care of a variety of jobs that would otherwise be cumbersome or difficult. Interesting products of roll forging are tapered parts such as shafts, brake levers, and rifle barrels. The rolls are machined with an interrupted section which is used as the starting point for the stock to be rolled. Tapered grooves in the rolls are of different depths where the reduction is such as to require a series of passes.

[1] Presses for the Jet Age, *Fortune*, Vol. XLIV, No. 6, pp. 111–113, 146, 148, December, 1951.

The five forging operations for producing a connecting rod can be seen in Fig. 11-11. The necessary upsetting, gathering, and bending are roll forged. The final two operations are performed in a forging press.

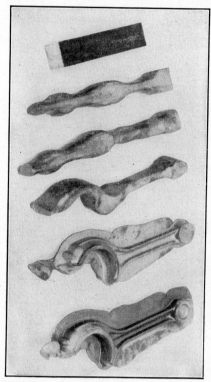

Fig. 11-11. Open-end connecting-rod forging. Operations: (1) first pass roll, (2) second pass roll, (3) bender, (4) blocker, (5) finish. (Courtesy of The National Machinery Co., Tiffin, Ohio.)

Tooling the connecting rod production in this manner speeds output and lowers die and equipment costs. Roll forging frequently serves for the preliminary operations of both impact and press die forgings.

Upset Forging. Forging machines are designed to operate horizontally with dies opening vertically —the reverse of forging presses. The products of forging machines are known as upset forgings from the fact that bar stock is gripped in dies and then gathered, or upset, where an enlarged volume of metal is needed in the forging. The range of products that can be produced on forging machines is extremely wide. Relatively simple shapes such as ball races are produced in a two-stage die. More complicated shapes such as motorcar hubs and the like are also produced by the machine forging method.

Forging machines are powered by electric motors through V-belt drives to inertia members that connect through air clutches to the crankshafts. The grip dies part vertically for insertion of the forging stock. Cams operate the punch, or male die, after the grip dies have closed. The die operation can be followed in Fig. 11-12, where a four-station die produces a clutch hub. The first operation is upsetting, wherein the bar stock is gathered for the requisite diameter. Subsequent stages continue the forging to finish size. The stock must be moved from each stage to the next upon completion of each operation. It is interesting to note that the hole is punched in a manner that forces the stock into the die cavity. As a result there is no loss of material from hole forming and there is no flash to be discarded. These are obvious advantages that weigh heavily in favor of machine forging as compared to other forging methods.

Fig. 11-12. Dies and tools for forging a small clutch hub off the end of the bar. (*Courtesy of The Ajax Mfg. Co., Cleveland.*)

PRECISION FORGING

The development of jet engines has posed the problem of fabricating component parts of a high degree of accuracy. One of the methods that is contributing to progress in this direction is that of precision forging of turbine buckets (Fig. 11-13). The alloys used in this application are those resistant to high temperatures, *i.e.*, they possess major percentages of both chromium and nickel. The precision forging of a turbine bucket starts with a roll-forging operation; following this, the semifinished

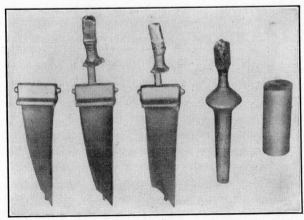

Fig. 11-13. Precision-forged turbine bucket for jet engine. (*Courtesy of The Steel Improvement and Forge Co., Cleveland.*)

forging is freed of scale and is reheated for the drop-forging operation. Precision forging of these alloys requires frequent reheating, since several operations are necessary.   Surface conditions are given close attention because the precision contours demand superior finish.

Extrusion Forging.   Extrusion forging differs from conventional closed die forging; the dies are designed in a manner that permits the heated stock to flow only into the designed shape of the forging.   The die set consists of a punch and a die similar to those in Fig. 11-14.   This die set

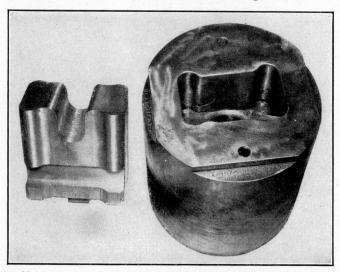

Fig. 11-14.   Spindle extrusion die.   (Courtesy of Ford Motor Company, Detroit.)

more nearly resembles the design associated with cold forming metal sheet than it does impact forging dies.   The stock used for an extrusion forging must be cut to close tolerances, since there is no flash on the finished forging nor is any metal allowed for a tong hold.

Extrusion

Nonferrous metals and alloys are fashioned into a multitude of shapes, bars, tubular products, and moldings by hot extrusion.   Steel is now being extruded by a process developed in France in which glass fiber is used as a lubricant on the hot steel.   This extrusion method is being introduced into the United States, indicating that there will be some interesting developments in steel products manufacture in the immediate future.   The end products of the hot extrusion process are generically termed extrusions.   A familiar illustration of the extrusion process is the removal of tooth paste from its tube.   In this example the tooth paste is the material to be extruded and the orifice of the tube acts as the extrusion die.

Extrusions are formed in horizontal extrusion presses of imposing operating capacities (Fig. 11-15). Presses are built in different capacities and on two operating principles. One design places the die ahead of the extrusion ingot; in the other design the die is carried in the piston, where it causes the extruded metal to flow through the hollow piston rod. The head-end die extrusion press is the more common type.

Fig. 11-15. A billet (center) is shown being forced by hydraulic ram into extrusion press cylinder. Billet has been heated to facilitate normal flow through the die. Formed extrusion will emerge from hydraulic press at far left. (*Courtesy of Aluminum Company of America, Pittsburgh.*)

The major production of extrusions is in the field of aluminum alloys, but magnesium, lead, tin, and copper-base alloys are also frequently specified for extrusions. Items like pin tumbler lock parts are sometimes produced as copper-base extrusions, while some aircraft moldings are magnesium-alloy extrusions. Extrusions are produced in lengths that are limited only by customer requirements, although manufacturers' specifications govern stock lengths, which in turn vary with the type of extrusion.

An aluminum-alloy extrusion starts with an ingot that has been cast to cylindrical shape in a metal mold. The ingot is permitted to cool prior to further processing. A continuous-type reheating furnace is auxiliary equipment in the extrusion shop. Heating the ingots is performed with care, since the final temperature is critical. Once the ingot has reached extrusion temperature—which, for these alloys, ranges between 800 and

900°F—it is placed in the extrusion press. Ingot diameter fits the extrusion cylinder bore.

The extrusion piston moves against the rear of the ingot, forcing the latter through the die located at the front, or opposite, end of the cylinder. Extrusion is a single-operation process in that the ingot behind the die is converted into the finished extrusion by passage through the die. The extrusion issuing from the die is cut to desired length, and extrusion continues until the ingot has been reduced to a small stub, which is then scrapped.

Extrusion offers the designer a product that is unobtainable by any other metal-forming method. In extrusions there are no hampering restrictions about metal placement, nor is there any requirement about taper or undercutting—the designer can dispose the metal with a view to greatest resistance to imposed stresses in end use.

Extrusion dies are designed in a manner that permits their insertion in or removal from the extrusion press as desired. Dies should be provided with smooth surfaces in order to avoid serious scratching of the extrusion. A positive method of identifying an extrusion is to note the die marks running longitudinally on its surfaces. When small, plain shapes are to be extruded, the die may have multiple openings, thus making several extrusions simultaneously.

Tubular products and hollow extrusions are produced from aluminum alloys. Dies for hollow extrusions are of two-part construction with parting line normal to the extrusion axis. The die part facing on the ingot holds the extrusion arbor, which in turn controls the internal shape of the extrusion. This die half is further equipped with rather large openings through which the extruding metal passes. The several streams of metal emerging from this die half are turned in toward the die arbor by the outer die half, whence they pass through the die opening. A hollow extrusion die for aluminum alloys actually combines in its design a pressure welding operation with a double extrusion process.

Forging Dies

The manufacture of forging dies, in common with other die work, demands the highest type of craftsmanship to ensure the accuracy demanded in the end product. Forging dies requires special skill, since they must be made to compensate for both forging contraction and die wear in service. It is customary to purchase die blocks in the hardened condition in order to avoid distortion, cracking, or spoilage of a die by heat-treatment after the die is finished. The die sinker has in addition to his other problems the difficult task of machining hardened steel.

The choice for forging die steels ranges from plain carbon, for short-run dies, through the alloy grades, and includes some high-speed steels for extrusion forgings. Air hardening steels find favor where dies are large and of heavy sections. In other instances dies are built up with extremely hard inserts; yet this procedure requires care, for any tendency to loosen during operation will ruin the die.

The final die impression is the first one made in a die block. Upon its completion, it is "proved" by pouring lead or wax into it to form a casting that reproduces the die cavity. This lead cast, or proof, is carefully checked for dimensional accuracy and is submitted to the customer for

Fig. 11-16. Single-impression finishing die for an aluminum-alloy housing forging. (*Courtesy of Drop Forging Assn., Cleveland.*)

his approval. The other impressions are sunk into the die block only after the final forging impression has been accepted. A single-impression forging die that is used on the finishing operation for an aluminum alloy housing is shown in Fig. 11-16. This housing is forged in five operations, requiring three forging hammers.

Die Typing and Broaching. Another procedure for making dies is that of producing an extremely accurate master die of high hardness. The typing blanks are heated and forced into the master die so that they assume the shape of its cavity. The die set shown in Fig. 11-14 was produced by this method. Die typing offers a quick and economical method for producing duplicate die parts. The procedure of forcing or pressing a hardened piece into a previously roughed-out die block, cold, for the purpose of forming a die half is known as broaching. Obviously there are shape limitations to be considered, even though die broaching offers a rapid method for producing duplicate die parts.

Hot Forming

Hot forming is primarily associated with the shaping of steel plate, although magnesium alloys, mentioned previously, also behave well in

Fig. 11-17. Final pressing of a locomotive boiler dome on a 1,000-ton four-post press. (*Courtesy of Lukens Steel Co., Coatesville, Pa.*)

this process. Since steel furnishes the bulk of the material for hot forming, this discussion is confined to that material. Hot forming is usually performed at a temperature above the lower critical of the steel and the piece is permitted to cool normally from the temperature at which the work is completed. Forming at elevated temperatures permits greater deformation of the workpiece, since it has greater ductility owing to the increased plastic flow potential. The final one of six operations in hot-pressing a boiler dome appears in Fig. 11-17. The member shown is formed from a steel circle 78 in. in diameter by 1⅛ in. in thickness, with an approximate weight of 1,500 lb.

One chief disadvantage of hot forming can be observed in Fig. 11-17, which shows the heavy formation of scale on the workpiece. Scaling reduces gage to some extent and also produces a roughened surface requiring considerable cleaning before a pleasing and satisfactory appearance is achieved.

Hot Pressing.   Hot pressing is used for large plates of heavy section or where a high degree of deformation is required without rupture.

Fig. 11-18.   Press forming gondola car end. (*Courtesy of American Car and Foundry Co., New York.*)

Primarily it is a production process, since die and equipment costs are of a magnitude that can only be absorbed by the production of a considerable number of units.   Because the plate is worked at elevated temperatures, a material-handling problem of some importance arises. Figure 11-18 shows the setup for hot-pressing the end plate for a gondola car.   This operation is so contrived that the finished pressing is discharged at the side of the press, an arrangement that conserves floor space.

Hot Spinning.   Dished heads of various designs that are used in pressure vessels are produced by either pressing or spinning.   Hot spinning has one primary advantage over pressing, since there are no restrictions on the dimensions of the die. Spun heads can be fashioned to any desired configuration on contour and also to diameters limited only by the capacity of the spinning machine. A remarkable example of hot spinning is the one in Fig. 11-19 which is working a clad plate into a head

Fig. 11-19. Forming an extremely large dished head by hot spinning at the Lukens Steel Company, Coatesville, Pa.

20 ft $4\frac{7}{32}$ in. OD. The spinning technique is shown clearly by the roller at left, bearing against the revolving plate which started as a circle. Two plates were welded in order to obtain a steel circle of sufficient diameter. Hot spinning has been successful on plate thickness up to 6 in. There is some tendency to reduce gage at some areas in the spinning.

Survey Questions

11-1. Is hot shaping a room-temperature operation?

11-2. What is the end product of hammering termed?

11-3. Explain the significance of the term "wrought."

11-4. Does hot shaping affect the mechanical properties of the production part?

11-5. How are ingots produced?

11-6. Distinguish between an ingot and a billet.

11-7. Explain the function of a blooming mill.

11-8. The term "pass" has what meaning in rolling?

11-9. What is meant by "rolling sequence"?

11-10. Are a three-high and a reversing mill the same type of equipment?

11-11. How is the capacity of a rolling mill stated?

11-12. From what materials are rolls made?

11-13. Where are clad plates or sheets generally used?

11-14. Are aluminum ingots produced in the same manner as steel ones?

11-15. Are any unusual precautions necessary for rolling magnesium-alloy sheets?

11-16. From what basic form of copper are sheets rolled?

11-17. How is seamless steel tubing produced?

11-18. Describe the operation of a steam hammer.

11-19. Give an application for pneumatic forging hammers.

11-20. Name several impact die forgings that are component parts of an automobile.

11-21. Are any of the nonferrous alloys shaped by drop forging?

11-22. Why does an impact forging die have a flash pocket?

11-23. Do drop hammers operate on a different design principle from steam hammers?

11-24. On what type of equipment are press forgings produced?

11-25. Give an example of an open die forging.

11-26. How will massive forging presses influence aircraft construction?

11-27. Does roll forging follow the impact principle?

11-28. Upset forgings employ what shape of raw material?

11-29. Name some products that are produced by precision forging.

11-30. What is an extrusion forging?

11-31. Wherein does extrusion offer greater flexibility than rolling?

11-32. How are extrusions produced?

11-33. List the metals that can be shaped by extrusion.

11-34. Is extrusion a room-temperature operation?

11-35. How are hollow extrusions made?

11-36. From what materials are forging dies made?

11-37. Describe die typing.

11-38. How is a die proved?

11-39. Hot forming is largely confined to what material?

11-40. By what method are dished pressure vessel heads produced?

11-41. Give an example of a hot-pressed component.

REFERENCES

Ashburn, Anderson, Associate Editor: Fundamentals of Forging, Forging Practice, *American Machinist*, Vol. 19, April, May, McGraw-Hill Publishing Company, Inc., New York, 1947.

Francis, C. B.: "The Making, Shaping, and Treating of Steel," 5th ed., Carnegie-Illinois Steel Co., Pittsburgh, 1941.

"Metals Handbook," American Society for Metals, Cleveland, 1948.

Naujoks, Waldemar: "Forging Handbook," American Society for Metals, Cleveland, 1948.

"Steel Plates and Their Fabrication," Lukens Steel Company, Coatesville, Pa., 1947.

"Steel Products Manual," American Iron and Steel Institute, New York, 1949.

CHAPTER 12

HEAT-TREATING

The term heat-treatment covers a host of processes applied to most of the engineering metals, both wrought and cast. Heat-treatment includes both heating and cooling operations—not heating alone. There are procedures that employ subnormal temperatures; solution heat-treated aluminum alloys are held at or near freezing in order to decelerate precipitation, and some steels are subjected to low temperatures during the stabilization treatment. From all this it is evident that treating metals thermally is a branch of metallurgy that has many ramifications and that requires both knowledge and judgment.

The mechanical engineer, if he is to be held responsible for a design, should insist that his recommendations be followed to the letter. There is no point in using a heat-treatable metal member unless that member is subjected to the particular heat-treatment which will develop the necessary properties. Neglect of this consideration arises all too frequently in manufacturing, with the result that costs are excessive or service life is sacrificed. When a metal has been chosen for a given member, the correct thermal treatment should be specified and a shop procedure established that will develop the required properties in that member.

The choice of an engineering material is frequently made from the narrow field of those known to the designer. He is generally opposed to specifying anything with which he is unfamiliar. As a result, high costs may attend the product, dooming it to obsolescence from its inception. The development of new alloys, coupled with an increasing knowledge of thermal treatment in all categories of metals and alloys, imposes the burden of continuing revision of designs and manufacturing methods on organizations or individuals dedicated to progress. They should be informed on these subjects to the point where the correctness of their considered judgment will not be open to the shadow of a doubt.

Steel

Steel accounts for the greater part of work in the heat-treat shop. Other metallic alloys that require thermal treatment will be discussed in a later section of this chapter. Steel is primarily an alloy of iron and carbon, with traces of other elements as residuals from the original raw materials or from processing materials. This base steel is termed carbon steel or plain carbon steel. The addition of other alloying elements to steel during its production cycle for the purpose of modifying its properties result in what is known as alloy steel. The behavior of an alloying element is different in its influence on steel when it is added individually from the behavior when it is added in combination with other alloys. As a result steel is a most versatile material; so much so that the mechanical engineer can find a steel suitable for practically any design requirement.

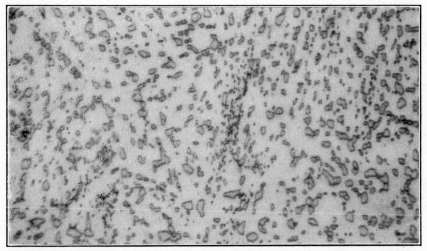

Fig. 12-1. 0.76 plain carbon steel. Spherodized carbides, brine-quenched and tempered 12 hr at 1250°F. ×2,500. (*Courtesy of United States Steel, Research Laboratory, Kearny, N.J.*)

The fact that base steel is an alloy of iron and carbon indicates that the presence or absence of carbon is of predominant importance. The carbon content determines the properties of a given steel. However, the amount of carbon is not in itself so important as the *form* of the carbon and the way in which it is distributed in the steel. For example, Fig. 12-1 shows a spherodized structure, in which the carbides are of globular form; this form of carbon and this distribution pattern impart toughness and machinability. This particular structure resulted from a heat-treatment designed to develop these specific properties in the steel. The structure was obtained by quenching the specimen in brine from its austenitizing temperature, followed by tempering at 1250°F for 12 hr.

The same steel transformed isothermally developed the structure pictured in Fig. 12-2. Examination of this micrograph shows a typically pearlitic structure which is characterized by alternate bands of cementite and ferrite, usually termed a lamellar structure. The heat-treatment consisted of an isothermal quench from austenitizing temperature at 1300°F for 3½ hr.

A study of the preceding structures, together with the procedures followed to obtain them, will clarify the fact that heat-treatment alone was responsible for the different structures and the changed properties of these specimens taken from the same steel.

Fig. 12-2.   0.76 plain carbon steel.   Coarse pearlite isothermally transformed, 3½ hr at 1300°F. ×2,500.   (*Courtesy of United States Steel, Research Laboratory, Kearny, N.J.*)

HEAT-TREATMENT

Heat-treatment of steel concerns itself with altering the form and distribution of the carbon.   In consequence the higher the carbon in a steel the greater will its effect be on the final properties of that steel. Heat-treatment can take many varied forms; the choice is based on the properties desired in the end product.   Among the better-known heat-treating methods can be listed: annealing, carbonitriding, carburizing, casehardening, hardening, homogenizing, isothermal transformation, nitriding, normalizing, patenting, and tempering.

Certain of these have a similar over-all objective; for example, carbonitriding, carburizing, casehardening, and nitriding function as surface hardening methods, whereas annealing, normalizing, and patenting act to modify the structure.   This statement must be interpreted broadly since, if there were several identical methods for producing the same result, confusion would result.

Hardening.   Heat-treatment is most frequently mentioned in connection with hardening.   Hardening is desirable from the standpoint of strength development, since steel has its highest strength when it is in its hardest condition.   A study of Fig. 12-3 will reveal the strength proper-

AISI—C 1080, Fine Grain

(*Oil Quenched*)

PROPERTIES CHART

(Average Values)

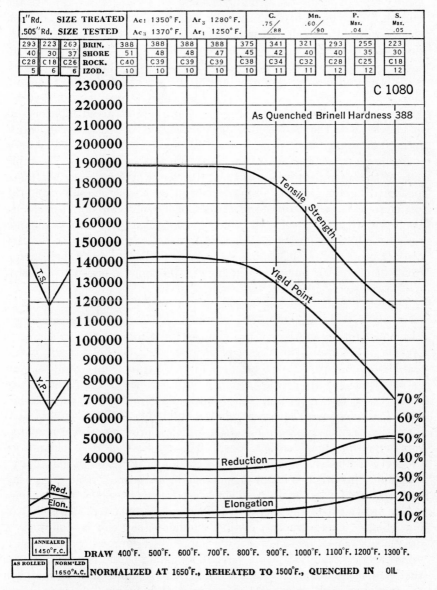

1″Rd.	**SIZE TREATED**	Ac₁ 1350° F.	Ar₃ 1280° F.	C. .75/.88	Mn. .60/.90	P. Max. .04	S. Max. .05

Table (top values):

			BRIN.	388	388	388	388	375	341	321	293	255	223
293	223	269											
40	30	37	SHORE	51	48	48	47	45	42	40	40	35	30
C28	C18	C26	ROCK.	C40	C39	C39	C39	C38	C34	C32	C28	C25	C18
5	6	6	IZOD.	10	10	10	10	10	11	11	12	12	12

C 1080

As Quenched Brinell Hardness 388

Tensile Strength

Yield Point

Reduction — 70% 60% 50% 40% 30%

Elongation — 20% 10%

ANNEALED 1450°F.C.

DRAW 400°F. 500°F. 600°F. 700°F. 800°F. 900°F. 1000°F. 1100°F. 1200°F. 1300°F.

AS ROLLED | NORM'LZD 1650°A.C. **NORMALIZED AT 1650°F., REHEATED TO 1500°F., QUENCHED IN OIL**

Fig. 12-3.   Properties Chart.   (*Courtesy of Bethlehem Steel Co., Bethlehem, Pa.*)

ties of C1080 carbon steel treated to varying degrees of hardness.   Similar property charts are available for all the better-known steels of the self-hardening types.

Hardness in steel is obtained by quenching from a temperature sufficiently high to ensure the structure's being wholly austenitic prior to the quench.   The phenomenon involved here is that of a solid solution change within the steel.   At room temperature and with a normal structure, carbon steel is composed of cementite (Fe_3C; iron carbide) and ferrite.   When steel is heated through its critical temperature range a transformation occurs; the structure of the steel undergoes a complete change.   The carbon has dissolved in gamma iron, resulting in the structure austenite.   An austenitic structure has a face-centered cubic crystal in contrast with the body-centered type common to steel below its transformation range.

Austenite forms at elevated temperatures and, in most steels, is stable only at those temperatures.   If then, the steel which has been heated to austenitizing temperature is permitted to cool at a normal rate, the austenite will revert to its original components of ferrite and cementite. However, when the steel is subjected to controlled conditions of cooling, the austenite can be transformed into various structures that impart distinct properties.   Quenching is the term applied to controlled cooling from the austenitic range.   Quenching is, therefore, a critical consideration in the steel-hardening routine.

The first step in hardening steel is to heat it to a temperature either in or above its transformation range in order that the iron may assume its gamma condition, in which it can dissolve the carbon and other elements present, thus forming the solid solution austenite.   The dissolution of the carbides may be partial or total, depending upon their magnitude as well as the time at temperature.   When either time or temperature are excessive, grain coarsening will result.   Plain carbon hypereutectoid steels (carbon above 0.8 per cent) show a rapid increase in the upper transformation temperature; see Fig. 12-4, which charts the critical temperature curve for plain carbon steel.   The alternative to avoidance of excessive temperatures is to permit a residue of undissolved carbides to remain.   This practice is not uncommon, since recommended quenching temperatures for hypereutectoid steels are frequently below the A_{cm} line.

The treatment of the specimen following its austenitization is that of quenching.   There are two distinct methods that can be followed: a drastic quench to be followed by a subsequent tempering (reheating), or an elevated temperature quench and a holding period of such duration that complete isothermal transformation occurs.   Both of these methods are employed in the heat-treat shop, and both have much to recommend them; yet they are not at all similar.   As has been said, austenite is unstable at temperatures below the transformation range, and any lowering of temperature will be accompanied by carbide separation. It follows from this that the more rapid the rate of cooling the less carbide separation will occur; if this separation can be largely avoided, dissolved carbides

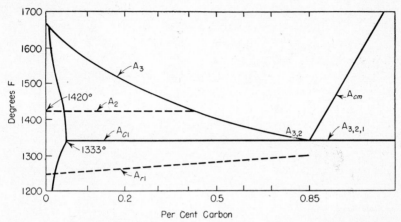

Fig. 12-4. Critical temperature diagram. (*From* **W. T.** *Frier, "Elementary Metallurgy,"* McGraw-Hill *Book Company, Inc., New York, 1942.*)

Fig. 12-5. Martensite, brine-quenched not tempered. ×2,500. (*Courtesy of United States Steel, Research Laboratory, Kearny, N.J.*)

will remain at room temperatures, resulting in a structure termed martensite, the chief constituent of fully hardened steel. Figure 12-5 shows martensite obtained in a specimen that was quenched in brine with no subsequent tempering operation. The structure is characterized by needles and is referred to as an acicular one; the white areas are retained austenite.

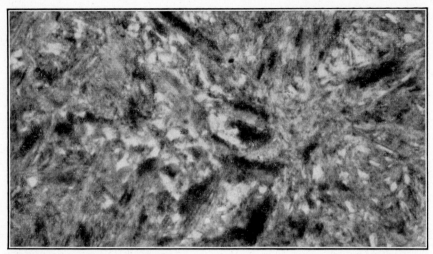

Fig. 12-6A. Martensite, brine-quenched and tempered 1 hr at 400°F. ×2,500. (*Courtesy of United States Steel, Research Laboratory, Kearny, N.J.*)

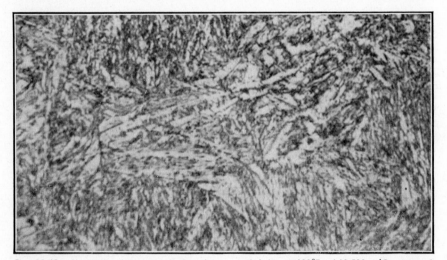

Fig. 12-6B. Martensite, brine-quenched and tempered 1 hr at 600°F. ×2,500. (*Courtesy of United States Steel, Research Laboratory, Kearny, N.J.*)

Tempering. Fully hardened steel contains stresses resulting from the quenching operation which can be relieved by reheating following the quench. This reheating operation is termed tempering, or drawing; in addition to stress relief it effects the recovery of a degree of ductility and toughness in the steel under treatment. The higher the tempering temperature, the greater the increase in ductility (Fig. 12-3).

Tempering applied to a martensitic structure causes its decomposition.

Fig. 12-6C.   Martensite, brine-quenched and tempered 1 hr at 800°F.   ×2,500.   (Courtesy of United States Steel, Research Laboratory, Kearny, N.J.)

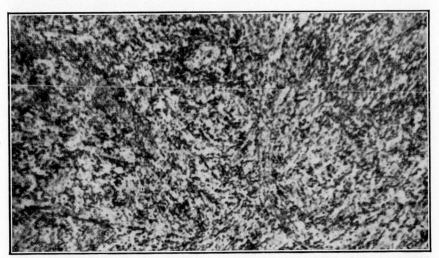

Fig. 12-6D.   Martensite, brine-quenched and tempered at 1100°F.   ×2,500.   (Courtesy of United States Steel, Research Laboratory, Kearny, N.J.)

The resulting structures can be identified as individual ones although the gradation from one to the next is not abrupt.   Examples of tempered structures are given in Figs. 12-6A, 6B, 6C, 6D.   These structures were obtained by tempering martensite (Fig. 12-5).   A study of this series of micrographs, which starts with a tempering temperature of 400°F (Fig. 12-6A) and concludes with a 12-hr 1250°F draw (Fig. 12-1), will reveal the effect of varying the tempering temperature.   Any further increase in tempering temperature in this series would completely obliterate the quench effect and the steel would enter its transformation range.

The procedure just described is correctly known as tempering martensite. The processing routine consisted of heating the member in its transformation range for a time interval at temperature to assure austenization of the structure. The member was then given a brine quench to room temperature in order to fully harden the steel. The hardening operation was followed by a temper or draw at the several temperatures shown on the micrographs. Tempering is employed as a means of increasing the toughness of the member. It is advisable to employ the highest tempering temperature that will meet the strength specification, since this will ensure the greatest toughness/strength ratio. Tempering results in a reduction in hardness.

The relationship of hardness and strength is such that when steels exhibit the same hardness they will have about the same strength (Fig. 12-7). This is a point that needs emphasis, since it has a decided bearing on the choice of steel for a given application. Obtaining the *same hardness* in a number of steels of different composition requires control of the tempering operation, because higher temperatures or longer periods are needed for one steel than for another even though the two have the same carbon content. Thus 1045 steel tempered for 1 hr at 960°F and 6145 steel tempered for 1 hr at 1240°F will both show a 300 Brinell hardness number (Bhn).

Isothermal Transformation.   The previously discussed method of heat-treatment is the one of greatest use in the heat-treat shop. The work of Davenport and Bain has been outstanding in developing a different concept for austenite transformation, one that is termed isothermal transformation. This is defined as "the process of transforming austenite in ferrous alloys to ferrite or a ferrite-carbide aggregate at any constant temperature within the *transformation range.*"[1]

Heat-treating by this method starts with the specimen being heated to and held in its austenite transformation range until the desired austenitic structure is reached. Following the time at temperature interval, the specimen is quenched to and held at the temperature that will give the transformation product desired. It is important to recognize that the interval for the start of the austenitic transformation is different for each temperature, and further, that the transformation period also varies with the temperature. Experimental data have been obtained for many steels, and from these data curves or charts of the isothermal transformation

---

[1] The joint AFA-ASM-ASTM-SAE Committee on Definitions of Terms Relating to Heat Treatment, "Metals Handbook," American Society for Metals, Cleveland, 1948.

have been drawn.[1] The curves are termed isothermal transformation diagrams, transformation-temperature-time (TTT) curves, or S curves, the last being the most commonly used expression. Such a diagram for 4140 steel is shown in Fig. 12-8; it charts the behavior of 4140 steel from austenite to martensite. Temperatures are plotted as ordinates and time

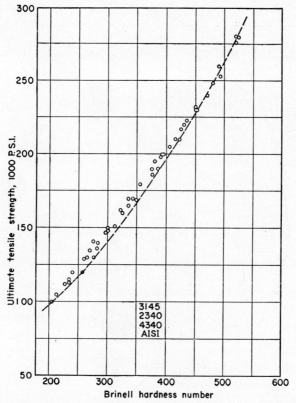

Fig. 12-7. The relation of ultimate tensile strength to Brinell hardness for three different steels of similar carbon content. (*Courtesy of United States Steel Corp., New York.*)

is plotted on a logarithmic scale that expands short and compresses long time intervals. The heavy curved line at the left marked "transformation begins" shows the time-temperature position for the start of austenite transformation. So long as the steel is in the area at the left of that line it retains its austenite structure; when the line is crossed, transformation of austenite begins. The heavy curved line at the right gives the position of the end of transformation, and the structures in the area to the right

[1] "Atlas of Isothermal Transformation Diagrams," Research Laboratories, United States Steel Corporation, Kearny, N.J.

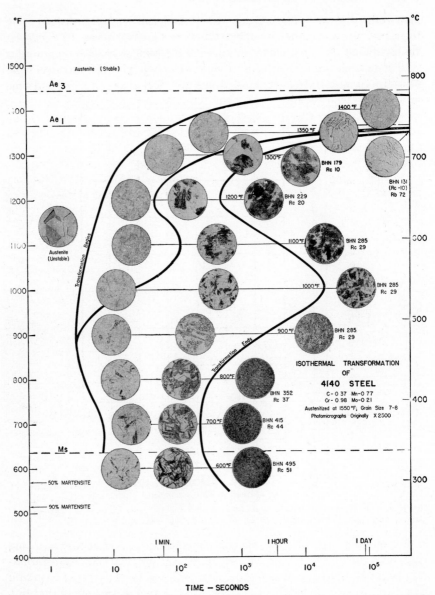

Fig. 12-8. Isothermal transformation diagram for 4140 steel. (*Courtesy of United States Steel, Research Laboratory, Kearny, N.J.*)

are those of complete transformation. These structures will not transform further, regardless of subsequent cooling rates. The area between the boundary lines represents partial transformation.

The dotted horizontal line Ms shows the temperature of the start of the martensitic transformation. Martensite transforms only on a falling temperature and not at a constant temperature as do the other transformation products. The chart shows that at an approximate temperature of 575°F there is a 50 per cent martensite transformation, which has increased to 90 per cent with the temperature lowered to approximately 520°F. The important assumption here is that the rate of quenching has

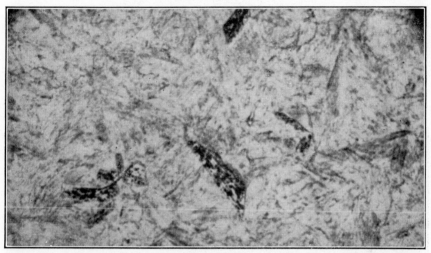

Fig. 12-9A. 4140 steel 5 per cent transformed, isothermally, at 800°F. ×2,500. (Courtesy of United States Steel, Research Laboratory, Kearny, N.J.)

been sufficiently rapid to *prevent any austenite transformation until the Ms temperature has been reached.* Failure in this respect means that some transformation occurred before the temperature for the beginning of martensite formation was reached, and as a result maximum hardness was not attained in the specimen. The rate of quench is the key to obtaining a fully martensitic transformation; however, in the heat-treat shop problems of steel composition as well as mass must be dealt with.

Alloying additions in steel have the effect of slowing transformation; therefore there is a greater time interval available for the quench. Alloy steels show the "beginning of transformation" curve moved to the right in the isothermal transformation diagram. Transformation is more "sluggish" both on quenching and on tempering for the alloy steels.

In Fig. 12-8 micrographs are included for several structures, showing partial as well as complete transformations at given temperatures. In order to add clarity to this diagram, Figs. 12-9A, 9B, and 9C are pre-

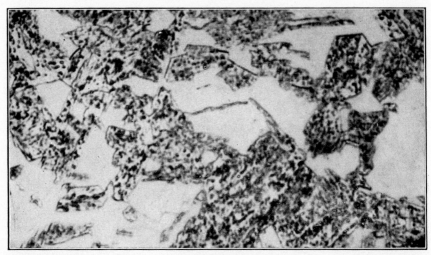

Fig. 12-9B. 4140 steel 50 per cent transformed, isothermally, at 800°F. ×2,500. (Courtesy of United States Steel, Research Laboratory, Kearny, N.J.)

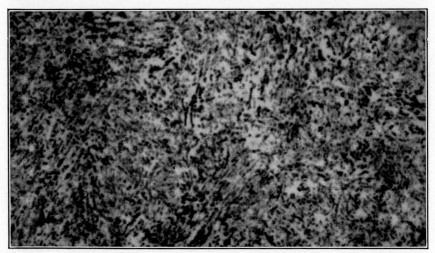

Fig. 12-9C. 4140 steel 100 per cent transformed, isothermally, at 800°F. ×2,500. (Courtesy of United States Steel, Research Laboratory, Kearny, N.J.)

sented. These are all taken from the transformation of 4140 steel at 800°F. The figures show, respectively, 5, 50, and 100 per cent transformation from austenite. The only difference between these structures is the element of *time;* temperature remained constant. This particular type of heat-treatment is also known as austempering.[1] The structure developed in Fig. 12-9C is termed Bainite.

[1] Trade name of process patented by United States Steel Corporation.

The two methods for heat-treating steel in order to develop the necessary strength coupled with toughness have been given in some detail. One method is based on the technique of tempering martensite, while the other represents transformation at a constant temperature (excepting martensite). To clarify further these two concepts of heat-treatment

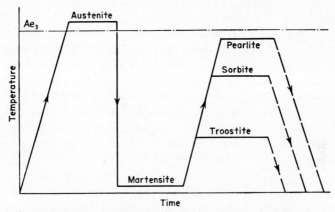

Fig. 12-10A. Schematic sketch of heat, quench, and temper.

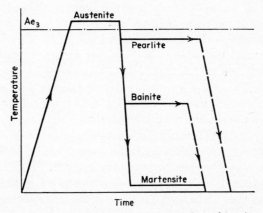

Fig. 12-10B. Schematic sketch of isothermal transformation.

Figs. 12-10A and 10B, showing schematically the routine followed in each of the two methods, are included. The terminology applied to tempered structures in Fig. 12-10A is currently considered obsolete.

Which of these two methods should be applied to a given heat-treating problem is open to some difference of opinion. Primarily the decision is based on the shape and size of the treated component. Isothermal transformations, when optimum results are expected, will function best on small-sectioned work. Quenching progresses inward from the surface; consequently a specimen of any appreciable volume will quench more slowly than will a thin section. The effect of mass on both quenching speed and depth of hardness should always be considered in connection with the establishment of a heat-treat procedure.

CASEHARDENING

The methods for hardening discussed thus far in this chapter have dealt with the self-hardening steels—those that harden directly on quenching. There are instances where steels are selected that can be endowed with the combination of a hard surface backed by a strong, tough core. This desirable combination of properties can be obtained by casehardening. A wide choice of steels is available, from the alloys which will produce excellent core properties to the low plain-carbon grades that are economical to buy and that machine readily. Steels selected for casehardening are generally of low carbon content, rarely exceeding 0.25 per cent.

The necessity of obtaining satisfactory surface hardness in such steels is met by carburizing the part prior to any quench or reheat and quench. Steel is carburized for the purpose of increasing the carbon, and in some processes the nitrogen, or both, in the surface of the steel. Of several methods used in the heat-treat shop for accomplishing this, the oldest and best-known is pack carburizing.

Pack Carburizing. The parts to be carburized are packed in a heat-resistant alloy steel box where they are surrounded by carburizing compounds. The latter are materials high in carbon of a form that will readily develop CO and CO_2 when subjected to elevated temperatures. Energizers such as barium carbonate are used to speed the reaction and thus to shorten the carburizing time cycle. Carburizing temperatures are in the 1650 to 1700°F range, for most steels.

Packing requires care inasmuch as the parts must be surrounded by an equal amount of carburizer for uniform results. The vitality of the carburizer is maintained by making additions to offset the loss incurred in the previous use. The prepared boxes, which are frequently cylindrical in shape, are sealed prior to being placed in the furnace. Upon completion of the carburizing cycle the boxes are withdrawn and contents emptied over a screen in order to separate the work from the carburizer.

Gas Carburizing. In this method a gaseous atmosphere is maintained in the furnace as the agency for imparting the necessary carbon to the steel surface. A diversity of practice governs the actual operation in that gases such as methane, ethane, and propane are used in the furnace atmosphere. There is the further practice of using oil vapors as a source of hydrocarbon, either separately or in combination with carbonaceous gases.

Gas carburizing has the advantages of cleanliness and reduced handling over the pack method.   Flexibility is another noteworthy feature, since atmospheric composition is readily controlled by the combination of input and venting.   Carburizing speed is claimed to be higher than it is when solid carburizers are used.

Liquid Carburizing.   The development of liquid carburizing can be traced to the older cyaniding pot principle.   Now, however, activated salts have replaced the potassium cyanide of former days.   This is a most fortunate circumstance, for the elimination of potassium cyanide (KCN) has removed a deadly poison from the heat-treat shop.   Sodium cyanide is the primary source of the carburizer, although calcium cyanide is of some importance in this connection.   Liquid carburizers are used mainly for relatively shallow case depths on the order of 0.025 in.

Carbonitriding.   This method is a combination of gas carburizing and nitriding.   The process consists of bleeding ammonia gas into a carburizing atmosphere in the furnace in order to develop both carbon and nitrogen in the surface of the steel.   The amount of ammonia gas required may be as low as 1 per cent where the work is given a quench upon removal from the furnace.   When air quench is specified, ammonia is used in larger volumes as a means of obtaining the desired hardness.

Heat-treating Carburized Steel.   The previous paragraphs have surveyed the more prominent methods used for changing the surface composition of the steel.   Note that the objective in each instance is that of modifying the steel in preparation for further processing.   It follows from this that *carburizing in itself does not harden steel*.   There are designs in which local areas are not to be carburized.   In such instances selective carburizing is used.   The surfaces that are not to be treated are masked by copper plating, coating with proprietary compounds, or covering with sand.   Following the carburizing process, the copper is ground off or removed by reverse plating.

A carburized part is a complex steel that has a high-carbon outer surface, with carbon content decreasing to the core, which has been unaffected insofar as chemical composition is concerned.   The usual carburizing steels develop a range of from 1.0 to 1.3 per cent C on the surface, or for the case, while the core retains its approximate original analysis.

Quenching directly from the carburizing operation is not as common as formerly.   Current practice is in the direction of pot cooling, followed by reheating to the transformation range of the case to be followed in turn by a quench and a draw.   This procedure, accompanied by the resulting data on properties, is given concisely in a properties chart (Fig. 12-11).   Carburized parts are also subjected to double heat-treatments wherein both case and core are processed.   Treatment to develop toughness in the core takes precedence over case considerations.

AISI—C1015, Fine Grain

PROPERTIES

(Average Values)

1"RD. TREATED .505"RD. TESTED	Ac_1 1390°F. Ac_3 1560°F.	Ar_3 1510°F. Ar_1 1390°F.	C. .13/.18	Mn. .30/.60	P. Max. .04	S. Max. .05

		T.S. Lb./Sq. In.	Y.P. Lb./Sq. In.	Elon. % 2 In.	Red'n. %	Brin. No.	Izod Ft. Lb.
AS ROLLED		61,000	45,500	39.0	61.0	126	81.5
NORMALIZED	1700°F. A.C.	60,000	48,000	38.0	61.0	121	82.0
ANNEALED	1600°F. F.C.	56,000	37,500	40.0	66.0	116	84.0

CORE PROPERTIES

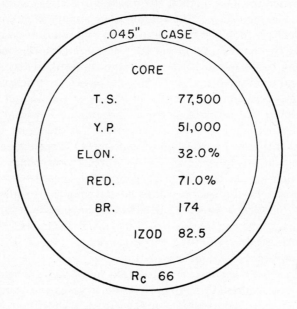

.045"   CASE

CORE

T.S.	77,500
Y.P.	51,000
ELON.	32.0%
RED.	71.0%
BR.	174
IZOD	82.5

R_c 66

SINGLE QUENCH AND TEMPER

(1) Carburized at 1675° F. for 8 hours

(2) Pot Cooled

(3) Reheated to 1425° F

(4) Water Quenched

(5) Tempered at 350° F.

Fig. 12-11.   Chart of properties for carburized and heat-treated C1015 steel. (*Courtesy of Bethlehem Steel Co., Bethlehem, Pa.*)

Nitriding. Surface hardening, in which the formation of iron nitrides predominates, is of interest to the designer. Best results for nitriding are obtained by employing nitralloy steels. These steels contain aluminum ranging from 0.85 to 1.20 per cent and as a result develop surface properties superior to any other nitrided steels. They contain appreciable percentages of chromium and molybdenum in addition to aluminum. The nitralloy steels are designated by types, viz., nitralloy 125 (Type H) and nitralloy 135 (Type G). The various types differ in both carbon content and alloy range.

Nitralloy steels are heat-treated to develop core properties prior to nitriding. It is customary to purchase such steel, if it is to be machined, in the heat-treated condition. When distortion is to be minimized, machined parts should be stress-relieved prior to nitriding. Forgings are produced from non-heat-treated stock, since subsequent heat-treatment is necessary as a finishing operation.

Nitriding is accomplished by subjecting the steel to an atmosphere rich in nitrogen; ammonia gas is most frequently used for this purpose, although organic nitrogen-bearing compounds as well as synthetic urea are important. This gas is bled into the furnace at a volume that will yield the proper dissociation rate for nitrogen:

$$2NH_3 \rightleftarrows 2N + 3H_2$$

The dissociation products escape through a vent, where their composition can be analyzed as a guide to gas-flow control. Temperatures for nitriding are comparatively low, ranging from 930 to 1000°F. This desirable low-temperature treatment is offset by the long time at temperature, which may extent to 90 hours or more. Case depths which average 0.015 in. are considerably less than in carburizing, despite the much longer treatment.

Advantages of nitriding are extreme hardness, 1000–1100 Vickers diamond (10 kg load), and retention of hardness to temperatures of 1200°F for intermittent heating. Corrosion resistance is also claimed for nitrided surfaces. From a manufacturing standpoint the important thing about nitriding is the fact that no quenching is necessary. Claims have been advanced to the effect that the part can be finished ground to size prior to nitriding without fear of distortion or growth after treatment. Where growth occurs, it is on the order of 0.001 in. per inch of dimension.

Interest in nitriding develops primarily from the hard surface potential backed by a tough core. Nitrided parts, such as valve stems, show excellent wear resistance and justify their higher costs. Nitriding can be done selectively by masking with solder or tin-plating. A gray mat surface is indicative of a splendid nitrided case, while a lustrous appearance means an inferior one. Annealing of nitrided surfaces is best accomplished by dispersing the surface nitrides; however, a surface once annealed will never produce a nitrided surface comparable to the original one.

Casehardening Reviewed. Casehardening means producing a hardened surface backed by the type of core necessary to meet design requirements. There are several methods of surface treatment. Some require subsequent heat-treating, some quench direct; in nitriding, no quench is needed. Casehardening is rarely applied to those steels whose compositions permit quenching from their transformation range for the reason that such steels are inherently capable of direct heat-treatments to desired properties. Casehardening is specified for those applications where surface hardness and wear resistance are to be combined with toughness.

Applied Heat-treatment

Annealing. Annealing is accomplished by heating the work—which should be protected from any decarburization influences either by packing or by controlled furnace atmosphere, through its transformation range— and holding for a period that will ensure uniform temperature throughout, to be followed by slow cooling away from the air. The latter aspect of the annealing cycle requires special emphasis, since it is the cooling rate that governs final results. For best results in annealing, the furnace heat is closed off and the work permitted to cool with the furnace. Such a procedure is costly from the viewpoint of furnace equipment use and can be successfully detoured by placing the heated pieces in lime, sand, or a similar insulating material that will ensure slow cooling.

Annealing is generally considered to mean softening. There are other interpretations of the term—some by custom and others by definition. Obviously, softening indicates a change in microstructure to pearlite (Fig. 12-2) which results in altered mechanical properties.

There are modifications applied to annealing, as is indicated by such terms as blue annealing, bright annealing, etc. In every instance, these terms refer to a specific annealing application designed to produce a unique end result.

Normalizing. Normalizing differs from annealing in both heating and cooling. Normalizing provides for heating well above the transformation range to temperatures higher than the annealing ones, since this process is widely used with alloy steels. After a short period at temperature, much shorter than in annealing, the piece is removed from the furnace and cooled in *still air*. In effect such cooling is a quench, a fact that explains the higher strength values as compared to annealing (Fig. 12-3).

Normalizing affects the part much in the manner of annealing, although it is sometimes specified in forgings for grain refining prior to annealing or to improve machinability. It is a faster method, owing to the increased cooling rate; however, because of the shorter heating time the structure and properties are not so uniform as in an annealed end product. The relative transformation temperature ranges for hardening, annealing, and normalizing are diagramed in Fig. 12-12.

Quenching. Quenching as a part of the heat-treating cycle is of fundamental importance. More frequently than not, failure to obtain expected hardness or the experience of outright cracking can be traced to improper quenching as to choice of both medium and technique. Quenching is a cooling operation. As the surface cools, convection of heat from the core starts cooling the center. The speed of quench varies with the composition and temperature of the bath as well as with its movement.

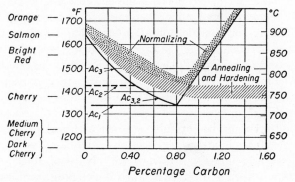

Fig. 12-12. Transformation temperature range for hardening, annealing, and normalizing. (*From "Metals Handbook," American Society for Metals, Cleveland, 1948.*)

Uniform results depend on maintaining the quenching bath at a constant temperature.

When the heated piece strikes the quenching bath, a vapor film forms which acts as an insulator. This holds true whether an air or a liquid quench is used. Obviously this film must be dissipated in order to obtain the desired quenching action. Movement, of either the piece or the quenching medium, will aid materially in bringing about this desired condition. The skilled heat-treater always moves the heated piece in the quenching bath either in a circular motion or in a figure eight. Such motion should not be so rapid that cavitation of the medium directly behind the piece will occur, since differential cooling rates as indicated by soft areas will result. The importance of agitating the quenching medium is shown in Table 12-1.

Agitation may be taken to mean the movement of the quenching medium against the work. There is considerable interest in spraying liquid under pressure in order to attain high velocity of movement and thereby to increase quenching rates. There are also installations using a mist or fog blanket as a quenching medium.

TABLE 12-1. SEVERITY OF QUENCH (H VALUE)*

Agitation	Oil	Water	Brine
None................	0.25–0.30	0.9–1.0	2.0
Mild................	0.3 –0.35	1.0–1.1	2.0–2.2
Moderate..........	0.35–0.40	1.2–1.3	
Good..............	0.4 –0.50	1.4–1.5	
Strong............	0.5 –0.80	1.6–2.0	
Violent............	0.8 –1.10	4.0	5.0

* "Metals Handbook," p. 495, American Society for Metals, Cleveland, 1948.

The use of oil as a quench needs some clarification, since all types of oil—animal, vegetable, and mineral—are used, either singly or in combination. The important consideration about quenching oils is their vapor pressure because this is the determinant of their effectiveness.

Distortion and Cracking. The choice of a quenching method as well as a quenching medium is predicated both on the steel analysis and on the end use of the product. The objective in quenching is the avoidance of warping, cracking, or variable hardness. It is for this reason that the design of the part must be carefully studied with regard to its behavior during quench. Such items as section thickness, section changes, cavities, edges, and bores will govern the choice of steel and quench. Quenching is not always directed toward developing hardness; rather a substantial portion is given over to delivering a tough end product free of cracks, warpage, and distortion.

When such precision-machined members as gears are to be quenched, the above considerations require especial attention. Warpage in gears can be controlled by using a fixture in which the gear is placed prior to immersion in the quench. In fact the complete quenching cycle can be accommodated in a quenching press (Fig. 12-13). In such a press the gear is positioned in a fixture that holds it to shape during the quenching cycle.

Close examination of the gear in position in Fig. 12-13 will show that the area within the ring gear is taken up by a segmented expander. This device operates to take advantage of plastic flow in the gear steel to combat the normal contraction caused by the quench. The quenching oil is not used indiscriminately as an immersion bath; instead it is delivered against the gear through jets whose streams are baffled in order to provide differential cooling as the gear sections require. This quenching cycle is far from routine in that all features of the quench operation must be coordinated.

The size of the section as well as the temperature gradient within the piece will exert a decided influence on the amount of distortion or cracking that may occur. As the outer layers cool they will contract; however, they are limited in this because the center has not as yet cooled sufficiently to conform. As a result the surface layers are in tension and the center in compression at the beginning of the quench. When the surface layers reach a temperature in the *Ms* range, transformation of the austenite to martensite sets in, with the result that the outside undergoes slight expansion, which tends to relieve the tension stresses somewhat.

Fig. 12-13. Close-up of ring gear in Gleason quenching press. *(Courtesy of Western Gear Works, Lynwood, Calif.)*

Martempering. Examination of the transformation stresses has led to the idea of circumventing them by a type of interrupted quench termed martempering. In this method the piece is quenched rapidly from its austenitizing temperature to the *Ms* range, where it is removed from the bath and permitted to cool in air to room temperature. Since martensite forms at and below the *Ms* temperature, this microstructure will develop during the cooling to room temperature. The transformation stresses will be of a much lower magnitude, since the drastic temperature gradient within the piece is largely eliminated. As a result, there is much less danger of cracking with this method than with the full quench.

Heating

The modern heat-treat shop can choose heating equipment other than furnaces. These newer developments, including such items as electrical induction, oxyacetylene and gas-flame heating, offer the heat-treater a *speed method* of heating. In addition to these, there are such items as salt, oil, and lead baths that can be described as secondary heating equipment, since the materials that compose the heating bath are, in their turn, heated from an outside fuel source.

FURNACES

The selection of a furnace is, broadly speaking, based on the two considerations of fuel cost and production requirements. The heat sources most commonly used are gas, oil, and electricity. The choice between these is governed primarily by local conditions of availability and cost. The point is that furnaces are designed for using any of these fuels.

Heat-treating furnaces avoid the use of direct flame in favor of muffles or indirect firing. Radiant tube heating, wherein the fuel is burned inside ceramic or alloy tubes, permits atmospheric control within the furnace and gives about the same type of performance as electrical resistance heating. Large-volume furnaces favor the radiant tube type of heating because of fuel economy.

Fig. 12-14. Box-type heat-treating furnace.
(Courtesy of Lindberg Engineering Co., Chicago.)

Once a decision has been made on the fuel to be used, production requirements dictate the particular type of furnace to be selected. The choice lies between batch and continuous, or production, designs. There is a wide range of furnace equipment, with the trend moving in the direction of a special design to meet an individual problem. For the most part the box, or hearth, type of furnace (Fig. 12-14) is in the majority.

Furnaces designed for production embody various features necessary to mass movement of material. Reciprocating hearth furnaces cause the material, which is fed in at one end, to move forward and be discharged at the end of the heating cycle. The shaker hearth is a similar development. Rotary-hearth furnaces are built with the hearth as a disk on which the work is placed so that as the hearth rotates the piece is subjected to a complete heating cycle. The loading and discharge doors can be placed where they best fit into the production sequence. Furnaces of this type are of considerable size (Fig. 12-15). There are some of circular outside shape that attain sizes as great as 50 ft in diameter.

The largest furnaces, although they are not of the continuous-production type, are of the car type. Work is loaded on cars which are pushed into the furnaces; a sand seal is used at car-deck level to prevent heat damage to the car's running gear.

Temperature Control. Furnace temperatures are measured by means of some type of thermocouple connected with a pyrometer of either indicating or recording design. Further, thermocouples are used as a means of automatic regulation of the furnace. Some of this control equipment is extremely sensitive in that the tolerance in temperature range is

Fig. 12-15. Rotary-hearth furnace equipped for the radiant-tube firing used for clean hardening. (*Courtesy of Surface Combustion Corp., Toledo, Ohio.*)

specified at less than 5°F. Close control requires refinement in instrumentation and continued calibration of the thermocouples used. A typical temperature control instrument installation is shown in Fig. 12-16.

Temperature control equipment is of no value unless it is respected and cared for accordingly. Many failures in the heat-treat shop are traceable to neglect of this equipment. Instruments should be checked periodically, and thermocouples require frequent calibration. The operating staff must be fully informed on temperature control to prevent such errors as connecting rare metal couples to base metal recorders and other lapses.

Controlled Atmosphere. Separately controlled atmospheres within a heat-treating furnace have been in use for some time. Finished machined parts can be processed without loss of surface hardness during heating because decarburization can be eliminated, as can carbon pickup. Another attribute of controlled atmospheres is that scaling can be prevented; as a result, clean, accurate work is possible without resort to pickling and other forms of cleaning.

Controlled atmospheres are generated in equipment that is auxiliary to

Fig. 12-16. Temperature-control instrument panel installations. (*Courtesy of Brown Instrument Division, Minneapolis-Honeywell Regulator Co., Minneapolis, Minn.*)

the furnaces. Atmospheres are produced from gases, liquids, and solids and also from combinations of these. This wide range of sources yields a large number of furnace atmospheres, each one designed to meet a specific condition. Peck[1] has divided furnace control atmospheres into nine categories, extending from completely burned fuel gas through completely burned dissociated ammonia. An example of a furnace installation complete with atmosphere generator is shown in Fig. 12-17.

Salt Baths. There are inherent advantages to the use of salt baths, such as the fact that the molten salt congeals on the newly immersed workpiece and insulates it from sudden heat shock. A similar protection

[1] C. E. Peck, industrial heating engineer, Westinghouse Electric Corp., in a lecture at the American Gas Association School, Columbus, Ohio, May, 1947.

Fig. 12-17. A combination preheat and high-heat controlled-atmosphere furnace for heat-treatment of high-speed steels. (*Courtesy of Lindberg Engineering Co., Chicago.*)

is afforded when the quenching cycle is reached. More important than these is the fact that the workpiece heats much more rapidly, with a time saving on the order of 4:1 to 6:1 over atmosphere heating. Heating will be uniform, since the molten salt completely surrounds the workpiece regardless of its shape. Scaling and decarburization are avoided when heating in salt baths because the workpiece is not in contact with the air. Composition of the salt bath requires close control in order to prevent

TABLE 12-2. TYPICAL SALT-BATH COMPOSITIONS*

Desig-nation	Weight percentage					Approx. melting point, °F	Recom-mended heating range, °F	Application
	NaCl	KCl	BaCl$_2$	NaNO$_2$	L NO$_3$			
I-1	45–55	45–55	. . . . .	. . . . .	. . . . .	1250	1350–1650	Neutral hardening
I$_2$-2	15–25	20–30	50–60	. . . . .	. . . . .	1100	1250–1700	Neutral hardening
I$_3$-3	20–30	. . . . .	70–80	. . . . .	. . . . .	1300	1400–1700	Neutral hardening
I-4	10–20	. . . . .	80–90	. . . . .	. . . . .	1400	1500–2000	Neutral hardening
L-1	. . . . .	. . . . .	. . . . .	40–50	50–60	290	325–1200	Austemper-ing

* Abstracted from "Metals Handbook," American Society for Metals, Cleveland, 1948.

any reactions with the metal being treated.   Some salt-bath compositions
and their applications appear in Table 12-2.

Furnaces for salt baths are built along different lines in respect to
methods of heating.   Those heated internally (Fig. 12-18) employ either

Fig. 12-18.   Immersion tube heated salt-bath pot furnace.   (*Courtesy of Surface Combustion Corp.,
Toledo, Ohio.*)

gas radiant tube, an electrical resistance element, or an immersed electrode as the heat source.   The immersed electrode construction is
capable of developing temperatures to 2400°F, which is the maximum
salt-bath temperature.

SPEED HEATING

The following paragraphs are devoted to describing heat-treating
methods wherein the heating is not performed in a furnace.   Instead
some other heat source, as exemplified by electrical induction, oxyacetylene, or gas flame is used.   The advantage of these methods lies in
the fact that heating time is reduced to a matter of seconds.   Local heating can be applied, removing the necessity for masking; of equal importance is the fact that workpieces of great size can be treated by heating
only the areas that require hardening.   Large-diameter gears and
machine tool ways are examples of components now locally hardened by
speed heating.   With a very rapid heating rate, the elevated temperature

is confined to the surface layers; thus the tendency to distort or crack the workpiece is reduced.

Induction Heating. Heating metals by high-frequency electrical currents is used in many phases of metal treating, forming, and joining. The induction heating circuit employs a high-frequency current whose source may be (*a*) motor-generator sets, (*b*) vacuum-tube oscillators, (*c*) mercury arc converters, or (*d*) spark-gap oscillators. Each of these varies somewhat as to available frequencies as well as capacities—a condition that limits equipment choice. Motor-generator sets, for example, are available for frequencies ranging from 1,000 to 30,000 cycles and have capacities reaching 1,500 kw.

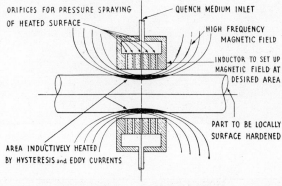

Fig. 12-19. Schematic diagram of induction heating. (*Courtesy of The Ohio Crankshaft Co., Cleveland.*)

The principle of the induction heating circuit is fundamentally that of a transformer, since the member carrying the current is the primary and the workpiece being placed in the inductor loop becomes the secondary. The flow of the current through the inductor sets up the familiar lines of force which cut through the workpiece that has previously been inserted in the circuit. The arrangement of an induction heating circuit for hardening can be seen in Fig. 12-19. Resulting heat arises from both hysteresis losses and eddy current losses; the former are generally disregarded and the heat source is considered to be the eddy currents, which are resistance losses.

The application of induction heating to heat-treatment is accomplished by adapting the inductor coil to the workpiece. An example of an induction hardening installation used for gears is shown in Fig. 12-20. There are some extremely ingenious induction hardening installations such as the figure-eight coils used for treating two camshafts simultaneously. These coils heat the cam face, then move to the next one, until all, plus the camshaft bearings, have been hardened on both shafts.

Fig. 12-20.   Hardening a gear by induction heating.   (*Courtesy of Induction Heating Corp., Brooklyn,* N.Y.)

Fig. 12-21.   Close-up of workpiece-holding device and flame head.   Note how individual flame tips are positioned so as to concentrate the desired volume of heat on the two diameters of workpiece. (*Courtesy of Cincinnati Milling Machine Co., Cincinnati.*)

The oxyacetylene flame is used for selective hardening in a manner similar to the previously described induction device. The flame is the same one used for welding. Torches bearing multiple flames have been developed for this application. The oxyacetylene flame, being capable of a temperature of 6300°F, gives an intense local heat; when several of these flames are used together, the workpiece can be heated rapidly. The flame heating principle is the basis for design of heat-treating equipment as shown in Fig. 12-21. Multiple-flame torches play against a rapidly revolving workpiece, which results in an extremely short heating period. The piece, when heated, is quenched by being dropped into a quench tank that is located directly below the heating station. Splined ends of shafts lend themselves admirably to this system of hardening. Gear teeth are flame-hardened by passing flames on opposite sides of the tooth, with a water quench following the progress of the flames.

Nonferrous Alloys

The increased attention being given to the light metals and nonferrous alloys in engineering manufacture was discussed in Chap. 2. It seems desirable, therefore, to direct attention to the fact that heat-treating is also applied to many of these materials. New methods, new techniques, and new concepts will be required of both supervisory and operating personnel, since the problems involved are largely of a nature that call for a clean break from the traditional heat-treat processing of steel.

ALUMINUM ALLOYS

Alloying elements used in aluminum are termed hardeners. The metallic elements most commonly found in wrought alloys are Cu, Mg, Si, and Mn, while Zn, Cr, Ni, Pb, Sn, and Bi are also present in certain alloys. They are capable of forming a considerable number of constituents. Mondolfo[1] has examined these in some detail. Heat-treatment of aluminum alloys concerns itself with the constituents and the form in which they are present.

There are three recognized heat-treatments applied to aluminum alloys: (a) annealing; (b) solution HT; (c) precipitation HT. Annealing has the same meaning as in ferrous alloys. Further, annealing is applied to the strain-hardening, heat-treatable, and casting alloys. Temperatures for annealing lie somewhat below those for solution heat-treatment.

Solution Heat-treatment. The alloy B26-46T (Alcoa 195), essentially composed of 4.5 per cent Cu, with the balance aluminum, is a prominent

[1] Mondolfo, Lucio F.: "Metallography of Aluminum Alloys," John Wiley & Sons, Inc., New York, 1943.

heat-treatable casting alloy, and will serve here in the description of solution heat-treatment. When this alloy is molten, all of the Cu is in solution; the Cu is completely dissolved in the liquid Al and the melt represents a molten solution of Cu in Al. With a lowering of the temperature, solid alloy will begin to form. The composition of these first crystals will be richer in Al than the indicated alloying properties. A continuation of the freezing process will find crystals, increasingly rich in Cu, forming in the melt until ultimately the final crystals forming are surrounded by melt containing 33 per cent Cu (eutectic). Upon solidification of this remaining liquid, it precipitates two constituents in a simultaneous action. One of these is a solid solution of approximately 5.5 per cent Cu, while the other is the intermetallic compound $CuAl_2$, which contains about 52 per cent Cu and is hard and brittle in nature.

Obviously the solidified casting lacks homogeneity insofar as the distribution of the Cu component is concerned. Since, therefore, the solubility of Cu in Al increases with temperature, the solution heat-treatment is applied to obtain a better Cu distribution. The temperature is raised to 960°F for this alloy, where all of the Cu is soluble in the solid Al. The specimen is held at this temperature; consequently a water quench quickly follows the heating period in order to retain the maximum amount of the solid solution. Quenching may be in boiling water as a means of controlling the warpage that can result from quenching strains.

The temperatures used for solution heat-treatment of Al alloys are chosen to be just below the melting point of the eutectic of that alloying system. The use of higher temperatures causes melting within the specimen, which is rendered unfit for service application and must be regarded as scrap for remelt. Solution heat-treatment improves the properties of Al alloys.

Precipitation Heat-treatment. Quenching was employed, following solution heat-treatment, to retain the solid solution change developed. However, since solubility decreases with lowered temperatures, there is a tendency for the dissolved alloying component to precipitate to the extent of room temperature equilibrium conditions. This phenomenon is also termed aging. In the duralumin-type alloys, especially 17S, aging is extremely rapid at room temperatures and is essentially complete in four days. In consequence, these alloys are not subjected to a precipitation heat-treatment, which means they are not reheated following the solution heat-treatment.

Reheating, following solution heat-treatment, for the purpose of precipitating the alloying components of an optimum critical size is termed precipitation heat-treatment. Its effects on the mechanical properties are increased yield and ultimate tensile strength as well as hardness; ductility may remain constant or tend toward lowered values, depending on the alloy. Fig. 12-22A shows the microstructure of 24S wrought alloy in the annealed condition and Fig. 12-22B the same alloy in the fully heat-treated condition—solution plus precipitation.

Fig. 12-22A.   Al alloy 24S-O, annealed condition, Bossert's etch.   ×100.

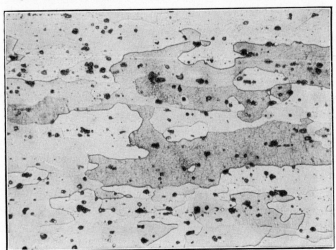

Fig. 12-22B.   Al alloy 24S-T4, solution plus precipitation heat-treated, Keller's etch.   ×300.

Natural aging following solution heat-treatment can be arrested by subjecting the material to subnormal temperatures. Rivets are stored at these temperatures in order that they may be headed readily prior to precipitation. Artificial aging is a term that is synonymous with precipitation heat-treatment. While all of the Al alloys will precipitate following solution heat-treatment, the time element may be so great as to

dictate artificial aging.   The corrosion resistance of some of the Al alloys
is closely interrelated with heat-treatment and deserves more than passing
attention.   Intergranular corrosion, or intergranular exfoliation, as it is
sometimes termed, has been known to result from imperfect heat-treatment.   This type of failure is critical, since the defect originates within the
metal and is not readily observed, as is surface corrosion.   Stress-carrying
members should be given especially close inspection for evidence of
intergranular deterioration.

COPPER-BASE ALLOYS

The range of copper-base alloys is very broad as to composition and,
further, is divided between wrought and cast products.   In view of this
diversity, any remarks on heat-treatment will need to be regarded as
applying to specific alloys rather than to the entire field.

Homogenizing is a high-temperature treatment used on some copper-
base alloys for the purpose of decreasing or even eliminating segregation
within the specimen.   Process annealing has a similar objective and finds
its greatest usefulness in processing brass.

Heat-treatment is specified for copper-base alloys that are susceptible
to solution and precipitation hardening of this group.   Beryllium copper
has the widest industrial application.   ASTM specification B194-49T
governs beryllium copper strip and shows a range in tensile strength from
150 to 180,000 psi extending from the soft to the full hard temper.

MAGNESIUM ALLOYS

Interest in heat-treatment of magnesium alloys is centered primarily
in the cast products.   In the wrought magnesium series alloy AZ80X is
specified for heat-treatment in some applications.

There are three heat-treatments applicable to magnesium-alloy cast
products: stabilizing, solution heat-treatment, and aging, or precipitation.
Stabilizing consists of heating the workpiece for 4 hr at a temperature of
500°F.   The temperatures for solution heat-treatment are related to the
specific alloy in question; however, a maximum of 800°F is general with
time at temperature extending from 10 to 20 hr.

The objective of heat-treatment of magnesium alloys is similar to
the objective in the case of aluminum.   Solution heat-treatment increases
toughness and resistance to shock.   The following precipitation or aging
treatment promotes higher yield strength and greater hardness but
sacrifices some ductility in so doing.   Magnesium alloys carry a heat-
treat designation as AZ92HT or AZ92HTA, depending on whether solution (HT) or solution plus precipitation (HTA) is specified.

NICKEL-BASE ALLOYS

There are several nickel-base alloys that respond to heat-treatment.
These are best known to industry under their trade names, among which

can be mentioned "K" monel, "Z" nickel, and Hastelloy. The heat-treatment consists of an aging process and is different from those associated with the light metals. The nickel alloys are heated in sealed containers or in controlled atmospheres with special attention given to the elimination of sulfur. Temperatures range from 1100 to 1600°F with time at temperature varying widely for the aging treatment. These alloys do not require a quench—rather, some are slow cooled to 900°F, while Hastelloy is cooled in air.

Survey Questions

12-1. Does heat-treatment include only treatments at elevated temperatures?

12-2. Why is a knowledge of heat-treatment fundamental to the mechanical engineer?

12-3. Basically, wherein do plain carbon and alloy steels differ?

12-4. Is the carbon content of a given steel significant?

12-5. Why is the form of the carbon important?

12-6. When should a spheroidized structure be specified?

12-7. What is the basic consideration in heat-treating steel?

12-8. How is a steel austenitized?

12-9. To what does the "critical temperature" of a steel refer?

12-10. In fully hardened steel, what structure predominates?

12-11. Does hardening steel increase its ultimate tensile strength?

12-12. Frequently "tempering steel" is an expression used to indicate hardening; is that correct?

12-13. Why is steel tempered?

12-14. Is the relationship of hardness to ultimate tensile strength similar for different alloy steel of the same carbon content?

12-15. Wherein does isothermal transformation of steel differ from the usual heat-and-quench procedure?

12-16. By what other terms is isothermal transformation denoted?

12-17. Of what significance is an isothermal transformation diagram?

12-18. How are S curves plotted?

12-19. Interpret the Ms temperature shown in Fig. 12-8.

12-20. How does the quenching effect function?

12-21. Why are various quenching mediums used?

12-22. Does the carburizing operation harden?

12-23. For what type of components should casehardening be specified?

12-24. Review the principal carburizing methods.

12-25. Wherein does carbonitriding differ from carburizing?

12-26. Should carburized gears be given a single or a double heat-treatment?

12-27. How do nitralloy steels differ from alloy steels?

12-28. Give three assets peculiar to nitriding.

12-29. Why is normalizing specified as a prior operation to annealing on some forgings?

12-30. Why is agitation important in quenching?

12-31. How is distortion controlled in gear quenching?

12-32. Does martempering offer unique advantages?

12-33. Describe the design features of a muffle furnace.

12-34. Are open-flame furnaces used for heat-treating?

12-35. On what basis is a furnace fuel selected?

12-36. Can batch-type furnaces be used for mass production?

12-37. What are salt baths?

12-38. How can the accuracy of temperature control equipment be maintained?

12-39. Why is controlled atmosphere important in heat-treating?

12-40. Are there any advantages to speed heating?

12-41. Where can induction heating be advantageous in heat-treating?

12-42. How is flame hardening performed?

12-43. In which group of nonferrous alloys is heat-treating most frequently specified?

12-44. Are aluminum alloys heat-treated primarily to increase hardness?

12-45. Does precipitation heat-treatment precede or follow solution heat-treatment?

12-46. Differentiate between natural and artificial aging of specific aluminum alloys.

12-47. What is the function of homogenizing certain copper-base alloys?

12-48. Are any of the magnesium casting alloys susceptible to heat-treatment?

12-49. Need precautionary measures be followed when heat-treating nickel alloys?

12-50. List the important objectives that can be attained by heat-treating.

REFERENCES

"Alcoa Aluminum and Its Alloys," Aluminum Company of America, Pittsburgh, 1950.

"Atlas of Isothermal Transformation Diagrams," United States Steel Corp., Pittsburgh, 1951.

Bullens, D. K.: "Steel and Its Treatment," 4th ed., John Wiley & Sons, Inc., New York, 1938.

Curtis, Frank W.: "High-frequency Induction Heating," 2d ed., McGraw-Hill Book Company, Inc., New York, 1950.

Francis, C. B.: "The Making, Shaping, and Treating of Steel," 5th ed., Carnegie-Illinois Steel Co., Pittsburgh, 1941.

Frier, W. T.: "Elementary Metallurgy," McGraw-Hill Book Company, Inc., New York, 1942.

Haughton, J. L., and W. E. Prytherch: "Magnesium and Its Alloys," His Majesty's Stationery Office, London, 1937.

"Heat Treating Aluminum Alloys," Reynolds Metals Co., Inc., Louisville, 1946.

Henry, O. H., and G. E. Claussen: "Welding Metallurgy," 2d ed., rev. by G. E. Linnert, American Welding Society, New York, 1949.

Hollomon, John H., and Leonard D. Jaffe: "Ferrous Metallurgical Design," John Wiley & Sons, Inc., New York, 1947.

Howe, Henry Marion: "The Metallography of Steel and Cast Iron," McGraw-Hill Book Company, Inc., New York, 1916.

"Metals Handbook," American Society for Metals, Cleveland, 1948.

Mondolfo, Lucio F.: "Metallography of Aluminum Alloys," John Wiley & Sons, Inc., New York, 1943.

"SAE Handbook," Society of Automotive Engineers, New York, 1942.

Samans, Carl H.: "Engineering Metals and Their Alloys," The Macmillan Company, New York, 1949.

Sauveur, A.: "The Metallography and Heat Treatment of Iron and Steel," 4th ed., Harvard University Press, Cambridge, Mass., 1935.

Simons, Eric N., and Edwin Gregory: "The Structure of Steel Simply Explained," Prentice-Hall, Inc., New York, 1938.

CHAPTER 13

TURNING LATHES

The shaping of metal through chip removal was undoubtedly first accomplished on a turning machine. Such machine tools are termed lathes in modern phraseology. Lathes had their beginning in antiquity and hence they can properly be credited with the honor of being the progenitor of the machine tool. With the advent of motive power the lathe became capable of a greater range of usefulness and it soon became known as the engine lathe, thus establishing its field of application. A further development saw the incorporation of a lead screw which enabled the lathe to increase its scope to include thread cutting. Improved design and constructional features have been continually added to this machine tool, which is currently known as the screw cutting engine lathe.

The Engine Lathe

Engine lathes are classified according to type as bench lathes, standard engine lathes, precision (toolroom) lathes, and special-duty lathes.

Fig. 13-1.   Jeweler's lathe, 3.94-in. swing, 12-in. bed length.   (*Courtesy of Louis Levin & Son, Inc., Los Angeles.*)

Each of these types fits a specific class of work. The selection of an engine lathe will therefore be governed by the class of work and the production needed. There are other methods of classification in which design details are the dominant feature.   In these categories are found such items as power application.   The preponderance of current models are geared-head drives, whereas formerly most were of cone-head design.

Bench Lathes.   Bench lathes are built in two basic styles.   The smaller is termed a jeweler's, or instrument maker's, lathe and is suited for turning small parts, usually from round stock of wire gage (Fig. 13-1). It has a single pedestal under the head-stock end of the bed; thus the latter is open at its other end.   These lathes are equipped with a cone

Fig. 13-2.   10-in. bench-type toolroom lathe.   (*Courtesy of Rivett Lathe & Grinder, Inc., Boston.*)

pulley that fits a round belt; by this means different turning speeds are obtained.

The bench lathe common in the machine shop is similar in appearance to the standard engine lathe except for size and type of mounting.   Obviously, from its name, a bench lathe is built to fit or to be mounted on a bench (Fig. 13-2).   A bench lathe is a precision machine tool in every sense.   This matter of precision is emphasized because a distinction exists between *bench* lathes and *bench-type* lathes.

Bench-type Lathes.   Bench-type lathes abound in home workshops; their cost varies with the construction and the degree of accuracy to be expected.   There are many of these lathes installed in industrial arts and apprentice training departments, where they serve admirably (Fig. 13-3).   When jobs fitting their capacity are available, bench-type lathes

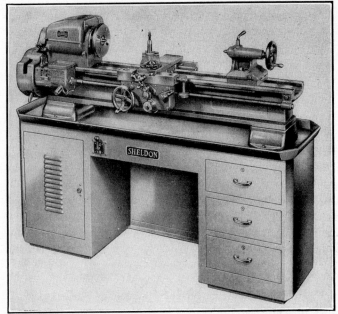

Fig. 13-3. Bench-type lathe, cabinet-mounted. (Courtesy of Sheldon Machine Co., Inc., Chicago.)

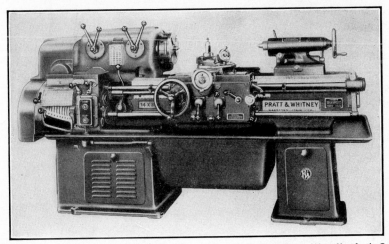

Fig. 13-4. Precision-.ype toolroom lathe. (Courtesy of Pratt & Whitney, West Hartford, Conn.)

are capable of delivering a low-cost product, and for that reason they are included in general machine-shop equipment.

Standard Engine Lathe. The standard, regular, or conventional engine lathe is the most widely used machine tool (Fig. 13-4). The distinguishing feature of a lathe countershaft bolted to the ceiling is rapidly passing from the shop in favor of the current trend toward individually driven equipment. This evidence of progress is inserted here merely to provide the occasion for remarking that in the days of the belt-driven, cone-head lathe the beginner was first taught the knack of shifting belts from one step on the cone to the next. The belted lathe had the virtue of being able to slip when the lathe was fouled by the novice!

There are many models of standard engine lathes, both as to specifications and as to manufacturers. The difference between the designs offered by the makers is analogous to that existing in the motorcar field; in other words, all engine lathes perform satisfactorily, but the controls, power applications, and construction vary. The purchaser should predicate his selection on those specifications most nearly meeting his requirements.

Functional Design. The standard engine lathe is capable of performing the following operations:

Primary functions

    1. Turning
        a. Cylindrical
        b. Taper
        c. Forming
    2. Facing
        a. Straight
        b. Forming
        c. Trepanning
    3. Boring
        a. Cylindrical
        b. Taper
    4. Threading
        a. External
        b. Internal

Secondary functions

    1. Drilling
    2. Centering
    3. Reaming
    4. Knurling
    5. Parting
    6. Chamfering

This listing does not preclude other machining operations from being accomplished by the engine lathe. Lathe operations are performed by rotating the work against a stationary tool, be it lathe tool, boring bar, twist drill, reamer, or any other. When a special setup is used in the lathe, the usual practice is to reverse this procedure by mounting the work on the carriage, where it is held stationary, and placing the cutting tool in a spindle chuck, thereby causing it to rotate. By this method an end milling cutter can be used on a workpiece mounted on the carriage. Another example is that of boring an open-end cylinder by grasping one end of the boring bar in the lathe chuck and placing the opposite end on the tailstock center. These cases are cited as typical of the flexibility of the conventional engine lathe. The extent of this work classification is limited only by the ingenuity of the tool engineer and the degree to which improvisation is permitted or found desirable.

Work-holding Methods. The workpiece needs to be held firmly in order that its rotation contact with the tool will prevent its slipping. There are three general methods for holding the part: gripping it in a chuck which is fastened to the spindle, mounting it on a faceplate, placing it on centers and driving through a dog contacting a small faceplate, or dog plate. The first method is termed chucking; the last is known as mounting on centers. In the instance of repetitive work where quantities justify the cost of such a procedure, specially built chucking fixtures or work-holding devices are used.

Chucks. It is impossible to make a definite statement about the class of work that is held in chucks. In general, such items as forgings, castings, and relatively short lengths of bar stock are usually considered suitable for this type of mounting. Jobs that require boring or other operations on an inside surface must be held in a chuck or chucking fixture. Lathe chucks are designed around three distinct operating principles. The chuck body is bolted to an adapter plate, or chuck nut, that fits the lathe spindle and is fastened thereto by threaded, cam-lock, or taper and keyed connections. On the opposite side of the body there are a series of jaws either three or four in number. These jaws are fitted to move in T slots by means of a

Fig. 13-5. Conventional independent four-jaw lathe chuck. (Courtesy of The Skinner Chuck Co., New Britain, Conn.)

screw that has a hollow head fitting the chuck wrench.

The independent type of chuck, which usually has four jaws, is constructed to permit the movement of each jaw separately (Fig. 13-5). Chucks of this type have the advantage of being able to grasp unsymmetrical work. There are a series of concentric grooved circles on the face of the chuck body that greatly aid the operator when chucking symmetrical work, since he can note the position of each jaw with respect to a given circle and then adjust the jaws accordingly.

The universal chuck usually has three jaws, but four are found in some designs. The jaws operate by a scroll that causes them to move in unison. When the workpiece is of a true diameter, it can be chucked centrally by turning only one chuck jaw screw. The difficulty with these chucks arises when careless operators place unsymmetrical work

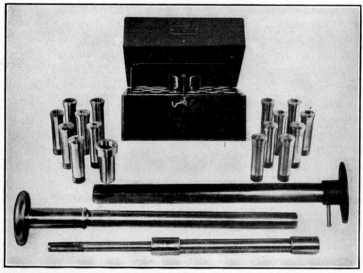

Fig. 13-6. Draw-in collet-chuck equipment, including a range of spring collets. (*Courtesy of The Hendey Machine Co., Torrington, Conn.*)

therein and then proceed to tighten the jaws, causing them to spring and lose their alignment. The combination lathe chuck is built to operate either as an independent or as a universal chuck. A locking device on the back of the chuck body controls its operation. Lathe chucks are accessory equipment and not supplied by the lathe builder.

Collet Chucks. When small, accurate bar stock is to be machined, a lathe can best be equipped with a collet chuck. There are several designs; all have the same objective of centering and holding the stock accurately. Collet equipment is shown in Fig. 13-6. It consists of spring collets in a range of sizes to fit the bar stock, a draw-in sleeve, a closer, and a knock-out rod. The collets themselves are slotted in order that they can be compressed around the work thereby gripping it firmly. Spring collet chucks should be used only to grip finished or machined surfaces. Furthermore, in order to avoid damage to the collet, these chucks should not be used to grip work that is more than 0.002 to 0.003 in. over or 0.005 to 0.008 in. under the nominal size of the collet.

A recent development in collet chucks is the Rubber-Flex Collet. This chuck is mounted directly on the spindle nose. It contains many thin strips of hardened steel bonded together by synthetic rubber. This type of collet has greater versatility than the spring type. A further advantage is that fewer collets are necessary to cover a range of sizes.

Mounting on Centers. Any workpiece that is of considerable length or otherwise of a shape requiring outboard support should be mounted on centers. Note that the length of the lathe is a limiting factor, since a piece longer than the distance between centers of a lathe cannot be mounted in this manner.

Where exceptionally long pieces are to be machined, the tailstock can be removed and a steady rest set up to support the outboard end (Fig. 13-7). Steady rest mounting is also used where end facing or internal machining is desired. Further, the steady rest is sometimes placed between centers as a means of preventing springing of the workpiece.

A follower rest which clamps to the carriage and moves with it is also employed as a means of preventing deflection of the workpiece. The fol-

Fig. 13-7. Conventional-type steady rest. (Courtesy of The Hendey Machine Co., Torrington, Conn.)

lower rest is equipped with two supporting points and the cutting tool acts as a third one.

Prior to mounting, the workpiece must be drilled with a center drill at each end. The center drill produces a 60° angle hole, which fits the angle of the centers. The center in the headstock spindle is termed the live center, since it rotates with the work. The tailstock center is the dead center because it is fixed and the work rotates thereon. Because of this bearing condition, *the tail center must be lubricated* and must be made of hardened tool steel. Where extremely high speeds or heavy cuts are used, the dead center is tipped with a cemented carbide or the tailstock spindle is designed to contain a rotating center. As the workpiece heats up, it expands, which means that the operator must be alert to retract the center in order to prevent burning. The center should at all times be set loosely enough to permit the workpiece to rotate freely but not so loosely as to allow chattering.

The work on centers is driven by a lathe dog whose tail engages a slot in the faceplate, or dog plate (Fig. 13-8). The dog is fastened by means of a setscrew. Care must be exercised to prevent this screw from marring a finished surface. A piece of soft metal such as copper or aluminum wrapped on the piece under the screw point will prevent disfiguration.

Fig. 13-8. Turning workpiece held on centers. Drive effected through dog and small faceplate. (*Courtesy of Springfield Machine Tool Co., Springfield, Ohio.*)

Mandrels. A workpiece that has been bored can be worked on centers by pressing it on a mandrel. The mandrel is hardened and has centers in its ends. There is a slight taper on the mandrel which acts to tighten in the bore as the mandrel is pressed home. Work on a mandrel presents all faces to the tool—an impossibility with a chuck. A conventional mandrel-held operation is pictured in Fig. 13-9. There are a number of different styles of mandrels, such as the cone, the expanding, the gang, and the nut types.

Straight Turning. Turning is the operation used for reducing an outside diameter. When the workpiece being turned is held by a chuck, fixture, or faceplate, there should be little difficulty about producing a true cylinder. When a taper develops on the workpiece, the difficulty can be traced to one of three sources: (1) tool wear; (2) tool mounted insecurely; (3) the ways of the lathe being worn, permitting uneven travel of the carriage, misalignment of the headstock, or deflection. The first two of these difficulties can be remedied, but a worn lathe bed is beyond repair short of a complete reworking and overhauling.

There is a greater likelihood of obtaining unwanted taper when turning on centers. If the tailstock center is misaligned in a horizontal plane, a taper will result on the workpiece. In consequence it is desirable to check center alignment prior to turning. Prior to placing the live center, the lathe spindle seat should be wiped clean with the finger tips to ensure complete freedom from any foreign particles lodging there. The center itself should be similarly cleaned at the time it is inserted in the lathe

Fig. 13-9. Turning cast iron mounted on a tapered mandrel.

spindle. The live center must run true. Its truth can be checked by a dial indicator placed in the tool post. Where extreme accuracy is desired, a very light cut should be taken off the live center to assure its concentricity.

The dead center is placed in the tailstock spindle by applying the precautions used for the live center. With both centers in place, the workpiece is mounted thereon and the tailstock spindle is locked. The cutting tool is set correctly and brought against the workpiece near the live center. The procedure from here on is as follows: Take a cut deep enough to develop a fully turned area on the workpiece. Engage the feed in a direction toward the headstock and machine an area ½ in. in length. Note carefully the reading on the cross-feed dial. Then withdraw the tool and move it to the dead center end and clear of the workpiece. Reset the tool to the precise previous dial reading and, with the power feed engaged, machine a similar area. Check these two turned areas with a micrometer caliper. The amount of setover for the tailstock will equal one-half the difference of these readings. It is usually necessary to repeat this operation before an accurate setover is obtained.

Taper Turning.   A primary asset of the engine lathe is its ability to turn controlled tapers.   The conventional lathe offers two distinct methods for accomplishing this end, viz. the setover tailstock for long tapers and the compound rest for short tapers.   In addition to these, a taper attachment, which is listed as auxiliary equipment by most lathe manufacturers, makes a third taper turning method possible.   The two latter methods can be applied for *external* as well as *internal* tapers, while the setover tailstock one is only possible for external tapers.

The setover tailstock method is difficult, since an accurate setover requires extreme care.   The measurement can be made by bringing the tool against the work (assuming correct center alignment) noting the cross-feed dial reading, and then moving the tool the amount of the calculated setover by again reading the dial.   The amount of setover is calculated from the specified taper dimensions.   A simplified method for calculating the amount of setover is based on reducing taper dimensions to taper per inch.   When that value is established, setover is calculated:

$$\text{Setover} = \frac{\text{taper per in.} \times \text{length of workpiece}}{2}$$

Since the small diameter is located at the end of the shaft, the tail center would be set over *toward* the operator.   This method of taper turning imposes severe operating stresses on the dead center, since the center in the shaft and the dead center are not concentric.

The compound rest, is the preferred method for turning steep tapers (Fig. 13-10).   A scale, graduated in degrees, is located at the base of the compound rest.   The base is of swivel construction and contains two locking screws.   In setting a taper, the witness mark is brought to the desired angle graduation and locked into position.   The angle setting is the complement of the angle shown on the drawing when that angle is measured from the center line of the work corresponding to the lathe axis.   The procedure varies here somewhat, depending upon the pattern of graduations, which is not the same on all makes of lathes.

The compound rest has a dovetailed slide which is actuated by a screw whose end carries a hand wheel for manual operation.   The compound is always manually operated, there being no power feed.   A necessary precaution is that of noting the position of the compound at the start of the cut, since sufficient travel is needed to cover the entire length of the taper cut in one setting.   Stopping the feed rod and lead screw will guard against accidental engagement of any power feeds on the carriage.   It is sound practice to check the compound taper setting by means of a vernier bevel protractor.

The taper attachment (Fig. 13-11) is employed on both long and short

Fig. 13-10. Compound rest holding tool post with toolholder. (*Courtesy of* **Reed-Prentice Corp.**, *Worcester, Mass.*)

Fig. 13-11. Taper attachment. (*Courtesy of Monarch Machine Tool Co., Sidney, Ohio.*)

tapers for center mounted work.   It has the advantage of permitting the workpiece to remain on center alignment, thereby eliminating the overload condition on the dead center and increasing accuracy.   The taper attachment carries graduations in terms of taper per foot as well as degrees of taper.

For repetitive work requiring great accuracy, the taper attachment is the best answer to taper turning. It is the best method for cutting tapered threads; the threading tool should be set normal to the axis of the work and not perpendicular to the tapered surface.

Form Turning and Facing. Accessory equipment is available from some lathe manufacturers for form turning and profile facing (Fig. 13-12). This development permits the use of an engine lathe for accurate form turning—a decided improvement over the tedious manual method of manipulating both cross and longitudinal feeds simultaneously.

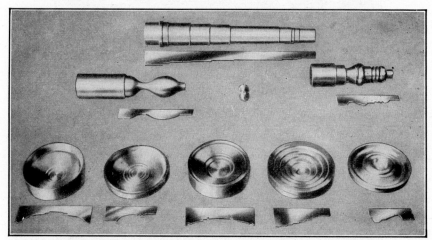

Fig. 13-12. Shaft and profile facing jobs. (*Courtesy of The R. K. LeBlond Machine Tool Co., Cincinnati.*)

Facing. Facing refers to taking a machining cut in a direction normal to the lathe axis. The cutting tool travels *across* the work, in contradistinction to turning, where the tool travels *along* the work. A straight facing cut produces a flat surface. The cutting tool can be manually operated, or, for uniform results, the power cross-feed is engaged. Tool travel can be either from the periphery toward the center or the reverse. Such items as method of mounting, bores, type of materials, and periphery shape are governing factors in deciding tool travel direction.

Precautions are necessary to ensure straight facing cuts. The carriage should be locked to the bed, using the locking screw provided for that purpose. Casting scale may be of sufficient hardness to cause undue tool wear, which will result in a taper on the facing cut. A typical facing operation is pictured in Fig. 13-13. Form facing and profiling are performed on an engine lathe equipped with a form-turning attachment.

Trepanning. Trepanning is a type of facing operation in which a modified parting tool is used for machining a concentric groove from the

face side.   A cutting-off operation will then part the trepanned piece
from its base material (Fig. 13-14).

A counterpart of a German high-speed trepanning lathe has been
designed in America.   An impressive saving in machining time and

Fig. 13-13.   Typical facing cut on aluminum-alloy casting.

Fig. 13-14.   Trepanning operation.   Cutting out center of solid bar stock with an L-shaped tool preparatory to parting off collars; note solid bar remaining after trepanning operation is completed.
(*Courtesy of Lodge & Shipley Co., Cincinnati.*)

material is possible with high-speed trepanning.   Gun tubes are of
special interest in this new trepanning concept.   The solid forging is
trepanned instead of being bored in the conventional manner.   The
material removed from the bore takes the form of a solid core instead of

the chips that result from conventional boring. This core is salvageable for further application; thus a pronounced saving in material is afforded. On 8-in.-diameter bars, 4 ft in length, trepanning at a rate of 480 in./hr was attained on a $2\frac{5}{8}$-in. smooth bore, with an $1\frac{1}{8}$-in.-diameter core resulting.[1] The speed of performance which it makes possible indicates that this trepanning method, where applicable, will make obsolete many present boring applications.

Boring. Boring is an internal machining operation whose objective is to increase the size of an existing hole or to bring it to concentricity.

Fig. 13-15. Boring an aluminum-alloy casting in a typical boring operation. Casting is mounted on a specially designed fixture.

For the most part, boring is confined to components gripped in a chuck or chucking fixture or mounted on a faceplate. Boring may take the form of a straight, a taper, or a formed contour.

In all these, the same general principles are used that were discussed in the section on turning. The difference between boring and turning is found in the tooling. Boring requires the use of a boring bar. This tool is available in a variety of designs, both as to mounting and as to method of clamping the cutting tool. The position of the cutting tool is important, since, where a blind hole is being bored, the cutting tool edge must project beyond the end of the boring bar in order that the bore can be made to full depth.

The possibility of deflection in the boring bar is always present during the boring operation. The deflection may be of sufficient magnitude to cause chattering or, what is worse, to produce a bellmouthed bore.

[1] Rylander, Andrew E.: Fundamentals of Trepanning, *Western Machinery and Steel World*, February, 1952, pp. 82–84.

Another defect arising from boring bar deflection is that a taper will result, with the large diameter being on the entering end. This difficulty can be eliminated by taking two cuts in the same direction; however, the boring bar setting must not be altered. A typical boring operation is shown in Fig. 13-15.

The position of the cutting edge of the tool with respect to the horizontal center line of the bore requires attention. It is common practice to set this edge exactly on the center line.

Taper bores are made by employing the same techniques that are applied to taper turning. The compound rest and taper attachment methods are applicable. It is a relatively difficult matter to measure a tapered bore. When possible, the male taper should be used as a gage, since such a procedure will save considerable time in bringing the bore taper to a proper fit.

Threading. Threads of all forms can be cut on a screw-cutting engine lathe. They can also be produced in either right- or left-hand styles, as well as in multiple threads. The only limitations are those imposed by the available change gear combinations. The thread pitches that a given lathe is capable of cutting can be read from the index plate on the change gearbox. Thread cutting, both external and internal, is presented in Chap. 16.

Secondary Functions. Lathe operations discussed thus far in this chapter have been those employing a single-point tool mounted directly or indirectly in the tool post on the carriage. The tailstock has been considered only in respect to holding the dead center. There are several functions that can be performed by replacing the dead center with a cutting tool.

Placing a taper-shank twist drill directly in the tailstock makes it possible to drill holes in a workpiece that is rotated by the chuck against the stationary drill. When a straight-shank drill is to be used, it is held in a drill chuck whose shank fits into the tailstock spindle tapered seat. It is desirable to place a lathe dog or other clamping device on the drill in order to prevent its rotation in the tailstock spindle.

A center drill, held in a drill chuck, is used to drill a small 60° hole in the end of the workpiece. The hole depth is governed by the function it is to perform. If it is to act as a starter for a following drilling operation, the center may be drilled to an appreciable depth. If, on the other hand, the center hole is intended for mounting the workpiece on centers, the center hole should not be large. The center drill pilot, being small, is prone to break off under conditions of too low rotation speed, heavy crowding, or roughened stock ends. Carelessness here will result in a broken pilot embedded in the workpiece where it will be difficult to remove or the workpiece will have to be scrapped.

A twist drill placed in the tailstock spindle will tend to follow the previously drilled center hole. Should the twist drill develop a tendency to wander, it can be guided by bringing pressure against it with the toolholder in the tool post. When drilling a deep hole, the drill should be backed off occasionally to free the chips.

Machine reamers are made with taper shanks that permit their placement in the tailstock spindle after the manner of a twist drill. A reaming operation is always a delicate one requiring judgment on the part of the lathe operator. A reamer should never be turned in a reverse direction. The correct amount of stock should be left for removal by the reamer—too much stock should never be allowed. Improper attention to correct reaming procedure will lead to chatter marks or a broken reamer. Excellent results are possible with lathe reaming; this is especially true when the reamer is used to follow the boring bar.

The sequence of operations for producing an accurate hole in solid stock starts with the center, or starting, drill. A drilling operation follows, wherein more drills of increasingly larger diameters are used. A boring operation may or may not be used then, depending on stock structure, to bring the drilled hole to concentricity and also to size it for the reaming operation. There should be about 0.005 to 0.015 in. stock remaining for the machine reamer to clean up to exact size. In these operations all the tools used are positioned in the tailstock spindle excepting only the boring bar, which is held in the tool post.

Parting. A parting cut is a cutting-off operation in which a narrow-bladed tool whose cross section resembles a trapezium is used. Since the tool is narrow and its end is unsupported, it has a tendency to deflect and chatter unless its cutting point is accurately positioned at the horizontal axis of the stock being cut. The cutting edge should be slightly tapered in order that there be a leading point which will cut through cleanly.

It is generally undesirable to permit sharp corners to remain on finished work. Breaking the corners, such as rim edges and entrances to bores, is known as chamfering. The operation consists of bringing the edge of the turning tool against the offending corner and relieving it so that a beveled surface results. Should a chamfer of any appreciable amount be required, the compound rest is used in order to machine the designed angle.

Knurling. This produces a surface that has a raised pattern for nonslip gripping. The knurling tool consists of a pair of narrow hardened steel rollers carrying a crosshatch pattern on their periphery. Rollers are rigidly held in a head or shank so they can rotate about their centers. One style of knurling tool holds three pairs of knurling rollers in which each succeeding pair has a finer configuration pattern. The head floats in a holder to permit the chosen pair of rollers to engage the workpiece uniformly. The rollers are forced against the workpiece under considerable pressure and are caused to turn by the former's rotation. The knurling tool is translated along the work in a reciprocating motion causing a raised pattern thereon. The longitudinal movement of the knurling tool can be activated either by power or by manual feed.

CONSTRUCTION OF THE ENGINE LATHE

The design of engine lathes varies with the different manufacturers and also between the models within one line of manufacture. As a result engine lathes have considerably different appearances even though they are all designed to perform similar functions. The earlier distinction as between geared headstock and cone pulley design has all but disappeared on lathes in the precision toolroom and manufacturing classifications.

The principal components of an engine lathe are the bed with its supporting mountings and the headstock with its accompanying drive, carriage, and tailstock. In addition to these main members, there is a change gear train, gearbox, feed rod, and lead screw. These are delineated in Fig. 13-16 together with additional functional features.

Lathe Bed. The bed is a gray iron casting because of this material's ability to dampen vibrations and provide excellent wearing surfaces. There are several cross ribs integrally cast into the bed for rigidity and stiffness. The length of the bed is commonly given as the dimension for specifying the size of an engine lathe; for example, a 13-6 lathe is one that can swing a 13-in.-diameter workpiece (or its equivalent) and that has a bed 6 ft long.

The top of the bed has machined ways which act to guide the longitudinal movement of both the carriage and the tailstock and also position the headstock for alignment. The ways, which are usually of an inverted V shape, are generally integral with the bed casting. On some designs the ways are flame-hardened and ground to alignment. The accuracy of the ways determines in great part the performance that can be expected from the lathe; worn ways cannot produce precision machine work. On the front side of the bed, below the ways, there is a geared rack bolted into position. The rack serves for moving the carriage, either manually or by power, through a gear train in the apron.

The lathe bed is mounted on legs at its ends. The trend is toward cabinet legs under the headstock, since this design permits housing the driving motor there is an inconspicuous, out-of-the-way place. There may or may not be a chip pan located under the bed.

Lathe Headstock. The headstock is, in effect, a transmission. It receives its power from an individual motor in most designs and transmits the power to the workpiece. The headstock also delivers power to the

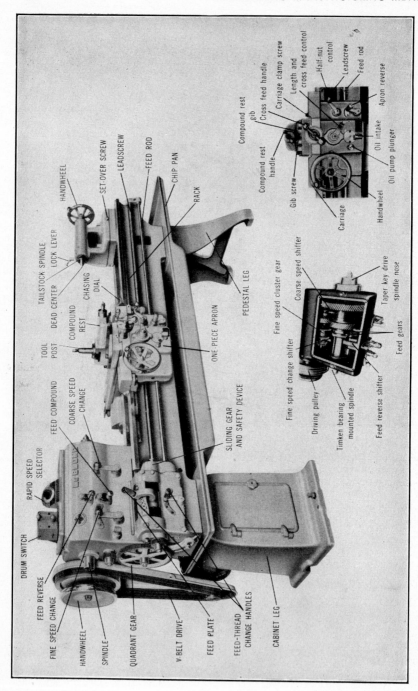

Fig. 13-16. Nomenclature of the components of a conventional-type geared-head engine lathe. Headstock and carriage shown in foreground. (Courtesy of The R. K. LeBlond Machine Tool Co., Cincinnati.)

change gear train for driving the carriage or cross-feed. For the most part, lathe headstocks are equipped with gear trains for imparting various rotational speeds and power increments to the workpiece.

A lathe spindle is a hollow shaft usually carrying an internal taper at its nose end. The taper is of a standard that will accommodate lathe centers and collet-chuck components. The diameter of the hole through the spindle is important, since it limits the maximum size of bar stock that can be projected through the spindle. The nose of the spindle is designed to hold the chuck, faceplate, or other work-carrying fixture. Formerly the nose carried a straight thread ending at a shoulder; there was no standardization in this construction. Present designs conform to American Standard B5.9–1948,[1] which features two types of spindle nose, designated as D-1 and type L respectively (Fig. 13-17). All dimensions and pertinent information regarding these are found in the above-mentioned standard.

Fig. 13-17. Type D-1, camlock spindle nose. (*Courtesy of Monarch Machine Tool Co., Sidney, Ohio.*)

The spindle influences the quality of production, since deflection or any other shortcoming of the spindle immediately become apparent in the workpiece. The condition of the spindle bearings, regardless of bearing type, is a critical matter. The height of the spindle governs the swing of a lathe because a workpiece cannot be held in a lathe whose maximum diameter measures more than two times the distance from the center of the spindle to the ways of the lathe bed. The gap bed affords a means of increasing the swing of a lathe for workpieces held in a chuck or on a faceplate. Gap bed design permits either the removal of a block section of the bed entirely or sliding a divided bed section longitudinally.

Change Gear Train. The general location of the first gear of the change gear train is at the spindle end opposite the nose. This gear train functions to transmit both power and speed of rotation to the change gearbox. In some designs there are tumbler gears for the purpose of changing the direction of rotation of the feed rod and lead screw.

[1] "Standard for Spindle Noses," American Standards Association, New York.

The gearbox, located on the side of the bed and below the headstock (Fig. 13-18), carries a series of gears so arranged that different speeds of rotation can be given to the feed rod and lead screw. An index plate on the front of the gearbox indicates the feed and screw thread pitch for each setting. The range covered by a gearbox is noted on its index plate.

The feed rod is a plain shaft with a spline running its entire length. Mounted in the apron is a floating sleeve equipped with bevel gears at its ends that is keyed to the feed rod. It is by this construction that power and motion are transmitted to the carriage.

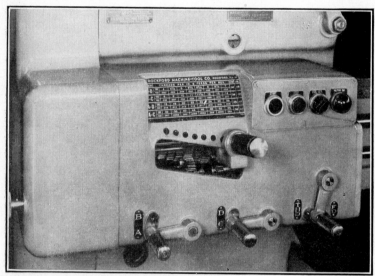

Fig. 13-18.   Change gearbox, quick-change type.   (*Courtesy of Rockford Machine Tool Co., Rockford, Ill.*)

The lead screw, on the other hand, is threaded most of its length. A split nut inside the apron can be made to clamp on this screw as a means of driving the carriage for thread-cutting operations. Note the difference in function: *The lead screw is used only for cutting threads and never for any other purpose.* On some lathes the lead screw and feed rod are combined into one; in such instances there is a spline in the lead screw.

Lathe Carriage.   The carriage is composed of saddle, apron, cross slide, and compound rest. The saddle is an H-shaped casting that rides on the lathe ways. It carries the crosslide and compound rest mechanisms and the taper attachment when one is present. The apron is fastened to the saddle in a position normal to it. All of the operating mechanisms for power longitudinal and cross-feeds as well as thread cutting are housed in the apron (Figs. 13-19 and 13-20).

The chief variations in lathe design center around the construction and

operation of the apron. There are some designs that have an apron
reverse whose purpose it is to change feed travel direction. The matter
of clutch design within the apron is also variable. Controls and safety
features are found in varying degrees in all apron mechanisms. The

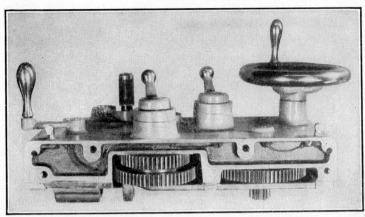

Fig. 13-19. Lathe apron, top view. Operating levers on front of apron, left to right: split nut,
apron reverse, cross-feed clutch, longitudinal-feed clutch, and longitudinal-feed handwheel. (Courtesy of Rockford Machine Tool Co., Rockford, Ill.)

Fig. 13-20. Lathe apron, rear view. Split nut at left in open position. Bevel gears at bottom provide apron reverse. This design employs separate lead screw and feed rod. (Courtesy of Rockford
Machine Tool Co., Rockford, Ill.)

apron also carries the handwheel that moves the carriage longitudinally.
This is the larger of the two handwheels on the front of the carriage.
The smaller handwheel, which is equipped with a graduated dial for
setting the depth of cut, operates the cross-feed.

Lathe Tailstock.   The tailstock, or footstock, as it is sometimes termed, consists of two castings.   The lower one is machined to fit the bed ways and slide thereon.   The upper casting, which is tongued to the lower one, is equipped with a spindle.   The latter can be extended or withdrawn by means of a handwheel.   The tailstock has two clamping screws that engage a clamp fitting the underside of the bed ways.   The clamping feature is used to hold the tailstock in position on the ways.   There is a locking lever for maintaining spindle position.   The tailstock is moved along the bed manually; however, on large lathes there is a geared mechanism for this purpose.   The tailstock can be removed from the lathe by loosening the clamp and sliding it off the end of the bed.

ATTACHMENTS FOR ENGINE LATHES

The taper turning attachment is a leading example of supplementary equipment capable of simplifying a lathe operation.   A thread chasing dial is indispensable for thread cutting; that this is recognized is indicated by the fact that many builders include the dial as standard equipment.

Less commonly known is the micrometer carriage stop which offers an accurate means of measuring longitudinal travel of the carriage.   The stop clamps to the top of the lathe bed and is equipped with a spindle whose extension is controlled by a micrometer dial.   A machined boss on the edge of the carriage is brought into contact with the spindle end.   This device is not to be confused with automatic carriage stops, which are used for spacing the position of shoulders or grooves on a workpiece.

In the second category of attachments are those that extend the scope of lathe functions.   Included are such items as bed turrets, which replace the tailstock and transform the engine lathe into a turret lathe.   Milling attachments of various kinds are available, as is grinding equipment.   Others are gear cutting, cutter relieving, and rapid traverse attachments.   Taken together, such supplemental equipment is of interest where the cost of a machine tool is not justified for a special job.

A somewhat different aspect of accessory equipment is to be found in the field of contour turning, especially production turning.   In the former instance, there are several systems available whose mechanisms may be controlled by means of mechanical, hydraulic, pneumatic, or electrical devices.   A well-established electrical control is known as the Keller (Fig. 13-21), while the Bailey pneumatic-hydraulic system has also found many adherents.

Repetitive turning on a production basis is possible on a standard engine lathe that requires only a control attachment conversion unit.   This type of equipment is proving popular because of its ability to reduce turning costs substantially.   The basis of the duplicating method is that of generating work shapes from a template, or master, by means of a hydraulically controlled cutting tool.   This design permits the tool to make an uninterrupted cut over the workpiece, regardless of contours such as shoulders, tapers, and the like. Components such as motor shafts, spindles, valve stems, and piston rods are readily adapted to this type of production turning.

Fig. 13-21. Keller control setup for form turning rolls. Note tracer and template at rear of carriage. (Courtesy of The Monarch Machine Tool Co., Sidney, Ohio.)

SPECIALIZED LATHES

There are lathe designs fitted to special work. They are, in effect, engine lathes suited to one particular type of work. Some depart widely from engine lathes in appearance as well as design. A center-drive axle lathe is an example, since the drive is located on the center of the lathe bed and there is a footstock at each end, the headstock, as such, being omitted (Fig. 13-22).

Other lathes fitting into the category of specialized equipment are oil-country lathes which feature an excessively large opening through the headstock, roll-turning lathes used for machining rolling-mill rolls, and crankshaft turning lathes that find their field of usefulness in automotive-engine and similar shops. The best method of describing this lathe classification is to state that when a turning problem of a specialized nature offers sufficient production possibilities, the lathe builders are capable of producing a piece of equipment that will effect a solution.

Examples include such designs as the one shown in Fig. 13-23. This lathe is a conventional type except that it has an unusually long bed, which makes possible its use on long shafts and pipe work. Lathes having an exceptionally large swing also belong in this classification.

Fig. 13-22. Betts-Bridgeford center-drive axle turning lathe equipped with two carriages. (Courtesy of Consolidated Machine Tool Corp., Rochester, N.Y.)

Fig. 13-23. Extended bed lathe, 252-in. capacity between centers. This lathe is equipped with three front-turning carriages and three heavy-duty steady rests. Equipment shown was used for turning 105-mm. high-velocity gun tubes. (Courtesy of Seneca Falls Machine Co., Seneca Falls, N.Y.)

Survey Questions

13-1. Enumerate the different types of engine lathes.

13-2. How are most modern lathes driven?

13-3. On what class of work are bench lathes used?

13-4. State the basic operations performed on a standard engine lathe.

13-5. By what different methods can a workpiece be mounted in an engine lathe?

13-6. Wherein do independent and universal chucks differ?

13-7. Give some advantages of collet chucks.

13-8. How are workpieces prepared for turning on centers?

13-9. Does the follower rest clamp on the lathe bed?

13-10. Are both live and dead lathe centers hardened?

13-11. Which center is adjustable and which one must be lubricated?

13-12. When is mandrel mounting desirable?

13-13. How should a cylindrical turning setup be checked to avert taper?

13-14. State three possible methods for turning a taper.

13-15. Describe a compound rest.

13-16. In what direction does the cutting tool travel when taking a facing cut?

13-17. In what respect does trepanning save material?

13-18. Are boring and drilling the same operation?

13-19. How can boring bar deflection be corrected?

13-20. Does a lathe offer any advantages in thread cutting?

13-21. Describe the setup necessary for cutting a left-hand thread.

13-22. How can a twist drill be guided to prevent eccentric drilling?

13-23. Do machine reamers differ from hand reamers?

13-24. Parting has what other name?

13-25. Give an application for knurling.

13-26. How is the size of an engine lathe specified?

13-27. State the principal components of an engine lathe.

13-28. Why are lathe spindles hardened and ground?

13-29. Where is the lathe change gear train located?

13-30. What functions does the feed rod perform?

13-31. Should the lead screw be used for driving the carriage for turning or boring?

13-32. List the principal parts of a lathe carriage.

13-33. How can the tail spindle be "set over"?

13-34. Is there any attachment that can be used for gaging longitudinal carriage travel?

13-35. How best can a lathe be rigged for repetitive turning?

13-36. Does an oil-country lathe have any distinguishing features?

13-37. On what type of work are roll-turning lathes used?

13-38. What type of machining equipment is selected for boring artillery gun tubes?

REFERENCES

"Changing the Shape of Metals with an Engine Lathe," Shell Oil Co., Business Collaborators, Inc., St. Louis, 1946.

Colvin, Fred H.: "Running an Engine Lathe," McGraw-Hill Book Company, Inc., New York, 1941.

Colvin, Fred H., and Frank A. Stanley: "American Machinist's Handbook," McGraw-Hill Book Company, Inc., New York, 1945.

Jones, Franklin D.: "Machine Shop Training Course," 3d ed., Vol. I, The Industrial Press, New York, 1944.

"Machine Shop Technology," 2 vols., National Metal Trades Association, Chicago, 1941–1942.

Oberg, Erik, and Franklin D. Jones: "Machinery's Handbook," 13th ed., The Industrial Press, New York, 1948.

Shuman, J. T., and L. H. Bardo: "How to Operate a Lathe," John Wiley & Sons, Inc., New York, 1944.

"Tool Engineers' Handbook," McGraw-Hill Book Company, Inc., New York, 1949.

Turner, William P., and Halsey F. Owen: "Machine-tool Work," 2d ed., McGraw-Hill Book Company, Inc., New York, 1945.

CHAPTER 14

TURRET LATHES

The turret lathe came into being as the result of new requirements in the metal shaping industry. The evolution of the idea of interchangeability of parts manufacture gave rise to new concepts of machining. A demand was developed for the repetition of accuracy over a substantial number of identical components. These new conditions were met by a revision of engine lathe construction through replacing the tailstock with a tool-carrying member termed a turret. The turret, whose original shape was cylindrical, was provided with a series of equally spaced mounting holes. Each of these holes, or stations, carried a tool arranged in a succession corresponding with the sequence of the machining operations to be performed on the workpiece. This tooling arrangement provided for both speedy and accurate machining.

The trend of current turret lathe design is toward both greater production and increased precision. These objectives are achieved by the combination of expert tooling and dependable equipment. Tooling a turret lathe for optimum performance is a task that demands of the tool engineer knowledge and vision of a high order.

Classification of Turret Lathes. Fundamentally turret lathes can be classified as either horizontal or vertical, depending upon the position of the main axis. Horizontal types are in the majority, primarily because they can be adapted to a greater range of work.

Horizontal turret lathes fit two general patterns so far as the class of work they will take care of is concerned. On this basis they are divided into the bar type and the chucking type. This terminology refers primarily to the raw material classification fitted to each. The bar-type turret lathe (Fig. 14-1) is specified for use with bar stock of every shape known to engineering production, be it round, square, hexagonal, or other. Since bar stock is of uniform cross section throughout its length, the stock is held by means of collets in the headstock. Jawed chucks can also be used on bar-type machines when the workpiece is a forging or a casting.

The chucking type of turret lathe (Fig. 14-2) is designed primarily for machining forgings and castings. Workpieces of this type are held in chucks mounted on the spindle nosepiece. There are a wide range of chucks available, ranging from two-jaw types through the conventional ones to specialized chucking fixtures. The need for such diversity arises

Fig. 14-1.   Bar-type turret lathe in operation.   Note bar stock under coolant stream.   (*Courtesy of Bardons & Oliver, Inc., Cleveland.*)

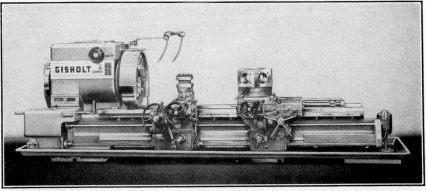

Fig. 14-2.   Large chucking-type turret lathe with $36\frac{1}{2}$-in. swing.   (*Courtesy of Gisholt Machine Co., Madison, Wis.*)

from the multiplicity of shapes that forgings and castings attain. The chucking type of turret lathe can also generally be equipped with collets for bar work.

Another method of classification of turret lathes is based on the turret mounting. The main ones are the saddle and the ram types. The former has heavier construction throughout the entire lathe than does the ram type The point of difference between them is traceable to the construction of the turret setting.

Saddle Type. The saddle type of turret is built with the turret mounted on a saddle that can be moved along the bed ways. The saddle is complemented by an apron that in appearance resembles engine lathe construction. The apron houses mechanisms for longitudinal saddle travel by both power and manual operation. There is also provision for power rapid traverse, a desirable feature for returning the saddle because of its comparatively long travel during the machining cycle.

Fixed-center turret construction is one in which the center of the operating turret station coincides with the lathe axis; there is no movement of the turret tool other than the longitudinal. If, then, a facing or similar machining operation is desired, that feature must be built into the tooling independently of the turret. The turret mounting is such that it must be indexed manually and then clamped into position by an extending side lever.

The cross-sliding turret is built to permit sidewise movement of the entire turret. This construction is of decided convenience where facing cuts need to be taken. A stop roll unit, located beneath the saddle, controls the longitudinal movement of the turret for a given cut. The cross-sliding turret is adaptable to machining contours, counterbores, threading, and internal tapers. It adds considerable scope to the potentialities of the turret lathe especially for short-run production and jobbing work.

The side-hung carriage is usually associated with the saddle turret. Its advantages—traceable to its cantilever construction, which provides no contact with the rear bed way—are found in permitting greater swing capacity. The carriage houses the operating mechanisms and work stops. The latter feature provides the means for producing duplicate parts without the necessity of measuring each one independently. Stops can be relied upon to produce repetitive work to limits of $\pm.001$ in. on the longitudinal dimensions.

Ram Type. On a ram-type turret there is a decided difference in turret mounting. The ram type does have a saddle; however, the latter fastens to the bed and the turret slides in a longitudinal direction thereon as the means of feeding the turret tool into the workpiece. Ram-type construction is found on bar as well as on chucking turret lathes. The ram type is readily distinguished by a prominently spoked turnstile handle with its end knobs (Fig. 14-3). This device functions to move the turret in longitudinal travel. In addition, by bringing the turret to the end of its travel, on the reverse stroke it automatically indexes the turret.

The stop screws controlling longitudinal turret travel are located at the rear of the turret slide.

The ram type of turret is usually equipped with a reach-over type of carriage because this lathe is used largely on bar work. The reach-over type rides on both bed ways and, in some designs, is supported by a lower rail. Because of its construction it is possible to add tooling at the rear or opposite to the square turret. The cross-slide unit, on any design, can be operated simultaneously with the turret; in this way, combined cuts can be taken on the workpiece.

Fig. 14-3. Ram-type universal turret lathe tooled for chuck work. (Courtesy of Jones & Lamson Machine Co., Springfield, Vt.)

Turret lathes can be provided with additional equipment. Taper turning attachments are of decided convenience where there is any appreciable amount of taper turning to be done. This attachment is placed on the front rather than the rear of the carriage. It is also possible to equip a turret lathe for thread chasing by the installation of additional components consisting of a lead screw with its accompanying split nut.

Headstocks. Headstock design for turret lathes does not follow a single pattern. The most elementary headstock design has a cone pulley drive. This construction is used only on small turret lathes, occasionally termed hand turret lathes. It is limited in the two essentials of power and speed range.

Spindle speed of wide range is available with the electric spindle turret lathe. A variable-speed electric motor is connected directly to the spindle inside the headstock housing.   Speeds as high as 3,600 rpm are obtainable with this type of drive.   There is a single lever controlling forward and reverse in addition to the full speed range.   Light work such as nonferrous alloys, plastics, and small ferrous parts are best suited to turret lathes embodying this headstock construction.

It is in the heavy equipment, however, that headstock development has shown marked progress.   All turret lathe builders offer a type of geared construction.   Some of these are built with a series of control levers for spindle speed changes since there are a substantial number of

Fig. 14-4. Automatic turret lathe equipped with hydraulic controls. (*Courtesy of Gisholt Machine Co., Madison, Wis.*)

the latter available.   A simplified headstock control employs but a single lever which functions in connection with a small handwheel located at the side.   This arrangement is termed a preselector because of the fact that the operator can select a succeeding speed while the lathe is in operation by merely turning the handwheel until the desired spindle speed is set.

Power is generally delivered to a geared headstock through a single pulley-type drive.   Power application is made through clutches that are located on the main drive pulley shaft.   Both forward and reverse spindle rotation are available by means of separate clutches which are frequently of the multiple-disk type.

Automatic Turret Lathes.   The substitution of various types of automatic control for manual operation is proving to be a revelation.   Figure 14-4 portrays the use of a hydraulic control system.   Conventional turret mounting and hand controls have been eliminated in favor of a hydraulic system. The entire appearance of the lathe has undergone revision. The multiplicity of levers has been replaced by a simple, easily operated hydraulic system. All this has been accomplished without sacrificing anything in the way of metal-cutting potentialities.

In harmony with automatic turning lathe design, turret lathes are employing various control systems. An example of an electrical control to provide automatic operation for the turret lathe is pictured in Fig. 14-5. Among the features of this design is one for providing an electrical

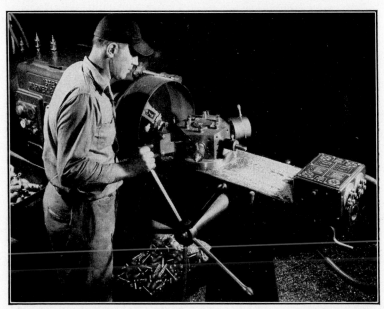

Fig. 14-5. Electro-cycle turret lathe, 16-in. capacity. (*Courtesy of The Warner & Swasey Co., Cleveland.*)

brake on the spindle that causes it to stop at exactly the same position each time. The particular model shown is especially recommended for machining brass, although it is also adapted to the other nonferrous alloys and plastic materials.

Automatic turret lathes are built for heavy-duty operation. Production potentials are high with a design like that shown in Fig. 14-6, since it has two spindles and dual tooling on the turret faces. The automatic features of this machine are such that changes of speed and feed can be accomplished while the machine is under cutting load. Automatic spindle stop is provided, permitting tools to return to neutral position without unnecessarily scoring the work.

Automatic horizontal turret lathes have all of the advantages of the conventional ones plus the gains resulting from an automatic cycle that relieves the operator of many manual duties. The nature of an automatic cycle is such that it tends to pace the operator, thereby establishing a dependable rate of production. There are some disadvantages to be considered, such as higher initial investment and increased tooling time; yet these are not significant where production runs are of a magnitude that will justify the installation of automatic equipment.

Fig. 14-6.   Two-spindle automatic turret lathe.   (*Courtesy of Potter & Johnson Co., Pawtucket, R.I.*)

Vertical Turret Lathes

Turret lathes are specified machine tool equipment primarily for turning, boring, and facing operations, including their modifications such as counterboring, chamfering, grooving, radii, and the like. Castings and forgings requiring several turned surfaces are especially well adapted to turret lathes. However, as these elements increase in size they become more difficult to place in a horizontal turret lathe. This problem is solved by the vertical turret lathe. A vertical turret lathe (Fig. 14-7) is equipped with a five-sided turret located on the horizontal crossrail. Its location is such that it can be traveled vertically in two directions as well as horizontally, forward and reverse. These movements can be conducted either under power or manually. In addition, a rapid traverse is available as a power drive. The turret is indexed by means of a crank located on its front face.

A side turret head entirely independent of the main turret is mounted at the side. It moves vertically as well as horizontally and permits machining a second operation concurrently with the main turret; such procedure is termed *combined cutting*. All operations are possible with the sidehead, although boring is done principally with the vertical turret. When two or more cuts are taken from the same station at the same time, the procedure is known as *multiple cutting*.

Vertical Turret Lathe Table. Vertical turret lathes are equipped with a circular revolving table that is, in effect, a chuck, or has a chuck built

Fig. 14-7. Vertical turret lathe, showing ram head (left), vertical turret and sidehead (right). (Courtesy of The Bullard Co., Bridgeport, Conn.)

into it. In addition, there are T slots in the table face for strapping on fixtures or clamping the workpiece directly. There is an accurately machined straight hole in the center of the table where plugs can be inserted as a means of locating fixtures for concentric rotation. The table is the basic locating and gaging surface for the vertical turret lathe and should be given the consideration that such a critical member deserves. A vertical turret lathe is specified as to size by the diameter of the table; thus a 36-in. vertical turret means that the table has a 36 in. diameter.

Automatic Vertical Turret Lathes. Repetitive work is best machined on an automatic vertical turret lathe.   The vertical automatic turret is constructed so that it can be operated either manually or automatically.

Turret Lathe Tooling

Genuine production gains resulting in low machining cost can be had from correctly engineered turret lathe tooling.   The tooling equipment is reflected in the ingenuity of the tool engineer.   Total production time for any turret lathe job is comprised of three elements: setup, handling, and cutting time.   It is the responsibility of the tool engineer

A

B

Fig. 14-8.   Turret lathe tools.   (A) Single cutter turner, (B) multiple cutter turner.   (Courtesy of Bardons and Oliver, Inc., Cleveland.)

to keep each of these three elements in their proper perspective regardless of production lot size.

Two broad basic principles to be observed concern themselves with the bar type and chucking type respectively. Insofar as the bar type is concerned, the cutting tool can generally be arranged whereby the bar stock is supported, in the manner of a steady rest, opposite to the cutting edge by rollers adjustable to stock size. This type of tooling is termed box tooling. A universal set of representative tools should be the basis of any tooling program; these tools can be adapted to a range of bar stock

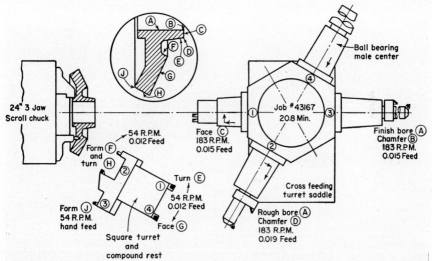

Fig. 14-9. Outline drawing of tooling for machining bevel gear blank casting. (*Courtesy of Gisholt Machine Co., Madison, Wis.*)

sizes. A group of universal bar-type tools is shown in Fig. 14-8. This group should be augmented by such additional items as a drill chuck, a self-opening die head, and flanged toolholders. Owing to the fact that bar turner cutters are usually held in a semivertical position, the cutting angles are ground on the top end rather than the side. Care must be exercised in getting the cutting edge and the rollers in proper position.

The tooling for chucking-type turret lathes varies considerably from bar equipment, since it tends in the direction of boring and turning. A further difference arises from the fact that castings and forgings do not follow the uniform cross-section pattern of bar work. A variety of tool heads and holders are necessary for chucking work. Heavy work demanding rigidity in the setup employs overhead pilot bars (Fig. 14-3 and 4). There is no such thing as a standard tooling setup for a turret, inasmuch as each job is in effect an individual problem. It seems wiser to adopt tooling to fit the necessities of a given workpiece than it is to attempt to use some so-called standard tooling setup just because it may be on hand. By way of illustration, Figures 14-9 and 14-10 show the tooling for a bevel gear blank casting. Note that the square turret carries a substantial amount of tooling while the hexagon turret has two skip-index stations.

Vertical turret tooling has but five stations to work with on the main turret. The square side turret provides additional tooling space, which is utilized to the extent that the workpiece will permit. Figure 14-11 is included to show the tooling layout for a typical casting. The sequence of cuts is designed to give the best possible cutting time for the job.

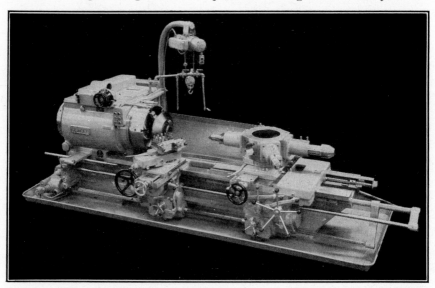

Fig. 14-10. Photograph of the tooling setup for gear blank outlined in preceding figure. (*Courtesy of Gisholt Machine Co., Madison, Wis.*)

Fundamental Tooling Considerations. In the operation of a turret lathe the over-all time required for machining a given workpiece equals the sum of the individual times for cutting, setup, and handling. Of these three elements, cutting time is the function of feed and speed which, in turn, is governed by the capabilities of the turret lathe and the tool material and design of the cutters.

Setup time is related to the tooling, since the simplicity of the tooling layout controls this factor. Any complications arising from special connections, and the like, will make themselves felt by increasing the time required to set up the job.

Handling time should be broken down into its elements: loading and unloading time as one set of factors, and machine handling or operating time as the second component. Machine operating or handling time is governed by the design of the turret lathe and the ability of the operator. On automatic turret lathes the automatic cycle governs both the cutting time and the indexing and tool approach time. These are then known as the cycle time, over which the operator has no control once the machine has been set up.

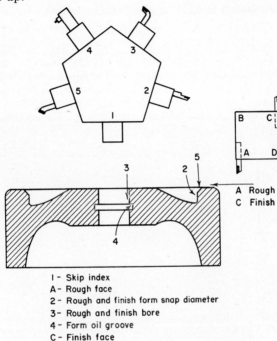

I - Skip index
A - Rough face
2 - Rough and finish form snap diameter
3 - Rough and finish bore
4 - Form oil groove
C - Finish face
5 - Chamfer

Fig. 14-11. Tooling layout for vertical turret lathe.

Survey Questions

14-1. Where is the turret located on a turret lathe?

14-2. In response to what need was the turret lathe developed?

14-3. Is a turret lathe capable of producing precision work?

14-4. Who, in the production organization, is responsible for tooling a turret lathe?

14-5. On what constructional feature are turret lathes classified?

14-6. Classify turret lathes on the basis of work types.

14-7. Select a turret lathe for machining forgings.

14-8. In what manner does turret mounting distinguish turret lathes?

14-9. What machining operation is facilitated by a cross-sliding turret?

14-10. In what turret-lathe design is the swing increased?

14-11. For what type of machining is the ram-type turret most suited?

14-12. Wherein do headstocks on turret lathes differ from those on standard engine lathes?

14-13. State the salient features of automatic horizontal turret lathes.

14-14. Do vertical turret lathes compete with horizontal types from the viewpoint of workpiece size?

14-15. Differentiate between the terms "combined cutting" and "multiple cutting."

14-16. What are box tools?

14-17. Fundamentally, what consideration must be observed in designing tooling for a chucking-type turret lathe?

14-18. Why is setup time of importance?

14-19. Define skip-indexing.

14-20. List the elements that are included in the cycle time.

REFERENCES

Boston, O. W.: "Metal Processing," 2d ed., John Wiley & Sons, Inc., New York, 1951.

"Flat Turret Lathe," Pratt & Whitney Aircraft Corp., Kansas City, 1943.

"Tool Engineers' Handbook," McGraw-Hill Book Company, Inc., New York, 1949.

"Turret Lathe Operator's Manual," The Warner & Swasey Co., Cleveland, 1940.

"Turret Lathe Tools," The Warner & Swasey Co., Cleveland, 1948.

"Vertical Turret Lathe," Pratt & Whitney Aircraft Corp., Kansas City, 1943.

CHAPTER 15

AUTOMATIC LATHES, CHUCKING MACHINES, AND SCREW MACHINES

Automatic Lathes

The automatic lathe embodies all the capacities of a single-spindle turning lathe with the addition of multiple tooling on a simultaneous cut. The automatic lathe is capable of carrying multiple tooling in a

Fig. 15-1. Automatic lathe, showing control camming and tool blocks. (*Courtesy of Jones and Lamson Machine Co., Springfield, Vt.*)

versatile arrangement that permits machining operations of similar or different characteristics to be performed at the same time. A second unique feature is its operating cycle. The sequence of machining a given workpiece, once decided upon, is set on the lathe's mechanism so that operation becomes entirely automatic.

It is possible to adapt the automatic lathe to short-run production, especially where a variety of workpieces have some dimensional requirements—face widths, for example—in common. Adjustments of this type are considerably less time-consuming than is a complete change-over from one style of workpiece to another. It is frequently possible to make such adjustments to fit small-lot production and still run the job at a saving over conventional lathe operation.

The automatic lathe can be applied to bar stock, forgings, and castings. Its greatest field of usefulness is in machining work held on centers. Thus, for example, the automatic lathe shown in Fig. 15-1 is available in a series of models ranging up to $17\frac{1}{2}$-in. swing with center distances as great as 87 in. and 75-hp input. The automatic lathe is generally of shorter bed length, for the same swing, than is an engine lathe of similar capacity. Multiple tooling requires high power input. The construction of automatic lathes features ruggedness without sacrifice in the precision of the machined product.

Construction Features. An automatic lathe is composed of a headstock, cycling mechanisms, a bed, tool-carrying components, and a tailstock. The general appearance of automatics varies substantially between the different makes and also between different models of a single manufacturer. Control and operational features are of different designs with the idea of rapid, effortless, and positive movement predominating. All the control systems previously described for specialized turning lathes have been engineered into automatics. An example of a hydraulically controlled automatic lathe is given in Fig. 15-2.

Two distinguishing features are the cycling mechanism and the tool blocks, or arms. The cycling is provided for the tool blocks in a manner enabling them to operate independently of each other. The front tools are provided with longitudinal as well as transverse travel, acting either singly or in combination. These movements can be modified with additional equipment in the form of cam bars, in order to provide taper and form turning where such operations are necessary.

The rear tool block is designed primarily for transverse movement used in facing, shoulder cutting, relieving, and chamfering operations. It does not, in general practice, move longitudinally; rather, cuts of any considerable width are made by employing wide tool faces either singly or in multiple. The cycle for the rear tool block is primarily that of feeding in toward the center: a slight sidewise movement away from the cut as a matter of tool relief to prevent scoring the workpiece, followed by a quick return to position. Cycling includes such features as infeed, travel, dwell, tool relief, and return to position. Rapid traverse is used wherever possible in the cycle. This applies specifically to tool approach and return when not engaged in actual cutting.

There is some difference in terminology relative to the tool-carrying components of an automatic lathe. The term tool block is used here, but such other expressions as tool slide and back arm have their adherents. Mention has been made of two tool blocks, front and rear; while this is the conventional construction, there are also designs in which a third block, placed above the workpiece and termed the overhead slide, is used. The advantage of the overhead, or additional, slide is that it offers increased tool-carrying capacity, thus making possible the use of smaller tools and reducing the likelihood of stalling the lathe.

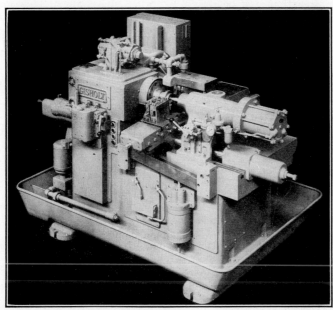

Fig. 15-2.   Hydraulic-type automatic lathe, 12-in. swing-over carriage.   (*Courtesy of Gisholt Machine Co., Madison, Wis.*)

Workpiece Drivers.   Substantial power requirements require positive workpiece driving mechanisms.   The workpiece must be mounted and released rapidly and located accurately.   The majority of the workpieces are mounted on self-mounting centers or on arbors.   The footstock spindle must be traveled twice for each workpiece.   This is taken care of in some designs by the use of either rapid hydraulic or pneumatic spindle movement.   Similar systems for clamping the footstock spindle are employed as an additional positive and time-saving device.

Chucking work is prominent on the list of automatic lathe operations. Some very ingenious devices have been built to accommodate workpieces. The tendency is toward chucks that operate with a hydraulic or pneumatic system.   There are also chucks embodying quick-opening mechanisms designed to save both time and effort.   Other equipment includes such items as magnetic chucks, power-operated collet chucks, and internal chucking devices.

Tooling Setups. Every setup needs to be engineered toward the objective of reducing the number of operations to a minimum. This imposes a demand for a single operation to perform the entire machining sequence; surprisingly enough, this objective is frequently attained.

The starting point of the tooling program concerns itself with the power input potential of the lathe. In order to meet this condition, the tendency on the part of the builders is to equip the automatic with ample reserve power that can be drawn on when necessary. This increased

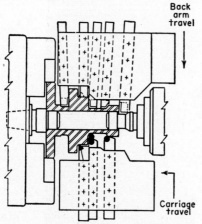 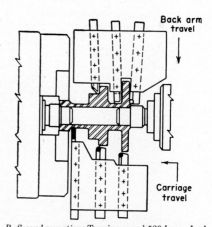

A, First operation: Turning speed 450 fpm—feed 0.015. Facing speed 580 fpm—feed 0.020. Power required—approx. 68 hp. Machining time—24 sec. Hold on stub centers and drive with two-jaw compensating air chuck. Depth of cut averages ¼ in. on a side. Rough turn, face, and form.

B, Second operation: Turning speed 520 fpm—feed 0.017. Facing speed 520 fpm—feed 0.025. Power required—approx. 35 hp. Machining time—28 sec. Hold on stub centers and drive with two-jaw compensating air chuck, turn, face, and form.

Fig. 15-3. Machining truck transmission cluster gear forging on automatic

power requirement is directly traceable to multiple tools, in contrast to the single tool on an engine lathe.

Actually the final tooling setup is reached as a result of experience on similar work. A given length of cut is frequently made with several tools set to the same depth, so that the longitudinal travel is much less than it would be with a single tool. The question of making concurrent cuts with the front and back tool blocks can best be answered by a study of the amount of stock removal, finish, and accuracy required. Some operations must be made at a lower rate than others because of these factors.

Tooling is an individual problem with every different workpiece. Surfaces requiring machining constitute the major problem, although the specification of the workpiece material is also important. The truck transmission cluster gear forging whose four operations are shown in Fig. 15-3 will serve as a typical example of both tooling and production;

specific information on operations as well as production times are given with each drawing. In addition, Fig. 15-4 is included to present the actual setup for operation *D*. Note that the individual tools differ in that some have inserted tips while others are clamped tips. These variations are traceable to the fact that economy in tooling governs final selections.

Tool blocks used on the automatic lathe are either universal, special, or solid types. The choice is generally predicated on the production run.

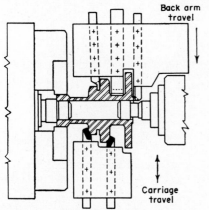

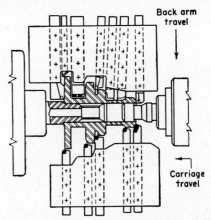

C, Third operation: Speed 470 fpm—feed 0.0075. Power required—approx. 28 hp. Machining time—18 sec. Hold on stub centers and drive with two-jaw compensating air chuck. Form, groove, face, and chamfer.

D, Fourth operation: Turning speed 660 fpm—feed 0.13. Facing speed 660 fpm—feed 0.025. Power required—approx. 20 hp. Machining time—23 sec. Hold on air-operated expanding fixture. Finish turn, face, and form. All diameters that must be concentric with one another and run true with the locating surfaces are machined in this operation.

lathe. *(Courtesy of Jones and Lamson Machine Co., Springfield, Vt.)*

Universal blocks are readily adaptable to a wide range of requirements in that individual tools of various shapes and sizes can be accommodated. The shortcomings of this equipment arise from the possibility that too much flexibility in toolsetting proves time consuming. In connection with machine operating time, it is well to consider the use of a solid tool block wherein the individual tools are preset to master gages in the toolroom; this effects a saving in setup time at the machine. The individual tools must always be set in the block in such a position that their cutting edges meet the oncoming metal. The tools in the rear tool block are inverted with respect to those in the front tool block. Where production is of a character as to cause retooling after a relatively short run, it is wise to maintain master samples as an aid in toolsetting. When a changeover is necessary, it is a relatively simple matter to mount the master sample in the lathe and set the tooling to fit.

Fig. 15-4. Tooling and setup used in operation *D* in preceding figure. (*Courtesy of Jones and Lamson Machine Co., Springfield, Vt.*)

Fig. 15-5. Automatic crankshaft turning lathe. (*Courtesy of The R. K. LeBlond Machine Tool Co., Cincinnati.*)

SPECIALIZED AUTOMATIC LATHES

Despite the impressive production potential of the automatic lathe, it is not a "one part" machine tool. Further development of the automatic lathe is the design for machining one part on a continuing basis (Fig. 15-5). This crankshaft lathe is capable of turning two forgings simultaneously. The example mentioned is not an isolated one; there are many other similar single-purpose automatic lathes.

Automatic Vertical and Horizontal Chucking Machines

There are several unique features incorporated in the design of the automatic vertical and horizontal chucking machines. The table carries

Fig. 15-6. Rotary-type vertical chucking machine, six-spindle, 20-in. capacity. Equipped with Woodworth expanding arbor fixtures. (*Courtesy of The Bullard Co., Bridgeport, Conn.*)

a number of spindle chucks so arranged that they match a corresponding number of work stations. Capacities vary in that six-, eight-, twelve-, and sixteen-spindle types are available. The term chucks is used here in a generic sense, since both conventional chucks as well as chucking fixtures are used.   The work stations carry the tooling, which is arranged in a variety of combinations engineered in a sequence so that, as the main table indexes, succeeding machining operations are performed.   The type and amount of tooling at each station must fit into a pattern that will machine the workpiece in one complete index cycle.   There may, of course, be duplicate tooling arranged to machine two workpieces per cycle.

It is frequently necessary to send the workpiece through a second machining cycle, since only surfaces accessible to the tooling can be

Fig. 15-7. A 12-in. six-spindle automatic horizontal chucking machine. (*Courtesy of The National Acme Co., Cleveland.*)

machined.   A repeat cycle, or second chucking, inverts the workpiece in order to expose the hidden surfaces of the first chucking operation. Second operations need not necessarily be done on this machine tool.   A typical example is found in machining an automobile motor flywheel, a casting that requires machining over its entire surface.

The automatic multiple-spindle vertical chucking machine (Fig. 15-6) is well adapted for machining castings and forgings although short lengths of bar stock are also considered suitable.   The keynote of these machines is their high production potential on repetitive work.   They are prominent equipment in those shops where production schedules are both tight and extensive.   These machines save considerable floor space as compared to their horizontal counterparts.   Tooling and setup are major and costly considerations that can be justified only by long-run production.

The presentation on chucking machines here has been devoted to vertical types.   There is at least one instance in which a builder refers to an automatic horizontal single-spindle turret lathe as a chucking machine.   There are also multiple-spindle horizontal chucking machines.

They are designed on two basic principles: in one the tool rotates, while in the other the workpiece rotates. In the former there are either four or seven spindles designed to give variable swing capacities. Work rotating designs are built in five-, six-, or eight-spindle models. There are also designs using eight horizontal spindles in an arrangement that employs double indexing in conjunction with duplicate tooling. By this device, two workpieces are completed with each cycle. The operating cycle is such that the two spindles at the center position are stopped in order that loading and unloading can be accommodated (Fig. 15-7).

Automatic Screw Machines

Automatic screw machines produce finished parts from bar stock. This is an accurate description so far as single-spindle machines are

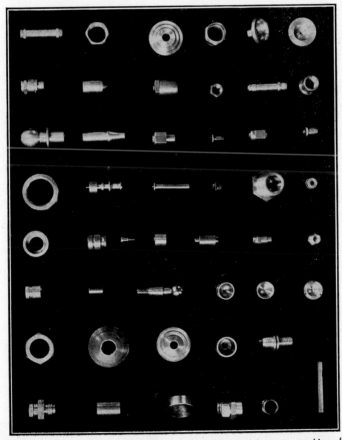

Fig. 15-8. View of various parts produced on Greenlee automatic screw machines (half size). (Courtesy of Greenlee Bros. & Co., Rockford, Ill.)

concerned; but it is not entirely true for multiple-spindle designs, since there are some chucking types built in that classification. The operating cycle of the screw machine is an automatic one whose various phases of operation are controlled mechanically by cam action. An operator is needed only for loading the bar stock and giving requisite supervisory attention. Even the manual loading function can be eliminated on those classes of work where magazine feed is possible. Screw machine products are generally small parts (Fig. 15-8). Larger production parts than those shown are possible, the limiting factor being that of machine capacity. Because of the multiplicity of tool carrying possibilities, every type of turning, facing, drilling, boring, reaming, threading, cutoff, and chamfering operation is possible. In addition, milling and broaching, which are never considered lathe operations, are also being included in screw machine production.

Single-spindle Automatic Screw Machines. The common characteristic of this type is that there is but one spindle. There are simultaneous machining operations by tools located in the turret and on the front and rear of the cross slide. Several designs of the single-spindle type are available, but two types predominate. These have two distinguishing features: turret position and type of cam construction, the latter being divided between disk- and drum-type cams.

Disk Cam Operated Screw Machine. In Fig. 15-9 the operating cycle, which includes bar feeding and clamping, is controlled by two cams carried on an operating shaft at the front of the machine, while an additional cam, located at the rear, governs the turret feed. The turret lies in a vertical plane and indexes in a direction parallel with the work. Turret mounting is on a slide that permits its movement into the work. All turret indexing and longitudinal travel are controlled by cams. For the most part the turret is of the six-station type, whose tooling, while of smaller proportions, bears close resemblance to that of the conventional turret lathe.

There are two cross slides which are designed to operate independently of each other and in a direction normal to the workpiece. Cross-slide movement to and from the work is controlled by cams that give desired feed to each tool. It is sound tooling practice to place all possible tooling on the cross slides as a means of relieving the turret. When this principle is followed, over-all machining time is reduced, since both side tools and turret tools can operate simultaneously.

Stock is positioned by being fed against an overhead swing stop, or, on occasion, a turret stop may be more convenient. The bar stock is fed forward automatically to its correct machining position immediately following the completion of the preceeding workpiece. The stock-feeding interval is referred to as an "idle movement," as are turret indexing and spindle reverse.

There is a considerable degree of flexibility in spindle speed, and this is useful as a means of accommodating the varying requirements of the different machining operations. These machines use a spindle speed as great as the workpiece and tooling will permit. Spindle speed changes are effected through the combination of change gears and clutches. Another important feature is that spindle rotation can be reversed—a desirable feature for backing off thread tools and in some turning operations.

Fig. 15-9. Single-spindle automatic screw machine. (*Courtesy of Brown & Sharpe Mfg. Co., Providence.*)

Tooling. Automatic screw machines favor circular tools for both cross slides. A circular cutoff tool is always placed on the back slide, which means that it must be in an inverse position. The cutoff tool is shaped to suit each individual job, since the width of the cut will be varied according to workpiece design and material.

Circular forming tools are placed on the front slide. These tools are simple or elaborate as the workpiece demands. The outstanding advantages of circular tools are that they can be turned to shape easily and that once the shape has been established it will remain true for the life of the tool. These tools can be sharpened by merely grinding the face of the offset. A disadvantage is that they must be positioned accurately with respect to the workpiece axis in order to machine the desired contour accurately. Turret tooling follows conventional turret lathe practice, but the tools are smaller and solid dies are common, since spindle reverse is available.

Drum Cam Operated Screw Machines. Single-spindle screw machines in which cycling operation is controlled by drum-type cams are sometimes termed ram-type automatics. Although their construction is considerably different from the disk-cam-operated type, in the final analysis production potentials and work types are similar for equal

Fig. 15-10. Single-spindle automatic. Rear view, guards removed to show drum-type cams. (*Courtesy of The Cleveland Automatic Machine Co., Cleveland.*)

machine capacities. The outward appearance of these two types of automatic screw machines is strikingly different, as are design details (Fig. 15-10). There are, in fact, two fundamental designs of the drum cam automatics: one, termed the turret type, is built in capacity ranges from $\frac{9}{16}$ to 10 in., while its companion style, the slide type, is available in capacities from $1\frac{1}{16}$ to $5\frac{3}{4}$ in. inclusive.

The distinguishing characteristics of these machines is their cam design. Drums, on which steel strips or contoured plates are bolted, act as cams that control the various automatic cycles. Because of this cam construction, these machines are extremely flexible; the strips or plates can be repositioned by merely relocating them on the drum surface.

There are three cams included in the operating mechanism. One cam, located on the spindle ram, controls the movement of the turret as to both indexing and longitudinal movement. A second cam functions as a cross-slide control, while the third cam directs the bar feed and chucking operations.

The turret is located on the front end of the ram, forward of the main operating cam. It rotates in a vertical plane normal to the workpiece axis. In this position the tools project away from the turret face and directly toward the workpiece. Tool mounting is variable, depending on types and individual operation requirements of turning, forming, threading, and the like.

Swiss-type Screw Machines. The development of automatic screw machines capable of high precision on small dimensions has come from

Fig. 15-11. Swiss-type automatic screw machine. (*Courtesy of George Gorton Machine Co., Racine, Wis.*)

Switzerland. Similar designs are produced in America with modifications in the direction of increased capacities (Fig. 15-11). The position of the tools is such that the stock is fed into them while rotating. Tool movement is controlled by a disk-type cam, as is the movement of the bar stock. Cam layout requires a high degree of accuracy as well as ingenuity. In fact the capabilities of this type of screw machine depend in large measure on the ability of the cam designer.

The headstock which carries the bar is reciprocated by cam action that must be synchronized with the tool rocker and cam and the frame cam controlling tool movement. Tooling is distinctive in that the tools are predominantly of the single-point type. Tools operate directly in front of the headstock bushing, thereby relieving the workpiece of any load-carrying requirement.

Swiss-type screw machines are employed primarily on small-diameter precision parts such as instruments, meters, watches, and clocks. The diameters and accuracy obtainable from these machines are unique. Tolerances on diameters are held as close as 0.0002 in. total, while shoulder lengths are produced to total tolerance of 0.0005 in. These tolerances are not the exception; rather, they have been held over long production runs. Surface finish is of a quality comparable to superior ground finishes.

Multiple-spindle Automatic Machines

Multiple-spindle automatic machines are fundamentally production types, and their acquisition should only be considered where production runs of some consequence are projected. Their initial and tooling costs are substantially greater and setup time is considerably longer than in the case of the single-spindle designs. The capacities of these machine tools have been expanded from the point where they were merely competing with single-spindle screw machines to the point where they operate in the field of turret lathe production. Their rugged construction and ample power input formed a combination capable of tooling applications unique among lathe accomplishments.

Regardless of the number of spindles on a given machine, its operation is such that all the tool slides are engaged on a workpiece simultaneously. The unit production time is equal to the greatest single-operation time. This is in contrast to the single-spindle machine, in which unit production time is equal to the sum of all the operation times, combined cuts being considered as a single operation time. A workpiece is completed each time the cycle indexes one position.

Spindles. Multiple-spindle machines are built in a variety of spindle combinations. The most usual arrangement is that with the spindle axes spaced equidistant in a radial pattern on the circumference of a circle. In this arrangement there are four, five, six, or eight spindles in the conventional designs. The choice of the number of spindles is predicated on such considerations as production requirements and product design. Another possibility with a large number of spindles arises from the fact that duplicate tooling can be utilized so that more than one part can be finished per cycle. Progress in the direction of product quality is enhanced by greater numbers of spindles, since tooling can be arranged for both roughing and finishing cuts. Six-spindle machines represent the greatest number of installations (Fig. 15-12). All spindle arrangements do not follow the radial pattern; however; one design employs a vertical in-line principle wherein the spindles are banked one directly above another.

Operating Principles.   The conventional design in multiple-spindle machines embodies the principle of the work rotating and the tooling remaining stationary.   There are other designs in which the tool rotates.

Fig. 15-12.   Six-spindle 1¼-in. capacity automatic screw machine.   (Courtesy of The New Britain Machine Co., New Britain, Conn.)

Tool-rotating types are not, in the strict sense, bar machines; rather, they are common for machining castings, forgings, and second operations on bar workpieces previously cut off.   Indexing is generally arranged for one position per operating cycle on the bar-type machines.   Skip indexing, on the other hand, is largely confined to the chucking-type machines.

Construction Features.   The two basic components of these machine tools are the spindle carrier and the main tool slide.   The spindle carrier, located on the inboard side of the headstock, indexes the headstock. When the machining activity is under way, the spindle carrier is locked into position rigidly.   Thus the spindle carrier controls and aids in the operating cycle.

The main tool slide is in a location that brings the individual tooling into alignment with the end of the bar stock.   Longitudinal feed is controlled by camming action in order that fluctuating tooling demands

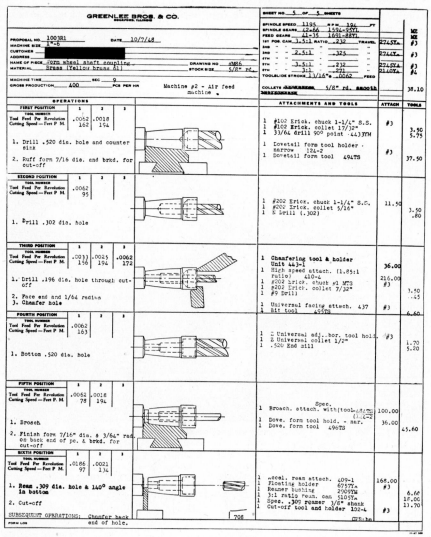

Fig. 15-13. Layout and tooling sheet for a brass worm wheel shaft coupling on a six-spindle automatic. (*Courtesy of Greenlee Bros. & Co., Rockford, Ill.*)

can be accommodated. Tooling here, for the most part, is of the end-working type of which roller and knee turners, drilling, boring, reaming, tapping, and threading are representative.

Cross slides are mounted directly on the headstock and are positioned to operate radially on the center line of the work. The movement of the cross slides is controlled by camming, and they operate independently of the main tool slide. There are instances, however, in which cross-slide and main tool side motions are synchronized. Additional slides are added from overarms in an arrangement termed swinging arm slides.

The tooling and production possibilities of a representative six-spindle automatic can be vizualized with the aid of Figs. 15-13 and 15-14. The first of these shows the operations, a working drawing, and tooling for each station; the second is a close-up view of one station. The production on this job is stated to be 400 parts per hour.

Fig. 15-14. Broaching attachment and tool mounting in fifth position for tooling sheet, Fig. 15-13. Six-spindle automatic. (*Courtesy of Greenlee Bros. & Co., Rockford, Ill.*)

Camless Automatics. While cams are used in conventional designs, there is a development in which quadrants equipped with stops act to replace cam action. This construction permits the adjustment of the feed stroke by setting the quadrants in place of removing cams. Because of this approach, no cam replacement is necessary and setup time is materially reduced. Short-run work can be placed on these machines to good advantage. A typical automatic built with quadrant feed adjustment is shown in Fig. 15-15.

Fig. 15-15. Five-spindle automatic bar machine equipped with quadrant feed control. (*Courtesy of The Warner & Swasey Co., Cleveland.*)

Survey Questions

15-1. Wherein are automatic and standard engine lathes similar?

15-2. Can an automatic lathe be used economically on short-run production?

15-3. Is an automatic lathe essentially a chucking-type machine tool?

15-4. What are tool blocks?

15-5. Where are cutting tools located on an automatic lathe?

15-6. Explain the function of the cycling mechanism.

15-7. How is an automatic lathe generally tooled for wide cuts?

15-8. Give some examples of parts that are especially well adapted to machining on an automatic lathe.

15-9. Are automatic lathes built for machining a single piece?

15-10. Define the term "second operation."

15-11. How many spindles are found on a vertical, automatic chucking machine?

15-12. Single-spindle-type automatic screw machines are confined to the machining of what form of raw material?

15-13. By what mechanism is the automatic-cycle operation on an automatic screw machine controlled?

15-14. List the possible machining operations within the capabilities of an automatic screw machine.

15-15. How does the turret function on an automatic screw machine?

15-16. On disk-cam-operated automatics, will the same set of cams serve for all machining jobs?

15-17. Name the different tool-carrying stations on an automatic screw machine.

15-18. Why are circular tools favored for automatics?

15-19. Are disk- or drum-type cams considered the more flexible design?

15-20. Enumerate several specific products that are best suited to Swiss-type, automatic screw machine production.

15-21. Is the number of spindles designed into multiple-spindle automatics a fixed one?

15-22. Does spindle position always follow a radial pattern?

15-23. On bar-type automatics does the work or the tool rotate?

15-24. Wherein do camless automatics differ from conventional designs?

15-25. Select some component parts of an automobile motor that could be machined on multiple-spindle automatics.

REFERENCES

Colvin, Fred H., and Frank A. Stanley: "Turning and Boring Practice," 3d ed., McGraw-Hill Book Company, Inc., New York, 1948.

"Construction and Use of Automatic Screw Machines," Brown & Sharpe Manufacturing Co., Providence, 1949.

Donaldson, Cyril, and George H. LeCain: "Tool Design," Harper & Brothers, New York, 1943.

"Handbook for Operators of Acme-Grindley Multiple Spindle Bar Machines," 6th ed., The National Acme Co., Cleveland, 1944.

"Set-up and Operation of B & S Screw Machines," a series of 14 pamphlets, Brown & Sharpe Manufacturing Co., Providence, 1948.

"Tool Engineers' Handbook," McGraw-Hill Book Company, Inc., New York, 1949.

Turner, William P., and Halsey F. Owen: "Machine-tool Work," 2d ed., McGraw-Hill Book Company, Inc., New York, 1945.

CHAPTER 16

SCREW THREADS .

The American Society of Mechanical Engineers accepted the responsibility for the development of screw thread standards by authorizing committee study of the problem as early as 1905.   In this worth-while endeavor it was joined by the Society of Automotive Engineers in 1911. There were three thread systems recognized until well after World War I: the United States Standard covered coarse pitch, the SAE fine pitch, and the ASME extra-fine pitch screw threads.   Coordination of these systems resulted in the establishment of the American National Screw Thread System, in which the coarse, fine, and extra-fine series were recognized. Congress established a National Screw Thread Commission in 1918 which provided the authoritative center for correlating the development work on screw thread standards.   For the first time in our history we were confronted in World War I with the necessity of screw thread fits in components originating in different factories in widely separated geographic areas.

An agreement was signed in Washington on November 18, 1948, by representatives of Great Britain, Canada, and the United States that created the Unified Screw Thread Standard for screws, bolts, nuts, and other threaded parts.   This standard brings affected screw threads of these three countries into complete accord, with the single exception that the British have a 12 pitch for their ½-in. coarse thread, while the American standard retains its former 13 pitch for this thread size.

Unified and American Screw Threads

The Unified standard is presented in American Standard B1.1—1949 in complete detail.[1]   The major revision of preceding thread forms is found in the root flat of the internal thread equaling P/4 while the crest dimension remains P/8.   The other important modification is found in the external thread, where both the root and the crest are rounded, although a flat crest, P/8, can be used.   Thread forms for both the internal and the external designs are sketched in Fig. 16-1.   It will be

[1] American Society of Mechanical Engineers, New York, 1949.

noted that the thread form shows something of the Whitworth influence on the external thread; however, the 60° thread angle of previous American standards is retained. These conditions mean that the newly developed Unified standard can be readily adapted to American practice.

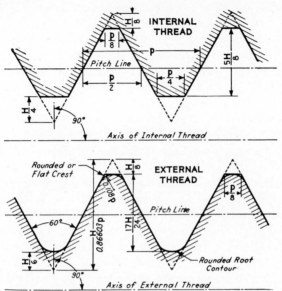

Fig. 16-1. Internal and external Unified and American thread forms, American Standard B1.1—1949. (Courtesy of The American Society of Mechanical Engineers.)

THREAD SERIES

The previously quoted American Standard B1.1—1949 covers both Unified and American standard threads. This fact is mentioned because the Unified screw threads are limited to the coarse and fine series of classes 1A, 1B, 2A, 2B, 3A, and 3B. When requirements go beyond these, other thread series should be investigated before the expedient of using special threads is resorted to.

Fine-thread Series—UNF and NF. In this series the former SAE standard is supplemented by ASME machine screw sizes below ¼ in. They are in general use in automotive and aircraft work, where fine threads are desirable because of prevailing requirements.

Extra-fine Thread Series—NEF. This is the same as the present SAE extra-fine series. It is used primarily in aircraft for thin-walled equipment where thread depth must be held to a minimum or where a maximum practicable number of threads is required within a given thread length.

8-thread Series—8N. This series starts with 1-in. diameter and extends through 6-in. diameter. These threads are used on bolts for high-pressure flanges, cylinder head studs, and like applications against pressure. They are set up to an initial tension resulting from elastic deformation in order that the joint will not open under the application of steam or other pressure. This series has a constant pitch value.

12-Thread Series—12UN or 12N. Note that this series is found in both the Unified and the American thread series. It is used in boiler work in sizes from ½ in. through 1¾ in. Machine construction uses this series for thin nuts on shafts and sleeves.

16-Thread Series—16UN or 16N. This is another constant thread series that is used for adjusting collars, bearing retaining nuts, and other applications requiring a very fine thread.

Special Threads. These comprise a group of nonstandard, or special, combinations of diameter, pitch, and length of engagement, whose basic thread form conforms to the Unified and the American National standard. A section of the ASA B1.1—1949 standard is devoted to special threads.

Thread Classes. Screw threads are classified or distinguished by the amounts of tolerance and allowance specified. This information is of direct concern to the manufacturing department, since it devolves upon them to produce thread fits in accordance with design specifications. Design specifications, in turn, are predicated on product end use as well as production cost.

There are several classes recognized in American Standard B1.1—1949; this is a revision of previously issued standards and therefore some additions are present. Classes 1A and 1B are designed for ordnance and similar special applications. Class 2A, on external threads, and 2B, on internal threads, are considered the standard ones for the usual production of bolts, nuts, and screws. A recent addition to this standard includes classes 3A and 3B, while classes 2 and 3 have been carried over from earlier standards.

The dimensions applying to each of these classes can be found in tabular form in the published standard. In order to use the information on screw threads correctly, the designer should use the designations incorporated in the standard. An example for an external thread follows:

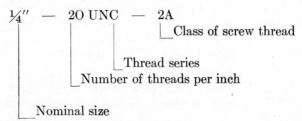

This designation applies to right-hand threads; when left-hand threads are wanted, the symbol LH follows the class designation.

ADDITIONAL STANDARD SCREW THREADS

There are additional standard screw threads for purposes of a special-ized nature such as pipe threads.   Other standard screw threads perform such functions as power transmission, as in the case of lead screws or closures exemplified by breach blocks.   The list of standard thread forms is quite extensive; since several are of limited application, only the better-known ones will be considered here.   A concise presentation of these is given in Fig. 16-2, where thread form and general dimensions are shown.

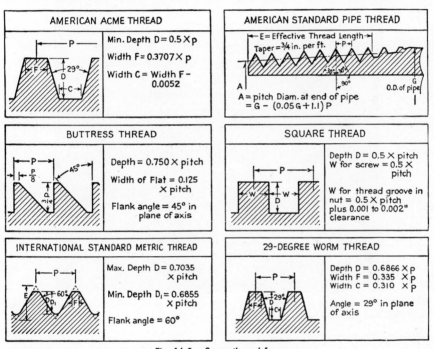

Fig. 16-2.   Screw thread forms.

Special Thread Forms.   The list of standard threads is being con-tinually augmented by special ones.   In each new development some specific condition is basic; for example, threads in which ball bearings form the contacting element comprise one such development.   Special thread forms must not be confused with nonstandard threads of indi-vidual pitch.   The policy of using nonstandard threads on an individual product has largely been abandoned in America.   We should recognize the profound influence that thread standards exert in engineering manufacture—we have better products at lower costs as a result of standardization.

Lathe-cut Threads

Mention was made in Chap. 13 of the fact that threads can be cut on engine lathes equipped with lead screws. This is a versatile thread-cutting method, since any desired thread form, external or internal, can be produced through the device of grinding the single-point tool to the contour of the wanted thread. The diameter of an external thread is limited by the swing of the lathe and the length is restricted to the dis-

Fig. 16-3. Thread cutting in a conventional engine lathe with workpiece mounted on centers and driven with bent-tail lathe dog.

tance between centers, except in those cases where expedients in setup are used. Internal threads are limited to the bore that the workpiece can accommodate, as it is by swing in the lathe. Since internal lathe-produced threads are generally cut with a holder of the boring bar type, mounted on a tool post, their length is limited by the boring bar overhang and rigidity. External and internal threads can be lathe-cut both as straight and as taper.

Another feature about employing the engine lathe for thread cutting is the wide range of thread pitches that are available. The index plate on the change gearbox shown in Fig. 13-18 indicates the thread pitches that this particular lathe can cut. Not all makes of lathes are identical in this respect. It is sound practice to check available thread pitch prior to purchasing a lathe. At the same time it is well to note whether an 11½ pitch can be had, since this pitch is common to several pipe sizes.

The engine lathe has the further virtue of being able to cut either right- or left-hand threads; the change-over is made by reversing the direction of rotation of the lead screw. Right-hand threads are cut by starting the tool at the right-hand end of the thread and feeding to the left (toward the headstock). A left-hand thread is cut by starting at the left and feeding to the right (toward the tailstock).

Multiple-start threads can also be cut on the lathe. This is not a simple task with the conventional lathe, since extreme care must be observed in index from one turned thread to the next. Assuming a double thread is to be cut, one thread of the desired pitch is cut, then, with the lathe stopped, the workpiece is indexed precisely 180° by one of several methods and the second thread is cut. Should a triple thread be desired, the index is 120°, while a quadruple thread indexes to 90°.

Setup for Lathe-cut Thread. The following directions are for one method of cutting a straight right-hand external thread on a workpiece mounted on centers (Fig. 16-3).

Adjust the lathe spindle speed to the appropriate range; then check lead-screw rotation by engaging split nut in carriage. (The carriage must travel to the left for cutting a right-hand thread.) Select wanted thread pitch on index plate of change gearbox. Carefully place levers, as indicated by index plate, in order that proper pitch will result. Other threads, such as internal, taper, or multiple-start, follow the same basic principles, with the necessary variations to suit their particular requirements.

The Threading Tool. Threading in a lathe is performed with a single-point tool. The tool is ground for the American standard thread form by fitting to a center gage whose included angle is 60°; other thread forms require their own gages. The general shape of the threading tool is shown in Fig. 16-4A; note that the tool bit fits the angle of the center gage accurately. The tool is mounted solidly in a toolholder in order to bring the tool point exactly on the center line of the work. As the tool is brought to the work, it is adjusted accurately to a position that is normal to the workpiece.

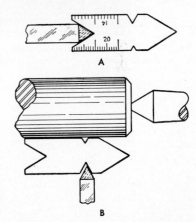

Fig. 16-4. (A) thread tool bit fitted to center gage, (B) thread tool bit positioned to workpiece by using center gage to secure alignment.

The center gage is placed against the work and the tool is positioned by bringing it into one of the side angle openings

(Fig. 16-4B).   Upon removal of the center gage the threading tool is brought in contact with the work.   The cross-feed dial reading is noted or, if lathe construction permits, the dial reading is placed at zero.   The carriage is moved to the right in order to permit the tool to clear the end of the workpiece.   The tool is then fed in for an initial depth of cut that approximates 0.015 in.

Cutting the Thread.   Cutting threads on a lathe is not an involved task if one fundamental is kept in mind.   Once the threading operation

Fig. 16-5. Threading dial on conventional engine lathe. Split-nut engagement lever shown with knobbed end. (*Courtesy of The Hendy Machine Co., Torrington, Conn.*)

has started, a positional relation has been established between the thread on the workpiece and the lead screw.   *This relation must be maintained throughout that thread-cutting operation.*   Failure to observe this precaution will result in a ruined thread, since each succeeding cut over the thread must accurately follow in the path of its predecessor.

In order to achieve this, the thread tool must enter the previous thread path each time at its exact starting point.   This requirement demands that engagement of the split nut with the lead screw must occur at an exact position for each cut over the thread, since it is lead-screw engagement that drives the carriage, with its threading tool, along the workpiece.   There are a number of methods involving the measurement of carriage travel by means of a scale placed on the lathe bed; however, these have been outmoded by the threading dial that is now a part of every lathe carriage.   The threading dial, usually located on the right-hand end of the carriage (Fig. 16-5), has a central circular scale that is driven from the lead screw. The scale is so graduated that one major division corresponds to one inch of carriage travel. Intermediate graduations coincide with fractions of inches of carriage travel.

When an operator has the lathe and workpiece set up ready for the first cut over the thread, he watches the dial intently and as a major graduation reaches the witness mark on the dial frame, he engages the split nut. This action results in the carriage, with its threading tool, being driven along the workpiece. The operator notes the reading, since, if a fractional pitch thread is to be cut, the thread dial engagement must be on an advanced graduation equal to the denominator of the fractional pitch. Thus if the original engagement when cutting a 11½-pitch thread is on dial graduation no. 2, each succeeding engagement for that thread must be on 2 or 4; obviously if the original engagement in this example is made at 1, each succeeding engagement must be on 1 or 3. By exactly the same process, even-numbered pitch threads can be cut by engaging the dial at fractional calibrations *if the pitch is divisible by that fraction*. A 6-pitch thread, being divisible by 2, can be "caught in" on the dial at any full inch or ½-in. graduation. An odd-numbered pitch such as 9, 11, 13, etc., must be engaged at the full inch graduations.

Completing the Thread. As the threading tool reaches the end of its desired path, it is quickly withdrawn from the cut and the split nut is disengaged. This combined operation requires accurate timing, especially when threading to a shoulder. When the threading tool has been withdrawn and the split nut disengaged, the carriage is moved manually a distance that will again bring the threading tool clear of the starting end of the thread. The cross-feed dial is set for the second cut, and when the selected threading dial graduation registers with its witness mark, the split nut is again engaged.

This procedure is repeated until the thread is cut to full depth as determined by fitting to some type of thread gage or mating nut. One precaution must be remembered: each succeeding cut is of less depth than its predecessor. The final cut is extremely light and is taken with a view to giving the thread a smooth, accurate finish.

Compound-rest Thread Tool Feed. The previous explanation of thread cutting in a lathe was based on the tool being positioned and fed at a 90° angle to the workpiece surface. This method is sometimes objected to because the width of the cut made by the threading tool tends toward a roughened thread. In order to overcome this objection, a threading tool can be ground to cut only one flank of the thread. Such a tool must be used in conjunction with a compound rest that is accurately positioned at 30° to the workpiece. The depth of cut is then made by feeding in the compound rest at each successive cut. When arriving at the end of the cut, the threading tool is backed out by means of the cross slide, which in turn has a reference setting to which the dial is positioned at the start of each successive cut. Reference setting, on some lathe designs, is obtained through the use of a stop.

PRECISION THREAD-CHASING LATHE

There are many demands for precision-cut screws of large dimensions, such as lead screws for machine tools, elevating screws on ordnance, and power transmission screws of many designs. Several lathes have been

Fig. 16-6. Precision screw-chasing lathe. (*Courtesy of Monarch Machine Tool Co., Sidney, Ohio.*)

developed, for cutting large screws of high precision with a single-point tool (Fig. 16-6). The features of this type of lathe which are departures from conventional lathe design are the steady rests mounted on the bed to permit continuous travel of the cutting tool. The lead screw is located in the center of the bed, where it operates in an oil bath. The lead screw is of high precision; for even greater accuracy the lathe is equipped with a lead screw variating attachment whose function is that of correcting previously determined lead error during the final chasing operation.

The lathe can cut screws to 9 in. in diameter and up to 15 ft in length. It can produce single- or multiple-start threads in both right- and left-hand styles up to and including 3-in. lead. Some idea of the precision of this lathe can be gained from the fact that it is said that its lead screw is finished with a limit of ±0.004 in., nonaccumulating, in its 15-ft length.

Thread Chasing

In order to avoid confusion about the nomenclature of threading as between cutting and chasing, it should be stated here that the term chasing is used in this chapter to mean threading by multiple cutting edges. It might be desirable to point out further that the term thread chasing is usually associated with mass production of screw threads by machine tools equipped with some type of die head. Die heads are assembled units with removable cutting elements, termed chasers. This construction is in contrast with the solid die, which is a single unit.

SELF-OPENING DIE HEADS

A self-opening die head has four or more chasers mounted in a carrier that is designed to open at the end of the thread-cut so that the die head can be speedily withdrawn from the workpiece. Die heads are used on

A

B

Fig. 16-7. (A) rotating-type die head equipped with insert chasers, (B) rotating-type die head equipped with hobbed cutters. (*Courtesy of The Eastern Screw Machine Corp., New Haven.*)

many different machine tools, including drill presses, turret lathes, chucking machines, automatic screw machines, and threading machines. Designs of self-opening die heads vary as to both condition of operation and mechanical construction. Selection of the die head is governed by such factors as size and type of screw material, thread size, machine installation, and production runs. Broadly classified, die heads are either rotating or stationary.

Rotating Die Heads. As the name indicates, the rotating die head is one that is used where the material to be threaded is stationary and

Fig. 16-8.   Phantom view of stationary-type die head.   (*Courtesy of The Geometric Tool Co., New Haven.*)

the die head rotates. Two designs are shown in Fig. 16-7. These heads are used on multiple-spindle screw machines, chucking machines, threading machines, and drill presses. They are constructed to open and close by means of a yoke. They can also be used in a stationary position in those instances where the workpiece rotates.

Stationary Die Heads. These heads are used where the workpiece rotates. There are several designs in respect to the opening and the closing mechanism. Die heads of the design shown in Fig. 16-8 find wide application as turret lathe tooling. The die head is self-opening at the end of the thread; however it is closed manually by means of the closing handle incorporated in the carrier. These heads are always constructed with a view to rapid and easy chaser removal.

Stationary die heads designed for Brown and Sharpe and similar automatic screw machines (Fig. 16-9) are much smaller and of different construction from the turret lathe types. In these installations the operation of the die head is synchronized with the operating cycle of the screw machine. In consequence the tripping and closing mechanisms are frequently built for external operation by suitable cam or stop devices on the machine.

Die Head Chasers. Chasers are of three distinct types as to design and appearance. Radial and tangential chasers are most common, but there are heads equipped with circular chasers. Radial chasers are produced in three types: insert chasers, milled chasers, and hobbed chasers. These classifications refer to the method of manufacture, which

Fig. 16-9. Die heads for B & S and similar screw machines. (*Courtesy of The Eastern Screw Machine Corp., New Haven.*)

imparts distinctive characteristics to each. The hobbed, or tapped, chaser represents a theoretically correct thread shape in that it fits around the screw much in the manner of a nut. The helix angle in the chaser is correct at all points. Another characteristic of the hobbed chaser is that it can be reground at both the chamfer and the cutting face repeatedly.

Insert chasers are free-cutting and are capable of exceptionally long runs between grinds. They are easily removed from the carrier and can be readily reground. A die head designed for insert chasers will accommodate several sizes to the full operating capacity of the carrier. Left-hand chasers require the use of left-hand carriers.

The design of tangential chasers imparts a free-cutting action and a natural clearance like those of a lathe tool. It is claimed, therefore, that these chasers are easily sharpened and that they produce a smoothly finished, accurate thread. The reduced area of contact results in low friction, and consequently maximum threading speeds are possible. A die head equipped with tangential chasers can be seen in Fig. 16-10.

This particular head is designed for cutting taper threads. The taper attachment causes the head to expand on the diameter as the work enters the die head. Cutting action is limited to the throat section of the

Fig. 16-10. Die head for cutting taper threads equipped with tangential chasers. (*Courtesy of Landis Machine Co., Waynesboro, Pa.*)

Fig. 16-11. Self-opening die head equipped with circular chasers. (*Courtesy of The National Acme Co., Cleveland.*)

chaser; this lessens cutting strains. The desired taper is regulated by cam action.

Circular chasers are made with ground annular grooves spaced at desired thread pitch. The circular form is interrupted in a manner that permits grinding a cutting edge on the chaser (Fig. 16-11). The correct thread lead is gained by grinding the face of the chaser-holding block to the required helix angle. Because of this design the same chasers, ground the opposite way, will produce left-hand threads. These chasers can be reground repeatedly or until 270° of the chaser circumference has been consumed.

Solid Dies. There are solid dies available which are used for every threading operation. Some of these are employed for restriking threads after a plating operation or for precision sizing. Manual threading is usually done with solid dies or with a die head containing two adjustable chasers which are positioned by screws. These chasers are removable for regrinding, a feature that the solid die lacks.

THREAD TAPPING

Internal threads are produced by taps whenever requirements permit. A table of tap drill sizes should be consulted prior to drilling a hole that is to be tapped. The tap drill size governs the minor diameter of the thread; a too large hole will result in a weakened thread. Solid taps are used where possible, since they are simple, rugged, and accurate. The threaded portion of the tap is produced either by machining or by grinding.

There are taps of many descriptions; each of these forms has been developed for a specialized application. Among those encountered in the general run of work are nut taps, pulley taps, pipe taps, boiler taps, stay-bolt taps, and spiral taps. Hand taps for American standard screw threads can be had in a series of three, respectively termed taper, plug, and bottoming. The difference between them is the amount of chamfer of the tap thread; thus a taper tap is used as a starting tap; while a bottoming tap is used on a blind hole where threads must reach to full depth.

Collapsible Taps. The counterpart of self-opening die heads is found in the collapsible tap (Fig. 16-12). This is used in both the rotating and the stationary type. When it is used as a stationary tap, collapsing is usually done by trip ring and resetting by a handle. If, however, the tap is of the rotating type, collapsing and resetting are accomplished by an outside yoke or by a trip plate and yolk. The collapsing feature pulls the blade-type chasers toward the center of the tap in order to clear the threaded hole as the tap is withdrawn.

Taps, regardless of design, are used in tapping machines in addition to the machine tools used for producing threaded components. Tapping machines represent specialized equipment designed for production run work. They can be had in every type of operating cycle, including fully automatic operation. There are tapping units available as accessory equipment for use on conventional drill presses.

Fig. 16-12. Collapsing tap for turret lathe installation. (*Courtesy of The Geometric Tool Co., New Haven.*)

THREADING MACHINES

When threading is a major part of machining a component, the operation is generally performed in a threading machine. Such machine tools are built in a variety of designs. The conventional threading machine has a single spindle equipped with a geared headstock that has several speeds (Fig. 16-13). The die head, which is of substantial construction, is arranged for automatic trip operation. Die heads are available for

Fig. 16-13. Single-spindle threading machine. (*Courtesy of The Hill Acme Co., Cleveland.*)

machine threads, pipe threads, and large-size API threads for oil well casings.

The carriage is generally arranged for manual thread start by means of a handwheel; there are designs equipped for lead-screw operation. Lead-screw engagement is accomplished through a bronze split nut actuated by lever and cam. Change gears are provided for the lead screw to meet screw pitch requirements. Threading machines can be used for tapping by attaching a tap chuck to the die head. Lead-screw-equipped threading machines are especially desirable for tapping work because of the power-fed carriage feature. It is possible to replace the thread chasers in the die head with blank milling chasers for hollow milling.

Threading machines are used for threading bolts, rods, and similar components in addition to pipe. In the latter application, the machine can be equipped so that threading, reaming, and chamfering are performed in a single operation. Pipe nipples are threaded on this equipment to good advantage.

Automatic Threading Machines. A further development is that of the hydraulically operated threading machine equipped for either automatic or semiautomatic cycling. In addition, the machine is built on the double-end principle; the heads can be used singly or in unison, depending on the type of workpiece. Double-end threading is applied to electrical conduit, tie rods, pipe, brace rods, and other workpieces requiring threads at both ends. Operation is simplified, since such functions as carriage movement, feeding, gripping, and releasing are all fitted into the hydraulic cycle which is controlled by a single lever.

Small Parts Threading. The automatic screw machine is always considered first where threading of small parts on a production basis is required. There are instances where such equipment is used for second operation work in connection with threading. Another solution to the problem of threading

Fig. 16-14. Threading machine for small-parts production. (*Courtesy of The Eastern Screw Machine Corp., New Haven.*)

small parts is found in a threading machine built for this particular purpose (Fig. 16-14). The machine is equipped with a variable-speed motor drive that makes the most efficient threading speed possible. Production rates as great as 1,000 parts per hour have been achieved; obviously, though, production is dependent on many variables not the least of which is the thread length.

HIGH-SPEED THREADING WITH SINGLE-POINT TOOL

A novel development, combining the single-point threading tool with an automatic operating cycle, is available in a threading machine designed and built in France. This threading machine is revolutionary in design,

Fig. 16-15. Automatic threading machine for single-point tooling. (*Courtesy of Cri-Dan, Paris, France.*)

since the conventional lead screw used on lathes is replaced with a high-precision cam that positively ensures the generation of the thread and the accuracy of the pitch (Fig. 16-15). In addition, the operating cycle is fully automatic. The operator needs only to change the workpiece and engage the clutch; all the rest of the cycle is automatic. Change-over time is as little as 15 min, and the machine has a maximum possibility of 50 cuts per minute.

Spindle speeds which range from 100 to 1,200 rpm are suited to all classes of thread and workpiece material. Thread forms offer no problem, since the single-point threading tool can be ground to suit. This machine is capable of cutting external, internal, right-hand, left-hand, conical, and multiple-start threads with capacities of up to 12-in. swing over the carriage and 5 ft between centers.

The carriage houses the operating cams and control dials. The cam can be designed to permit a number of cuts to be taken over a given thread. Operation is fully automatic, including rapid return from end of thread to its beginning. The relation between spindle speed and longitudinal travel is controlled by change gears. During the cutting cycle the saddle is clamped to the bed and only the longitudinal and cross slides are operative. Threading to a shoulder poses no special problem, since the threading tool shape can take care of this as it does on the lathe.

THREAD ROLLING

The production of screw threads by the rolling method is unique in that there is no metal removed from the workpiece. In effect, thread rolling is a cold-swaging operation in which the workpiece surface is caused to flow into the rolling die cavities. It is obvious therefore that the external diameter of the workpiece will govern the final major diameter of the thread. The workpiece section must be prepared to a predetermined diameter, which is generally about equal to the pitch diameter of the thread. Since the final major thread diameter is usually of a standard size, it is necessary to prepare the workpiece diameter to a nonstandard size or undersize. This means that where a thread covers only a portion of the length of the workpiece, a shoulder must be formed prior to rolling.

Thread rolling is applied only to external threads. There are no limitations as to thread form, since every type of standard thread including wood and lag screws and other similar threads are produced by rolling. Rolled threads can be produced in right- or left-hand, multiple-start, and conical types. They can be applied on short surfaces or full rod length. Rolled threads are accurate and uniform, since the roller dies are never resharpened and as a result are not subject to the vagaries of adjustment. The dies continue in service until their entire face has virtually failed. The rolls perform in a manner similar to burnishing, with a resulting smooth finish on the thread surface.

Thread-rolling Methods. There are two principal methods for rolling threads. In one system, flat dies having ribbed surfaces at the proper helical angle pass over each other in a reciprocating motion. At the start of the cycle the workpiece is placed against the forward edge of the stationary die; the movable die then comes forward, thereby causing the component to roll and feed inward across the die face. The completion of the stroke cycle delivers the threaded piece from the dies.

The second basic method employs cylindrical dies, either two or three per die head. The cylindrical roller dies are power driven, hence the workpiece feeds forward through the central space at their junction. A thread-rolling machine employing thread die rollers is shown in Fig. 16-16; the workpiece is guided by the knobbed lever shown in the center foreground. Thread-rolling machines are built in every cycling category, from manual to magazine-feed, hydraulically controlled operation. Thread-rolling heads are occasionally installed on turret lathes.

Fig. 16-16. Thread-rolling machine employing three roller dies. (*Courtesy of The National Acme Co., Cleveland.*)

THREAD GRINDING

One means of producing precision threads, both internal and external, is by grinding. Thread grinding is accomplished by rotating the workpiece against a grinding wheel whose periphery has been shaped to the desired thread form. There is a relative axial traverse between the workpiece and the grinding wheel of one thread lead per workpiece revolution. Another thread-grinding method employs a multi-rib wheel in which several adjacent grinding ribs are present on the wheel surface. This type of wheel is generally employed on short threads whose total length is but one pitch longer than the wheel face width. In this instance the work rotates only one revolution while generating the complete thread length. Wheel face contours are preserved by diamond dressing and also by crush forming.

Thread grinding is especially suited to producing accurate threads in hardened steel where no other thread-producing method can be applied. Ground threads are characterized by their precision and excellent finish. Since grinding eliminates the possibility of cuts or tears, ground threads are specified where fatigue and bending stresses are of consequence. Lead screws are commonly specified as ground threads, as are other components where precision is important.

Thread-grinding Machines. Even though grinding threads on a production basis is a relatively recent development, thread-grind-

Fig. 16-17. Universal precision thread grinder equipped with hydraulic controls. (*Courtesy of Ex-Cell-O Corp., Detroit.*)

ing machines in many types and styles are available. External grinding machines are in the majority, but there are also several styles of internal ones. Universal thread grinders (Fig. 16-17) are designed for every type of operation from manual through hydraulically controlled automatic cycles. Threads are also ground on centerless grinding equipment.

THREAD MILLING

Threads can be cut by milling; in this process either a single form cutter or a multiple one is employed. There is a considerable difference between these two methods. The single form cutter is used for long threads of relatively coarse pitch such as lead and feed screws, multiple worms, and other heavy types; both the workpiece and the cutter rotate. Correct thread lead is obtained by moving the cutter carriage longitudinally by means of a lead screw.

A multiple cutter has annular rows of teeth that are perpendicular to the cutter axis; however, these cutters are devoid of lead. In consequence the cutter length must exceed the required thread length by several thread forms to allow for overrun. In operation, the cutter is "plunged" to thread depth and the workpiece need be rotated but $1\frac{1}{10}$ revolutions in order to complete the thread to length. This type of thread milling offers competition to self-opening die work on large production runs. Accuracy of milled threads is one of the chief assets of this method of thread production, since close tolerances and excellent finishes are characteristic. A further advantage of thread milling is the possibility of cutting large thread forms on small-diameter stock.

Fig. 16-18. Thread milling with hob-type thread-milling cutter. Modified buttress thread milled on radial aircraft engine cylinder barrel. (*Courtesy of The Lees-Brandner Co., Cleveland.*)

Thread-milling Machines. The machine tools employed for thread milling (Fig. 16-18) are different in design and appearance from conventional milling machines. Their operating cycles vary in accordance with production requirements. There are also differences in operating mechanisms. Since thread milling is applicable to both external and internal threads, thread millers are built to accommodate either system. Universal thread millers which can be used for generating both external and internal threads are also available.

Survey Questions

16-1. Which engineering society did the first recognized work on screw thread standardization?

16-2. Who were the sponsors of the "Unified Thread Standard"?

16-3. Define the term "standard thread."

16-4. Wherein do the Unified and American thread forms differ?

16-5. Aircraft and automotive construction is based on which thread series?

16-6. Where is the 8N thread series used?

16-7. How are screw threads classified?

16-8. Show how the designer can place complete thread information on his drawing.

16-9. Give some advantages of lathe-cut threads.

16-10. Where are multiple-start threads used?

16-11. How is the threading tool accurately aligned to the work in lathe thread cutting?

16-12. Where is the thread-cutting dial usually located?

16-13. Can threads be cut on a lathe that lacks a threading dial?

16-14. Is the thread-cutting tool ever set at 30° to thread being cut?

16-15. Give some applications for precision-cut threads.

16-16. Explain thread chasing.

16-17. Where are self-opening die heads of greatest utility?

16-18. Do tangential chasers offer unique advantages?

16-19. Can circular chasers produce both right- and left-hand threads?

16-20. For what class of work are collapsible taps used?

16-21. Name several types of threading that are adapted to threading machines.

16-22. How are small parts threaded on a production basis?

16-23. Is high-speed threading ever done with a single-point tool?

16-24. Wherein do rolled threads differ from cut threads?

16-25. When are ground threads specified?

16-26. Are milled threads of interest in production work?

REFERENCES

Donaldson, Cyril, and George H. LeCain: "Tool Design," Harper & Brothers, New York, 1943.

Jones, Franklin D.: "Machine Shop Training Course," 2 vols., 3d ed., The Industrial Press, New York, 1944.

"Pipe Threads," American Standard B2.1—1945, American Standards Association, New York, 1945.

"Screw Thread Cutting Manual," Geometric Tool Co., New Haven, 1946.

"Screw-thread Standards for Federal Services," Handbook H-28, National Bureau of Standards, Washington, 1944.

"Tool Engineers' Handbook," McGraw-Hill Book Company, Inc., New York, 1949.

Turner, William P., and Halsey F. Owen: "Machine-tool Work," 2d ed., McGraw-Hill Book Company, Inc., New York, 1945.

"Unified and American Screw Threads," American Standard B1.1—1949, American Standards Association, New York, 1949.

CHAPTER 17

BORING

The boring mill has the distinction of being the largest or most massive of the machine tools. There may be a few exceptions to this generalization, for example, the large metal planer. But it is certainly true that no other machine tool combines size and flexibility to the degree found in the modern boring mill. An idea of the size attained by boring mills can be gained from Fig. 17-1.

Fig. 17-1. A boring mill equipped with 40-ft table erected in a pit. Right rail head protracted, left rail head plumb. (*Courtesy of The Niles Tool Works Co., Division, Lima-Hamilton Corp., Hamilton, Ohio.*)

The term boring when used in connection with machining metal refers to enlarging an existing hole. It does not mean the production of a hole in a solid piece, this is known as drilling. In its restricted sense, then, a boring mill would be used to machine a previously made hole regardless of whether that hole resulted from drilling or from coring done in the casting or from punching, as in a forging. However, boring mills have been broadened in scope to the point where they are capable of performing a variety of machining operations. Some boring mills are so versatile that their functions overlap those of other conventional machine tools.

Vertical Boring and Turning Mills

The machine tools accurately fitting into this category are in effect vertical turning lathes, insofar as their functioning is concerned. They have a rotating table whose diameter is used to specify their size. Thus a 36-in. boring and turning mill is equipped with a table having a 36-in. diameter. These machine tools are built with a crossrail that mounts a saddle for holding the cutting tool.

Construction Details. The design details of vertical boring and turning mills are such that as sizes increase, more tool mounting is provided. The crossrail may carry two or more saddles, which can be arranged to follow in the same cut or they can be used for combined cutting. Sideheads mounted on the housing can be added in some designs as a means of providing additional tooling capacity.

Operation. Vertical boring and turning mills make boring, facing, or turning cuts either singly or in combination. It is because of this flexibility that these machine tools are frequently used for facing and turning operations. Gear blanks of a suitable size are a favorite workpiece. The outside diameter can be turned, one side or the rim and hub faced, and the bore made in one setting. The gear blank is then turned over and the second side finished; thus the machining is completed to the point of cutting the teeth.

Vertical boring and turning machines are capable of producing accurate work in every phase of their operation. In consequence they are frequently chosen in preference to other machine tools for facing workpieces of all shapes; the only requirement is that the piece be of a size that can be swung on the mill. These machines offer a degree of flexibility that is extremely desirable in contract and semi-production manufacturing. As a means of offering greater flexibility, some designs are arranged for sliding housings so that the table can be clear.

Automatic Vertical Boring and Turning Mills. A specialized design for machining rolled steel car wheels has been developed in which the operating cycle is automatic (Fig. 17-2). One head cares for boring and facing the wheel hub while a second one faces the rim. Two sideheads turn the wheel tread in an operation where all four of these heads operate simultaneously. They are equipped with rapid traverse and operating feed all built into the automatic cycle; at the completion of the cycle, heads return to their starting position.

Fig. 17-2.   Automatic vertical boring mill tooled for machining car wheels.   (*Courtesy of Giddings & Lewis Machine Tool Co., Fond du Lac, Wis.*)

Boring Machines

Vertical boring machines are designed for single-purpose use where high production runs prevail.   In contrast with the previously described vertical boring and turning mills, these boring machines employ the principle of a rotating tool on a stationary workpiece.   Furthermore, their operation is limited primarily to boring.

Inclined Boring Machines.   A popular method of machining the bores on a V-type motor block is that of using a boring machine designed to fit the block dimensions.   These machines are of special design to meet the dimensional requirements of the motor block casting.   Certain components of these machines are common to them and to their vertical prototypes, and operation methods are the same.   A difference arises from the manner in which castings are loaded or unloaded or transferred in or through these machines. Inclined boring machines usually rough-bore the casting by employing a number of boring tools equal to the number of cylinders in the block casting (Fig. 17-3). Production rates vary somewhat with loading and operating time; an output of 65 cylinder blocks per hr is not unusual.

Fig. 17-3. Inclined-bed-type boring machine, showing motor block casting mounted for cylinder boring. (*Courtesy of The Ingersoll Milling Machine Co., Rockford, Ill.*)

Horizontal Boring, Drilling, and Milling Machines

The machine tool known as a combined boring, drilling, and milling machine is capable of performing many of the machining operations associated with individual machine tools in these three classifications. Fundamentally it is a boring machine designed for operation with a rotating tool on a stationary (nonrotating) workpiece. Frequently, however, the cutting tool rotates and traverses in a simultaneous movement; this is different from the operation of the milling machine, where the tool rotates on a stationary axis.

The basic operations performed by these machines are boring, drilling, and milling, including modifications of each one. In common with many machine tools, the horizontal boring, drilling, and milling machine can be adapted to other than their fundamental operations. They perform such further machining operations as facing, turning, and threading, as well as tapping, reaming, shaping, forming, and duplicating. A wide choice is available, including rotary tables which are most convenient for positioning the workpiece for subsequent operations; both horizontal and vertical tables are used in this manner.

There are several types of these machines, classification being based primarily on table arrangement. The three best-known ones are the

Fig. 17-4. Table-type horizontal milling, drilling, and boring machine equipped with electric pendant control. (*Courtesy of Lucas Machine Division, The New Britain Machine Co., Cleveland.*)

table type, the floor type, and the planer type. A fourth is known as the portable type because of the fact that it is taken to the job for such applications as work on board ship.

Table Type. The table type was the forerunner of subsequent model developments in horizontal boring, drilling, and milling machines (Fig. 17-4). The essential components of this machine are base, saddle, table, main column, headstock with one or more spindles, end column, and end support. Of these components only the bed and main column are fixed; all the other members are capable of movement.

The basic feature of these machines is that cuts can be made longitudinally, laterally, and vertically. The workpiece can be moved horizontally by sliding the saddle on the bed and transversely by table movement on the saddle. The headstock in turn can be moved vertically on the main column; this allows for the raising or lowering of the tooling as desired.

Table-type machines are the most versatile of all the designs because of their ability to maneuver in three planes. They are constructed for accuracy, a characteristic which is furthered by such refinements as depth gages and direct-reading dials for speeds and feeds and micrometer adjustments to all units. Speed and feed selectors, independent reverse to all units, and remote control are other features characterizing table-type machines.

Table types are the smallest of these machines, although some imposing models are built. They are especially convenient for machining gear cases, machine-tool components, Diesel- and gas-engine members, machinery parts, castings, weldments, and forgings where there are several pads, holes, or bores. It is possible to perform many machining operations with one setup.

Floor-type Machines. Floor-type machines mount the workpiece on floor plates instead of a table. It is for this reason that these machines take care of heavier work than the table ones. The basic difference between the two, however, is the fact that in the floor type the spindle traverses past the workpiece while in the table type the workpiece is traversed past the spindle.

The columns are mounted on runways which, because of sectional construction, can be extended to any reasonable length, as can the floor plates. In consequence the floor-type machines can be built to great size for machining extremely large workpieces. Some designs do not make use of an end column for support; rather, a very rugged main column is relied upon to give the necessary rigidity and support to the tooling. The choice of support is predicated on the workpiece shape and machining requirements. Floor-type machines are chosen for machining reduction gear cases, turbine housing, electrical generator frames and other components of large size.

Planer-type Machines. This design has a reciprocating table—a modification of the table type, since the saddle-table unit is replaced. Instead of the table and saddle unit being adjustable to and from the face of the headstock, the column and end column are each separately provided with adjustment to and from the bed and table (Fig. 17-5). The planer-type machine is selected for those jobs that require exceptional rigidity on heavy and long work.

Multiple-head Types. This machine departs from the basic design to the point where its scope and appearance are notably changed. A second column is used in such a position that the table is straddled. In addition there is a crossrail which accommodates one or more vertical headstocks. Each column carries one or more heads designed to swivel when angular work such as large V-type motor blocks are to be machined. In appearance, multiple-head machines are similar to large milling machines although construction details are unlike (Fig. 17-6).

Multiple-head machines are used on semi-production work where simultaneous operations are needed. The heads can be operated singly or in combination. Because of this design, vertical operations can be

Fig. 17-5. Planer-type horizontal boring, drilling, and milling machine equipped with 8-in. bar driven with a 75-hp motor. The workpiece shown weighs 50 tons. (*Courtesy of The G. A. Gray Co., Cincinnati.*)

in progress while sideheads are being used. The swivel-head features eliminate the necessity for angle plates and other auxiliary tooling or multiple setups. The jobs for which these machines are ideal are castings that require machining on three sides, since these can be accomplished at the same time and with a single setup.

Tooling. Tooling combinations are extremely widespread; however, since such tools are fundamentally designed for boring machines, boring bars are of chief interest. Boring bars are of two main types, known as stub bars and line bars respectively. The spindle has a Morse taper socket which fits the end of the boring bar and is equipped with a locking device.   Boring bars are not integral parts of the machine in any sense.

Stub bars are supported solely by the spindle connection, which means that their alignment depends on this fastening.   Stub bars are limited in their application to workpieces that can be brought close to the head-stock; any excessive overhang will develop vibration during machining. It is desirable to employ stub bars whenever machining requirements will permit, since they are easy to install and require no additional alignment.

Fig. 17-6.   Multiple-head horizontal boring, drilling, and milling machine.   (*Courtesy of Giddings & Lewis Machine Tool Co., Fond du Lac, Wis.*)

The line bar is of a length that will give its outboard end a bearing in the end column support, requiring careful alignment between the two columns.   When the bar is of any extended length, intermediate bearing supports are desirable.   These can be arranged by using boring fixtures designed to hold suitable bearings.   It is possible to use the workpiece itself as a means of providing intermediate bearing supports for the line bar where bushings can be inserted in previously machined holes.

Boring bars are frequently made of soft steel to permit ease of slotting and modification.   They may develop wear at the bearing surfaces and have only a short service life.   This condition can be remedied by attaching hardened steel wear strips, which are then ground to the required bearing diameter.   Hardened steel bars are another answer to the problem of bearing wear.

Boring bars are equipped with single cutters or fly cutters which correspond to single-point tools. This is by far the most common type of boring tool. It is possible to use a double-end boring tool under some conditions; either a single tool bit or two independent tool bits are used for double-end boring. Boring bars can be provided with attached heads capable of carrying several tools for making concurrent cuts.

PRECISION PRODUCTION BORING

The continued demand for precision boring, on a production basis, is being met by the development of machine tool equipment utilizing the

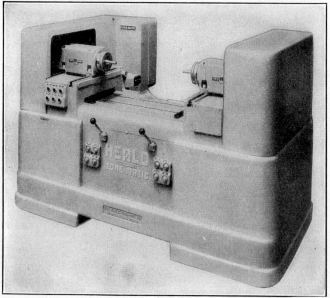

Fig. 17-7. Precision boring machine for use with single-point tool. (Courtesy of Heald Machine Company, Worcester, Mass.)

principle of extremely hard single-point tools operating at high speed. An early term for the basic method was diamond boring; this has been replaced by the coined word "borizing." The machine tool equipment built for this process is extensive in that single- and multiple-spindle designs as well as a variety of operating combinations, including fully automatic cycling, are available.

Machine tools of this classification are not confined to boring alone, since such additional operations as turning, chamfering, grooving, and facing are also performed on a precision production basis. Mechanical details of these machines vary as to work placement, spindle location, number of heads, and operating mechanisms.

The cutting tool used is an extremely hard one such as a diamond or cemented carbide.   The tools rotates, while the workpiece is stationary; however, both can be moved for longitudinal or cross feeds (Fig. 17-7).

Any engineering materials not exceeding 400 Bhn can be machined to a high degree of accuracy.   Efficient production can be expected when tolerances for dimensional accuracy, roundness, and straightness are on the order of 0.0001 to 0.0002 in.   The degree of finish depends on the material, machine equipment, and mounting; finishes equaling 1 micro-inch root-mean-square have been achieved on a production basis.

Jig Borers

In the area of precision locating and boring of holes the jig borer is pre-eminent.   This equipment is undoubtedly the most accurately and soundly built of all machine tools.   It produces precision work to the degree where measurements in ten-thousandths of an inch are considered routine, and operates with this precision over its entire lifetime.   Every device and every precaution that can contribute to precision is called into play in the building of a jig borer.

The term jig borer does not do justice to the capabilities of this machine tool (Fig. 17-8).   The primary function of jig borers is to produce accurate jigs, fixtures, dies, and similar work.   With the increased demand for precision in small-lot manufacturing, the jig borer should come into its own, as it can be fitted into such production programs in an altogether satisfactory manner.   Its ability to produce precision work without the necessity of using jigs has given rise to the application of the expression jig eliminator to the jig borer.

Construction Features.   The degree of precision is the same for all jig borers in the same classification.   Construction details vary although, as has been said, close attention is given to lifetime accuracy.   This ideal is achieved by designing, machining, finishing, and erecting the components with expert care.   Consideration is given to such details as temperature changes and the anticipated behavior of the constructional material over a period of time.   Thus hardened steel parts as well as castings are stabilized to prevent any change in dimensional accuracy over their lifetime.

The precision that the jig borer is capable of results from the methods used for controlling the table movement transversely and longitudinally. Vertical movement is cared for primarily by gaging tool depth although the spindle head can slide on the machined ways of the column.   The table is restricted to movement in one plane—longitudinally and transversely.

A unique means of controlling table movement on some models consists of measuring the travel entirely independently of its operating mechanisms.   Built-in measuring devices control the movement in a horizontal plane. Each slide is equipped with a "trough" wherein end measures of full inch increments are placed. The fractional inch measurements are made by means of an inside micrometer graduated to read to 0.0001 in. placed against the end measure rods. There is also a ten-thousandth dial indicator built into each slide. The indicators function as pressure gages to maintain a zero point and a constant measuring pressure. With this measuring system, the operator is not required to

Fig. 17-8. Jig borer equipped with end measures for gaging table movement. (*Courtesy of Pratt & Whitney, West Hartford, Conn.*)

develop a sense of "feel." Any slight movement of the table will be shown instantly on the dial indicators, which serve as a positive check throughout any given setting.

Two additional devices for measuring table movement are the graduated scale and the precision, or micrometer, lead screw. The graduated scale has the advantage of being free from any possibility of wear; however, when working to ten-thousandths, such extremely fine calibration lines are needed that they can only be read with an optical device. Repeated readings require undue concentration and hence fatigue on the part of the operator.

Accurately made lead screws have much to recommend them. They constitute the most rapid means for positioning, since the same device that moves the table also measures that movement. The manufacture of a precision lead screw, which is held to approximately 18 in. in length, involves many problems such as lead error and temperature change; however, the task is not insurmountable, as is evidenced by its use in jig borers (Fig. 17-9).

The Sipp jig borer, manufactured in Switzerland, uses a long lead screw equipped with cam lead error correction. The Hauser type of jig boring machine, also produced in Switzerland, operates on the co-ordinate system. Movement of table, boring head, and traverse slide are in accordance with the axis of co-ordinates, by means of high-precision micrometer screws fitted with correcting devices (Fig. 17-10).

Jig Borer Tools. Work is held rigidly while the cutting tool rotates in jig borer operation. A single-point tool is favored, since it generates a theoretically true hole, owing to its rotation about the exact center of the hole. There are a considerable number of boring heads, drill chucks, spotting tools, boring bars, boring tools, and precision end mill reamers

Fig. 17-9. Jig borer built with precision lead screw for table movement. (*Courtesy of Moore Special Tool Company, Inc., Bridgeport, Conn.*)

in a variety of styles and sizes available for tooling a jig borer. Tooling, when mounted directly in the borer spindle, is equipped with taper shanks; the spindle nose usually has a threaded end nut, or keeper, but this detail varies with different models. Solid boring tools are graded in sets according to capacity; they are made from high-speed steel or, in some cases are carbide tipped.

Accessory equipment extends the scope of jig borers. The extent to which such added expense is justified can only be determined by the job itself. Such items as tilting rotary tables, plain rotary tables, both manual and motor-driven types, and power traverse units are most common. There is much small equipment—for example, gages, precision angle plates, parallel bars, indicators, and proving bars—that completes the tooling requirements.

Fig. 17-10. Swiss-built precision jig boring machines. (Courtesy of Henri Hauser, Ltd., Bienne, Switzerland.)

DEEP-HOLE BORING

When holes whose length is greater than 20 diameters are to be bored, a nonrotating boring bar equipped with a pilot is generally used in an operation termed deep-hole boring. In some instances this method is

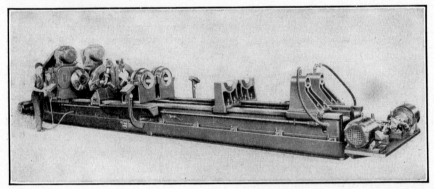

Fig. 17-11. Deep-hole boring machine. (Courtesy of W. F. and John Barnes Co., Rockford, Ill.)

employed on holes as shallow as 10 diameters. Regardless of the choice, deep-hole boring is of special interest on long production runs where the operation is integrated with the production program.

The deep-hole boring machines are designed for horizontal (Fig. 17-11) or for vertical operation. The tooling is designed to permit the flow of coolant to wash the chips through the hollow tool shank. The tool is fed by means of a whip support in which the tool is clamped. The cutting is done by any one of a number of designs, including such items as single or two-lipped deep-hole drills, pack bits, multi-lipped hollow core drills, and multi-fluted reamers.

Survey Questions

17-1. How does boring differ from drilling in metal?

17-2. When a vertical boring mill is specified, how is its size stated?

17-3. Name the operations that can be done on a vertical boring and turning mill.

17-4. Where are inclined, vertical boring mills used to advantage?

17-5. In what design types are horizontal boring, milling, and drilling machines available?

17-6. Of these types, which one is smallest?

17-7. What class of work is machined on the planer type?

17-8. How does a boring bar function?

17-9. Are boring bars accessory equipment or integral parts?

17-10. Of what material are boring bars usually made?

17-11. Describe fly cutters.

17-12. Is precision boring a production method?

17-13. Give an example of diamond boring.

17-14. For what type of machining are jig borers designed?

17-15. Need any precautions be observed when installing jig borers?

17-16. What is the chief characteristic of any jig borer?

17-17. Name some accessory equipment for jig borers.

17-18. In deep-hole boring, does the boring bar rotate?

17-19. When is a boring operation considered to be of the deep-hole type?

17-20. Is the tooling for deep-hole boring the same as for precision boring?

REFERENCES

Colvin, Fred H., and Frank A. Stanley: "Turning and Boring Practice," 3d ed., McGraw-Hill Book Company, Inc., New York, 1948.

Donaldson, Cyril, and George H. LeCain: "Tool Design," Harper & Brothers, New York, 1943.

"Handbook for Horizontal Boring, Drilling and Milling Machines," Giddings & Lewis Machine Tool Co., Fond du Lac, Wis., 1947.

Moore, J. Robert: "Precision Hole Location," The Moore Special Tool Co., Bridgeport, Conn., 1946.

"Tool Engineers' Handbook," McGraw-Hill Book Company, Inc., New York, 1949.

Turner, William P., and Halsey F. Owen: "Machine-tool Work," 2d ed., McGraw-Hill Book Company, Inc., New York, 1945.

CHAPTER 18

PLANING, SHAPING, AND SLOTTING

Basically, the machine tools used in planing, shaping, and slotting function to produce a flat surface or a modification thereof. The work-piece moves in a horizontal plane in a reciprocating motion under the tool in a planer; this movement is reversed in the case of the shaper and the slotter. A simple analogy is that of a carpenter using a hand plane on a piece of wood to bring it to dimension or to smoothness or both.

Metal Planers

The metal planer consists of a bed, a table, a housing, and crossrail components; these are found in several arrangements, and it is the

Fig. 18-1. Double housing planer equipped with two rail heads and two sideheads. (*Courtesy of Hamilton-Thomas Corp., Hamilton, Ohio.*)

arrangement that gives each type its name. The double-housing planer is the best known and most widely used type (Fig. 18-1). All planers, regardless of type or operating mechanism, feature a table reciprocating on the bedways. The workpiece is mounted rigidly on the bed in order to prevent any movement from tool cutting action. The planer tool is carried in a head mounted on the crossrail that permits lateral or vertical travel. The arrangement of heads is varied, several heads being installed both on crossrail and columns on large-size planers, as shown in Fig. 18-1.

Capacity. The double-housing planer can only machine workpieces within certain limits of width, height, and length. The restriction on width is governed by the clearance between the two housings; the maximum height is held to the vertical distance between the table and the crossrail when the latter is elevated to its upper limit; the length that can be planed is governed by maximum table travel. The limiting, or capacity, dimensions are stated in inches for width and height and feet for length and are always given in that order. A planer specified as a 48 by 36 by 12 size will accommodate a workpiece 48 in. wide, 36 in. in height, and 12 ft in length.

Openside Planers. Planers having a single vertical column are termed openside planers. Since but one housing is used, the workpiece can extend beyond the table width. Extension may be so great as to require an auxiliary support in the form of a track to carry the overhung workpiece. Openside planers offer greater versatility because of the increased range of work that can be machined.

Crossrail construction on openside planers requires special attention inasmuch as there is no support offered to the outboard end. There is a design known as the convertible openside planer in which a second housing can be placed if desired. This design offers the advantages of a double-housing and an openside planer in a single machine tool.

The direct motor drive employs a reversing electric motor. The table is driven by means of a gear rack fastened to its underside, resulting in dependable, trouble-free operation. The rack is driven by a gear train connecting with the motor. Spur-gear and helical types are found in current designs as well as a worm-drive type.

Hydraulic drives on planers follow in general the principle used on other machine tools (Fig. 18-2). A constant-speed motor drives a pump that circulates oil through the hydraulic system. The table is connected to a piston rod, which in turn connects to the piston located in the main drive cylinder. Advantages claimed for this equipment include such items as great flexibility in cutting speed and simplicity resulting from the elimination of gear trains. The hydraulic pump unit is connected directly to the electric motor in a combined unit that is self-contained and located independently of the planer.

Heads located on the crossrail are sometimes of right- and left-hand pattern in order that they may work close to each other. Heads are mounted on saddles similar to those on boring mills where swivel action is provided for angular cuts.

Workpiece Mounting. It is a wise precaution to give close attention to mounting the workpiece, or pieces, on the planer bed. Above all, the workpiece should be clamped only where solid support is afforded; straining the workpiece by clamp bolts should be avoided. One method of

Fig. 18-2. Hydraulically driven and controlled openside planer. (*Courtesy of Rockford Machine Tool Co., Rockford, Ill.*)

checking the clamping effectiveness is to place tissue paper or cellophane between workpiece and table; if at any point the paper can be pulled free, there is no support for the workpiece at that point.

Uneven surfaces are supported by inserting wedges or shims between them and the table. Clamping should then be done directly over the shims or immediately adjacent to them. Frequently one face of the workpiece is rough planed and then turned over for the planing of the opposite side. When opposite faces are rough-planed before finishing cuts are taken, the danger of warpage on finish planing is largely overcome.

Planer Applications.   Planers are chosen for machining flat surfaces on a wide range of work.   A listing of typical planer work would include such components as machinery bases, rolling-mill frames and housings, printing-press machinery, steam- and drop-hammer parts, textile machinery, machine tool members such as beds, slides, carriage and tables.   A planer is rarely regarded as a mass-production tool; rather it fits into industries of the toolroom and job-shop type.   It does offer the possi-

Fig. 18-3.   Contour-machining turbine buckets on a hydraulic planer equipped with duplicator, at the Allis-Chalmers Mfg. Co., Milwaukee.

bility of machining many duplicate parts with a single setup by stringing them on the table.   They are suited to such jobs as T slots, V ways, angular surfaces, and horizontal slotting.   Planer tables are ideal for mounting work-holding fixtures and chucks for small or odd-shaped workpieces.

Accessory Equipment.   There is a wealth of accessory equipment available for adapting planers to specialized work.   These include such appurtenances as radius planing and duplicating devices.   An example of a tracer installation for planing contours is shown in Fig. 18-3.   It can be seen that complicated shapes rarely associated with the general concept of planer work are possible when suitable accessory tooling is engineered for a given job requirement.

Planer Tools.   The planer employs the single-point tool principle of metal removal.   A planer tool can have many modifications in shape, size, construction, arrangement, and material; the selection for a given application is based upon requirements for that job. Planer tools are either forged in their entirety from high-speed steel or they are built up using a medium carbon steel shank welded to a short piece of high-speed steel. Another method, and one of considerable prominence, is that of tipping a medium carbon steel shank with high-speed steel, cemented carbide, or cast alloys.

MILLING PLANER

The evolutionary trend in machine tool design is evidenced by the development of the milling planer (Fig. 18-4). Basically this machine is

Fig. 18-4. Heavy-duty double-housing milling planer 66 in. by 66 in. by 20 ft. (*Courtesy of The G. A. Gray Co., Cincinnati.*)

a planer equipped with milling, drilling, and boring heads. The advantage of this equipment is that planing, milling, drilling and boring operations can be accommodated with a single setup. The milling heads are powered by their own individual motors; this adds versatility to the milling planer, which is built in either double-housing or openside styles.

Shapers

A shaper is a machine tool that provides a reciprocating movement of the cutting tool over the workpiece. At the same time the workpiece is moved across the tool path to give the requisite feed. In shaper operation the tool travels in the same horizontal path for each stroke. In consequence the contour of the resulting machined surface is governed by the path of that surface. The tool is mounted so that it can be fed vertically or be given angularity by manual means.

By far the greater part of shaper work is confined to machining flat surfaces or modifications thereof. The tool cuts on the pushing or outward stroke as it travels across the work; there is one design in which this action is reversed. Shapers are designated by their maximum stroke; thus a 24-in. shaper refers to one capable of machining a surface 24 in. in the direction of tool travel. Shapers range in size from the bench models with 6-in. stroke to the large industrial types with a 36-in. stroke. The stroke length can be adjusted from the minimum up to the capacity of the shaper.

HORIZONTAL SHAPERS

Among shaper installations horizontal types are in the majority. They are capable of a great range of machining operations on both external and

Fig. 18-5. Horizontal plain-table heavy-duty crank shaper. (*Courtesy of Hamilton-Thomas Corp., Hamilton, Ohio.*)

internal surfaces. A shaper is constructed with a housing containing the operating mechanisms and a ram that travels in ways at the top of the housing (Fig. 18-5), together with a driving motor and a crossrail carrying the table on the front to the housing.

The operating end of the ram carries the toolhead, which is equipped with swivel mounting carrying graduations permitting the tool slide to be set for angular cuts.   A clapper box is fitted to the lower end of the slide and it, in turn, carries the tool post.

The clapper box pivots at its upper end to permit tool freedom on the reverse stroke.   For the most part the tool drags lightly on the workpiece during this part of the stroke, although there are some designs in which the tool is raised and held free of the surface on return by mechanical or hydraulic means.   The tooling is similar to that of planer types, but smaller, and tool bits in holders are much more common than are solid forged tools.

The ram is reciprocated with a quick return motion that imparts a noticeably greater speed to the return stroke than it does to the cutting stroke.   This is achieved, on the mechanical types, by the basic principle of a crank and pin arrangement that, for the most part, is derived from the Whitworth quick-return motion.   Hydraulic drives are built on a different principle but achieve the same result.

The table can be traversed by a manual crank for setup or hand feed of an individual nature.   However, when performing conventional operations, the table traverse, which actually feeds the workpiece, is driven mechanically.   The drive is arranged so that the table can be traversed in either direction by a control lever.   In addition, many designs are equipped with a rapid traverse.

It is the type of table mounting and support that identifies the shaper as either plain or universal.   Those of the latter type are usually equipped with tables having two working surfaces, one of which is solid for planing flat and angular work, while the other has a tilting surface useful for combination and compound angle work.   In addition, the worktable can be rotated about its axis with graduations provided for accurate settings.

Operating Drives.   Mechanical details differ to the extent that some makers employ helical gearing whereas others provide spur-gear trains. Some modification of a sliding-gear transmission is employed, either singly or in combination, with a double main gear, to develop the ram speed range, which may offer as many as sixteen speeds.   The speed range varies with different makes and models; by way of example, one design offers 12 to 200 strokes per minute.

A hydraulic shaper is designed on the principle of the hydraulic system of power transmission, (Fig. 18-6).   The main ram drive and also the table traverse are operated hydraulically and mechanically.   The latter, as in mechanical types, has rapid traverse both horizontally and vertically.   Hydraulic ram operation results in a constant cutting speed throughout the stroke, and the range of strokes per min is infinite within the limits of the machine.   The hydraulic cylinder is located below and parallel to the ram to which it is directly connected resulting in a design whereby the power stroke is approximately on a straight line with the tool cutting point.

Shaper Accessories. Workpiece mounting governs the extent to which the conventional shaper can be employed for contouring and other specialized operations. There is a trend toward placing accessory equipment on the shaper itself for contouring by tracer attachments (Fig. 18-7). A work-holding fixture is used to give the workpiece proper positioning under the cutting tool. There are an infinite number of fixtures and accessories for shapers. Automatic power down-feed, auxiliary front

Fig. 18-6. Plain horizontal-type hydraulic shaper. (*Courtesy of Rockford Machine Tool Co., Rockford, Ill.*)

cross-feeds, indexing centers, profilers, circular feeding heads, table front hand feeds, and an array of vices are available for shaper application.

Draw-cut Shapers. All the shaper designs presented in this section have been of the push-cut type, wherein the tool cuts on its forward or outward stroke. That principle is basic and is the method favored by the great majority of shaper manufacturers. The draw-cut principle of shaping metal reverses the above procedure in the sense that cutting is performed on the inward or return stroke (Fig. 18-8). The advantages of this design are its capacity for taking extremely heavy cuts without fear of deflection and chatter. The ram is equipped with an overarm support throughout its travel, which, coupled with adequate table support, offers the necessary rigidity for heavy cutting.

Fig. 18-7. Plain horizontal shaper equipped with automatic contouring device.   Feeds are controlled by a hydraulic follower.   (*Courtesy of The Cincinnati Shaper Co., Cincinnati.*)

Fig. 18-8. Heavy-duty draw-cut die-block shaper. (*Courtesy of Morton Mfg. Co., Muskegon Heights, Mich.*)

Construction details, especially insofar as ram movement is concerned, differ noticeably from those of the conventional horizontal shaper. Rigid construction capable of taking care of heavy cuts is evident in this design. The workpieces are generally die blocks of steels that are not readily machinable; however, the "pull-cut" action causes the forces at work to be directed toward the main frame, thereby eliminating any danger of deflection with resultant tool dig and chatter.

VERTICAL SHAPERS

This classification may be open to question, since in many instances vertical shapers are also termed slotters—and with good reason, because

Fig. 18-9. Hydraulic vertical shaper machining internal ratchet teeth in a crane ladle control gear. (Courtesy of Rockford Machine Tool Co., Rockford, Ill.)

the latter expression is descriptive of their general application. In the main, vertical shapers are larger and more elaborate machine tools than are their counterparts of the horizontal type. Vertical shapers have a horizontal table; in some designs this is rotated by power while in others the table is stationary. The ram moves in a vertical plane with the familiar reciprocating motion. The operating details of ram drive and table movements (Fig. 18-9) are basically those of the horizontal shaper. Some designs feature adjustable forward inclination of the ram as a means of machining angular surfaces. This is especially useful for machining die clearances.

The table on vertical shapers can be moved both longitudinally and transversely with respect to the tool. The stroke is adjustable, the usual range being 6 to 36 in.; longer strokes can be had in large machines.

Operating design details of vertical shapers are divided between

Fig. 18-10.   18-in. crank-type slotter with Whitworth quick-return ram movement.   (Courtesy of Consolidated Machine Tool Corp., Rochester, N.Y.)

mechanical (Fig. 18-9) and hydraulic types. There is nothing unusual about either of these, since they both have been presented previously and both principles have proved themselves under shop conditions.

Applications of the Vertical Shaper. Vertical shapers are large, substantially built machine tools whose primary application is that of planing surfaces such as splines, ratchets, slots, keyways, and pads.

The vertical shaper is suited to machining large workpieces, since they can be placed on the table to advantage without the necessity of undue fastening and bracing or the fear of bending which would be present if the mounting were made on conventional horizontal shapers. They are

Fig. 19-1. Peripheral milling using slab and forming cutters as a gang setup. (Courtesy of Barber-Colman Co., Rockford, Ill.)

Fig. 19-2. Face milling armature plates with a 12-in. carbide-tipped cutter on a 24-in. circular milling fixture designed to hold two different sizes of these plates. (Courtesy of Cincinnati Milling and Grinding Machines, Inc., Cincinnati.)

the latter is parallel to the cutter axis is a modification of face milling.

In these two methods surface generation is different, owing to the type of contact rotation between the cutter and the workpiece and, predominantly, the manner of chip formation. Surface appearance is distinctive, since cutter behavior is not the same for both methods; however, in both methods the major portion of the chip load is carried by the circumferential teeth.

Surface Generation

There are two distinct possibilities in peripheral milling insofar as cutter action on the workpiece is concerned. The action that is most

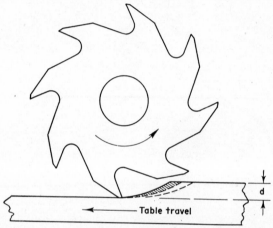

Fig. 19-3. Up milling—path generated by a plain milling cutter tooth. Note shape of chip.

used is variously designated; such terms as conventional, out-cut, and up milling, and feeding against the cutter are used. The other method, which is the reverse of this one, is termed down, climb, or in-cut milling, or feeding with the cutter.

Up Milling. This represents the practice of feeding the workpiece against the cutter in such a manner that the chip varies in thickness from a minimum at the point of contact to a maximum at tooth exit (Fig. 19-3). The tendency is to push the work along the table in a direction away from the cutter. Surface finish, in up milling, is a function of cutter speed and keenness coupled with choice of feed as well as cutter material and coolant; it is not primarily dependent on milling principle. However, the forces exerted by the cutter against the workpiece and the table tend to keep the lost motion in the milling machine feed screw and nut in a direction away from the cutter, a condition that promotes a smooth cut.

Down Milling. When down milling—the reverse of up milling—is used, the action of the cutter is that of starting the chip with maximum thickness and finishing with a minimum one. The rotation of the cutter is in the direction of workpiece travel (Fig. 19-4). One result of down milling is that the finished surface will bear evidence of tool revolution; similarly, coarse feeds in up milling will also cause tool revolution marks. The frequency and spacing of these marks are a function of cutter rotative

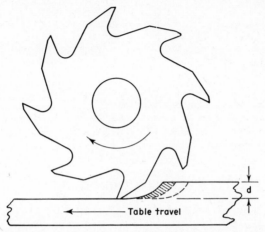

Fig. 19-4.   Down milling—path generated by a plain milling cutter tooth.   Note shape of chip.

speed and workpiece feed. It is contended that the degree of surface finish obtainable with this principle rivals that obtainable by up milling.

Down milling should never be attempted with a milling machine that has not been expressly built for this technique. The action of the cutter against the workpiece and table tends to pull them under the cutter, because of lost motion in the feed screw. Failure to take this precaution will certainly result in broken cutters, scrapped workpieces, or sprung arbors—or all three. A proper machine for down milling must be equipped with a compensating nut that will eliminate lost motion in the table screw where mechanical feed is used; some designs employ a hydraulic table feed.

Down milling is used to advantage where thin workpieces are to be milled, since the cutting action tends to keep such parts firmly seated in the work-holding device.

Face Milling. A face-milled surface is generated by the peripheral cutting edges of the face-milling cutter teeth. The distinction between peripheral and face milling cutters is shown in Fig. 19-5A and 5B. A face-milled surface has a pleasing appearance characterized by an arc-like pattern resulting from the feed. Nonuniformity of surface will result from failure to keep all cutting edges in the same plane.

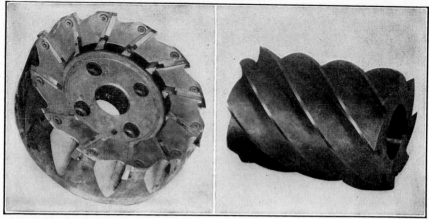

Fig. 19-5A. Face milling cutter of inserted-tooth type. Insert blades are tipped with carbide. (*Courtesy of Kearney & Trecker Corp., Milwaukee.*)

Fig. 19-5B. Plain milling cutter with helical teeth used for flat peripheral milling cuts.

Milling Cutters

Milling cutters are available in both standard and special types in a range that will produce every kind of contoured surface, from plain to complicated. Standard types are defined and classified in American Standard B5.3—1950.[1] For the sake of consistency, the terminology used in this section will follow this standard, which also includes dimensions covering the listed milling cutters. These dimensions are followed by the cutter manufacturers, so that a milling cutter of a given type and size can be obtained from any one of the several sources.

Classifications of Milling Cutters. There are two principal classifications, each of which has subdivisions; the two main divisions are based on relief of teeth and on method of mounting, respectively.

1. Classification based on relief of teeth
   a. Profile cutters
      All forms of cutters which are sharpened by grinding on the periphery of the teeth; the clearance, or relief, is obtained by grinding a narrow land back of the cutting edge. Shaped profile cutters are characterized by curved or irregularly shaped cutting edges.
   b. Formed cutters
      In cutters of this classification, the eccentric relief back of the cutting edge is of the same contour as the cutting edge itself. These cutters are sharpened by grinding the face of the teeth.

---

[1] American Standards Association, New York.

2. Classification based on method of mounting
  a. Arbor cutters are those with a center hole for mounting on an arbor.
  b. Shank cutters have either a tapered or a straight shank integral with the cutter.
  c. Facing cutters attach directly to the milling machine spindle end or to a stub arbor.

Among all the types of milling cutters, only face mills and end mills can be classified as to direction of rotation. The "hand" of a cutter is determined by the direction of rotation necessary to make it cut. A cutter is *right-hand* if it rotates counterclockwise and *left-hand* if it rotates clockwise, when viewed from the front end as mounted on the spindle. Cutters other than face and end mills are changed from one hand to the other by reversing their mounting on the arbor.

ARBOR-MOUNTING TYPE

Plain Milling Cutter. This cutter is a cylinder carrying teeth only on its circumferential surface. The tooth pattern is generally helical, with helix angles of 25 to 45°; when the helix angle is greater than 45° the cutter is known as a helical mill. The helical form enables each tooth to take a gradual cut, so that shock is reduced and chattering tendencies are eliminated. Plain milling cutters with straight teeth are also available.

Side Milling Cutter. In simplest terms, this is a plain milling cutter with the addition of teeth on both sides. The side teeth extend only a portion of the distance from the circumference to the center. When teeth are present on but one side, this type is termed a half-side cutter.

Straddle mills consist of two or more side cutters spaced on an arbor for the purpose of making parallel cuts, as in the case of boltheads and the like.

Interlocking cutters are similar in design to side milling ones except that they are made in a unit of two interlocking sections for the purpose of milling slots to exact width. They are maintained at a constant width by shims inserted between their inner hub faces.

Staggered-tooth Milling Cutters. Cutters of this type are of a narrow cylindrical shape and have teeth on the circumferential surface; these teeth, alternately of opposite helix angles, do the cutting. The side teeth, which extend a short distance from the circumference to the center, are for chip clearance only; they are not ground for cutting purposes.

These cutters are free-cutting and are capable of greater speeds and feeds than conventional plain types. Because of the alternate right- and left-hand helix angle of the teeth, and large undercut, these cutters operate almost without chatter. They are especially adapted to milling slots, in which depth exceeds width. The tops of the teeth are only two-thirds of the full cutter width.

Metal-slitting Saw Cutters. Another modification of plain milling cutters is the slitting saw. These saws are plain milling cutters with the sides relieved, or "dished," to afford side clearance. They are generally made in ⅜-in. maximum thickness and have more teeth for a given diameter than does a plain milling cutter. Metal-slitting saws are procurable in both side and staggered tooth patterns. Applications such as cutting off work or milling narrow slots are suited to cutters of this type.

Angle Milling Cutters. Cutters in this category are both single-angle and double-angle, with teeth on the conical surfaces. Single-angle cutters are made both with and without teeth on one flat side or both. These cutters are used for milling grooves of various kinds and also for milling the edge of a workpiece to a given angle.

Inserted-tooth Cutters. Cutters of this type are made for heavy-duty application. The body of the cutter is made of non-cutting material which can be either machined or cast. The body is slotted at its circumference for the insertion of the cutting blades. These are made from high-speed steel, cast nonferrous alloys of the Stellite type, or cemented carbides. Provision for securely anchoring and adjusting the blades is made adjacent to their slots. There are examples of inserted-tooth cutters in which the cutter body is cast around the cutter blades; such blades cannot be replaced.

The advantage of inserted-tooth cutters is that they are less expensive, since low-cost material is used for the body of the cutter (Fig. 19-5A). An additional favorable factor is the removable blade, which permits renewal or the insertion of a different contour. A single cutter body can serve indefinitely with blade renewals as the only expense.

Fly Cutters. This is a single-point tool rotated by an arbor. It is not a production tool but finds its greatest application in experimental work, since the single cutter can readily be ground to any desired shape. The potentialities of fly cutters are oftentimes overlooked. The single-blade cutter can be ground to a contour or shape and used instead of a form cutter where the latter is unavailable. Too, its single-point cutting principle can be employed for obtaining an excellently finished and precision surface.

Formed Cutters. There is a wide range of cutters in this classification, including such diverse types as gear cutters, sprocket cutters, convex cutters, concave cutters, corner-rounding cutters, thread-milling cutters, and hobbing cutters. In manufacturing intricate duplicate parts such as those for typewriters, sewing machines, ordnance, and instruments, formed cutters are prominently used. Formed cutters are generally of curved irregular outline. The contour of the tooth will remain unchanged so long as the face of a tooth is maintained in its original plane with respect to the axis of rotation. These cutters are used for duplicate interchangeable work and can be resharpened until the teeth become so slender as to be unable to withstand the forces of cutting.

Fig. 19-6. Arbor-mounting-type milling cutters.

The cutters described thus far are all of the arbor-mounting type. They are shown in Fig. 19-6, where their distinguishing features can be noted.

SHANK-MOUNTING TYPE

End Mills. These cutters are distinctive in appearance; in addition to teeth on their circumferential surface, they also have teeth on one end. The teeth may be parallel to the axis of rotation or of a helical pattern in either right- or left-hand styles. Those of moderate angle are frequently termed spiral end mills. End mills are made in five general types, known respectively as solid, shell, hollow, helical, and two-lipped, or slotting.

Solid end mills are made with toothed portion and shank (which is either tapered or straight) as an integral unit. They find application in profiling, facing narrow surfaces, spotting bosses, milling slots and keyways, and light milling operations.

Shell end mills are distinctive in that the tooth end is recessed to receive a nut- or screwhead for fastening the cutter on an arbor. The cutter is usually driven from the key slot across its back face. In tooth design these mills follow solid end mills. The chief asset of shell end mills is that their replacement cost is less because the arbor need not be renewed each time the cutting element breaks or wears out.

Hollow end mills are of tubular cross section, with teeth on one end and an internal clearance. Hollow end mills are used for milling bosses, removing cylindrical projections from solid metal, and sizing cylinder stock. Their shank, which is straight, is a continuation of the cutter body. These cutters are predominantly used for tooling automatic screw machines.

T-slot Cutters. These cutters are of the integral shank type. The cutting element has teeth on its periphery as well as both sides. Such cutters are used for machining the wide groove of a T slot. The vertical groove must be milled first in order to provide clearance for the shank of the T-slot cutter.

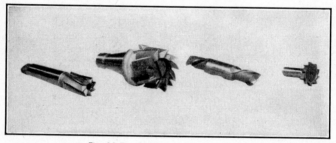

Fig. 19-7.   Shank-type milling cutters.

Woodruff Keyseat Cutter. This type of cutter has but one application—the milling of semicylindrical keyseats in shafts for seating Woodruff keys. These cutters are made in shank as well as arbor types. The former have teeth only on the circumferential surface and are made in the smaller sizes. Arbor types are a minimum of 2 in. in diameter, with staggered front teeth for cutting and side teeth for clearance.

The cutters in this last group are of the shank type for mounting directly into the spindle nose. There is a great diversity of styles and sizes in this classification; several are shown in Fig. 19-7.

Carbide Milling. The development of using carbide-tipped milling cutters is so widespread that it appears destined to cause re-evaluation of milling possibilities generally. Carbide-tipped cutters, or carbide cutters, as they are more commonly termed, won popularity in connection with wartime production requirements. There are many grades of carbides and several sources of supply, with the result that carbide cutters are being engineered to meet specific production problems.

Their chief application has been in face milling cutters, although other aspects have shown promise. The problem of shock has limited their acceptance for use on certain cutter types. Another deterrent is that many milling machines now installed are incapable of delivering the high speed and power that carbide milling demands. Milling machine designers are cognizant of carbide milling possibilities and are responding with improved models featuring rigidity in the machine, cutter mounting, and work-holding tables.

Milling Machines

The design of milling machines has advanced to the point where some models appear to have only one element, the rotating cutter, in common with the basic types. Such a diversified concept is convincing testimony of the soundness of milling as a machining method. While many modifications exist, three fundamental classifications are generally recognized: (1) column-and-knee type; (2) manufacturing, or bed type; (3) special type.

COLUMN-AND-KNEE TYPES

There is some variation in terminology in this classification, knee-and-column, knee-type, column-type, and column-and-knee type all referring to the same basic design. There are two distinct styles, horizontal and vertical (referring to spindle position). Operating details and construction are similar except for the spindle position.

Horizontal Type. Milling machines of this general classification have as their main components a column base, knee, saddle, table, overarm, drive, and feed mechanisms, together with necessary controls. The foundation of these milling machines is the main casting, which serves as the column bed. The bed is machined on its underside in order to give the entire machine a level setting. The column part of this foundation casting houses the driving mechanisms and the spindle. At its top, provision for the overarm is made and its front face is machined for attaching the knee and permitting vertical travel of the knee.

The knee is a casting that mounts normal to the column; it carries the vertical operating mechanisms, and its upper surface is machined for the saddle movement. The knee is supported and traveled by means of a telescoping, elevating screw located on its underside, away from the column.

The saddle, in its turn, is designed for cross movement normal to the column; its action is similar to that of the cross slide on a lathe. The saddle usually houses the power feed for the table.

One important feature to be noted is the distinction between plain and universal milling machines. Universal types have a swivel block mounted directly on the knee; the universal saddle mounts on the swivel block. The swivel block functions to permit angular movement of the table in a horizontal plane. The universal feature is desirable for such operations as milling helical flutes in cutting tools, cutting helical gears, and other similar work.   Plain milling machines do not have the swivel table feature; otherwise they are the same as the universal ones.

The milling machine table is mounted on the saddle in a design that permits longitudinal travel.   Together with this longitudinal travel, the cross travel of the saddle on the knee and the vertical travel of the knee on the column give the three-dimensional movement characteristic of the column-and-knee-type milling machine.   Table movement can be either manual or with power.   There is a range of power feeds, including rapid table traverse.   Table drive is usually accomplished by a screw.

Spindle.   The milling cutter is given its rotation by the spindle, which is in effect the main drive shaft for the milling cutter.   The spindle is a critical component, since to a large degree its accuracy determines the precision that can be expected from the milling machine.   Spindles are mounted in antifriction bearings and are capable of a range of speeds. Speed range is obtained through suitable gearing that is housed in the milling machine column.   Spindles must be accurately aligned with the table top.

The spindle nose is made to accommodate the arbors, cutter shanks, and chucks and to provide positive drive for them.   The nose has an inside taper.   Prior to 1927, taper was not standard with all manufacturers; that year, taper was standardized at 3.50 in./ft.   Further uniformity has been achieved through invoking American Standard B5.18—1943.[1] This should be consulted for complete information on milling machine spindle noses and keys.   There are four sizes of spindle-nose openings; however, sizes no. 40 and 50 are most used on column-and-knee milling machines.   Arbors are held in the spindle with a draw-in rod that is threaded into them.

Overarm.   The overarm is mounted and guided at or near the top of the column.   This may be either a single or a double element.   Its purpose is that of providing alignment and support for the arbor and other attachments.   It can be adjusted in its longitudinal movement and is held in position by a clamping mechanism at the top of the column. Braces can be placed on the outboard end of the overarm to give it rigid support from the knee, where the lower end of the braces attach (Fig. 19-8).

Controls.   All three of the slides, the table, saddle, and the knee are equipped with manual as well as power feeds.   The travel movement is subject to accurate control, since each slide is equipped with a micrometer dial.   Power feed is used when the milling machine is in operation; hand feed is employed for setting up the job and for positioning the travel stops.   It is important to see that stops are fastened into position prior

[1] American Standards Association, New York.

to operation, especially when rapid traverse is to be used.   Rapid traverse functions to bring the workpiece to the cutter or to return the table at the finish of an operation.   Available feeds cover a broad range, especially now that carbide milling is important.   Spindle speeds likewise offer a considerable choice.   All feeds and spindle speeds can be changed through levers and dials located conveniently for the operator.

Fig. 19-8.   Double overarm with braces on horizontal column-and-knee-type milling machine. This model has a built-in automatic table cycling design.   (*Courtesy of Kearney & Trecker Corp., Milwaukee.*)

Automatic Cycle.   Automatic cycling is used on milling machines as a means for increased production at less cost per workpiece by adjusting to an automatic repetitive cycle (Fig. 19-8).   This control is incorporated into a standard milling machine to permit individual, small lot, or production runs to be made.   It also permits calculating predetermined cycle time, thereby assuring uniform hourly production rates.   Automatic controls govern cycle operation, which can be applied both to horizontal and to vertical column-and-knee milling machines.

Typical cycling arrangements are known as plain, intermittent, and continuous cycles (Fig. 19-8A).   The automatic operation of the table movement is governed by dogs located on the table edge.   These dogs are positioned to suit the desired operation sequence.   The established cycle includes loading and unloading time as well as feed reverse and

How Job Is Done

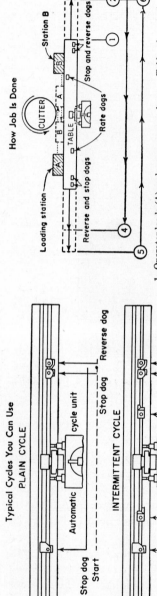

How It Works

1. Operator loads (A) and engages mono-lever. Table advances in rapid traverse to point of cut on workpiece (A) at (2).

2. Feed dog changes rapid traverse to selected table feed for cut on (A). Operator loads at station (B).

3. Upon completion of cut, stop and reverse dogs reverse table and rapid traverse to point of cut on workpiece (B).

4. Feed dog changes rapid traverse to selected table feed on (B). Operator unloads and reloads at station (A).

5. Stop and reverse dogs reverse table in rapid traverse to point of cut on workpiece (A).

6. Cycle repeats from (2).

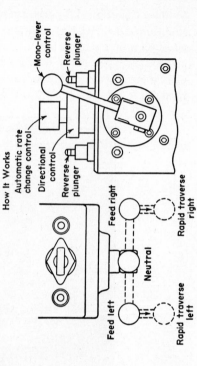

Typical Cycles You Can Use

PLAIN CYCLE

INTERMITTENT CYCLE

CONTINUOUS CYCLE

Fig. 19-8A. Typical cycle settings used for automatic-cycle milling (with automatic table cycle and mono-lever control). *(Courtesy of Kearney & Trecker Corp., Milwaukee.)*

rapid traverse. Frequently it is possible to have two identical fixtures or stations located at opposite ends of the table in an arrangement whereby one station is unloading and loading while the other station is under the cutter.

It is claimed that automatic cycling is profitable on production lots as small as ten. Savings in milling time on small lots set up for automatic cycling are substantial. It is possible to have the advantages of automatic equipment and operation without the necessity for large investments: a standard milling machine with automatic cycling accessories

Fig. 19-9. French-built column-and-knee-type milling machine featuring a unique universal head together with optical dial reading. (*Courtesy of C. Gambin & Cie, Billancourt, Seine, France.*)

covers all requirements. This dual arrangement offers possibilities of substantial cost cutting.

Other Column-and-knee-type Machines. While hand-type milling machines are not usually thought of as belonging in a production scheme, they are nevertheless of importance. There is abundant evidence that these millers do fit into production lines. Hand milling machines are of importance to the job shop because of their modest initial cost and also because of the range of work they can take care of. Any milling machine installation program would do well to include them.

The Gambin milling machine built in France employs an optical principle for reading and positioning controls accurately (Fig. 19-9).

The claim is made that an extremely high degree of precision work is produced with this type of control. It is interesting to observe that the French milling machine is very similar in appearance to American-built ones.

Vertical Milling Machines. The column-and-knee design is applied to vertical milling machines. Vertical milling machines derive their name from the spindle position, which is vertical to the table and parallel to

Fig. 19-10. Vertical milling machine, column-and-knee type, equipped with swivel head. (*Courtesy of Brown & Sharpe Mfg. Co., Providence.*)

the column. Some designs are equipped with a swivel head (Fig. 19-10). The swivel-head feature permits the spindle to be positioned at any point in a 180° arc that lies 90° each way from the vertical.

Ram-type Milling Machine. Another modification of the column-and-knee principle is embodied in the ram-type milling machine (Fig. 19-11). While this design is built in both plain and universal table types, it has two distinguishing features. First, in effect this miller combines the horizontal and vertical milling machine principles into one design, since its milling head can be positioned for horizontal, vertical, or angular milling by simple adjustment, without the addition or removal of any attachments or accessories.

The second feature is that the ram, which carries the milling head, can be moved outward or inward with respect to the table, thus bringing the milling cutter to the workpiece for greatest rigidity in setup. The table is equipped with cross and longitudinal power feeds, and the saddle assembly has vertical travel; these means afford tri-directional table movement.

Attachments and Accessories. Certain items of standard equipment, such as controls and drives, are considered part of the milling machine and are included in the original purchase price. However, arbors and some similar items are classed as extra equipment. In addition, there is a range of attachments and accessories available to the column-and-knee type of milling machine. These are available for the purpose of increasing the scope of the machine either in its adaptability or in its production capacity. Taken in their broadest sense, attachments can be grouped as (1) cutter-driving and related attachments; (2) work-holding attachments and fixtures.

Fig. 19-11. Ram-type milling machine, plain table model. (*Courtesy of Van Norman Co., Springfield, Mass.*)

Universal Milling Head. This head attaches to the front of the column so that the milling machine spindle of the horizontal type acts as the driving unit for the head. This head can be swiveled through a complete circle in a vertical plane. A horizontal miller can by this means be converted to function as a vertical one and perform angular milling as well.

Additional heads or accessories include slotting attachments that give the cutter a reciprocating motion as in a slotter. Others deserving of mention include rack milling, circular milling, cam milling, helical milling, and thread milling attachments of various designs. Some of these—the rack milling attachment, for example—are accompanied by other equipment such as indexing attachments.

Dividing Head. A dividing head is included as standard equipment with some milling machine models, but in most cases it is considered to be extra equipment. Thᴜ universal dividing head is an extremely accurate and at the same time a versatile indexing attachment. It holds mandrel-mounted workpieces between its center and a footstock center, or a chuck can be attached for holding workpieces by chucking in a horizontal, vertical, or angular plane. It has an indexing feature and can be attached to gearing for helical milling operations. The usual

Fig. 19-12. Dividing-head setup for indexing spur gear. (*Courtesy of University of Washington Machine Tool Laboratory.*)

setup is that in which the dividing head is mounted directly on the milling table, with the index plate facing outward for both mandrel and chuck work (Fig. 19-12)

The dividing head is equipped with an index plate. This plate carries a number of hole circles in a concentric pattern. Each successive circle carries a larger number of spacing holes in a pattern where, by interchanging index plates, a large index range is available. Index plates usually carry hole space circles on both sides in a supplementary arrangement; this eliminates the necessity for two separate plates.

The crank on the dividing head is turned as a means of imparting an indexed motion to the head spindle. The ratio of the dividing head depends upon its type. Formerly the ratio of 40:1 was considered standard. With that ratio, 1 complete turn of the crank indexed the work $\frac{1}{40}$ revolution. Thus if a 40-tooth gear was wanted, the crank on the dividing head would be given 1 complete turn; for an 80-tooth gear, the crank would be given $\frac{40}{80}$, or $\frac{1}{2}$ turn, whereas a 20-tooth gear would be indexed $\frac{40}{20}$, or 2 turns. Other indexing can be readily calculated and the increment obtained by setting off the calculated number of hole *spaces* on the index plate.

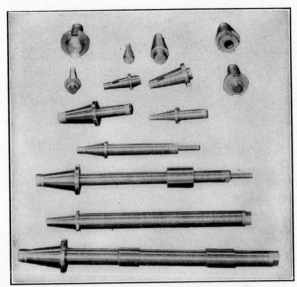

Fig. 19-13. Milling arbors and spindle accessories.

Other developments include the 5:1 ratio hypoid dividing head. On this design, 5 complete turns of the crank equal 1 complete revolution of the spindle. Index plates carrying hole circles similar to those previously described are included with the dividing head. The indexing crank is equipped with a plunger pin that serves to anchor the crank in its exact location on the index plate. Through an extension of the indexing principle on the 5:1 dividing head, it is possible to obtain 1,296,000 equal divisions in one circle.

Milling Machine Arbors. In order to get the benefit of the full possibilities of a milling machine it is necessary to equip it with a complete set of arbors. Arbors are available in several types and sizes. Three styles are regarded as basic (Fig. 19-13); they are classified as style A, B, and C, respectively, and are made in accordance with American Standard B5.9—1948.[1] A standard numbering system is applied to arbors, and

[1] American Standards Association, New York.

the following specifications are listed in sequence: taper size, diameter, style, length from shoulder to nut, and size of bearing. Thus, for example, arbor no. 41¼A 16-3 specifies an arbor of no. 40 taper, 1¼-in. diameter, style A, length from shoulder to nut 16 in., equipped with a no. 3 bearing. Arbor styles A and B are designed for use with cutters having center hole mounting. These cutters have a keyway by means of which they are keyed to the arbor. Cutter spacing or positioning, as the case may be, is by means of spacing collars. The collar-cutter assembly is held snugly by tightening the nut on the end of the arbor. A supply of collars of different widths should be maintained in order to fill out arbor spacing correctly.

The arbor-cutter assembly is held in position in the milling machine spindle by means of a draw-in rod that reaches through the spindle and screws into the tapered end of the arbor. The arbor is supported on its outboard end by a bearing in the overarm support. Style C arbors, being of the stub type, have no provision for, nor do they require, this outboard bearing support.

A small pilot end distinguishes the style A arbor, which is used for light work generally. The style B arbor, on the other hand, is of uniform diameter throughout its length and is used where less clearance is necessary and heavy milling, such as carbide milling, is performed. The stub arbor, style C, is designed for holding shell end mills and face milling cutters that are too small to be bolted directly to the spindle nose. The cutters fit the end of the arbor and are held in position by means of a screw whose head fits the cutter recess. All arbors are equipped with a keyway which makes up with a key in the spindle nose for driving the arbor-cutter assembly.

Arbors for milling machines are precision equipment. The accuracy of a milled surface depends in large measure on the truth of the arbor. Abuse and careless handling will result in poor performance. Arbors should be wiped, as should the spindle taper, prior to insertion; *the wiping must be performed when the spindle is at rest* as a safety precaution.

BED-TYPE MILLING MACHINES

Milling machines of the bed type are designed primarily for production and, for this reason, are also termed manufacturing or production millers. The versatility of the column-and-knee type is largely sacrificed in an all-out effort to gain greater milling production. This statement should not be interpreted to mean that bed-type millers are a one-part or specialized design; on the contrary they are capable of a wide range of application.

The term bed-type is derived from the fact that the bed casting is large and rugged and supports all the machine components (Fig. 19-14). In this particular design there are two columns in a parallel setting so arranged that the spindle head can be adjusted vertically between them.

The table movement is confined to longitudinal travel, which is obtained by either hydraulic or mechanical means, depending on the design. Rapid traverse as well as feed in both longitudinal directions is available. There is no three-directional table movement on bed-type millers; rather, a job is set up with the objective of repetitive operation.

Frequently a production job is tooled in a duplicate arrangement with an identical fixture in accurate alignment located at each end of the

Fig. 19-14. Bed-type milling machine, showing single-column design. (*Courtesy of The Ohio Machine Tool Co., Kenton, Ohio.*)

table. This arrangement provides for up-milling one workpiece and down-milling the other in a continuing operation cycle. A substantial saving in time is realized, since loading and unloading can be done while milling is proceeding at the opposite station.

Duplex Milling Machines. There are several modifications of the basic bed-type design. One of these is termed a duplex miller because it has two heads, facing each other yet served by a common table (Fig. 19-15). This construction permits two separate or identical milling operations to proceed concurrently, although each one is driven independently.

Duplex milling machines are particularly adaptable to milling parallel surfaces on the opposite sides of workpieces, as illustrated by the cylinder head casting in Fig. 19-15. On this and similar work where carbide face milling cutters are utilized, high production rates can be expected.

Tracer-controlled Bed-type Milling Machines. There are several variations of automatic and semiautomatic bed-type designs. Tracer-controlled cycles arranged for automatic control of the cutter and spindle position with respect to the table and workpiece are, in effect, adaptations of similar principles used on lathes. Their chief utility is in connection with milling curved surfaces and those of irregular contour. Templates

Fig. 19-15. Duplex milling machine face milling two sides of a cylinder head casting. (*Courtesy of Cincinnati Milling and Grinding Machines Co., Cincinnati.*)

are employed as a means of guiding the tracer in its path over the workpiece.

Hydraulic controls have been introduced on some tracer-type millers as a means of reducing physical effort on the part of the operator. Power feeds on these machines are also served by hydraulic means. The combination of mechanical and hydraulic movements is noteworthy as a recent design trend. Aircraft work requiring radii, contours, and curved surfaces is a fruitful field of application, as are some types of forming and drawing dies.

SPECIAL MILLING MACHINES

Planer-type Milling Machines. There is some question about including planer-type mills under the classification of special milling machines.

This doubt stems from the fact that planer types have established themselves rather clearly as an individual classification. They are built in two-column styles and openside models as well as in a number of variations of these concepts. The similarity to the planer, insofar as appearance is concerned, is clear from Fig. 19-16. The planer-type miller shown is equipped with two sideheads in addition to a railhead, each of which is individually motor-driven. The cutter-head assemblies can be positioned to suit the requirements of the workpiece. Further, the cutter head on the rail can be given either vertical or cross-feed travel.

Fig. 19-16. Double-housing planer-type heavy-duty milling machine equipped with four milling heads. Workpiece capacity, 84 in. by 84 in. by 18 ft. (*Courtesy of Consolidated Machine Tool Corp., Rochester, N.Y.*)

Feed, rapid traverse, and return are obtained from variable-speed hydraulic motors connected to feed screws. The milling cutter spindles are equipped with endwise micrometer adjustment. When electric limit switches are incorporated into the control of the movement of the different units, a semiautomatic cycle for production milling of a wide variety of work can be established. Planer-type millers, termed rail-type by some makers, are built to accommodate modern high-speed carbide milling cutters and, when thus tooled, deliver outstanding production records.

Milling machines of this type are especially well adapted to a wide variety of milling operations on large iron and steel castings, weldments, and machinery components. Work-holding fixtures can play an important part in increasing both the flexibility and the production possibilities of the planer type of milling machine.

Drum-type Milling Machines. Milling machines fitting this classification are primarily designed for machining individual workpieces. The design is a striking departure from that of the usual milling machine, where the workpiece is placed on a horizontal table. Here a table rotating in a vertical plane is fitted between two upright housings in an arrangement whereby several milling spindles are employed in a design in which machining operations on either one or both sides of the workpiece are possible (Fig. 19-17).

Fig. 19-17. Drum-type milling machine for continuous milling top and bottom of motor block castings. This milling machine weighs approximately 62,000 lb. (*Courtesy of Davis and Thompson Co., Milwaukee.*)

In the example shown there are two face mills operating simultaneously on the same side of the casting. One of these is taking the roughing cut, while the other is making the finish cut. All operations are continuous, so that the production loss normally encountered in loading and unloading workpieces on standard-type machines is eliminated. Cutter location is such that the roughing cut is completed on a workpiece prior to the start of the finishing cut thereon.

While the job setup shown in Fig. 19-17 is that of facing both the top and the bottom of a motor block casting, there are many other components suited to this general type of face milling. Among these are

such items as automotive cylinder heads, transmission cases, and flywheel housings, in addition to miscellaneous machine members which
require parallel milling of opposite faces.

Vertical Rotary Continuous Milling Machine. This type of miller is
used throughout the automotive, tractor, and agricultural machinery
industries. The table rotation can be either continuous of or intermittent feed or traverse. The last arrangement is generally made when
workpieces are widely spaced on the table so that the air gap between

Fig. 19-18. Crankshaft turn mill setup for machining six-cylinder automotive crankshaft. (*Courtesy
of Gisholt Machine Co., Madison, Wis.*)

them can be automatically traversed at the same time. The machine is
usually built with one rough-milling and one finish-milling spindle. The
vertical spindle head is adjustable on the upright and each spindle is also
adjustable. Spindle drive is through pick-off gears in order that spindles
can be given independent speeds.

Crankshaft Turn Milling Machines. A unique development in specialized milling machine equipment is that of turn milling crankshaft bearing
surfaces. In this design, milling cutters are employed for turning the
crank throws and milling the cheeks in a simultaneous operation. The
crankshaft turn miller is adapted to machining crankshafts used in
automobiles and trucks (Fig. 19-18). Essentially it is designed for high

production of one size of crankshaft over long runs. For machining a six-throw crankshaft, six milling spindles, each carrying a single cutter, are used. Each cutter is 24 in. in diameter and is driven by a 20-hp motor.

The operating cycle, which is fully automatic, is started by placing the crankshaft in the machine, where it is locked into position hydraulically. Two upper and two lower slides feed to a preset depth; at the same time the two front horizontal slides move into position and then feed to their

Fig. 19-19. Pratt & Whitney-Keller three-spindle duplicator, milling an aluminum-alloy core box, using the center spindle. (*Courtesy of University of Washington Machine Tool Laboratory.*)

preset depth. The crankshaft then rotates slowly 360° on its own centers. The milling cutters follow the crankpins around their orbits, milling the pins and adjacent cheeks in a simultaneous operation. At the completion of one revolution of the crankshaft, all slides return rapidly to the starting position and the cutters stop. The machine is then ready for the unload, reload operation. Six throws of a typical automotive crankshaft can be machined ready for grinding in 2.0 min, floor-to-floor time.

Tracer Milling Machines. There are several different models of tracer milling machines, in respect both to operating characteristics and to design principles. Irrespective of these variations, basically tracer milling technique is that of controlling and guiding the cutting tool across the work by means of a tracer or feeler. The tracer element moves in contact with the surface or contour of a master as it controls the cutter in its movement (Fig. 19-19). The master may be a model, a pattern, or a template. In Fig. 19-19 a wooden core box is being used as the master. However, it is common practice to mold the master of plaster because of the facility with which this can be achieved. Where considerable production is desired, a metal master is employed on account of its greater

Fig. 19-20.   Vertical single-spindle profiling machine.   (Courtesy of University of Washington Machine Tool Laboratory.

durability. Plastics are also used for masters where conditions dictate their use.

Tracer milling is prominent for contour machining and the machining of complicated parts. Formerly this technique was confined primarily to die making and kindred work; it remains important in that field especially on auto body and other dies. However, stepped-up aircraft manufacture offers many opportunities for tracer milling. There are numerous aircraft components that can best be machined on this equipment. In order to meet production requirements, tracer milling machines are built in multispindle types. The miller in Fig. 19-19 is capable of milling three identical workpieces simultaneously from one master.

The tracer millers described thus far have horizontal spindles and in consequence are termed horizontal types. There are also examples of vertical spindle designs in both single- and multispindle models. Manually operated vertical tracer milling, or, as they are sometimes called, profiling machines are considerably less complicated in construction (Fig. 19-20).

The profiler shown has a single vertical spindle driven by V belts. A template is followed by means of a tracer that is mounted adjacent to the spindle. The workpiece is mounted on the horizontal table, which is in turn moved longitudinally. The spindle head is traversed on the crossrail by means of a separate handwheel. All movement is made manually on this profiler—there are no automatic controls or power feeds. Machining is performed by end-mill-type cutters; a single cutter is used in the single-spindle machine. Two-spindle machines of the identical type are also available.

Rotary-head Milling Machines. These millers are derived from the vertical column-and-knee type of milling machine. They can mill

Fig. 19-21. Vertical rotary-head milling machine profiling a vertical surface. (*Courtesy of Kearney & Trecker Corp., Milwaukee.*)

intricate shapes without the use of models or templates (Fig. 19-21). The construction is such that the spindle can be offset from the center of the head. This device, coupled with the use of a rotating table, enables the machine to mill any geometrical shape. These machines are provided with power feed and are capable of production milling.

Survey Questions

19-1. Does a milling machine use a single-point cutting tool?
19-2. Where are milling machine installations most common?
19-3. Classify milling as to types.
19-4. Into what two categories is peripheral milling divided?
19-5. Give some applications for down milling.
19-6. Are milling cutters standardized as to types?
19-7. On what class of work are formed cutters used?
19-8. How many surfaces can a side milling cutter machine simultaneously?

19-9. Mention several types of milling cutters that are arbor-mounted.

19-10. Can end mills be arbor-mounted?

19-11. Wherein do T-slot cutters differ from end mills?

19-12. Do inserted tooth cutters offer any unique advantages?

19-13. Explain carbide milling.

19-14. On what distinctive lines are milling machines designed?

19-15. Column-and-knee-type milling machines are either of the plain or universal types. What features distinguish them?

19-16. How does the overarm function?

19-17. Are vertical milling machines equipped with an overarm?

19-18. To what feature does rapid traverse apply?

19-19. Why is cycle milling of importance?

19-20. Do any milling-machine designs include a universal head?

19-21. Where can ram-type milling machines be used to advantage?

19-22. When is a dividing head necessary?

19-23. Are all dividing heads designed for 40 : 1 ratio?

19-24. What are index plates used for?

19-25. To what standard do milling machine arbors conform?

19-26. Are these arbors regarded as precision equipment?

19-27. Should bed-type millers be considered as tool-room equipment?

19-28. Mention machining requirements suited to duplex milling machines.

19-29. Is tracer equipment ever used with standard-type milling machines?

19-30. Suggest some applications for planer-type milling machines.

19-31. Are drum-type milling machines flexible in their application?

19-32. Can crankshafts be machined on milling equipment?

19-33. On what class of work is tracer-type equipment of greatest interest?

19-34. What are Keller duplicators?

19-35. Do profilers differ from Keller duplicators?

19-36. Are models or templates always necessary for milling intricate shapes?

19-37. How are automobile body dies usually machined?

19-38. What type of aircraft parts are machined on duplicators?

REFERENCES

Colvin, Fred H., and Frank A. Stanley: "Drilling and Surfacing Practice," 3d ed., McGraw-Hill Book Company, Inc., New York, 1948.

Ernst, Hans: "Milling Machine Practice," Cincinnati Milling Machine Company, Cincinnati, 1942.

Jones, Franklin D.: "Machine Shop Training Course," 3d ed., Vol. II, The Industrial Press, New York, 1944.

"Milling Machines, Planers and Shapers," Technical Manual, TM 1-421, War Department, Washington, D.C., 1942.

"Milling Practice Series," Books One and Two, Kearney & Trecker Corp., Milwaukee, 1942, 1945.

"Practical Treatise on Milling and Milling Machines," Brown & Sharpe Manufacturing Co., Providence, 1947.

"Tool Engineers' Handbook," McGraw-Hill Book Company, Inc., New York, 1949.

"A Treatise on Milling and Milling Machines," 3d ed., Sections One and Two, Cincinnati Milling Machine Co., Cincinnati, 1945.

CHAPTER 20

BROACHING

Broaching, as a machining method, has several characteristic features that distinguish it as to both fundamental operation and equipment. It is unique in that roughing, finishing, and, in some applications, burnishing are performed by a single broaching tool in one operation. In broaching more than in any other machining method the tool rather than the machine controls production rate and quality. This statement should not be interpreted to mean that broaching machines serve only incidentally; rather, it is intended to focus attention on the fact that any consideration given to a possible broaching application must start with the broaching tool.

The term broach is applied both to the broaching tool and to the broaching machine. In this chapter the term broach will be used consistently to identify the broaching tool, whereas "broaching machine" will refer to the machine in which the broach is operated.

Metal removal is accomplished by a broach designed with a series of multiple teeth, or cutting edges, positioned in tandem, in an arrangement whereby each successive tooth is slightly higher than its predecessor and, therefore, each tooth takes a cut. The amount of metal removal is a function of the tooth depth and the number of teeth in the broach. It can be understood from this that broaching is in effect a generating process. The shape of the broached surface, the feed, and the cutting speed are dependent on broach design. The broaching machine may impose limitations such as power availability and length of stroke; however, these are secondary considerations and can be disregarded where production runs are concerned. Correct machine selection is always critical under such circumstances.

Broaching was originally conceived of as a method for machining internal surfaces, and in this field it retains its preeminence. Further extension of the broaching method has lead to the inclusion of surface broaching, for which the largest broaches are used. Broaching has, by custom, been divided into internal and surface types, each one having modifications suitable for given requirements.

Broaching is primarily a production process in the sense that a broach is made for a given job and is not, except in rare cases, adaptable to a range of applications. This situation is different from milling, where general cutters such as plain mills, for example, can be used on a variety of workpieces requiring flat surface machining. There can be no denying the fact that broaching offers serious competition to milling in those areas where it can be applied. Swidlo states that cost of manufacture of the Garand semiautomatic M-1 rifle decreased by 57 per cent when broaching was substituted for milling.[1] Equally interesting results are reported in automotive, agricultural, and home appliance manufacture. Broaching has its limitations, especially in connection with size of workpiece.

Broaches

A broach is a precision metal-cutting tool. It can perform a complete machining job, from roughing to finish, because it is a combination of the several types of tools usually needed for such a machining sequence. There are literally a multitude of broach designs, since their adoption is increasing with the wider knowledge of the broaching method. Two representative broach designs, one of the pull and the other of the push type, are shown and the various sections of the broach are detailed in Fig. 20-1. The front pilot serves to align and steer the broach squarely as a means of guaranteeing correct positioning in the workpiece. The roughing teeth perform the function of major metal removal. Since they take rather deep cuts, it is common practice to nick these teeth in order to achieve a discontinuous chip. The nicking follows a staggered pattern to prevent any uncut surface remaining.

Semifinishing teeth take a shallower cut than do the roughing ones, while the finishing teeth serve to bring the broached surface to dimension. The rear pilot acts to keep the broach square with the hole as it passes out of the workpiece. On some broaches, burnishing buttons serve the dual function of burnishing and guiding.

A broach has a chip removal problem that is unique among metal-cutting tools. There is no opportunity for the removal of chips when they are formed, as there is in the case of single-point tools and milling cutters. Each broach tooth must accommodate its own chip and carry that chip through to the completion of the cut. It is only after the tooth leaves the workpiece that the chip can clear the broach tooth. This imposes limitations on broach design, since sufficient space must be provided for a chip pocket. The pitch of the broach teeth, their depth, shape, and length of land, all must conform to a pattern that will result

[1] Swidlo, I. A.: Broaching vs. Milling, *The Iron Age*, Dec. 7, 14, 21, 28, 1944, and Jan. 11, 1945.

in allowing sufficient chip space and proper cutting action. The chip spiral is also affected by the thickness of the material cut.

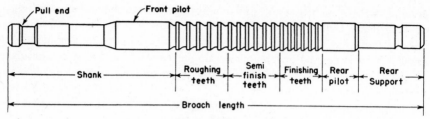

PULL TYPE INTERNAL BROACH

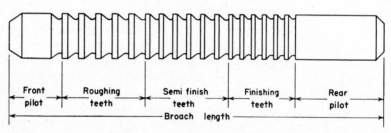

PUSH TYPE INTERNAL BROACH

Fig. 20-1.   Pull-type internal broach.   Push-type internal broach.   (*From "Metal Cutting Tool Handbook," Metal Cutting Tool Institute, New York, 1949.*)

The terminology applied to an individual broach tooth includes many expressions common to other metal-cutting tools (Fig. 20-2). The tooth radius requires attention when resharpening, lest compound and discontinuous curves result that will interfere with correct chip formation.

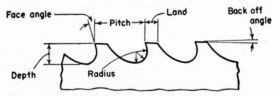

Fig. 20-2.   Typical broach tooth form.   (*From "Broaches and Broaching," The Broaching Tool Institute, New York.*)

Pitch of the broach is extremely critical, since broach strength depends largely on this factor. Pitch also determines the number of teeth that will be cutting metal at a given instant. The nature of the material being broached governs the pitch, as do length of cut and chip thickness. Since cast-iron chips crumble and do not spiral as do steel ones, cast iron requires less chip space; therefore, finer pitch can be used on the broach in the case of cast iron than in the case of steel. The usual recommendation calls for a minimum of two teeth being in engagement in the cut; a greater number is preferable for both broach alignment and elimination of chatter. It is sometimes desirable to use differential spacing in a pattern as a means of eliminating vibration during cutting; in this practice the same pitch is used for a group of teeth, followed by a different pitch for the succeeding group.

The teeth on a broach are not always normal to the broach axis; this is especially true of surface broaching, where the principle of shear cutting is used. Shear cuts give a better surface finish and eliminate vibration, since several teeth are engaged simultaneously. Shear angles are generally in the range of 5 to 20°. Disposal of chips on shear cuts poses the problem of the chips crowding to one edge, thereby causing roughening at that surface.

The depth of cut per tooth depends on several factors. When the cut is too great, broach strain, and even failure, is likely to result; a cut that is too shallow is also undesirable, since rubbing rather than cutting action will result. The material being broached plays the largest part in determining the depth of cut. The cut per tooth in free-cutting steel, ranges around 0.0015 in.; for splines the diameter is around 0.006 in.; depth of cut on round broaches is about 0.003 in.

These values are greatly exceeded in the jump-broach design. This development is aimed toward cutting beneath the scale of a cored or forged hole. Broach teeth of the same diameter occur in pairs. The first tooth is splined and therefore takes out half of the metal of the circumference. The following tooth, which is of the same diameter, but solid, cuts the remainder of the circle. Such broaches have a normal step, or increase, in tooth diameter from one pair to the next of 0.030 in. The steps are lessened materially at the sizing section. These broaches are much shorter than those of standard length because of the substantial cuts made by the double jump teeth.

Speed of broaching varies with different materials and different jobs. A general rule is to broach workpieces at a rate between 12 and 24 fpm, while small jobs are cut at 30 ft or more. The capacity of the broaching machine is a determinant, since it limits the possible speed.

Broach Construction. Internal broaches are usually of one-piece construction regardless of their contour or length. They are made of high-speed steel almost without exception, although carbide tipping is used on some applications, especially for finishing teeth. Making a broach is a costly procedure, since its accuracy must be consistently maintained. There is always the possibility of difficulty in machining or in heat-treating, a difficulty that increases with broach length and contour. This problem is solved in some instances by using shell construction, similar in principle to that of shell end mills (Fig. 20-3).

Surface broaches are either solid or built-up, depending primarily on their size and type. Large surface broaches are invariably of the built-up type, with the teeth made in sections and mounted in a holder. When several cuts are to be made simultaneously with the same broach, it is not uncommon to mount teeth in subholders, which in turn are mounted in a main holder. The advantage of sectional broaches is obvious, since any tooth breakage can be repaired by removing the affected section without scrapping the entire broach. Examples of built-up surface broaches and broach sections are given in Fig. 20-4. Section broaches are an extremely convenient design where contour changes are wanted because the transition can be built into sections that are more conveniently machined than are long, cumbersome solid broaches.

Fig. 20-3. Shell broach. (*Courtesy of Colonial Broach Co., Detroit.*)

Broach Sharpening. A sharp broach, like any metal-cutting tool, will deliver the sort of production that is expected of it. A dull broach will not produce to dimension and will require excessive amounts of power for its operation.

Only enough metal should be ground from a tooth to bring that tooth to the required degree of sharpness. Each tooth should be considered as an individual grinding job. There are broaches where the step per tooth is critical and the exact amount of metal must be ground from each tooth.

Broach Shanks. When a broach is used, it is pulled or pushed through the workpiece in the case of internal broaching. Surface, or external, broaching is performed in a similar manner; however, there are some examples where the broach is held stationary and the workpiece is moved past the broach while it is in contact with the surface to be machined.

Pull broaches operate either as a pull-up or a pull-down type. In the former, the broach is pulled upward, through or past the workpiece, which is held below the broaching machine platen. The pull-up, pull-down distinction does not apply to horizontal broaching for obvious reasons. The broach must connect with the broaching machine ram in order that the pulling effort can be accomplished.

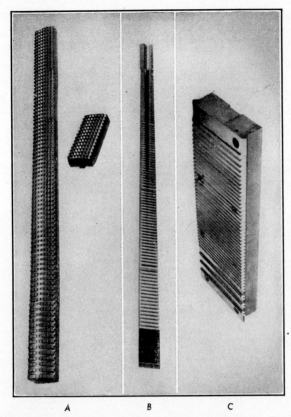

Fig. 20-4. A, broach for internal involute teeth, built of six replaceable sections. B, five-section generating-type broach used to machine a convex surface. C, flat broach. (*Courtesy of Colonial Broach Company, Detroit.*)

Broaching Machines

Basically a broaching machine is of simple construction and operation, since its only function is that of exerting sufficient force to move the broach. As broaching increases in importance in the machining field, refinements and automatic cycling, indexing, rapid traverse, and other functions are being incorporated in the design of the machine to the point where it is difficult to recognize the basic machine as a simple one.

Broaching machines are built in two principal types, termed horizontal and vertical, respectively. Each of these has many modifications; the principal one is that of having more than one ram. Rams are driven either hydraulically or mechanically; those machines known as screw-type broaching machines employ the latter method. Design trends are in the direction of hydraulic operation as production requirements become more imposing.

Horizontal-type Broaching Machines. Broaching machines of the horizontal type are built with the broach operating in a horizontal plane (Fig. 20-5). They are regarded as the most universal of all types because of the diversity of work they can handle. On internal broaching, the operator of the broaching machine generally needs to pass the pilot end of the broach through the workpiece and make connection with the pull-head. Horizontal machines are also adapted to surface broaching. There are applications such as automotive cylinder heads where the broach is connected permanently to the ram for surface broaching.

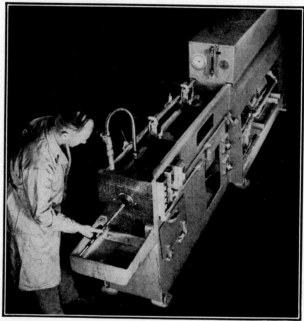

Fig. 20-5. Horizontal broaching machine tooled for internal broaching. (*Courtesy of The Lapointe Machine Tool Co., Hudson, Mass.*)

While this application is that of producing a flat surface, external broaching in horizontal machines is also applied on contours. Horizontal broaching machines are built in a wide range of sizes and with a wide range of operating characteristics that include automatic cycling, indexing, and helical broaching. Where broaches are of some length, intermediate supports such as crossheads are provided to preserve alignment.

Vertical-type Broaching Machines. As the name indicates, the broaches are operated in a vertical plane in these machines, which means less floor space than horizontal installations. On production work, vertical broaching machines invariably carry two broaches which can be operated in several sequences, such as pull-up and pull-down or parallel operation in one cycle (Fig. 20-6). In addition, automatic broach handling is featured, which relieves the operator of the task of manually threading the broach through the workpiece. A further advantage of the vertical design is the ease with which fixtures can be placed on the table.

Vertical broaching machines are built in three general styles, known respectively as pull-up, pull-down, and push-down types. The pull-up concept was first used in broaching. It is especially effective for internal broaching where no relationship needs to be maintained with an external surface. The workpiece is held beneath the table and the broach is pulled upward through it.

Pull-down styles were a development following the pull-up type. The workpiece is placed above the table and the broach is pulled down through it. Automatic broach and ram connections coupled with rapid ram reverse stroke combine to give these machines high production capabilities.

Push-type broaching machines are designed in several styles. One type is built for pushing internal broaches; in another instance the ram is designed for surface broaching. There is a distinction in appearance between these types, since in the latter the ram operates against the machine column in suitable guides for proper alignment and requisite stiffness to prevent broach buckling. There

Fig. 20-6. Vertical broaching machine equipped with two broaches. (*Courtesy of American Broach and Machine Co., Ann Arbor, Mich.*)

are vertical broaching machines that offer a universal pattern of push as well as pull types.

Specialized Broaching Machines. Special broaching machines are of such a diversity of types that it is impossible to give due credit here to all of them. Suffice it to say that there is nothing static about this trend, nor has a plateau been reached. New concepts are continually being brought to broaching machine design, as exemplified by Fig. 20-7. This broaching machine employs a rotary principle which is a distinct departure from the idea of translation that is universal with broaching. Broaching machine design innovations include multiple-spindle horizontal types, cylinder line broaching, helical broaching, horizontal multiple with indexing, and chip conveyor types, to mention a few.

Broaching Fixtures. Following the selection of a broach, tooling the operation is the next consideration. Broaching fixtures are designed to hold the workpiece during the machining operation. The usual considerations regarding loading and unloading the workpiece need to be studied. It is here that the ingenuity of the tool engineer is given full scope. Fixtures must be able to align work with the broach for correct

Fig. 20-7. Double-end rotary broaching machine of special design. (*Courtesy of Colonial Broach Co., Detroit.*)

cut. Such a requirement poses a difficult problem in cases where rough castings or forgings must be held in alignment. One method of solving this problem is by designing a compensating fixture capable of equalizing the holding position.

After alignment problems are solved, attention should be given to fixture design from the viewpoint of operating ease. Loading and unloading times are critical in broaching as in other machining operations. In consequence, fixture design is pointed in this direction. An example of a tip-down fixture on a double-ram machine is shown in Fig. 20-8. A design of this nature greatly facilitates loading and unloading operations. Clamping devices, while largely of toggle design, include mechanical as well as pneumatic and hydraulic principles. Whatever system is followed, it is always necessary to secure a solid mounting of the workpiece in order to avoid slippage or shifting.

Indexing broaching fixtures play a prominent part in tooling for production. An especially fine example of this design is its application to stacking (Fig. 20-9). The workpieces shown are metal stampings of automotive window-operating mechanisms. Production possibilities

Fig. 20-8. Tip-down-style broaching fixture. *(Courtesy of The Lapointe Machine Tool Co., Hudson, Mass.)*

Fig. 20-9. Indexing fixture for window gear mechanism. Note provision for coolant supply. *(Courtesy of The Lapointe Machine Tool Co., Hudson, Mass.)*

are high and machining cost is low, since these parts are geared segments that would be difficult to machine by conventional methods.

Broaching fixtures are not confined to workpiece holding; there are situations in which they also act as broach guides or supports. This is achieved either directly by the fixture itself or by employing accessories such as the horn which is common in such operations as spline broaching. The spline broach is rectangular in cross section and as a result requires support in the bore of the workpiece. A horn is inserted in the workpiece both to guide and to support the broach. The horn design is deserving of more than passing consideration. If it is not of sufficient length, the broach may tend to deflect at its juncture with the workpiece, resulting in erratic dimensions and, possibly, broach damage. The horn should extend beyond the workpiece in both directions to ensure correct broach cutting action.

The demands on broaching fixtures for horizontal broaching are similar to those for vertical broaching. If a distinction is to be made in broaching fixtures it should be between internal and external types. This is

Fig. 20-10. Horizontal broach serrating a steering bracket. Note broached part shown resting on broaching fixture. (*Courtesy of National Broach and Machine Co., Detroit.*)

readily understandable, since in internal broaching the bore serves as a guide and positioning member and there is no necessity for additional appurtenances.

Horizontal external broaching is for the most part associated with heavy work involving a combination of large broaches and substantial machine equipment (Fig. 20-10). A survey of automotive-parts machining procedures gives evidence of considerable interest in this type of broaching application. The methods vary with different shops; yet motor block castings have been broached both top and bottom, as have their attachment pads and other finished surfaces. Indications are that further substantial progress in this direction can be anticipated.

Case Studies of Broaching

There have been repeated references in this chapter to individual broaching applications. However, broaching accomplishments are so widespread that they touch on virtually all machining requirements short of cylindrical turning. Because of the breadth of broaching applications, it is an impossibility to do justice to all of them. However, this chapter should not be concluded without calling attention to the broaching applications wherein two or more complementary broaching operations perform the necessary machining. In the example shown in Fig. 20-11

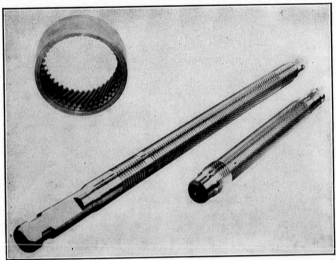

Fig. 20-11. Roughing and finishing broaches for machining internal helical gear teeth. (*Courtesy of National Broach and Machine Co., Detroit.*)

the necessary production is obtained from four broaching machines that replace the total of twenty-one machine tools of various types formerly needed. The teeth of the helical overdrive ring gear are completely machined in two broach passes to a tolerance of 0.0002 in. on all tooth characteristics.

Another application of multiple broaching is shown in Fig. 20-12. The part is produced in an automatic screw machine, yet the added requirement of splines must be met. This is accomplished by three broaching operations, as shown. Formerly there were holes drilled and the remaining metal was removed by two broaching operations. Substitution of a third broaching operation for the drilling has resulted in an over-all production increase of more than 80 per cent, due primarily to the elimination of index drilling.

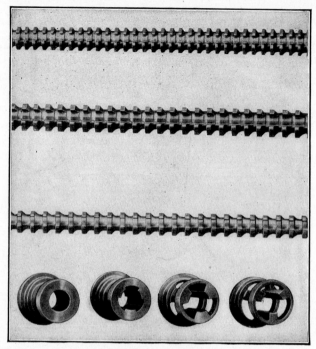

Fig. 20-12. Roughing and finishing internal spline broaches. Workpiece is shown before and after each operation. (*Courtesy of National Broach and Machine Co., Detroit.*)

Survey Questions

20-1. In broaching, does the tool or the machine generally determine the production rate?

20-2. A single broaching operation is capable of what different machining operations?

20-3. Does the term "broach" refer to the tool as well as the machine?

20-4. How is the amount of metal removed by a broach governed?

20-5. Is broaching confined to internal surfaces?

20-6. Can broaching be considered as a general-purpose machining operation?

20-7. With what machining method does broaching compete?

20-8. Distinguish between a pull- and a push-type broach.

20-9. How does a broach clear the chips it produces?

20-10. For what type of work is a jump broach best suited?

20-11. In what units is broaching speed measured?

20-12. Of what materials are broaches made?

20-13. Do shell broaches offer any unique advantages?

20-14. Are there sectional broach designs other than shell types?

20-15. What precautions are necessary when sharpening a broach?

20-16. Basically what designs do broaching machines follow?

20-17. Vertical broaching follows what two methods?

20-18. State some advantages for broaching fixtures.

20-19. When should tip-down fixtures be used?

20-20. Is it possible to broach stacked parts?

20-21. Can gears be cut by broaching?

20-22. Give some examples of flat broached surfaces.

20-23. What are spline broaches?

20-24. Wherein does rotary broaching differ from the usual procedure?

REFERENCES

Burden, W. Wilson: "Broaches and Broaching," Broaching Tool Institute, New York, 1944.

"Metal Cutting Tool Handbook," Metal Cutting Tool Institute, New York, 1949.

"Tool Engineers' Handbook," McGraw-Hill Book Company, Inc., New York, 1949.

CHAPTER 21

DRILLING

Drilling a hole is an operation in which an end cutting tool, termed a drill, is rotated about its major axis as it is fed into the workpiece (Fig. 21-1). An exception to this general statement is the case of impact, or star drills, as they are generally termed. The latter are not used on metal; their field of application includes concrete, stone, brick, and

Fig. 21-1. Drilling operation using a twist drill. Note that drill flutes provide for chip escape and also serve as coolant carriers. (*Courtesy of The American Tool Works Co., Cincinnati.*)

similar materials. A combination of the two procedures alluded to above is applied to flat drills and star drills in jackhammers, where the drill is given some rotation while it is under impact. An innovation in drilling is that of holding the drill stationary and causing the workpiece to rotate, as in some screw-machine and turret-lathe tooling.

Drills are for the most part of the twist type, although flat drills are of importance in certain classes of drilling. There are some specialized types of drills which have been developed to take care of individual requirements. Classification of drills is based on details such as method of manufacture, material, shape, length, design (helix or flute), shank type, point characteristics, and, above all, size (diameter).

Twist Drills

Twist drills are composed of point, body, neck, and shank, all included in a solid tool. The most widely used type of drills, viz. straight- and taper-shank twist drills, are covered by American Standard B5.12—1949, entitled "Twist Drills—Straight Shank and Taper Shank."[1] The terminology used in that standard is followed in this chapter (Fig. 21-2).

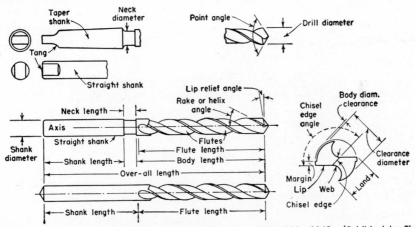

Fig. 21-2. Standard twist drill terms. Proposed revision ASA B5.12—1949. (Published by The American Society of Mechanical Engineers, New York.)

This nomenclature pertains to conventional twist drills primarily; there are many types of specialized drills, and there are innovations present on most of them. By way of example, the flute helix can be either right- or left-hand, thereby establishing the direction of rotation for the drill. A left-hand twist drill must be rotated clockwise—the direction of rotation is determined by viewing the drill from its point while its axis is along the line of sight.

The history of drilling tools indicates that early drills were flat, or rectangular in cross section. The edges of the flat were generally convex by an amount fitting to the hole diameter. The cutting end of the drill was pointed, like that of currently used twist drills. The other end of the drill was forged or turned down to a round shank that fitted into the drilling machine spindle or chuck where it was fastened.

[1] American Society of Mechanical Engineers, New York.

Flat drills were further improved by twisting them about their major axis. This construction resulted in improved drilling, since it aided in guiding the drill in the hole and provided a means for chip escape and rake angle that was not present in the flat drill design. The manufacture of twist drills by this method has largely been abandoned in favor of forming the flutes by machining them from solid stock. This operation is performed by a method that in its general principles is similar to the cutting of a helical gear. In two-fluted twist drills, the fluting is usually a single operation, the two flutes being cut concurrently. Machine tools are specially designed for this purpose, with basic features differing in that some are vertical and others are of the horizontal type of operation. Twist drills are made from high-speed steel as well as carbon steel. Production drilling is largely done with high-speed or carbide-tipped drills. There are twist drills with 0° helix angles; these are known as straight fluted drills and find application for drilling copper alloys and sheet stock.

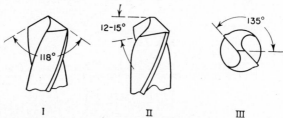

Fig. 21-3. Drill point angles. I, conventional drill point; II, angle of lip clearance with workpiece face; III, angle of lip clearance with chisel edge.

Helix Angles. Twist drills are available in a range of helix angles. Since the function of the flutes is that of forming proper cutting edges, chip curling, chip removal, and coolant carrier, it is obvious that the nature of the metal being drilled will be the determinant of the helix angle. Conventional twist drills have helix angles of approximately 24°. When drilling materials where chip formation is voluminous owing to high penetration rates, helix angles should be increased. Drilling the softer types of aluminum alloys is best accomplished with twist drills having 48° helix angles. The classification known as high-helix drills include those twist drills whose helix angles range upward from 30°. There is also a series termed low-helix drills using helix angles ranging downward from the conventional 24° angle. Drills in this category are mainly those used for drilling plastics and others used for copper-base alloys. In addition to variations in helix angles, these drills have further modifications such as changes in web thickness, polished flutes, and other innovations designed to aid their performance.

Drill Points. The performance of a twist drill is dependent on the treatment accorded to its point. This takes precedence over all other considerations. Helix angles were given prior mention only because they are built into the drill; they are not subject to change, whereas drill-point angles can be ground to suit the use for which they are intended.   There are three different angles that require consideration in connection with a properly ground, or "pointed," drill, viz., point angle, lip relief, and chisel edge (Fig. 21-3).   Recommended values for these angles are not fixed; however, Table 21-1 indicates accepted practice in this regard. Twist drills when received from the manufacturer generally conform to the specifications given in the first line of the table.

TABLE 21-1*

Types of drilling	Reference—Fig. 21-3		
	I	II	III
General shop usage............	118	12–15	125–135
Gray cast iron................	90–118	12–15	125–135
White cast iron...............	118–135	5–7	115–125
Mild steel—wrought or cast....	118	12–15	125–135
Alloy steel...................	125–135	6–10	115–125
Aluminum alloys..............	118–130	12	125–135
Magnesium alloys.............	118 max.	12–15	120–145
Copper alloys................	115–130	10–15	115–125
Plastics—molded.............	70–95	12–15	125–135

* Compiled from manufacturers' and material suppliers' data.

Improperly pointed drills will not produce acceptable work.   A dull drill will cause trouble by burning the drill point, with the result that either the drill will be ruined or an inordinate amount of grinding will be necessary to resharpen it.   A high degree of skill is required to sharpen a drill properly by offhand grinding.   It is a far better procedure to employ a suitable drill-grinding machine (Fig. 21-4) for this purpose, since this equipment will produce a correct drill point.   In the drill-grinding machine shown, the grinding wheel rotates, reciprocates, and oscillates in a unique path while in contact with the drill point, which rotates about its own axis.   An example of a drill point ground in this machine is shown in Fig. 21-5.   There are other designs of drill-grinding machines; one of these operates on the principle of manually swinging the drill in its holder across the grinding wheel.

Essentials of Drill Sharpening.   While it is true that correctly sharpened drills are obtained from drill-grinding machines, it seems desirable to detail the essentials necessary to a properly functioning drill.   The three characteristics shown in Fig. 21-3 must be understood in their respective relation to drilling results.

a. Lip clearance. If there is no lip clearance, the drill will not cut because it cannot penetrate. It is not merely ground on the circumference of the drill; it covers the entire surface back from the point. The *heel* of the drill, which is the surface back of the cutting lip, should be ground away at an angle, as indicated in column II of Table 21-1. This

Fig. 21-4. Drill grinding operation. Note sparks from drill point and position of the drill. (*Courtesy of University of Washington Machine Tool Laboratory.*)

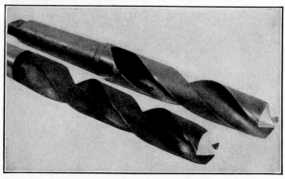

Fig. 21-5. Correctly ground drill points. Note especially the upper point (ground in the operation shown in the preceding figure), with its thinned web.

angle is in all cases the one measured at the circumference of the drill. The angle of the lip clearance should be gradually increased, however, as the center of the drill is approached until the line across the chisel edge of the drill gives the values shown in column III.

Faulty lip clearance angles are the cause of much drilling difficulty. If the angle of lip clearance is too great, the edges of the cutting lips will fail because of a lack of support when they enter the workpiece. A too shallow angle will prevent proper cutting action.

b. Length of lip. It is necessary that the lips of a drill be of identical length. Should one be longer than the other, they will not remove equal amounts of metal. Such a condition frequently leads to drill breakage. Another fault resulting from unequal lip lengths is that an oversize hole will be drilled. Too much emphasis cannot be placed on the subject of properly ground drill points.

The web of a twist drill increases in thickness in a direction away from the drill point. In order to secure the desired drill-point angles after repeated resharpening, it is necessary to thin the web by grinding. Twist drills decrease in diameter from the point to the shank in a variable amount of from 0.0005 to 0.00075 in. per inch of length. This affords relief from the drill binding in the hole.

Rates for Drilling. The "speed" of a drill refers to its peripheral speed and is measured in feet per min. The term speed should not be confused with rotational speed, which is measured, in revolutions per min. More faulty work results from driving drills too slow than from driving them too fast; this applies especially to small drill sizes.

It is sound procedure to inaugurate a drilling operation by combining high speed and low feed. Feed rates are governed by drill size and are stated in thousandths per revolution. A very general rule to follow in this regard is a feed of 0.001 to 0.002 in. for drills under $\frac{1}{8}$ in.; 0.002 to 0.004 in. for $\frac{1}{8}$ to $\frac{1}{4}$ in.; 0.004 to 0.007 in. for $\frac{1}{4}$ to $\frac{1}{2}$ in.; 0.007 to 0.015 in. for $\frac{1}{2}$ to 1 in.; and 0.015 to 0.025 in. for drill sizes greater than 1 in. The drill should be started with a light feed and care must be exercised in lightening the feed at the time the drill breaks through, especially when drilling sheet stock or working on curved surfaces.

DRILL TYPES AND DESIGNATIONS

Reference has been made to the fact that drills are available in a broad range of types and styles. Among these, the two-fluted, or two-lipped, twist drills are regarded as conventional. So far as sizes are concerned, classification is designated as follows:

Numerical—No. 80 to No. 1 (0.0135 to 0.228 in.)
Alphabetical—Letters A to Z (0.234 to 0.413 in.)
Fractional—$\frac{1}{64}$ to 4 in. and over by 64ths.

This listing refers to standard stock sizes; these include metric sizes, which are considered standard. There are other sizes to be had by special order.

Shank Styles. A drill is held in the drill chuck or spindle by means of its shank, which provides the driving effort. Shanks are either straight or tapered, the former applying to small- and the latter to larger-diameter drills as a general rule. There are also squared taper shanks such as those found on wood bits; a modification of this design is termed the ratchet shank (Fig. 21-6).

Taper shanks are of different sizes, following the Morse taper system. These drills fit directly into the drilling machine spindle which is equipped with a Morse taper hole. The range is from no. 1 for ⅛-in. taper-shank drills to no. 6 for drills of 3½-in. diameter. Placing a drill in the machine spindle offers no problem so long as the shank size is equal to or smaller than the spindle hole. In the event that the taper shank is smaller than the spindle, it can be brought to size by using drill sleeves. Sleeves are graduated by taper sizes so that they nest in a perfect fit. They are separated by inserting a key, or drift, that acts as a pry against the tang.

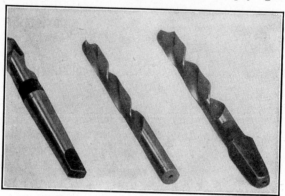

Fig. 21-6. Shank styles common to twist drills.

The advantages of taper-shank drills are their freedom from slippage when in use and the fact that they rotate in truth unless injured by abuse. Straight-shank drills require the use of a drill chuck for a driver. Drill chucks are equipped with a taper shank for spindle fit. Chucks are self-centering on the drill and are operated either manually or with a key. A drill should always be firmly held in the chuck; if slippage occurs, the shank will be fouled and will run out of truth.

Special Drill Types. In addition to the conventional drill types there are a host of special ones designed to fit local applications. In this category such items as three- and four-fluted core drills, oil-groove drills, oil-hole drills, multi-cut drills, step drills, hard-steel drills, threaded-shank aircraft drills, and crankshaft drills are included. Drills are also classified as short length, taper length, jobbers' length, automotive series, and long length.

RELATED TOOLS

Reamers. A reamer is a rotating cutting tool, generally of cylindrical or cornical shape, that is used for enlarging or finishing an existing hole.

A reamer is designated by its nominal size or diameter; its length is measured parallel to its axis.

Reamer nomenclature and specifications are stated in ASA standard B5.14—1941. There is a vast number of reamer types both in conventional and in special categories. One series of reamers is of the shell type which has its counterpart in milling cutters.

A finishing reamer is expected to remove a very small amount of metal. Reaming is, in effect, a sizing, or scraping, operation. Hand reamers

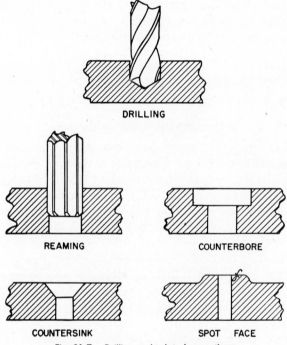

DRILLING

REAMING   COUNTERBORE

COUNTERSINK   SPOT   FACE

Fig. 21-7.   Drilling and related operations.

should not be expected to remove more than 0.002 to 0.003 in. of stock on the diameter. Machine reamers, on the other hand, can take care of greater amounts. In no case should stock removal exceed 0.012 in.; removal of from 0.003 to 0.005 in. is preferable.

Counterbores. A counterbore is a tool designed to enlarge a previously formed hole for a part of its depth and at the same time to produce a shoulder at the bottom of the enlarged portion (Fig. 21-7). The counterbore tool is frequently equipped with a pilot that fits the base hole diameter, where it acts to ensure concentricity with the original hole; however, there are counterbores that do not have this aligning feature.   There are step counterbores that produce more than one diameter in a single operation.

Countersinks.   Tools in this classification fall somewhere between drills and counterbores.   Countersinks are employed to produce a taper in an existing hole (Fig. 21-7).   A hole is countersunk to accommodate a fastener head such as a screw, rivet, or the like.   Countersinks used for woodscrews have an included angle of 82°, while machine screws are 60, 82, or 90°.   Another series that is used for ships plates, boilers, and tanks have 37, 45, 53, or 78° included angles.

Spot Facers.   A further operation related to drilling is termed spot facing.   Spot-facing tools are modified counterbores.   The difference between them is that spot facing is applied to the face or top of a machine boss that generally has a hole normal to its surface.   Spot facing produces a finished surface that acts as a seat for bolt- or screwheads or for mountings.   The spot-facing tool, commonly termed spot facer, takes several forms, but in every case it is an end cutting tool.

Upright Drilling Machines

The familiar term "drill press" has, technically, passed from drilling-machine terminology.   The more accurate expression "drilling machine" has been substituted to describe the category which includes the single-spindle general purpose machine tool.   The more important ones are the sensitive type, the bench type, and the floor type.   Each of these has some design modifications made by the different manufacturers of drilling machines.

Sensitive Drilling Machine.   Drilling machines of this type are small, high-speed ones intended for driving letter-size and other small drills.   These drilling machines are virtually indispensable to such operations as those of the tool and die shop, the template shop, and the instrument shop and laboratory.

Bench-type Drilling Machine.   The drilling machines in this classification are for the most part small editions of the column floor types.   Their name is descriptive, since they are intended for mounting on a bench or table.   They are usually equipped with a V-belt drive employing a stepped pulley for spindle speed variation.   Hand feed is common on the usual design since these machines are generally limited to driving drills up to $\frac{1}{2}$ in. in diameter.   Bench-type drilling machines are popular in all branches of manufacturing, in addition to being prominent in hobby and home workshops.

Floor-type Drilling Machines.   In this group is found the familiar column drilling machine.   The two principal types in this classification are the round-column and the box-type upright.   These designs differ in both column as well as table treatment.   They are both specified as to size by the distance from the center of the spindle to the face of the column.

Round-column Type. This drilling machine has great adaptability. The driving head is mounted at the top of the column. The drilling round table is clamped to the column in a manner that permits its vertical movement as well as its being swung about the column (Fig. 21-8). This table can also be rotated about its center for convenience in bringing mounted workpieces under drill.

The round table can be swung clear in order that large workpieces can be placed on the floor plate. This feature contributes in a major way to the adaptability of the round-column upright drilling machine. The spindle carries a Morse taper for direct insertion of taper-shank drills or for drill chucks. There are several spindle speeds obtainable from the change gearbox that receives its power from a directly connected motor. Both hand and power feeds can be employed, the choice depending on the particular job.

Box-column Upright. These drilling machines are built with a box-type column that enables them to handle heavier drilling operations. The front of the column has machined ways for adjusting the drilling head vertically. A second set of ways serve as table guides. The table is of the compound type permitting movement

Fig. 21-8. 21-in. all geared upright round-column drilling machine. (*Courtesy of The Cincinnati Bickford Tool Co., Cincinnati.*)

in both directions in the horizontal plane. Table movement can be measured on dials which are graduated to read in thousandths of an inch; this makes possible accurate workpiece alignment.

Upright Gang Drilling Machines. There are operations adapted to a single table served by several individual spindles. Machines that handle such operations are in effect a series of box-column drillers connected to a single table (Fig. 21-9). A variety of arrangements are possible, although four or six spindle types predominate. The individual spindles can be set up for different speeds in order to accommodate varying requirements of a workpiece that can be passed from one drilling operation to another.

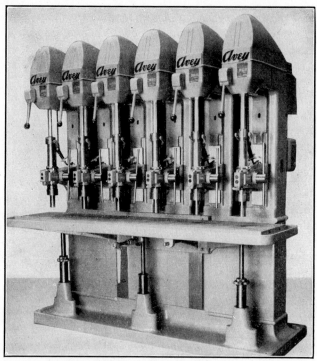

Fig. 21-9.   Six-spindle upright gang drill equipped with multi-strand V-belt drive.   (*Courtesy of The Avey Drilling Machine Co., Cincinnati.*)

RADIAL DRILLING MACHINES

There is a distinctive classification of upright drilling machines known as radial drills.   They derive their name from the design whereby an arm, carrying the drilling head, is constructed to permit it to be swung in a complete circle about its upright column.   Radial drilling machines have a working capacity that is capable of more substantial operations than those associated with the conventional type of upright drilling machine.   They are designed and built to accommodate drilling, boring, reaming, tapping, spot facing, and related operations.

The radial drilling machine is simple in construction, since it consists of a base, a vertical column, and an arm carrying the drilling head.   The head traverses on the radial arm either by power rapid traverse or by manual movement.   The head carries the drill spindle; the lower end of the spindle is equipped with a Morse female taper whose size, depending on the machine capacity, usually ranges between no. 4 and no. 6. There is a range of spindle speeds provided that can be readily engaged by means of conveniently located controls. Feeds are likewise obtainable in a wide choice by suitable controls; however, manual feed is also available when desired. The machine spindle moves in a vertical plane on most designs; these are termed plain-type radials. In universal and semi-universal radials, the spindle can be rotated to angular positions with the radial arm.

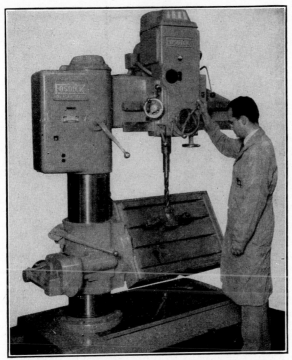

Fig. 21-10. Radial drilling machine equipped with column-mounted swivel table. (*Courtesy of The Fosdick Machine Tool Co., Cincinnati.*)

The workpiece is fastened to the base of the radial drilling machine where the piece to be drilled is too large for table mounting. However a separate table, in a variety of designs, can also be had where smaller workpieces are being machined (Fig. 21-10). Such tables are generally built of swiveling construction and carry graduations for exact positioning. Not all manufacturers use the same design; in some machines this table mounts on the bed rather than on the column.

Traveling Radial Drilling Machines. The utility of a radial drill can be expanded by altering its design so that the column, with its accompanying radial arm and head, can be traversed along a longitudinal bed table (Fig. 21-11). This feature is sometimes modified to the point where power is applied for the traversing movement in a design known as the truck type. In this type a truck or tractor carrying the column and radial arm travels on rails, whereas in the conventional traversing type the movement is along the machine bed. The job setup shown is

Fig. 21-11. Traversing-type radial drilling machine tooled for machining Diesel-engine blocks mounted in a swinging fixture. (*Courtesy of The American Tool Works Co., Cincinnati.*)

indicative of the machining possibilities possessed by this design when accompanied by versatile fixtures.

Production-type Drilling Machines

Undoubtedly the most diversified line of machine tools is found among production-type drilling machines. This term has been used to cover an extremely wide field; in consequence, some doubt can be expressed as to its appropriateness. Irrespective of the choice of terms, the development of machines for performing drilling and related operations is continuing at a rate that indicates further startling innovations can be expected.

MULTIPLE-SPINDLE DRILLING MACHINES

Multiple-spindle drilling machines afford a means of drilling a number of holes simultaneously (Fig. 21-12). The number of spindles is fixed in some designs; in others, spindles can be added to the capacity of the machine. Construction and operating details are different among the various manufacturers of these machine tools. Multiple-spindle designs are most common in vertical styles; however, the same principle has been adapted to horizontal drilling machines.

Fig. 21-12. Vertical multiple-spindle drilling machine. Thirty $\frac{1}{4}$-in. drills in the front row and thirty-one $\frac{1}{4}$-in. drills in rear, all spaced on 1-in. center distance. Production time 0.29 min per piece. (Courtesy of Baker Brothers, Inc., Toledo, Ohio.)

SPECIALIZED HEAVY-DUTY DRILLING MACHINES

Machine tools fitting into this classification are of highly specialized designs. They are a distinct departure from the all-purpose drilling machine, since they are built for maximum production on a given workpiece. Instead of an abbreviated survey of a field that is replete with spectacular accomplishments, summaries of a few representative cases chosen at random are offered here.

CASE STUDIES OF SPECIALIZED DRILLING MACHINES

Case I. The series of operations performed on a crankshaft in the two-way horizontal machine with auxiliary units and trunnion-type fixture (Fig. 21-13), are the following:

	Left-hand side	*Right-hand side*
Station 1	load and	Unload
Station 2	$2\frac{9}{64}$-in. drill-1 hole	$1\frac{1}{8}$-in. end cut-1 hole, $\frac{7}{8}$-in. drill-1 hole
Station 3	spotface and chamfer	$\frac{3}{8}$-in. drill and chamfer (6), $1\frac{1}{8}$-in. core drill (1)
Station 4	$\frac{1}{2}$-in. C' bore (1)	0.875 drill (1)
Station 5	$\frac{7}{8}$ drill web hole	$1\frac{7}{32}$-in. C' bore, 0.484 bore and cham
Station 6	Cham $\frac{1}{32} \times 45°$ OD	1.6094-in. semifinished C' bore
Station 7	Mill $\frac{3}{16}$-in. keyway, rear	$1\frac{1}{16}$-in.-diam. undercut and cham
Station 8	Blank	0.3906 ream (6) holes
Station 9	Blank	0.4995 ream (1) hole
Station 10	$\frac{1}{2}$-20 tap 1 hole	$\frac{7}{16}$-20 tap (6) holes

Production for the above operations is estimated at 32 pieces per hour net.

Fig. 21-13. Two-way horizontal machine for drilling and reaming operations on a crankshaft. (Courtesy of Baker Brothers, Inc., Toledo, Ohio.)

Auxiliary equipment includes a milling attachment mounted on a drive bracket. The fixture is a trunnion type having automatic power index with ten stations. A study of the operations shows that drilling is but one of the types of machining, since related operations are also included. This versatility adds much interest to an evaluation of the suitability of this type of equipment for a specific installation.

Case II. This case has been chosen because it presents a vertical drilling machine that is tooled for reaming valve guides (Fig. 21-14). Fixturing and automatic ejection have solved the problem of loading and unloading workpieces. This particular machine is adapted to reaming two sizes of intake and exhaust valve guides, the larger having a hole $\frac{5}{16}$ by $3\frac{1}{4}$ in.

Eight twenty-station automatic indexing-type fixtures are mounted on an eight-spindle vertical drilling machine. After the operator has filled the stations of the loading magazine, the machining and ejection cycles are automatic. Any number of stations to the capacity of the fixtures can be loaded at a single station. While these fixtures are of the

Fig. 21-14. Eight-spindle vertical drilling machine equipped with automatic broaching and indexing fixture. (*Courtesy of Davis and Thompson Co., Milwaukee.*)

indexing type, there is no lost time for indexing, since this occurs between the work stations.

The production of valve guides on this machine is reported by the owner of this equipment to be 2,520 pieces per hr.

Portable Horizontal Drilling and Tapping Machines. A development of more than passing interest is that of a portable drilling machine designed to be taken to the work instead of having the work brought to it. This particular development features a central column carrying a crossarm containing the machine head, which can be rotated 360° and swiveled 180° (Fig. 21-15). The top of the column has a built-in bail for ease of lifting by a crane. To give the machine stability, stabilizing spreader arms are hinged to the machine runway.

This particular design is extremely flexible in that the head can be arranged for drilling vertically upward or downward as well as horizon-

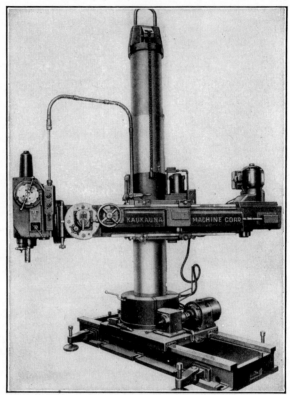

Fig. 21-15. Portable universal drilling and tapping machine. (*Courtesy of Kaukauna Machine Corporation, Kaukauna, Wis.*)

tally or at any angle. In addition, the entire rail and head stock are provided with vertical traverse on the column, thereby allowing for considerable spindle height. The entire column assembly has horizontal traverse on the runway, so that positioning in that direction as well is afforded.

Survey Questions

21-1. In the machine shop, are drilling and boring synonymous?

21-2. Were there any drill types that preceded twist drills?

21-3. How are twist drills made?

21-4. Give some applications for straight fluted drills.

21-5. Of what importance are helix angles?

21-6. Name the three different angles on a drill point.

21-7. Unequal lip lengths cause drill breakage; do any other difficulties result from this defect?

21-8. List twist-drill size classifications.

21-9. By what means are twist drills driven?

21-10. On what class of work are core drills used?

21-11. Do oil-hole drills have advantages? Explain.

21-12. Is a finishing reamer essentially a stock-removing tool?

21-13. Can counterbores and countersinks be used interchangeably?

21-14. Will the same countersink serve for wood screws and machine screws?

21-15. Where are sensitive drilling machines used?

21-16. Are gang drills regarded as general purpose equipment?

21-17. From what construction feature do radial drilling machines derive their identity?

21-18. What are universal radials?

21-19. Wherein do multiple-spindle drilling machines differ from gang drills?

21-20. Are all drilling machines built with vertical spindles?

21-21. Can drilling machines perform machining operations other than drilling?

21-22. Are drilling machines "tooled up" for production work?

21-23. How are taper-shank twist drills held in the spindle?

21-24. What style taper is standard on a taper-shank drill?

21-25. Do production-type drilling machines use standard or special twist drills?

REFERENCES

"Tool Engineers' Handbook," McGraw-Hill Book Company, Inc., New York, 1949.

CHAPTER 22

GRINDING AND FINISHES

Grinding is a machining method wherein metal is removed in the form of chips by means of a rotating grinding wheel. The latter is unique among cutting tools since it is, in effect, self-sharpening and at the same time possesses a multitude of cutting edges. Grinding is distinctive as a machining method in that it is a means of shaping extremely hard

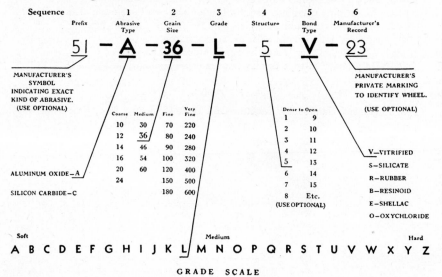

Plate 1. Standard marking system chart. (From "Markings for Grinding Wheels," American Standard B5.17—1949, The American Society of Mechanical Engineers, New York.)

metallic materials. Grinding is also employed on all other metals common in engineering manufacture. It can also be used on hard and brittle nonmetals such as ceramics, plastics, and glass. In addition, grinding is the only method for machining some thin metallic workpieces that are difficult or impossible to hold in other machine tools.

Mass production has developed only as rapidly as have grinding techniques. True interchangeability manufacture resulted when grinding was capable of producing the required accuracy. While grinding is generally considered solely as a method of finishing, it is also capable of removing metal rapidly and at relatively low cost. Grinding is frequently in the rare position of applying the finish to workpieces that are the finished products of other machining methods. The precision built into machine tools results from their component parts being finished by grinding or a related method.

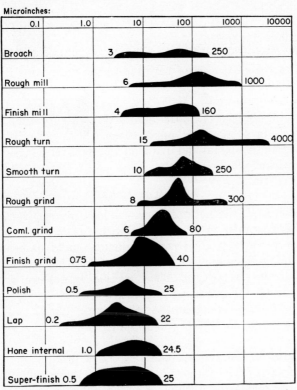

Plate 2. Industrial finishes. Height of curve is proportional to the frequency of occurrence of a particular roughness. (*Courtesy of Physicists Research Company, Ann Arbor, Mich.*)

Grinding Wheels

Grindstones. Earliest records of grinding indicate that the grinding wheel was fashioned from a slab or block of natural sandstone. Those wheels were termed grindstones. Grindstones revolved slowly and the grinding operation was extremely time consuming. One salient drawback to grindstones was their tendency to wear out of round: no amount of dressing would provide a remedy, since the stone lacked uniform hardness throughout its cross section.

Natural Abrasive Wheels. The artificial grinding wheel, so termed in contradistinction to the natural grindstone, was introduced at the close of the Civil War. This wheel employed the natural abrasive *emery* for the cutting element. Emery is found in many countries including the United States (southern section). It obtains its cutting ability from the corundum and abrasive iron oxide contained in its composition. The corundum content ranges from 70 per cent to as low as 30 per cent, so that emery is a variable product. Emery wheels have been superseded by artificial abrasive wheels almost entirely. Even though they have become obsolete, the term emery wheel continues to be applied, incorrectly, to grinding wheels.

Corundum is a natural aluminum oxide containing variable amounts of impurities. Its high degree of hardness is the reason for its ability to perform satisfactorily in a grinding wheel. Quartz is another type of natural abrasive; however, it is not commonly used. Diamond is another natural abrasive; it is the hardest known substance and is used in some specialized grinding applications. Owing to its nature, it requires a distinctive bond, and diamond wheels must be used differently from conventional grinding wheels.

ARTIFICIAL ABRASIVES

As has been said, the natural abrasives lack uniformity and in consequence deliver erratic results. A realization of this fact motivated a search for an artificial abrasive whose quality could be controlled and whose cost of production would be reasonable. The quest for such a product led to the discovery of silicon carbide by Acheson around 1890. Jacobs is credited with inventing the process for making aluminum oxide in an electric furnace at about the same time. These two inventions provided the basis on which the grinding wheel industry has been developed.

Silicon Carbide. Silicon carbide (SiC) is a product of the electric resistance furnace. The furnace is charged with pure silica, petroleum coke, sawdust, and sodium chloride. The chemical reaction wherein silicon and carbon unite to form SiC is accompanied by the formation of CO, which escapes through the porosity caused in the furnace bath by the presence of the sawdust. The salt acts as a fluxing agent by forming chlorides with the impurities of the charge.

Silicon carbide particles are angular in form and fracture easily. They are harder than aluminum oxide but lack the latter's toughness. This abrasive is chosen for grinding hard materials of a brittle nature such as cemented carbides, ceramic materials, and cast irons. It is also favored for grinding materials of low tensile strength such as brass, bronze, copper, and aluminum alloys. There are many trade names applied to silicon carbide—Carborundum, Crystolon, Electrolon, "C" abrasive, Natalon, and Sterbon, among others.

Aluminum Oxide. Aluminum oxide (Al_2O_3) is produced in an electric arc furnace from bauxite. Bauxite contains ferric oxide, silica, and rutile, along with aluminum hydroxide. It is calcined prior to being charged into the electric furnace along with iron borings and coke breeze. The resulting melt is composed of approximately 95 per cent Al_2O_3, 3 per cent TiO_2, 1.5 per cent SiO_2, and 0.5 per cent Fe_2O_3.

Aluminum oxide crystals are tough and therefore do not tend to fracture readily. This characteristic makes them unsuited for grinding hard materials, since they tend to dull prior to fracture. They perform best when grinding tough materials such as the various grades of steel, wrought iron, and malleable cast iron. Modifications in the manufacturing

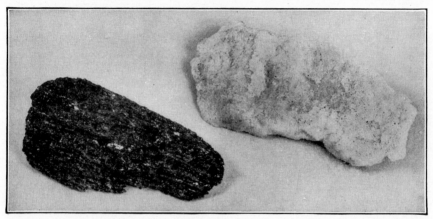

Fig. 22-1. Abrasive materials prior to crushing and grading: silicon carbide, dark in color; aluminum oxide, white. Note difference in structure.

process will alter the structure of the crystals and broaden their scope of applications. Aluminum oxide abrasives are known by such trade names as Alundum, Borolon, Aloxite, Sterlith, "A" abrasive, Alowalt, and others.

Abrasive Grains. The artificial abrasives are recovered in lump form upon cooling from their molten state. The characteristics of the grains is noticeable upon solidification (Fig. 22-1) in that silicon carbide has a brittle grain whereas aluminum oxide is tough in comparison. The lumped material is sent through jaw crushers as the first step in size reduction. The resultant pieces are further reduced by being passed through steel sizing rolls.

Abrasive materials are crushed in a manner that will control both the shape and the size of the individual grain (Fig. 22-2). The size classification is made by screening through standard cloth screens by mechanical means. Standard grain sizes on the Department of Commerce specifications list are the following:

Silicon carbide

Screened sizes: 8, 10, 12, 14, 16, 20, 24, 30, 36, 46, 54, 60, 70, 80, 90, 100, 120, 150, 180, 220, 240

Aluminum oxide

Screened sizes: 4, 6, 8, 10, 12, 14, 16, 20, 24, 30, 36, 46, 54, 60, 70, 80, 90, 100, 120, 150, 180, 220, 240

Commercial grain size classification includes three grades:

Coarse grain from 6 to 24 inclusive
Medium grain from 30 to 60 inclusive
Fine grain from 70 to 600 inclusive

Choice of grain size is governed by both the intended application and the finish desired on the ground workpiece. Small amounts of impurities are added by some producers to color the finished abrasive.

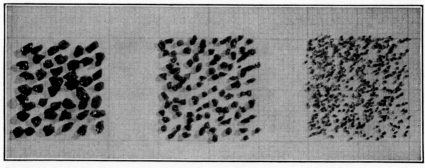

Fig. 22-2.   Unretouched photograph of standard aluminum oxide abrasive grains on graph paper having 20 lines per in.   (*Courtesy of Pacific Grinding Wheel Co., Everett, Wash.*)

BONDING TYPES

A grinding wheel is composed of two components—the abrasive grain and its bonding agent. The bond in a grinding wheel acts to hold the grains in position and also to release them when they become dulled. There is no single bonding agent that will perform suitably for every grinding requirement; this accounts for the six different ones regarded as standard by the Grinding Wheel Manufacturers' Association. These six bond designations are V, vitrified; S, silicate; B, resinoid; R, rubber; E, shellac; O, oxychloride. Some variations and additions are employed by individual manufacturers as a means of developing a product of individual characteristics. A representative group of grinding wheel shapes is shown in Fig. 22-3.

Vitrified Bond. This is the most prominent of all bonding agents. It is also known as glass bond and porcelain bond. Basically this is a clay bonding agent with which other ceramic materials are mixed. The bond and abrasive grains are thoroughly mixed and processed as a batch. The wheels are then shaped and dried. A firing operation in a kiln is the final operation in developing the bond strength. Vitrified bonds are strong and rigid.

Silicate Bond. This bond is composed of silicate of soda (water glass) combined with a metallic oxide, which, when baked, renders it insoluble in water. It is not a strong bond but it releases abrasive grains faster than the vitrified type. It is used for grinding edged tools and in other applications where operating temperatures must be at a minimum. Wheels above 36 in. in diameter are usually made with this bond.

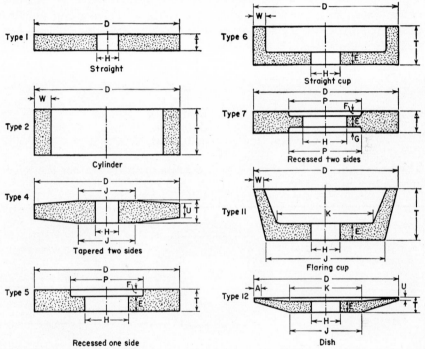

Fig. 22-3. Shape types of grinding wheels. (*From "Grinding Wheels," Simplified Standard, No. 45–47; The Grinding Wheel Manufacturers' Association, Worcester, Mass.*)

Resinoid Bond. This is a plastic made of synthetic organic material. It has great strength and considerable elasticity, hence it is being employed to give the grinding wheel a wide range of properties. Resinoid bonded wheels cut rapidly and can be operated at high speeds.

Rubber Bond. This bond is a form of hard rubber and is used primarily for making hard, coarse snagging wheels, thin cut-off wheels, and finish wheels for producing fine finishes on hardened steels.

Grinding Wheel Structure. Wheel structure refers to the precise method of spacing the cutting units (abrasive grains) in the grinding wheel. It is obtained by exercising close control over the size and distribution of the pore spaces between the abrasive grains. The importance of structure shows itself in the performance of the grinding wheel, since it functions to provide chip clearances in the voids or pores. Structure is specified by a numerical series using the numbers from 0 to 15, inclusive. The lower numbers are used to designate the close, denser structures, while the higher ones indicate the opener, or more porous, structures.

Grinding Wheel Grades. The grade of a grinding wheel refers to its degree of hardness. This characteristic is dependent upon the bonding of the wheel, since the inherent hardness of the abrasive grains remains unaffected by both bond and grinding wheel manufacturing process. Grading is designated by letters in the following sequence:

	Grade
Very soft	C, D, E, F, G
Soft	H, I, J, K
Medium	L, M, N, O
Hard	P, Q, R, S
Very hard	T, U, V, W, X, Y, Z

These designations do not apply to a definite quantity; rather the reference is to a range of hardness.

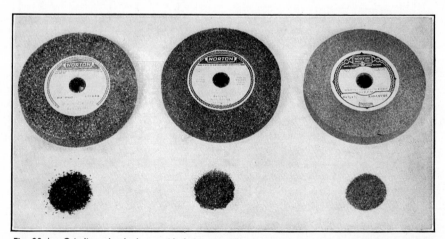

Fig. 22-4.   Grinding wheels shown with their respective abrasive grains.   Coarse, medium, and fine grain sizes appear from left to right.   (*Courtesy of Norton Company, Worcester, Mass.*)

Grinding Wheel Designations. Wheel selection frequently spells the difference between a successful grinding job and one that is unsatisfactory. A plan for grinding wheel designation as sponsored by the Grinding Wheel Manufacturers' Association is given in Plate 1 (page 374). This is a reliable guide to the selection of grinding wheels. However, all grinding wheel manufacturers do not adhere strictly to the chart designations, since some of them offer products whose characteristics do not conform exactly to those listed. There are cases in which a grinding wheel manufacturer employs his individual system of designation. This is mentioned because confusion may arise in correlating actual grinding wheel markings with those shown as standard in the chart. Figure 22-4 gives examples of grinding wheels and their respective abrasive grain.

Grinding—A Cutting Action. Automatic self-sharpening is the accepted basic principle of the cutting action of the grinding wheel (Fig. 22-5). Each abrasive grain acts as a cutting tool that takes its individual chip from the workpiece. A definite relation exists between chip thickness and chip space. The former quality will in turn be affected by keenness as well as depth of cut. Keenness results from the behavior of the bond, since a weak bond will release the

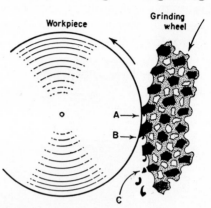

Legend:
A – Chip starting to form
B – Chip completely formed
C – Weak abrasive grain fractured
after impact with workpiece

Fig. 22-5. Schematic sketch of the cutting action of a grinding wheel.

grains readily, thereby causing the wheel to wear rapidly. A strong bond has the opposite effect and may not permit the release of grains until they become dulled to the point of losing their cutting efficiency.

GRINDING WHEEL CARE AND OPERATION

Dressing. Dressing, truing, and balancing are critical to all grinding wheels intended for precision grinding results. Dressing is necessary to relieve the "loading" of the wheel. The tools used for dressing and truing are of three general basic types: abrasive, diamond, and steel. There are several styles of each of these.

Truing. Truing refers to the treatment of a grinding wheel face by which it is shaped to grind a desired contour. Filleting is an example of the necessity for truing a wheel face. A given workpiece may require a series of different fillet sizes all to be ground in a single setting; this can be accomplished by truing the wheel as required.

Crush Dressing. A hardened steel crusher, formed to the desired wheel-face contour, is brought in contact with the grinding wheel as it slowly revolves. This type of dressing readily brings the wheel face to desired shape. Crush dressing aids in rapid production of formed parts.

A shortcoming of the use of crush dressing is a slight sacrifice in the quality of finish as compared to other types of dressing.

Grinding Fluids. Increasing attention is being given to the choice of fluid necessary for successful grinding results. Water was the original fluid used in grinding. It has been largely superseded by soluble oils, since these fluids have splendid coolant action, prevent rusting, and possess lubricating qualities. Various types of oils are used for grinding, especially on thread grinding and similar contour work.

Fig. 22-6. Coolant delivered through grinding wheel to workpiece. (*Courtesy of Gallmeyer & Livingston Co., Grand Rapids, Mich.*)

Grinding fluids keep the workpiece cool, thereby preventing surface cracks and distortion. They also aid materially in improving the surface, since chips are washed away, and there is some indication that a desirable lubricating action is present. Placing the grinding fluid at the contact surface is the aim of every coolant delivery system. In some grinding operations, there is a veritable flood of coolant delivered under considerable pressure to ensure proper coolant results.

A recent development is that of delivering the coolant directly through the grinding wheel itself (Fig. 22-6). Specially designed open-structured grinding wheels, whose sides are sealed, are necessary for this technique. The grinding fluid is delivered to a hollow section at the hub and is caused to flow outward by the centrifugal force developed by the rotation of the grinding wheel.

Dry Grinding. Grinding with fluids, whatever their nature, is termed wet grinding. The majority of finish and precision grinding is of this type. A considerable amount of grinding is performed without the use of fluid on the workpiece or wheel in a method known as dry grinding. Most offhand grinding and snagging falls into this classification. There are instances where a change from wet to dry grinding has proved beneficial in eliminating defective work. Surface grinding frequently employs dry grinding, as does disk grinding.

Grinding Speeds. The speed of grinding is measured in feet per minute of the surface of the grinding wheel; grinding speed is stated in surface feet per minute. It is calculated by multiplying spindle revolutions by wheel circumference in feet. A usual speed of 6,500 sfpm is common to the majority of grinding operations; however, this is not to be regarded as a fixed figure, since both greater and lesser speeds are used.

TABLE 22-1. MAXIMUM RECOMMENDED SAFE OPERATING SPEEDS*
(Speeds shown are in surface feet per minute)

Type of wheels	Vitrified and silicate bonded wheels			Organic bonded wheels		
	Soft	Me-dium	Hard	Soft	Me-dium	Hard
Type 1, straight wheels (including plate mounted and inserted nut wheels)	5,500	6,000†	6,500	6,500	8,000	9,500
Type 4, taper wheels	5,500	6,000†	6,500	6,500	8,000	9,500
Types 5 and 7, recessed wheels	5,500	6,000†	6,500	6,500	8,000	9,500
Type 2, cylinder wheels (including plate mounted and inserted nut wheels)	4,500	5,500	6,000	6,000	8,000	9,500
Types 11 and 12, dish and flaring cup wheels	4,500	5,500	6,000	6,000	8,000	9,500
Type 13, saucer wheels	4,500	5,500	6,000	6,000	8,000	9,500
Type 6, deep recessed cup wheels	4,500	5,000	5,500	6,000	7,500	9,000
Cutting wheels larger than 16 in. diameter						7,500–14,000‡
Cutting wheels 16 in. and smaller						10,000–16,000‡
Thread grinding wheels	8,000	10,000	12,000			12,000
Automotive and aircraft crank grinding wheels (on standard machines)		7,300	8,500			

* Abstracted from American Standard B7.1—1947, American Standards Association, New York.

† On precision machines vitrified wheels in medium grades may often be operated at speeds up to 6,500 fpm.

‡ Depending on stability, design, and condition of machine.

Cutoff wheels operate in the highest grinding wheel speed ranges and, in general, organic bonded wheels operate safely at speeds above the vitrified types. Workpiece speeds in cylindrical grinding are low in comparison with grinding wheel speeds employing a starting speed of 125 sfpm. A guide to safe grinding wheel speeds is presented in Table 22-1. It is recommended that this table be consulted in the interests of correct grinding results combined with safe operation.

Grinding Operations

Tool and cutter grinding machines are designed primarily for sharpening tools and cutters that are cylindrical in cross section or that operate on the principle of rotation about a center. To be sure, linear cutters such as planer knives and die segments can also be ground on these machines when they are equipped with the necessary work-holding accessories. Among the tools ground on these machines such items as reamers and taps are in the majority; in the cutter classification hobs and milling cutters of a wide assortment of designs form the bulk of the grinding.

Cutter and Tool Grinding. Regardless of the elaborateness of the grinding equipment, there remains the necessity for skill and knowledge of a high order on the part of the operator if cutters and tools are to be correctly sharpened. Wheel selection is important in order to prevent heating, with its subsequent loss of hardness. The grinding machine and its related equipment must be kept in good order and accurate alignment. Spindles must be free of vibration and table movement easy and smooth. A decision must be made on whether to take roughing and then finishing cuts or merely a single cut.

The position of the grinding spindle with respect to the work is a critical matter. Gear tooth cutters must be ground on a line normal to their horizontal axis when mounted in the grinding machine. Tooth rests should fit the teeth properly and care must be exercised in holding the tooth firmly against the tooth rest while grinding (Fig. 22-7). The most desirable procedure is that of having the tooth ground in contact with the rest. There is also the matter of cutter tooth position with respect to the grinding wheel, since the cut can be made either toward the cutting edge or the reverse. Both techniques have their respective advantages; however, the finer the finish on the cutting edge the longer the tooth will remain sharp. Frequently cutting edges are lightly honed immediately after grinding as a means of improving the cutting surface. Tool angles are ground to standards prevailing for the particular tool or cutter being sharpened. Information on this is available from cutter manufacturers as well as from ASA standards.

The condition of finish on any machined surface depends to a large extent upon the accuracy with which the cutting tool employed for machining has been ground. A cutter should never be used after it ceases to cut freely for the reasons that it will produce an inferior finish, it may destroy the accuracy of the workpiece, and it will require increasingly more power. There is little to be gained from allowing a cutter to become dull to the point where excessive grinding is necessary, since resharpening will be a time-consuming operation and will prove costly as well. Sharp tools and cutters aid in economical production, as they do in improving quality of finish.

Fig. 22-7. Tooth rest in position against the tooth being ground on a large end mill. (*Courtesy of Norton Company, Worcester, Mass.*)

Grinding Cemented Carbide. Cemented carbides are used on both multiple-point and single-point cutters and tools. Inserted tooth milling cutters and similar tools are ground on tool and cutter grinding machines of the types previously described. Single-point straight-shank tools with carbide tips are ground offhand, for the most part, on specially designed grinding machines. These machines carry a grinding wheel at each end of the centrally mounted motor spindle. The motor should be reversible in order that both right- and left-hand tools can be ground. A roughing wheel is mounted on one end of the spindle and a finishing wheel on the other. Adjustable table rests, equipped with graduated dials for obtaining recommended tool-cutting angles, are adjacent to the grinding wheels.

The grinding wheels are mostly of cup shape, although straight wheels are more economical for grinding the steel shank of the tool. Silicon carbide grinding wheels of soft grade only should be used for grinding cemented carbides. Grinding wheel manufacturers are tending toward using a friable type of silicon carbide abrasive for this application. Diamond wheels are also recommended for this purpose but they are not as commonly employed as the silicon carbide ones. Especially fine finishes are obtained by finishing on an iron lapping disk charged with diamond powder.

Care is required for proper grinding results inasmuch as the tool is a composite of a steel shank and a carbide tip. It is recommended that the steel shank be ground on a separate wheel as a means of preserving the carbide grinding wheel. Grinding should be in a direction from carbide tip toward the shank. The tool should be rocked from side to side as a preventive against grooving the grinding wheel. Any necessary top dressing is always done prior to grinding the other tool faces.

Production Grinding

In its inception, precision grinding was considered supplementary to lathe machining. In general, the workpiece was turned on the lathe and the final sizing and finish were achieved by grinding. This concept of grinding has been expanded for several reasons, chief among them being the degree of finish grinding can produce and the fact that grinding is capable of machining material too hard to be turned in a lathe. The same situation applies to flat surfacing; grinding is capable of operations that cannot be achieved with the machine tools designed for flat surfacing.

Production grinding has gained increased stature as knowledge of its potentialities has broadened until it has become a serious competitor, in some areas, to the more traditional machining methods. Processing a workpiece must be studied today with a view toward grinding from the rough to the finished size. This transition has been materially helped by the ability of the foundry to produce castings of narrowing tolerances. The same situation applies to forgings and those other production methods which contribute the raw material of the machining department. In its own field, grinding is developing along lines familiar to other machine tools. Automatic operation and cycling, multiple cuts, and greater diversification in grinding machine and grinding wheel types have all contributed to the increasing attention being given to grinding as a machining method over and above merely one for finishing as was formerly the case.

Production grinding is applied to external and internal surfaces as well as contouring in a variety of forms. Grinding machines can be classified on the basis of design types as:

Cylindrical............ $\begin{cases} \text{On center} \\ \text{Centerless} \\ \text{Chucking} \end{cases}$

Internal.............. $\begin{cases} \text{Chucking} \\ \text{Fixture} \\ \text{Centerless} \end{cases}$

Surface............... $\begin{cases} \text{Horizontal} \\ \text{Vertical} \end{cases}$

Specialized or individual

Disk.................. $\begin{cases} \text{Horizontal} \\ \text{Vertical} \end{cases}$

Within these classifications, all design features, from manual to fully automatic operation, are available. Selection of a grinding machine is not unlike that of any machine tool, since there are modifying factors such as production requirements, workpiece size and shape, workpiece material, stock removal, finish requirements, and operation costs that need to be evaluated.

CYLINDRICAL GRINDING

This term had its origin in the fact that initially, grinding for a precision finish was performed on components of cylindrical shape. The meaning of the expression cylindrical grinding has been expanded to the point where the term is applied to tapers, cams, and external grinding of contours. It is understood that the workpiece is rotated in the same direction as that of the grinding wheel, but at a decidedly slower rate.

Work mounting or holding determines the type of grinding machine. The more flexible machines are those which hold the workpiece between centers, since they can accommodate a wider range of workpiece sizes. Such machines are specified as to capacity by two dimensions; 6 by 30 in., for example, means that the maximum workpiece would be 6 in. in diameter with a length of 30 in. The tailstock center is cut away in order that the grinding wheel may pass completely beyond the work. In some designs, a work-holding chuck is used in place of center mounting; however, this feature is employed only where required by workpiece shape.

A cylindrical grinding machine is equipped with a wheel head which carries the grinding element. A wheel spindle, whose bearing mounting is critical, carries the grinding wheel. The spindle is generally driven by multiple V belts from the motor, which is independently mounted in order to eliminate vibration from the wheel. Provision is made for traversing the workpiece across the wheel face in order that the workpiece length can be completely ground. There are designs in which the workpiece merely rotates whereas the wheel head traverses, but this type of construction is uncommon.

Table traverse can be operated manually but in production grinding automatic movement is general. Traversing is either by mechanical or by hydraulic means. It is said of the latter that there is less opportunity for vibration and in consequence design is tending in that direction. Table traverse is handled in an automatic cycle designed to eliminate the necessity for the operator to move any control levers during the grinding cycle.

The cylindrical grinding machine is equipped with an infeed whereby the wheel is fed into the work. The depth of cut for the wheel is a variable quantity and differs as between roughing and finishing cuts. Roughing cuts of 0.003 in. are taken, but on finishing this value is reduced to as little as 0.0001 in. Workpiece diameter is measured by micrometers or gages unless the grinding machine is equipped for automatic gaging. In the latter instance, infeed is included in the automatic operating cycle of the grinding machine.

In cylindrical grinding it is necessary to have a rigid work mounting in order to prevent deflection of the workpiece. A usual method, for pieces of any length, is to include steady rests that bear on the workpiece and support it. The forces from grinding wheel action tend to push the work outward as well as downward; hence the shoes in the rests must be positioned to counteract that tendency. It is also necessary to adjust these shoes after each cut in order to maintain a proper bearing against the workpiece.

There is a dwell time at each end of the traverse stroke in order to permit grinding the workpiece to size at its ends. It is here that the "spark-out" is noted: the volume of sparks emitting from the grinding operation is an indication of the depth of cut. When spark volume vanishes, it is evidence that the wheel is no longer cutting.

Cylindrical Grinding Techniques. Workpieces whose lengths are greater than the width of the wheel face are ground by traversing. There are occasions where the length to be ground can be accommodated without traverse movement. In such cases plunge grinding is employed; in this process the grinding wheel is moved into the work. Crankpin grinding is an example of the plunge-grinding technique. This procedure is used for grinding contours where the wheel has been dressed to suit.

Another interesting development in cylindrical grinding is that of making multiple or concurrent cuts (Fig. 22-8). On this job two different diameters are being ground simultaneously. Wheel diameters are maintained by a built-in truing device which, in turn, is operated by interchangeable flat cams. This particular job setup is indicative of the potentialities of multiple cuts—there are examples of several wheels grinding concurrently on a single workpiece.

Plain cylindrical grinding machines having a wheel slide or angle head causing the wheel to feed at an angle of 60° to the work axis, instead of the conventional 90°, are employed for grinding cylindrical surfaces and shoulders on a production basis. The grinding wheel is dressed so that its periphery can grind the cylindrical surface of the work and face-grind the shoulder simultaneously. By dressing the wheel periphery in multiple steps or by mounting several wheels on the spindle, it is possible to grind a number of different diameters and shoulders concurrently.

Cylindrical Grinding Machines. The conventional cylindrical grinding machine is referred to as a "plain" grinding machine. It is built primarily for grinding cylindrical shapes; however, it is not uncommon to

Fig. 22-8. 10 by 18 in. plain cylindrical grinding machine set up for grinding two diameters on an automotive part concurrently. (*Courtesy of Cincinnati Milling and Grinding Machines, Inc.*)

equip these machines with attachments for cam grinding and other work of a similar nature. There are modifications of the basic design which have been developed for individual work classifications. An example is the gap machine, which has a gap in the bed to accommodate large flanges.

Roll grinders are built in an extremely wide size range for grinding rolls for many industrial uses. Rolling sheet in steel or aluminum requires rolls of considerable dimensions, especially in the category of back-up rolls. The paper industry also requires roll-grinding equipment as a critical part of its production machinery.

Other production-type cylindrical grinders include crankshaft grinding machines of many designs. Another example is that of piston grinding machines, which have an important part in automotive production, as do valve grinding machines employed for grinding valve seat inserts.   Camshaft grinders for grinding cam faces as well as line bearings are well known to automotive production.

Cylindrical grinding machines, regardless of type, are designed and built for accuracy.   Controls are equipped with dials for precision setting and movement.   Rigidity is incorporated in all critical members to ensure continued and long-lived accuracy.   Refinements are continually being added; a striking example of this trend is the use of a strain gage connected with an electronic amplifier as a means of accurately aligning the swivel table on either straight or taper work.   The tendency toward fully automatic operation is increasingly apparent in cylindrical grinding machine design.   Built-in sizing arrangements which control the entire

Fig. 22-9.   Universal-type cylindrical grinding machine. (*Courtesy of Brown & Sharpe Mfg. Co., Providence.*)

grinding cycle, including rough and finish grind feeds and speeds, rapid traverse, and automatic sizing, provide a grinding service that exemplifies the transference of skill and reduces the dependence on artisanship in production work.

Universal Cylindrical Grinding Machines.   Manufacturers refer to these grinding machines as universals; however, it seems desirable to include the term cylindrical in their descriptions, since they are primarily employed on that class of work.   Grinding machines in this classification are distinctive in that they are equipped with a headstock carrying a rotating center and that, in addition, the headstock swivels (Fig. 22-9). The wheel head is of special design; it can also swivel.   On some makes, the grinding wheel can be mounted in any one of three different positions on its spindle.   The combination of swiveling headstock and wheel head makes this classification of grinding machines truly universal in operation.   Internal grinding is also done on this type.

INTERNAL GRINDING

This method of grinding is confined to finishing holes or bores. It is capable of producing excellent surfaces with a high degree of accuracy. Its development has been such that it has replaced some reaming operations for reasons of economy as well as of excellence of finish. Precision within 0.00025 in. is readily attained, while limits as close as 0.0001 in. lie within the capacity of internal grinding. Here, as in other types of grinding, hard materials can be finished to desired accuracy; distortion

Fig. 22-10. Internal grinding machine, plain type. (*Courtesy of The Heald Machine Co., Worcester, Mass.*)

in bores and holes of heat-treated workpieces are corrected by this grinding method. Internal grinding machines are designed and built to take their place in any production program requirement.

Chucking-type Internal Grinders. In this type the workpiece is held in a chuck mounted in the work head. Several design modifications exist on the various features of internal grinding machines (Fig. 22-10). The work head is a typical example, since the work spindle rotates in some models, while in others it is stationary. It may have a reciprocating motion, or the grinding element may reciprocate. Either work head or wheel head or both may be equipped with cross slides. The table may or may not traverse, and its movement can be manually or mechanically operated, or both.

Internal Grinding Techniques.   Accepted procedure for grinding bores on relatively small work is that of bringing the grinding wheel into contact with the entire internal surface by rotating the workpiece with its axis parallel to that of the grinding wheel.   For better visibility, grinding contact is made on the side away from the operator.   Plunge grinding is used for producing contoured internal surfaces, but straight bores are not plunge-ground.

Large workpieces are mounted on a face plate for grinding in a planetary type of internal grinding machine.   The grinder is designed to provide the grinding wheel with rotation about its own axis as well as to travel the wheel in an orbit whereby it can contact the entire surface of the bore to be ground.   The workpiece, in this case, is held stationary. Both wet and dry grinding find application over the range of internal grinding.

Internal grinding has been developed on the automatic-cycle principle to the point where the operator is required only to load, start, and unload the machine.   The various modifications embodied in these automatics follow the dictates of the grinding job requirements.   There are few application limitations for internal grinding, since straight, taper, and contoured bores are ground without difficulty.   Production machines for multiple operations are also available.

CENTERLESS GRINDING

This grinding method is different from cylindrical grinding, since here the workpiece is not supported on centers.   This omission is of genuine advantage in many respects, chiefly in the elimination of the centering operation, resulting in lower costs, and also in the fact that a more accurate cylinder can be generated on slender workpieces, since there is no axial thrust from the centers.   Centerless grinding is admirably suited to repetitive production work because, once the job setup is made, the operator can load while the previous piece is being finished.   Applications for centerless grinding are widespread.   Shafting, rods, and bars of stock lengths are ground by the centerless method on the one hand, while workpieces whose length is less than that of the grinding wheel face are examples of the other extreme.

There are three conventional methods for advancing the workpiece in centerless grinding; these are termed through feed, end feed, and infeed. A given grinder design incorporates one of these principles; the methods are not used interchangeably on a single grinding machine or with the same workpiece.   To these three methods must now be added a fourth one, which is known as the rotary infeed.

The operating principle of cylindrical centerless grinding employs three basic elements—the grinding wheel, the regulating wheel, and the work rest blade in a fixed relationship (Fig. 22-11). The grinding wheel, traveling at a speed ranging around 6,500 sfpm, contacts the workpiece, whose rotation is in the opposite direction. A regulating wheel of the same rotation, whose speed varies from 15 to 300 rpm, bears on the opposite diameter of the workpiece. The result of these movements is that the workpiece and grinding wheel are traveling in the same direction at their contact line; however, since the workpiece is rotating at a slower rate, there is relative motion, which causes the grinding effect. A work

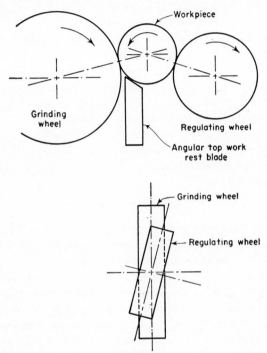

Fig. 22-11. Diagram of centerless grinding operating principle.

rest or blade supports the workpiece, thereby holding it in its correct geometric position. The centers of the grinding and regulating wheel are in a plane, but the workpiece center is above this horizontal. Lowering the center of the workpiece has the effect of reducing its diameter, while raising it has the opposite effect.

The regulating wheel is placed at an angle with the workpiece axis in order for feed to be imparted to the workpiece. This wheel is an abrasive one that is dressed by means of a built-in diamond wheel dresser. Its face is dressed concave for the purpose of ensuring line, rather than point, contact with the workpiece. Workpiece feed rate is a function of the inclination of the regulating wheel axis, together with its diameter and speed of rotation.   Control of the regulating wheel is important in both end-feed and through-feed centerless grinding.

Infeed Centerless Grinding.   This method is, in actuality, a form of plunge grinding.   There is no feed of the workpiece, whose length is less than the width of the grinding wheel face.   By installing segmented wheels, a variety of diameters can be ground simultaneously.   This method is commonly employed on workpieces having one surface to be ground, such as bolts or shouldered pieces.   In setups of this type, it is usual to contour the regulating wheel as well as the grinding wheel to fit the design of the surface to be ground.

Centerless Internal Grinding.   A somewhat specialized application is that of internal grinding of workpieces whose outside surfaces have been cylindrically ground.   However, where suitable applications are found, this method is highly satisfactory.   The operating principle of centerless internal grinding machines is based on supporting the workpiece exterior between two pressure rolls, while the regulating wheel forms the third point of contact.   In consequence, the truth of the internal grind depends entirely on the accuracy of the external surface.   There are examples of this method being built into grinding machines with fully automatic cycles.

SURFACE GRINDING

Machining and finishing of flat surfaces that are free from projections and of a size not to exceed machine capacity belong in the field of surface grinding.   While this grinding method is one capable of producing accurate surfaces, it is, nevertheless, of interest on first operation work as well.   Its common application is that of precision grinding.

Surface grinding machines are classified according to spindle treatment as horizontal or vertical types.   As a general thing, the vertical spindle surface grinding machine mounts a cup wheel as its grinding element, whereas the horizontal one is equipped with a straight wheel.   Machine size influences wheel type in that segmented wheels are conventional for large vertical machines.

Magnetic Chucks.   The workpieces are usually held by magnetic chucks, either directly or indirectly.   Nonmagnetic materials are mounted in fixtures which may or may not be held magnetically.   Magnetic chucks are built in a variety of styles, depending on the type of work they are to accommodate (Fig. 22-12).   They are a satisfactory holding device provided the workpiece facing surface is relatively flat; if it is not, the use of shims or wedging is necessary, but neither is entirely satisfactory.   A source of direct current is required for chuck operation; further equipment includes demagnetizing accessories.   These chucks must be used with care to prevent overheating.   Magnetic chuck development has been successful in perfecting a permanent magnet type; these do not require a source of direct current for operation.

Horizontal-spindle Surface Grinders. The grinding machines in this classification are built with a horizontal grinding wheel spindle located at the center of the machine. The wheel head is mounted on a vertical column that is cast integrally with the machine bed. There is some variation in this design, depending on the size of the machine. The wheel spindle usually is built for two or more speeds with a V-belt drive, although direct drive is also used. The table of the machine has longitudinal travel that is either manually or mechanically operated. Straight

Fig. 22-12. Magnetic chuck installed on a horizontal surface grinder. (*Courtesy of Mattison Machine Works, Rockford, Ill.*)

wheels are conventional for horizontal-spindle surface grinders, and the usual operation is that of grinding flat surfaces.

Vertical-spindle Surface Grinders. The chief characteristics of these grinding machines is the vertical position of the spindle. In constructional features they closely resemble the horizontal-spindle ones, so far as smaller machines are concerned. A conventional vertical-spindle machine mounts a cup wheel for flat surface work; segmented wheels are favored for some operating conditions.

Production-type Vertical-spindle Surface Grinders. There are several features included in these grinders that set them apart from the conventional designs. Larger capacity and heavy, rigid construction, along with rotating tables, comprise some of the noteworthy modifications. Automatic operation and size control, coupled with one or two wheel heads, provide production potentials of a high order. The grinding wheels are plain or sectored, depending on the job. However, the striking production possibilities of these machines command attention (Fig. 22-13). These grinding machines are tooled for repetitive operation on the single-purpose principle. As an example of production, hardened alloy steel bearing race rings are ground to ±.0005 in. on two sides at the

Fig. 22-13. Dual-spindle automatic vertical surface grinding machine designed for mass-production requirements. (*Courtesy of The Blanchard Machine Co , Cambridge, Mass.*)

rate of 1,200 pieces (2,400 surfaces) per hour. The actual production obtainable is dictated by the shape, size, and surfaces of the workpiece.

FACE GRINDING MACHINES

The grinding machines in this classification are built for heavy work, as is indicated by their driving motors, which range from 20 to 75 hp on the largest models. These machines have a horizontal grinding spindle that mounts either a cylindrical or a segmented wheel from 20 to 48 in. in diameter. The machines are rigidly built and of considerable capacity, with table sizes as great as 36 by 180 in. Despite their size, the machines are built for accuracy, with automatic feed ranges from 0.0005 to 0.005 in.; in addition, hand feeds are also available.

Face grinding machines are employed in such diverse installations as tool, production, and maintenance shops in virtually all industries, in metalworking, in railroad shops, in paper and pulp mills, in terracotta and rubber plants, in steel mills, and in foundries. Installations are common for surfacing machine bases, motor frames, pump parts, foundry flasks, shear blades—in fact, any machined face, free from projections, where a flat surface is required. Work mounting is either directly on the table or on angle plates.

DISK GRINDING

A distinctive method of metal removal wherein a disk rather than a wheel is the grinding element is of interest to every work type from snagging castings to precision finish. This method has frequently been termed surface grinding, a phrase that, while accurate, may lead to some confusion with other surface grinding methods.

Disk grinding uses an abrasive disk that is fastened to a steel disk mounted on the grinding machine spindle. Fastening is either done mechanically, by bolting, or it is done by gluing the abrasive disk to the metal one. Abrasive disks are in no sense similar to the sanding disks familiar to the woodworking shop. On the contrary, abrasive disks are made similarly to grinding wheels; however, the former may have steel wire or other strength-reinforcing agencies incorporated in them. The large sizes are generally of segmented construction for ease of both manufacture and mounting.

Disk Grinding Machines. Disk grinding is no longer an offhand grinding process. The degree of finish, production, and precision obtainable by disk grinding is directly related to the design of the disk grinding machine. Horizontal and vertical, single and multiple spindles, conventional and single-purpose, automatic and manual operation, and combinations thereof have all appeared in disk grinding machines.

Offhand Grinding. The general metalworking shop would find itself hard-pressed without offhand grinding. This method finds manifold uses, from tool grinding to dimensional work (Fig. 22-14). In the toolroom there are many examples of resharpening tools by this method. Precautions against overheating the workpiece and placing undue pressure on the grinding wheel are necessary, and choosing the correct wheel is vital. Safety considerations in offhand grinding include the proper positioning of the work rest to prevent the workpiece from wedging and *grinding on the face and not the side of the wheel*. Eye protection is basic, as is the use of wheel guards. The grinding wheels must be balanced and should be dressed as occasion demands.

Snagging. This is the rough grinding method whose chief application is the removal of metal in volume in the shortest possible time.

Fig. 22-14.   Offhand grind of a shaper tool.   (*Courtesy of University of Washington Tool Laboratory, Seattle.*)

Fig. 22-15.   Snagging a gray iron casting on a conventional grinding wheel stand.   (*Courtesy of Norton Company, Worcester, Mass.*)

Removing casting fins, gates, risers, and scabs is a common application for snagging.   The method is applied as a first operation in a host of other applications on forgings, weldments, cutoff bars, shapes, and plates.

Most snagging is done on conventional grinding stands carrying a wheel at each end of the spindle (Fig. 22-15).   Straight wheels are used, and they attain considerable size for large work. Snagging is also done by bringing the grinding wheel to the workpiece with swing-frame or portable-type grinders. Snagging is primarily a manual grinding operation and, with labor costs looming more important, automatic machines are an intriguing possibility.

Abrasive Belt Grinding. The use of abrasive paper glued into an endless belt which then becomes the abrasive element of a grinding machine is finding increased application. This is a development from the original idea of polishing and buffing with abrasive paper or cloth. Several different types of machines are currently available for abrasive belt use. A conventional design (Fig. 22-16) has a vertical belt travel provided with suitable backing to carry the grinding thrust. This method is capable of producing excellent surfaces but is not regarded as a volume metal removal process. Abrasive belt grinding is performed dry for most applications, although there are some specially prepared materials designed for use with the wet method.

Abrasive belt grinding is proving itself as a finishing method for turbine blading of jet engines. Blades are roughed out on duplicator mills and ground to size and finish with abrasive belts. Developments are rapid, since entire new machine tools are being designed such as cylindrical grinding machines using abrasive belt grinding elements.

Fig. 22-16. Abrasive belt grinding machine. (*Courtesy of University of Washington Tool Laboratory, Seattle.*)

Finishes

In discussing finishes, it is intended to refer not to the dimensional requirements but rather to the condition of the surface insofar as its roughness is concerned. Such expressions as surface roughness and surface finish are common; yet it is contended that the term surface finish is an erroneous one, since each of the words composing that term has a distinct meaning. That the term has considerable standing is shown by its use as the title of a standard.[1]   The definitions in that standard are largely based on information in American Standard B46.1—1947, "Standard of Surface Roughness, Waviness, and Lay."[2]

Definitions applying to the more common terms used in a discussion of finishes are abstracted here from the above standards:

Surface—The surface of an object is the boundary which separates that object from another substance or object.

Nominal Surface—A two-dimensional boundary of separation which is absolutely true and smooth and whose shape and extent is defined by a drawing or descriptive specification.

Surface Qualities—The physical characteristics of a surface, such as roughness, waviness and flaws.

Roughness—That deviation from nominal surface evidenced by minute contiguous irregularities occurring on the nominal surface.   Roughness in itself does not alter the trueness of a surface.

Roughness Number—A physical measurement in RMS microinches which represents the maximum permissible degree of roughness of the surface to which it is applied except that, where two numbers are used, the larger shall be the maximum and the smaller the minimum permissible degree of roughness.

Microinch (Mu In.)—One millionth (.000001) part of the U.S. Standard linear inch.

RMS—The square root of the mean of the sum of the squares of the height (in microinches) of the irregularities.   This value can be calculated but is usually read from a meter or instrument made for measuring surface roughness.

Waviness—That deviation from nominal surface evidenced by recurrent irregularities having the form of waves.   These deviations are usually of greater magnitude than surface roughness which may be superimposed on waviness.

Flaws—Irregularities which occur at one place, or at relatively infrequent intervals in the surface; *e.g.*, a scratch, ridge, hole, peak, crack, or check.

Lay—The direction of the predominant surface pattern.

The significance of these definitions is that they emphasize the fact that the designer can communicate his desires to the shop by means of standard drawing symbols covering these important aspects of finishes. The standard drawing symbols are published in the Standards, as are scales for roughness and waviness.   The point is that the designer is no

[1] "Surface Finish," Aeronautical Standard AS107A, Society of Automotive Engineers, Inc., New York, 1945.
[2] American Standards Association, New York.

longer required to rely upon generalities insofar as desired surface quality is concerned.

The chief sources of surface roughness are the feed marks or ridges caused by cutting tool or grinding wheel and the minute particles from the built-up edge shed on the surface in the process of machining. The degree of roughness is the direct result of the machining operation, since any given single machining method is capable of producing differing degrees of surface roughness.

In the surface-finishing methods in common use the primary objective is the removal of the metal film on the workpiece surface that is variously termed fragmented, amorphous, noncrystalline, and/or smear metal. The concept of finish concerns itself with this metallic layer which is not considered a homogeneous part of the base metal. When this layer is removed from a surface, an excellent finish of high quality results. *The extent of this metal layer is variable.* The dulling of a cutting tool or grinding wheel will cause imperfect cutting action: the base metal will be torn rather than cleanly cut, and increased surface roughness will result. This condition explains the variations in finished size of components subjected to identical machining and finishing processing. The range of surface roughness characteristic of different machining as well as polishing methods is shown in Plate 2, page 375, where the ranges of roughness are given in microinches rms plotted logarithmically.

Surface Roughness Measurement. An accomplished mechanic will frequently depend upon his sense of feel in estimating surface quality. This is implemented by drawing the fingernail over a surface and noting its character. A more scientific version of this procedure substitutes an instrument for the fingernail.

One such instrument, known as a profilometer, employs a small diamond-tipped aluminum stylus mounted between two button anvils at the end of a handle. When this assembly is drawn along the surface, the diamond tip moves vertically with an amplitude determined by the surface roughness. This mechanical motion is transformed into an electrical current, which can be read directly in microinches on a meter of the instrument. There are several styles of tracers, each design suited to a specific surface style or geometry. This instrument can also be equipped with a recorder. It is common practice to use these instruments directly at the machine tool for control purposes.

Another instrument for measuring surface roughness is known as the Brush surface analyzer. It employs a tracer-generated current that records average scratch depth to an increased scale on a calibrated paper tape. Any single recording covers a $\frac{1}{16}$-in. travel of the tracer point, with the result that the tape will not show extremely long-range defects such as spirals from cross-feeds. The average scratch depth must be computed from the tape; yet this pictorial record is extremely valuable in studying surface roughness (Fig. 22-17).

Measurement of surface roughness is only meaningful to the degree to which it is understood and utilized. It does not follow that every mating surface, regardless of material or function, should approach zero micro-inch roughness. The ideal finish is that one which will permit the optimum oil film to be maintained under both load and operating conditions for a given application.

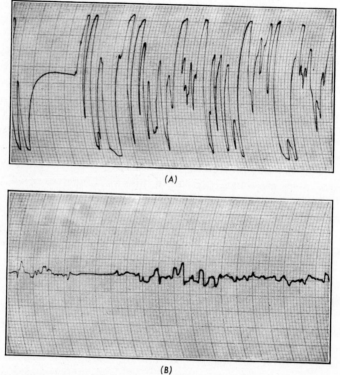

(A)

(B)

Fig. 22-17. Charts made on Brush surface analyzer; 1 mm = 1 microinch. (A) coarse ground surface, (B) fine ground surface.

Honing. Honing is essentially an abrading procedure that is applicable to all metals and to many nonmetals such as plastics, rubber, ceramics, and glass. The abrading, or cutting, element is known as a hone, and it is in the form of a stick. The hone is composed of an abrasive material bonded to shape in a manner similar to grinding wheel construction. Hones are graded and identified by a standard code sponsored by the Grinding Wheel Manufacturers' Association.

Honing can be accomplished manually, but in production, honing machines are usual. The honing unit consists of one or more honing sticks mounted in an adaptor with a suitable mandrel. This unit is free to float and, in the case of internal honing, follows the existing hole. The finish surface pattern is that of a crosshatch which is the natural result of hone travel during its operation. The severity of the finish pattern is a function of hone fineness and pressure. The latter is, in turn, dependent upon the hardness and toughness of the material being honed but will range from 150 to 450 psi. Results obtained in honing are largely governed by the reciprocating and rotational speeds.

The widest application of honing deals with internal, cylindrical applications; however, other surface geometry, including flats, are also honed. Honing machines are built for every type of application. Their development includes production designs of multiple-spindle type. Honing is regarded as a precision finishing method capable of closely controlled accuracy.

Lapping. Lapping is a method of finishing whose objective is that of refining the geometrical accuracy and surface finish by means of a loose abrasive. In order to accomplish its purpose, an element known as a lap is charged with abrasive powder whose vehicle can be either grease, oil, or a soap and water compound. The workpiece is then subjected to the action of the abrasive-charged lap, whose motion is dictated by the geometry of the surface being lapped. The relative motion between the workpiece and the lap is not positive in the sense that a definite path is followed. Rather, the action is a floating one in which there is a guiding action designed to prevent a repetitious path from being followed as a means of uniform treatment of the workpiece surface and also of developing new contact points between the lap and its workpiece.

The lap element is generally a close-grained gray cast iron, although practically all of the usual engineering metals, such as copper-base alloys, lead, tin, and aluminum alloys find specialized application. Copper, for example, is used primarily as the material for diamond lapping. Non-metals such as wood, felt, and leather also are suitable for lap elements, especially on hardened steel surfaces. Metallic laps are prepared by rolling or pressing the abrasive into them.

Abrasive powders are graded as to fineness and are further classified as soft, medium, or hard. They are employed for polishing gems and are worked in connection with soft laps. Lapping abrasives are procurable in stick form similar to those common in buffing operations.

Lapping is either a manual or a machine process. Flat surface hand lapping is relatively easy. The flat lap is charged uniformly with abrasive over its entire surface area and then moved over the workpiece surface in a figure-eight motion with slight pressure application. In production work, lapping is carried on as a mechanical process. Lapping machines are built primarily to suit a specific job (Fig. 22-18).

Lapping is also applied to specialized applications such as gear lapping, spherical lapping, centerless lapping, and lapping gage block surfaces. The latter are processed by means of non-rotating laps. Excellent surface quality is provided on small parts by employing an oscillating-spindle lapping machine wherein the piece is frequently lifted from the rotating lap member.

Superfinishing. A newcomer among surface finishing methods had its beginning in 1936 with the process termed superfinish. Its objective is

Fig. 22-18. Lapping machine, showing use of one-piece work holder for cylindrical lapping. (Courtesy of Norton Company, Worcester, Mass.)

that of removing amorphous metal resulting from previous machining methods, regardless of type. It is capable of reducing surface roughness and lessening inequalities in surface geometry (Fig. 22-19).

Superfinishing is an abrading process in which the abrasive element is in the form of a stone or stick. The stone is given an oscillating traverse while in contact with the rotating workpiece. This operation uses slight pressure, on the order of 20 psi, while work rotation ranges from 50 to 60 spfm—the workpiece, meantime, being flooded with lubricant. Superfinishing is not intended primarily as a dimension-changing process; it is designed for stock removal averaging 0.0001 to 0.0002 in. on a diameter.

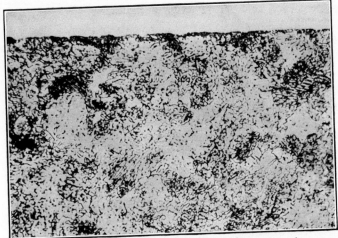

Fig. 22-19. Superfinish profile X 750, microinch 8 to 10 on C-1095 steel. (*Courtesy of Chrysler Corp., Detroit.*)

Fig. 22-20. Superfinishing machine for crankshaft bearings. (*Courtesy of Gisholt Machine Co., Madison, Wis.*)

However, an unlimited choice of surface patterns ranging from a mirror finish to 30 microinches rms may be applied.

Superfinishing machines in a variety of designs, of which Fig. 22-20 is an example, are available to industry. This is a machine and never a manual method. It is used in the automotive industry for such components as tappets, crankshaft bearings, clutch plates, brake drums, bearing races, and many others. Production potentials are high with machines adapted to specific parts. By way of example, brake drums are completed at the rate of 150 per hour on a single-spindle machine, while tappet bodies are superfinished at the rate of 720 per hour on a twelve-spindle machine.

Vapor-blast Finishing. Another recent development for surface finishing is that of employing a wet blast carrying an abrasive material. Compressed air at 85 psi drives the abrasive-carrying liquid through the gun nozzle at a rate that causes a vapor blast to result. Various types and sizes of abrasives are used, depending on the finish desired. Castings are processed with a 40-80 quartz or silicon carbide abrasive, whereas machined surface may go to the extreme of a 1,200 mesh "Novaculite" abrasive in a process also termed liquid honing.

This finishing method is indispensable for such applications as contoured dies where tedious hand processing has been standard practice. Another application is that of de-burring small, intricate parts where featheredges remain from previous machining. It is satisfactory for use on glass and plastics, but owing to its nature its action is not as rapid as that of other finishing methods.

Buffing and Polishing. Mention must be made of these two time-honored methods of producing surface finishes. They are not intended as dimension-attaining methods but are useful in achieving eye-pleasing finishes. Buffing and polishing are performed by several different methods and are applied to metal and nonmetals.

Survey Questions

22-1. Is grinding a chip-removal machining method?
22-2. How has grinding contributed to mass production?
22-3. Is production grinding performed with grindstones?
22-4. Name some natural abrasives that are used for grinding.
22-5. How are artificial abrasives produced?
22-6. Of what importance is abrasive grain classification?
22-7. Which of the bond types is most widely used?
22-8. Are all grinding wheels of the same hardness?
22-9. Give the standard that governs grinding wheel markings.
22-10. Why are grinding wheels dressed?
22-11. Are truing and dressing the same operation?
22-12. What are grinding fluids?
22-13. Where is dry grinding used?
22-14. In what units is grinding speed measured?
22-15. Is skill necessary for tool and cutter grinding?
22-16. Does grinding cemented carbide require any special consideration?
22-17. On what type of surfaces does production grinding apply?
22-18. Is cylindrical grinding confined to true cylindrical surfaces?
22-19. Why is dwell time necessary in cylindrical grinding?
22-20. When can plunge grinding be specified?

22-21. Where is internal grinding applied?

22-22. Is internal grinding a precision method?

22-23. Where does centerless grinding show to best advantage?

22-24. How is the workpiece supported in centerless grinding?

22-25. Is centerless grinding confined to external surfaces?

22-26. To what type of operations is surface grinding suited?

22-27. When are magnetic chucks included in tooling a grinding job?

22-28. Should disk grinding be referred to as surface grinding?

22-29. Describe the grinding elements used in disk grinding.

22-30. Can offhand grinding be considered as a precision grinding method?

22-31. Where is snagging important?

22-32. How are jet blades finished economically?

22-33. Define "roughness" as applied to surface finish.

22-34. Give some of the causes of surface roughness.

22-35. What is the primary objective of surface finishing methods?

22-36. Name some instruments used for measuring surface roughness.

22-37. Describe the cutting element used in honing.

22-38. Is honing a manual or machine method or both?

22-39. Does lapping have a dual objective?

22-40. Can a superfinished surface be detected by its surface pattern?

22-41. Has superfinishing been adapted to mass production?

22-42. Give some applications for vapor-blast finishing.

22-43. Are buffing and burnishing similar polishing methods?

REFERENCES

"Better Grinding," 2d ed., Landis Tool Co., Waynesboro, Pa., 1947.

Colvin, Fred H., and Frank A. Stanley: "Grinding Practice," 3d ed., McGraw-Hill Book Company, Inc., New York, 1950.

"Grinding Wheels," Pacific Grinding Wheel Co., Everett, Wash., 1948.

"Handbook on Abrasives and Grinding Wheels," Norton Co., Worcester, Mass., 1946.

Heywood, Johnson: "Grinding Wheels and Their Uses," 2d ed., Penton Publishing Company, Cleveland, 1942.

"Tool Engineers' Handbook," McGraw-Hill Book Company, Inc., New York, 1949.

"Wear and Surface Finish," Gisholt Machine Co., Madison, Wis., 1947.

CHAPTER 23

GEARING

The production of satisfactory gears involves more than gear cutting equipment and its proper operation; of equal importance is the selection of a correct gear material. The gear material chosen must bear close scrutiny in respect to functionality, machinability, heat-treating behavior

Fig. 23-1. Representative gears. (*Courtesy of Western Gear Works, Seattle.*)

as to both hardness and distortion, forgeability, weldability (for fabricated gears), and, above all, manufacturing costs.

Gear Classifications

Gears are employed as a positive means of transmitting motion or power; some gear types are shown in Fig. 23-1. There are modifications of this principle in the sense that changes in direction as well as changes in speed can be effected by gearing.   Bevel gears are designed to change direction of the transmitted motion, while worm gears combine this feature with a change in speed, as between the worm and the worm gear.   There are shape modifications, especially in spur gears, whose objective is that of transmitting motion at a nonuniform rate.

Spur Gears.   These are the most widely used gears.   The face of the spur gear is parallel to the axis, which limits application to transmitting motion between parallel shafts.   Spur gears can be regarded as the least complicated ones to cut, since they have uniform straight teeth.

Helical Gears.   The teeth of these gears are in the form of a helix with respect to their axis.   This tooth design results in more than a single

Fig. 23-2.   Bevel gears with herringbone teeth.   (Courtesy of Douglas Fraser & Sons, Ltd., Arbro -.3 Scotland.)

tooth being in contact, which ensures silent operation and provides greater gear strength.

Herringbone Gears.   These are a modification of the helical type in the sense that they are in effect a double helical.   They are employed for transmitting motion between parallel shafts.   There is a novel design in which bevel gear teeth use a herringbone pattern (Fig. 23-2).   These gears eliminate the tendency toward side thrust that is characteristic of helical gears.   From the manufacturing viewpoint, there are two types of herringbone gears.   The conventional one has a circular recess extending around the circumference of the gear at the junction of the teeth; the second type omits this clearance groove and has solid teeth that meet at the center of the gear face.   Herringbone gears are usually of large size and are applied in gear drives of considerable capacity.

Bevel Gears.   Gears of this type are employed for transmitting motion between shafts located at an angle to each other.   Bevel gears include several modifications both as to tooth and as to design concept. Those having straight teeth are best known. Spiral bevels, which were formerly the standard method for motorcar rear-end drives because of their quieter operating characteristics, are also well known in machinery design and construction. Spiral bevel gears are one example of the curved-tooth type of bevel gear; other examples are the hypoid and the zerol.

Hypoid Gears. These gears are similar to spiral bevels, with the difference that the pinion axis of the hypoid is offset either above or below the gear axis. They resemble spiral bevels in that the teeth are curved and oblique in a pattern that permits gradual engagement and overlapping tooth contact. The offset of the pinion permits the crossing of the

Fig. 23-3.   Square spur gears demonstrate the rack and pinion principle of operation.

gear and pinion shaft, permitting several pinions to be mounted on a common shaft. Most motorcar rear-end drives employ hypoid gears, since the offset pinion permits a lowered drive shaft, thereby reducing the tunnel height in the floor boards.

Zerol Gears. These have curved teeth that lie in the same direction as those on straight bevel gears. The most accurate description of these gears is that they are spiral bevel gears in which the spiral angle is zero. They are cut on the same equipment that is used for spiral bevels.

Worms and Worm Gears. Gears of this type are employed in applications where a substantial reduction in relative motion is desired, especially where the drive shafts are at right angles to each other. The usual concept of a worm-gear drive is that of a screw driving a nut. There are two elements, the worm and the worm wheel, comprising a worm-gear drive. The worm has a constant thread form and uniform axial lead, while the worm wheel is constructed to partially envelop the worm. Single-thread worms are conventional because of their lower cost of manufacture; however, there are multiple-thread designs as well.

Cone-drive Worm Gearing. This is a modification of the conventional worm-gear drive. The difference between the two is that in the cone drive there is a double enveloping of one gear by the other. This design employs a concave-faced worm in place of a straight-faced one.

Geared Rack. This is a spur gear whose pitch diameter is infinity. A rack of a given pitch will mesh with any gear of the same pitch and tooth form. A well-known application of a rack is its use on an engine lathe as a means of traveling the carriage longitudinally. A combination of quadrant spur gears and four racks results in a "square" gear (Fig. 23-3).

Gear Cutting Methods and Machines

Every metal-shaping process has its examples of gear making. Cast gears, or gears with cast teeth, are produced in ferrous as well as nonferrous metals. They are precision-cast, die-cast, or cast in green-sand and in dry-sand molds. Generally such gears are assembled into the end product with no machine work on their teeth beyond de-burring. Die casting and investment casting are both capable of producing gear teeth whose accuracy approaches those produced by machine cutting.

Press-forged gears of nonferrous metals are well known; since they are forged in a die, they compare in accuracy and finish with machine-cut gears. Gear blanks are produced in large volume by impact die forging.

Metal stampings are common for gears that are intended for slow speeds and low power input. These stampings are sometimes stacked and then riveted into what amounts to a laminated whole. This procedure is followed in order to develop the necessary face width for the gear.

Flame machining is successful for producing gears of intermediate and large sizes. Templates are employed in some cases, while in others the desired torch movement is obtained from the cutting machine mechanism. An economical method for producing geared racks is that of flame-cutting the tooth outline along the major axis of a steel bar, thereby yielding two racks with a single torch cut.

Gear Milling. Cutting gear teeth in a milling machine is the most flexible method. Gears of all sizes, within the capacity of the machine, and of all pitches can be cut on a milling machine that is equipped with an index head. Furthermore, different gear styles such as spur, bevel, worm-wheel, and helical gears, are regularly milled. Related items such as roller and silent chain sprockets, metric gears, and ratchets are also produced by milling. The milling machine performs equally as well with single and multiple gear cutters as it does with gear hobs. For the most part, the milling method is selected for use with single cutters for producing gears in small quantities.

The majority of modern spur gearing is designed with teeth of the involute shape or a modification thereof. A single cutter, such as is used in gear milling, produces a satisfactory gear tooth. Any standard involute gear cutter will cut a range of gear teeth. In order to cut any gear from 12 teeth to a rack, a series of eight cutters is necessary for *each pitch*. These cutters are numbered and their cutting ranges are as follows:

Cutter no.	Gear tooth range
1	135 teeth to rack
2	55–134
3	35–54
4	26–34
5	21–25
6	17–20
7	14–16
8	12–13

Where accuracy is desired on the high end of each range, it is recommended that cutters in the half-number size be used for obtaining better tooth form. Thus, for example, cutter no. $1\frac{1}{2}$ will cut gears from 80 to 134 teeth inclusive.

Single tooth involute cutters are available for either $14\frac{1}{2}$ or 20° pressure angles. The tooth form is obtained from the cutter shape. In gear milling, the full tooth depth and form are cut in a single pass. It is desirable on some work to employ a roughing cut ahead of the finishing one as a matter of increased production as well as of greater accuracy. Roughing cuts are made by gear *stocking cutters*. These cutters are generally characterized by steps on their side cutting faces. These steps may be placed on opposite sides of alternating teeth or on both sides of all faces. The cutters are designed to leave ample stock for the finishing cut, which can be made at high speeds since stock removal is not a problem.

Multiple cutters are made in sets to cut two or three teeth in a single pass; however, they are individual types in that they will only cut the number of teeth for which they are designed. Their design varies to the extent that the combinations as between roughing and finishing and between duplex and triplex are nonstandard. Roughing and finishing may be either separate or combined operations (Fig. 23-4).

Gear Hobbing. Hobbing is a process in which gear teeth are generated as the result of the combined rotating movement of the gear blank and the hob. The hobbing process is shown diagrammatically in Fig. 23-5 for both complete and single-tooth generating action. The cutting element, or cutting tool, in the hobbing process is known as a hob. A hob is a threaded, gashed cutting tool that is essentially a fluted hardened steel worm equipped with proper clearances for cutting action. Single-thread (or start) hobs are most generally used, although where a high degree of accuracy is desired on gears of coarse pitch, a roughing cut is taken with double- or triple-thread hobs and the finishing cut with a

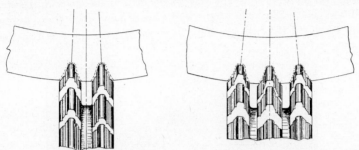

Fig. 23-4. Duplex and triplex multiple roughing gear cutters. (Courtesy of Michigan Tool Company, Detroit.)

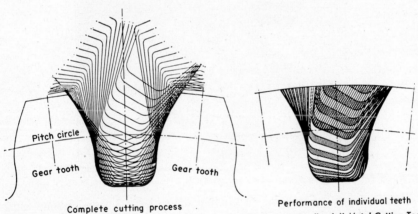

Pitch circle

Gear tooth   Gear tooth

Complete cutting process   Performance of individual teeth

Fig. 23-5. Generating action of hobs. (From "Metal Cutting Tool Handbook," Metal Cutting Tool Institute, New York, 1949.)

single-thread hob. A single-thread hob cuts but one tooth, whereas a double-thread tooth cuts two teeth concurrently.

Gear hobbing can be visualized as the action of a rack and a gear when meshed: as the rack is moved in the direction of its major axis, the gear will rotate. In gear hobbing, an axial section of the hob is representative of the basic rack. Because of the lead or helix of the hob, succeeding axial hob sections advance this basic rack in the direction of the hob axis as it rotates. It can be seen that as the hob completes a full revolution, it will have advanced one full gear tooth.

Hobbing is a continuous cutting operation in which both the hob and the gear blank motion is rotative, with the added feature that feed is a straight-line motion. A hob is capable of cutting any number of teeth within a given pitch. Furthermore, gears produced by a hob of a given pitch will mate perfectly. A typical hobbing operation is shown in Fig. 23-6, which shows a spur gear being cut. The resemblance of a spur hobbing operation to a worm and worm gear in mesh is quite striking. The hob is set to the helix angle of the thread in order that the path of the hob teeth, as they rotate, may be parallel with the teeth of the gear being cut.

Fig. 23-6. Typical spur gear hobbing operation. (Courtesy of Michigan Tool Co., Detroit.)

Hobbing can be applied to cutting spur, helical, herringbone, and worm gears. This method is also employed for such forming as splines, ratchets, square ends, sprockets, cams, and, in fact, almost any contour that is based on a circle and that permits hob clearance while generating. Hobs for special work such as splines are designed to cut only one distinct part and are not to be confused with gear hobs for flexibility. The hobbing principle has been modified to the point where it is built into machine tools for turning shafts having several diameters or special shapes.

GEAR HOBBING MACHINES

The selection of a gear hobbing machine affords a considerable choice of types and models. So far as design is concerned, there are two basic types—the horizontal (Fig. 23-7) and the vertical hobbing machine. The capacity of a hobbing machine is governed by the maximum diameter of gear that it will cut; this is in turn modified by the pitch of the gear.

Undoubtedly the hobbing machine has a closer resemblance to the milling machine than it has to any other machine tool. Hobbing can be likened to milling in that there are two operating principles—climb hobbing and conventional hobbing. It is frequently possible to stack gear blanks as a means of faster production. A typical production study shows seven gear blanks, 7.750 in. OD with 1-in. face, 8 pitch, 60 teeth

Fig. 23-7. Horizontal hobbing machine. (Courtesy of Barber-Colman Co., Rockford, Ill.)

being hobbed to semifinish at a rate of 21.8 min per load or 3.1 min per gear.

Vertical-spindle Hobbing Machines. In this design, as its name indicates, the construction is such that the spindle is vertical. The hobbing head attaches to the main column, the tailstock being movable on the outer column. The gear blank is held in a vertical position for the hobbing operation. Operating principles follow those of the horizontal types. Vertical hobbing machines are built as either single- or multiple-spindle units. Design and construction embody such features as automatic cycling, shifting hobhead, centralized controls, and other details that promote rapid, accurate production.

GEAR SHAPING

A fundamental method of gear shaping is that of using a shaper equipped with a formed tool and a template. This is an expedient for a repair job. There are instances, however, especially for large gears, where a shaper or planer is similarly used. The small shop has the problem of cutting a bevel gear on a shaper owing to the lack of proper gear cutting equipment. Gear shaping is also applied to mass production; there should be no confusion on this point, since there are two widely different concepts involved.

Generating Gear Shapers. In its basic principles, generating gears can be likened to two gears in mesh, one of these being the cutter and the other one the gear blank. The cutter has a reciprocating motion

Fig. 23-8. Conventional gear shaper cutters. The one at the center is reversed in order to show its bottom, or cutting, face.

and at the same time a slow rotation while the gear blank also rotates slowly in engagement with the cutter. The reciprocating motion of the cutter does the shaping. The cutter spindle is driven in relation to the gear blank spindle rotation so as to afford the correct ratio between the number of teeth on the cutter and those on the gear. There are examples of gear shaper operation in which the cutter merely reciprocates without rotating. Since this is a gear generating process, one cutter will produce mating gears of any number of teeth. Cutters are ground with a concave face that provides the necessary cutting edge (Fig. 23-8).

This principle of generating with a reciprocating cutter makes possible a substantial range of work. Internal gears, which prior to this development were difficult to produce, are readily cut by gear shaping. Spur gears, helical gears, herringbone gears, segment gears, contoured gears, face gears, splines, cams, hourglass worms, and profiles can all be cut by this method, although in some instances auxiliary equipment is necessary. Other unique possibilities include eccentric spur gears, three-lobed holes, square holes, irregularly shaped pawls, sprockets, ratchets, racks, interrupted gears, and gear segments.

Gear Shaping Machines. There is no counterpart to gear shapers among machine tools. In Fig. 23-9 the gear cutter is shown at the left with the two gears that are being cut mounted on their spindle in the center of the machine. The actual cutting operation can be noted as being one in which a single gear tooth is cut at a time. As the reciprocat-

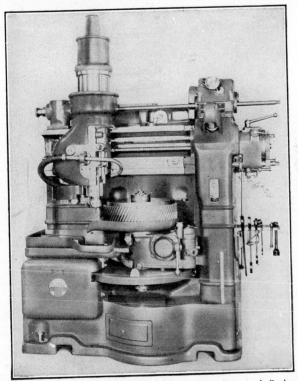

Fig. 23-9. Gear shaper designed to cut external as well as internal spur or helical gears. (Courtesy of The Fellows Gear Shaper Co., Springfield, Vt.)

ing cutter and the gear rotate, the cutter is fed into the work until correct tooth depth has been reached.

Shear-speed Gear Shapers. Another development in gear shaping machines is one that, primarily, reverses the principles involved in the previously discussed types. The shear-speed gear shaper cuts all gear teeth simultaneously. The gear blank reciprocates vertically. The cutter head is equipped with cutter blades that advance radially an equal amount with each workpiece stroke (Fig. 23-10). The cutter blades are retracted automatically in order to afford clearance for the workpiece. The entire operating cycle is automatic, including gear blank clamping. As a result, high production rates are readily achieved.

Fig. 23-10. Cutter tool head for a shear-speed gear shaper. (Courtesy of Michigan Tool Co., Detroit.)

BEVEL GEAR MANUFACTURE

Bevel gears have individual features, for example, the pitch angle, pitch-cone apex, and face-cone apex. The tooth shape on bevel gears is such that their manufacture requires distinctive techniques.

Bevel Gear Blanks. A bevel gear is actually made in two separate machining phases. The first phase deals with the bevel gear blank. The design of the bevel gear blank must extend beyond mathematical and functional considerations and into the field of production problems. Such items as heat-treatment, mounting possibilities when cutting (which includes correct relation of hub and bore for rigidity), hub lengths for cutter clearance, and webbing require consideration. Locating surfaces are important to mounting the blank correctly in the gear cutting machine.

Bevel Gear Planer. The bevel gear planer cuts the top and bottom sides of a tooth separately (Fig. 23-11). The resemblance to a planer is that a single-point tool is reciprocated as the tooth-cutting element. This cutting tool operates on a slide carried by an arm so designed that it can swing about the apex of the gear pitch cone in a vertical as well as in a horizontal plane. The positions of this arm are, in turn, controlled by a roller that rides on an element termed the "former," which represents the shape of the desired gear tooth. An individual former is provided for each side of the tooth, and sets of formers are available for both large and small pitch angles. The bevel gear planer operates on the copying and not the generating principle. The gear planer is used primarily for cutting gears of large diameter and heavy pitch.

Straight Bevel Gears. Straight-toothed bevel gears are usually produced by the generation method in a machine that has two single-point tools with straight cutting edges. These tools reciprocate on straight slides in their cutting cycle, which includes machining both sides of a tooth simultaneously. During the cutting cycle the tools and the gear blank have relative rotations, thereby producing the required tooth

Fig. 23-11. Bevel gear planer, showing tool operating mechanism. (*Courtesy of Gleason Works, Rochester, N.Y.*)

profile. The cutting tools represent an imaginary crown gear, and since they have straight cutting edges, any number of teeth can be cut by changing the relative motion of the tools and the gear blank.

Bevel gear generators generally make a roughing cut that is followed by a finishing cut. There are some modifications of this procedure, especially in fine-pitch gears, where roughing and finishing are performed in one operation. This is accomplished by using cutting tools that are made with both a roughing and a finishing section. Conventional finishing tools are of uniform section throughout their entire length, whereas roughing tools are of several designs, some of them being combination tools that include a slotter and a side cutting tool. Bevel-gear cutting equipment is also available, in which a rotating cutter whose teeth are positioned radially, is employed for roughing operations on a limited range of gear sizes.

Spiral Bevel Gears. Gears in this classification have several type modifications of tooth shape and form. There are two main styles: in one category of spiral bevel gears the teeth are generated, while in a second style, termed formate, the gear is not generated but its mating pinion has generated teeth that are modified to suit the gear teeth, which have no profile curvature. Formate gears have the same appearance as generated ones except for a slight difference in the profile shape of the teeth.

Fig. 23-12. Generating a spiral bevel gear with a rotating circular cutter. (*Courtesy of Gleason Works, Rochester, N.Y.*)

Spiral bevel gears, except for the larger sizes which are cut on generating-type planers, are made on gear cutting machines that utilize a face-mill type of cutter having multiple blades extending from a slotted head in the direction of its axis (Fig. 23-12). Cutting edges of the teeth are straight, yet tooth profiles of proper curvature result from relative rotation of the gear blank and the cutter spindle cradle. As this cradle returns to its starting position, the blank is indexed for the next tooth. There is considerable flexibility offered by these gear cutting machines, since hand of spiral, spiral angle, tooth bearing, and tooth size can all be varied by changing the relative position of the cutter and blank. Hypoid gears are cut on these gear cutting machines with some adjustment in setup.

FABRICATED GEARS

The great majority of cut gears are made from blanks that have been machined from forgings, castings, or bar stock. Material selection is based on cost and service requirements primarily. Where large gears are concerned, there is a tendency to replace castings with weldments (Fig. 23-13).

There are other types of gear blanks in which composite construction is used. A timing gear in which the gear face and web are cast aluminum alloy with a ferrous metal hub has proved successful in automobile

Fig. 23-13.   Gear blank weldment.   Note three plate web members.   (Courtesy of Western Gear Works, Lynwood, Calif.)

motors. This construction is used to ensure quiet operation in the gear train. There are other developments that achieve the same result by using nonmetallics for the gear teeth in conjunction with a metallic hub.

Gear Finishing Methods

Gear Shaving. This gear finishing method is applicable to all types of spur and helical gears of both external and internal types. Its sequence in the manufacturing program is variable to the extent that shaving may either precede or follow heat-treatment. Most automotive shops shave gears prior to carburizing and hardening, a practice that is preferred by the gear-making industry generally.

Gear shaving is a machining process that produces fine, curled, hairlike chips; it is in no sense a cold-working process similar to burnishing. There are two basic principles around which gear shaving machines are designed. The most popular method employs a rotary shave cutter (Fig. 23-14), of which there are several styles. In the other design, a rack-type shaving tool consisting of a series of blades performs the necessary cutting action.

Rotary Shaving. In rotary shaving, the gear and cutter are mounted as intermeshing gears. The cutter has gashed teeth, but these do not extend to the root nor onto the crest; shaving action is confined to the sides and does not involve the periphery of the cutter. There are several principles of mounting the gear with respect to the shaving cutter. In one style these two elements are mounted on crossed axes in order to

Fig. 23-14.   Gear shaver cutters.   (*Courtesy of National Broach & Machine Co., Detroit.*)

provide cutting action with a minimum of pressure. Stock removal results from axial motion of the cutting edges of the cutting teeth enhanced by the reciprocating motion between the cutter and the gear.

Additional rotary shaving methods include tangential shaving, which is a modification of the crossed-axis principle to the extent that the relative motion between gear and cutter is a tangential reciprocation of the cutter across the work. Narrow-faced gears are especially well adapted to this shaving method. In another method, the cutter and gear axes are parallel. Cutting action is obtained by reciprocating the cutter at a high frequency. Internal gears are shaved by this method.

Rack Shaving. The shaving, or generating, rack which is made up of individually replaceable teeth is mounted on the shaving machine table.

The gear is mounted on centers with its axis at an angle to the rack. As the rack reciprocates, the gear rolls with it, while at the same time it moves crosswise on the rack as a means of obtaining uniform rack wear. The gear is fed downward during the operation until its correct size has been reached. This method is most suitable for high production, since original tooling is somewhat more costly than with rotary shaving; yet rack tool life is so long that unit production costs are low. A rack of a given pitch will shave all gears of that same pitch and pressure angle.

Crown Shaving. The objective in crown shaving is that of shaping a tooth to provide a very slight crown at its center. This is accomplished by shaving the ends of the teeth, with the result that there will not be a concentrated load occurring there. Crown shaving can be accomplished by either rotary- or rack-type shaving machines.

Gear Shaving Procedures. In rotary gear shaving the procedure includes underpass shaving, traverse shaving, and traverpass shaving, which is a combination of the two other methods. Shaving cutter speeds are varied to suit the conditions of the gear as to material and hardness as well as finish desired. The usual speed, calculated for the pitch circle, lies between 300 and 400 sfpm for satisfactory results. Table feed is also a variable quantity, although a value of 0.010 in. per revolution of the gear can be regarded as a mean value.

Gear shaving concerns itself with tooth finish and not with gear diameter. The pre-shave cutting of a gear allows stock on the *thickness* of the tooth only. The amount of stock to be shaved varies with the diametral pitch: the coarser the pitch, the greater the amount. Thus gears of 2 to 4 diametral pitch allow 0.003 to 0.004 in. per tooth, while those of 16 to 18 diametral pitch have an amount of but 0.001 to 0.002 in. Uniform stock removal across the tooth is desirable for uniform cutter wear and best finish results.

OTHER GEAR FINISHING METHODS

Gear grinding is applied where distortion is severe or a considerable amount of stock needs to be removed following the hardening operation. In common with precision grinding methods generally, gear grinding is capable of producing both an excellent finish and a high degree of accuracy. Critical gear installations frequently specify grinding for the method of finish. Gear grinding is considered to be the oldest method of precision gear finishing.

Gear lapping is a finishing method whose objective is that of correcting and removing small imperfections. Gear lapping machines are built in various styles and cover the complete range of gear requirements. Operating characteristics follow those common to conventional lapping machines.

Burnishing is a cold-working process that employs an extremely hard work gear in rolling contact with the gear being finished. Burnishing was formerly looked upon with favor, but it has been largely superseded by shaving. A burnished gear carries considerable residual stress, which is undesirable in connection with any succeeding heat-treatment.

Shot peening is sometimes used as a final finishing operation on gearing as a means of placing the outer layer of metal on the teeth in compression for better service life. This method is not considered a finishing one in the sense of attaining dimensional accuracy or surface excellence.

Gear Tooth Pointing. When gearing is designed for sliding engagement, it is desirable to point, chamfer, or round off the end of the gear teeth that are to mesh with each other. Among the several methods used for pointing are grinding and machining.

GEAR CHECKING EQUIPMENT

No matter how carefully gears may be designed and manufactured, the possibility of error is always present. The variation permissible in gearing depends upon its end use. As loads and speeds are increased, the requirements for accuracy increase to the point where this characteristic becomes critical. There is a wealth of gear checking equipment available; included are instruments for bench-type checking as well as machinery for testing gears in operation.

Fig. 23-15. Gear sound tester. Designed for operating gears at various loads and speeds. (Courtesy of National Broach & Machine Co., Detroit.)

The amount and character of the noise that a gear installation emits is a clue to its accuracy. Every pair of gears develops its own characteristic sound when in operation. Such sounds have been classified to the extent that an experienced inspector can interpret them as to source and cause. Several types of testing equipment have been developed for the purpose of screening gearing to eliminate noise (Fig. 23-15). The tester illustrated has a sounding box designed to amplify gear noises to the point where they can be recognized. It can be operated in the shop without interference from outside noises, since it is soundproofed to isolate the gearing sounds. The gear testing equipment termed "speeders" has several modifications of this principle built in.

Equipment for checking gear accuracy is all characterized by its precision potentials. Pitch distances, for example, are measured by gage blocks; in other designs, recording equipment is employed to chart runout, or wobble. Dial gages and sine bars are basic elements of other gear checking equipment. Master gears are another means for ascertaining gear accuracy.

FINE-PITCH GEARING

A classification in which the diametral pitch is 20 or finer is known as fine-pitch gearing (Fig. 23-16). Considered from the standpoint of theoretical design, there is no characteristic distinguishing this from coarser pitch gearing of involute form. There is some difference in manufacturing procedures, since fine-pitch gears require special attention in such matters as clearance and top land dimensions. The concept of fine pitch includes spur, helical, and worm gearing. Complete specifications and engineering information on fine-pitch gearing are available in several standards published by the American Gear Manufacturers' Association.

Fig. 23-16. Fine-pitch bevel gears. (Courtesy of Western Gear Works, Lynwood, Calif.)

Survey Questions

23-1. Give some leading applications for gears.

23-2. Wherein do fabricated gears differ from other types?

23-3. Which classification of gears has the greatest application?

23-4. Where are hypoid gears frequently employed?

23-5. How does a geared rack function on an engine lathe?

23-6. By what methods are gears cast?

23-7. Are gears produced by any methods other than casting or machine cutting?

23-8. What machine tool is regarded as having the greatest versatility for gear cutting?

23-9. Are spur gear teeth always of involute shape?

23-10. Will a single cutter suffice for cutting all gear sizes of a given pitch?

23-11. When should stocking cutters be used?

23-12. How are multiple cutters used?

23-13. In gear hobbing, what elements rotate?

23-14. Mention the various gear types that can be produced by hobbing.

23-15. How is the capacity of a gear hobbing machine determined?

23-16. Distinguish between climb and conventional hobbing.

23-17. On what two general design principles are gear hobbing machines designed?
23-18. Describe the principle of gear shaping.
23-19. Is gear shaping a mass-production method?
23-20. How does the operating principle of a shear-speed gear shaper differ from conventional designs?
23-21. On what machine tools can bevel gear blanks be produced?
23-22. Is the cutting of a bevel gear confined to reciprocating tool equipment?
23-23. What gear cutting machines are used for cutting spiral-bevel gears?
23-24. Why are gears shaved?
23-25. Is there more than one basic method of gear shaving?
23-26. Does gear shaving have any effect on the size of a gear?
23-27. When is gear tooth pointing necessary?
23-28. Why are gear teeth shot-peened?
23-29. How does gear sound-testing equipment function?
23-30. Does fine-pitch gearing differ in design from coarser pitch types?
23-31. Name the organization that primarily sponsors gear manufacture.

REFERENCES

American Gear Manufacturers' Association, Gear Standards Publications.
Davenport, G.: "The Hobbing Method of Cutting Gear Teeth," McGraw-Hill Book Company, Inc., New York, 1940.
"Gear Materials and Blanks," American Standard B6.2—1933, American Standards Association, New York, 1933.
"Gears: Cutting, Finishing and Checking," Michigan Tool Company, Detroit, 1945.
"Kent's Mechanical Engineers' Handbook," 12th ed., John Wiley & Sons, Inc., New York, 1950.
"Letter Symbols for Gear Engineering," American Standard B6.5—1943, American Standards Association, New York, 1943.
"Metal Cutting Tool Handbook," Metal Cutting Tool Institute, New York, 1949.
"Modern Methods of Gear Manufacture," 3d ed., National Broach and Machine Company, Detroit, 1950.
"Tool Engineers' Handbook," McGraw-Hill Book Company, Inc., New York, 1949.

CHAPTER 24

TRANSFER AND SPECIAL MACHINES

A novel development, and one that is proving to be the beginning of a new trend in engineering manufacture, is that of the automatic transfer machine. This principle is being applied to machining components whose production requirements are impressive. There appears to be no standard terminology applying to this new method. Among the terms used to designate these machining lines are automatic transfer processing machines, automatic processing machines, transfer-matics, transfer machines, and process-through machines. Basically this equipment is composed of several individual machine tools arranged in accordance with a predetermined machining sequence yet integrated into a composite whole. The result is that of machining on the principle of the production line.

A beginning was made by assembling several multiple-spindle machine tools into a line. The workpiece was successively machined in each one in accordance with the chosen sequence of operations. Drilling and tapping were the primary considerations of these early machines. The workpiece was loaded, clamped, and transferred manually from one station to the next. Continuing study and investigation resulted in the successful completion of a transfer machine in which both clamping and transferring became automatic functions of the machine. Essentially this achievement formed the basis of the automatic transfer machine in its present state of development.

This equipment demonstrated its ability to machine aircraft engine cylinder heads for both the B-17 and the B-29 heavy bomber program in World War II. One transfer machine built for this program had 81 stations and its total length was 200 ft. The experience gained in wartime applications has served as a basis for further development of the automatic transfer machine for peacetime production requirements.

Automatic transfer machines are individual in the sense that they are built to meet specific requirements. The problems are not confined to production possibilities, nor do unit production costs constitute the sole consideration; the chief factor surrounding their installation deals with the type of industry they are to serve. In the automotive industry, where design changes are continually being made, it may be necessary to write off the cost of an automatic transfer machine over a model year whereas in another industry, in which design modification is less frequent, a greater period of time might be allowed for amortizing the investment. It is possible to modify existing stations on automatic transfer machines to accommodate revisions in workpiece design.

Transfer Machines

The first transfer-type machines were confined to drilling and tapping operations. These operations continue to be in the forefront; however, related ones have been added, including rough, semifinish, and finish boring, facing, chamfering, reaming, countersinking, counterboring, rough and finishing milling.

Individual machine tools that form part of an automatic transfer machine may be of conventional design insofar as operating principles are concerned. Multiple-spindle drilling machines serve as an example. Obviously design and construction modifications are frequently necessary in order to integrate the individual unit into a transfer machine.

Another production accomplishment is that of processing two work-pieces simultaneously. Such a procedure is possible where parts are of a size to permit double mounting on a single work-holding fixture. This procedure necessitates duplicate tooling throughout all machining stations. There is little that is fundamentally new from a machining viewpoint in the automatic transfer machines. Their distinguishing characteristics are those of integration, synchronization, and workpiece handling.

Machine Operation. It is incorrect to assume that these machines are automatic to the point where the human element can be completely eliminated. These machines operate by electrical and hydraulic circuits. Not only is the human element needed; it must be of the highest skill, intelligence, and resourcefulness since any down time is critical with production rates high. Even though push-button controls and signaling devices are built into most automatic transfer machines, they cannot operate without supervision and care.

Machine Achievements. Transfer machines are at their best for heavy production runs. They are not suitable for every type of manufacture nor are they confined to machining operations. The A. O. Smith Co. automobile frame plant[1] furnishes an example of long standing of the application of a variation of the automatic transfer machine principle to the fabrication of steel strip. Metal stamping, with automatic transfer presses, was presented in Chap. 10, together with illustrations

[1] Milwaukee, Wis.

of requisite equipment. A somewhat similar development has occurred in production foundries where castings are produced on another variation of the process-through principle including sand conditioning systems, machine molding, conveyor pouring, mechanical shakeout, and flask return.

Irrespective of the end product, the objective in all these developments is that of achieving greater production at lower cost. This major accomplishment is traceable to the elimination of lost time in workpiece movement. As material-handling time is decreased, man-hour requirements are lowered in direct proportion. In order to understand the progress that has been made by this innovation, the following cases, whose data have been provided by the respective machine tool manufacturers involved, are included.

PROCESS MACHINES

An automatic process machine consisting of four stations for machining truck cylinder blocks is shown in Fig. 24-1. The first station is a six-

Fig. 24-1.   Four-station automatic process machine for machining truck motor block castings.   (Courtesy of Ingersoll Milling Machine Co., Rockford, Ill.)

spindle cylinder boring machine that rough-bores the block casting. The next machine chamfers the top of the bores. A third machine mills bearing ends and bearing notches. The fourth machine is a four-spindle, two-traveling-head milling machine that machines the side pads. The four machines are connected by a hydraulically operated transfer mechanism and the workpiece is clamped hydraulically. Chips are disposed of through a conveyor running under the machine. Guaranteed production from this four-station automatic process line is 56 cylinder blocks per hr at 100 per cent efficiency.

TRANSFER-MATIC

An automatic transfer machine for machining automatic transmission cases for motor cars is shown in Fig. 24-2. A novel feature of the general arrangement of this machine is its ability to return the work-holding

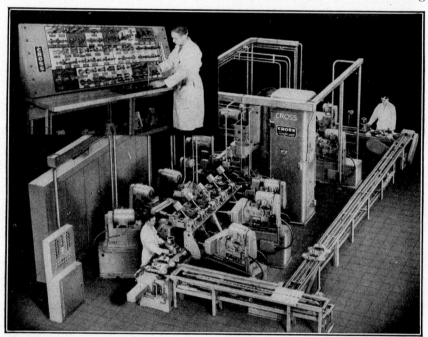

Fig. 24-2. Transfer-matic built for machining automobile automatic transmission cases. Note preset tool board pictured at upper left. (*Courtesy of The Cross Company, Detroit.*)

fixture to its starting point. This feature is made possible by a four-sided, or rectangular, layout, as distinguished from the better-known straight-line principle common to automatic transfer machines.

The machine has 15 stations, equipped with a total of 84 tools which drill, ream, bore, and tap 48 holes. With this tooling, a production rate of 67 transmission cases per hour is obtained at 80 per cent efficiency with two operators—one for loading and the other for unloading. One operator loads the workpieces on pallet-type fixtures which are transferred from station to station hydraulically. Accurate location and clamping of the work-holding fixture at each station is accomplished by hydraulically operated shot pins and cam-actuated clamps. The operating cycle is interrupted automatically if critical tools are either improperly set for depth or accidentally broken.

Unique accessories to the transfer-matic are a special bench and tool board for carrying two complete sets of *preset* tools and a complement of tool-setting gages; the tool bench is shown at the upper left in Fig. 24-2. There is a decided time-saving potential inherent in these preset tools, since when they are mounted in the machine no time is consumed for adjusting and setting.   Machine down time is thus materially lessened.

Case Studies of Transfer Machines

TRANSMISSION END BELL HOUSINGS

The casting machined on an automatic transfer machine is shown in Fig. 24-3, upper left view with the holding fixture below.   The other

Fig. 24-3.   End bell transmission casting, shown with work-holding fixture.   (*Courtesy of Greenlee Bros. & Co., Rockford, Ill.*)

views show different positions of the casting mounted on its holding fixture.   The fixture serves to locate the casting accurately for its processing.   At one station the fixtures are rotated 90° and at another they are tilted in order to permit machining from six directions.

The automatic transfer machine for processing this end bell transmission casting is shown in Fig. 24-4.   This machine consists of 22 stations. It is designed to permit machining from six directions—top, bottom, and four sides.   This machine performs a total of 95 drilling, reaming, spot-facing, chamfering, and tapping operations simultaneously, in a cycle time of 72 sec. Its capacity is 40 completed pieces per hour at 80 per cent efficiency. The discharge end is shown together with the hydraulic-

Fig. 24-4. Twenty-two-station automatic transfer machine built to machine end bell transmission casting. (*Courtesy of Greenlee Bros. & Co., Rockford, Ill.*)

pump units and electrical control board. The machine has a total over-all length of 47 ft.

REFERIGERATOR COMPRESSOR BODIES

In the automatic transfer machine shown in Fig. 24-5, cast-iron refrigerator compressor bodies are machined by placing two workpieces on each holding fixture for simultaneous processing.

This is a 24-station machine that performs 31 different machining operations with a total of 152 tools. Specifications of this automatic transfer machine include the following components:

Tools: 50 drills, 12 face mills, 2 side mills, 2 end mills, 12 boring tools, 38 chamfering tools, and 36 taps, totaling 152 tools.

Stations: 19 working, 2 inspections, 1 loading, 2 idle, totaling 24 stations.

Electrical: 39 motors, 169 total hp; 8 miles of wiring, 148 limit switches, 78 indicating lights, 107 push buttons, 226 magnetic starters, contactors, and timers.

Machine cycle: 30.5 sec.

Production rate: 188 workpieces per hour at 80 per cent efficiency.

Over-all length of machine: 98 ft, 8¼ in.

Prior to the placing of the workpiece, it has been turned, faced, and bored and the main center bearing rough-machined. The workpiece is located in the work-holding fixture by means of two dowel-pin holes that are previously machined in the skirt of the casting.

Fig. 24-5. Twenty-four-station automatic transfer machine for processing refrigerator compressor bodies, which are shown on their workpiece mountings. (*Courtesy of Greenlee Bros. & Co., Rockford, Ill.*)

All operations of this machine are synchronized. Heads are fed automatically by hydraulic power. All units must perform their operations and return to the rest position before the fixtures can be released for transferal to the next station. One operator takes care of the loading and he controls all functions of the machine

This automatic transfer machine was placed in operation in 1946. It was modified in 1947 and again in 1949 in order to accommodate design revisions of the workpiece. Although its rated capacity is 188 parts per hr, actual production records over a 6-month period reveal an average production rate of 212 parts per hour. Since its installation it has machined more than 2 million compressor body castings.

Special Machines

The perfecting of single-purpose, high-production designs simplifies choice between a conventional, or general-purpose, and a specialized machine tool. The final selection is predicated on production requirements considered together with cost pattern. The machine tool builder will offer a design to meet the specifications as presented; this may be a modification of some existing piece of equipment or it may be an entirely new concept. In any event, the specialized machine is selected in preference to the conventional or general-purpose one if an economy study shows it to be superior. This trend in machining equipment is rather pronounced in the automotive industry and in similar fields where high production prevails.

SPECIALIZED TRANSFER MACHINE

An example of a specialized transfer machine is shown in Fig. 24-6. This machine core-drills and reams automotive axle housings. It is

Fig. 24-6.   Fully automatic transfer machine that requires no operator for loading or unloading. (*Courtesy of Baker Brothers, Inc., Toledo, Ohio.*)

novel in construction, since it is adjustable for castings within the range of 60 to 96 in. Another interesting feature is that it does not require an operator. Workpieces are taken from a previous machining operation and placed on its loading platform, where a call switch for cycling the transfer machine is located. As a result, unless a workpiece is in the loading position the machine does not cycle. A ramp at the unloading end carries away the finished part by gravity.

SPECIALIZED MACHINE TOOL UNITS

Earlier in this chapter the nature of automatic transfer machines was discussed. They are composites of a number of special single-purpose machine tools designed for integration into the transfer machine. The individual units are as diverse as the workpieces machined thereon. In

Fig. 24-7. Specialized production machine for milling, drilling, reaming, counterboring, and tapping bottom of single, double, and four-cylinder crankcases. (Courtesy of Barnes Drill Company, Rockford, Ill.)

many of these specialized units, several different machining operations are performed, the exact design depending on the requirements of the transfer machine as a whole (Fig. 24-7). The example shown is not an unusual one; limitations of space prevent an extended exposition of the many specialized machine tool units that have been developed for combination in transfer machines.

Survey Questions

24-1. Is the principle of the automatic transfer machine confined to machine tool equipment?

24-2. Give some of the terms applied to the automatic transfer machine.

24-3. What was the forerunner of the present transfer machines?

24-4. Where can automatic transfer machines be used to best advantage?

24-5. List the chief machining operations that are included in transfer machines.

24-6. Are simultaneous machining operations possible?

24-7. Just what are the unique features of automatic transfer machines?

24-8. How does the term "stations" apply here?

24-9. Can automobile frames be produced on automatic transfer machines?

24-10. Can a foundry be fitted into the transfer machine program?

24-11. How are the controls on automatic transfer machines handled?

24-12. What is meant by preset tooling?

24-13. Under what circumstances are special machines chosen in preference to general-purpose types?

24-14. Is there any transfer machine that does not require an operator for loading or unloading?

24-15. How are machining fixtures applied to automatic transfer machines?

CHAPTER 25

CUTTING ELEMENTS FOR MACHINE TOOLS

In the terminology of metal cutting, both the machine tool and the cutting tool used in that machine are designated as "tools," and this causes some confusion. There is no similarity between these "tools," since the latter is complementary to the former. For this reason—to differentiate between the actual cutting tool and the machine tool in which it is used—the expression *cutting element* has been introduced in the present chapter heading. This choice of terminology is at variance with accepted usage but is made in the belief that it will aid in the clarification of the term *cutting tool* as that term is applied in machining generally. The distinction having been made clear, the standard terminology, which includes both the expression *tool* and *cutting tool*, will be employed in the text of this chapter. By way of definition, a cutting tool has a cutting edge, single or in multiple, which is used to produce the machined surface on the workpiece being processed in a machine tool.

Machining Research. Scientific studies in machining were begun in 1880 by Frederick W. Taylor at the Midvale Steel Company in Philadelphia. The results of his research, which included investigations at the Bethlehem Steel Company, among other manufactories, were presented in December 1906 as part of his inaugural address as president of the American Society of Mechanical Engineers. This monograph, "On the Art of Cutting Metals," is a learned paper of outstanding brilliance and completeness.[1] He acknowledges the contributions to these studies by his colleagues, White, Gantt, and Barth, among others. The monograph is of such fundamental importance to an understanding of the subject of metal cutting that it is recommended for study by every student interested in this field.

Some of the discoveries and developments made by Taylor and his associates have, with the passing of time, proved of fundamental significance. The use of cooling water introduced at the point of the cutting

---

[1] *Trans. ASME*, Vol. 28, pp. 32–350, 1907.

tool is one of the recommendations that has continued in favor and has received further study and improvement. Barth lead this group of investigators in the application of mathematics to the physical experimental data which resulted in the perfection, about 1901, of a slide rule for calculating machine tool operating data.

A significant discovery in cutting tools occurred in the period 1898–1900, during which the Taylor-White Process of heat-treating chrome-tungsten steels, was perfected. This development, supplemented in 1906 by the discovery that small vanadium additions to chrome-tungsten steels improved red-hardness and tool life, gave industry modern high-speed steel. The introduction of these steels proved revolutionary: they were given universal application for cutting tools for machining metals as well as nonmetals. They continue to occupy a position of importance, although the introduction of cast nonferrous tool elements and more latterly, cemented carbides, has lessened the employment of high-speed steel.

The research in cutting metal has been shared by many investigators in several countries; this work belongs to no one group of men. Fundamental and fruitful as the Taylor investigations proved to be, they are not alone in the field. Engineering literature is replete with the names of researchers in metal cutting. Prominent among these are Klopstock and Schwerd in Germany; Rosenhain and Sturney in England; Boston, Gilbert, Ernst, Martellotti, Merchant, Schmidt, Trigger, and Chao in the United States.

Fundamental Factors. The solution of the problem of machining a given component involves many variables; however, the shape and type of cutting tool, its composition, the capacity of the chosen machine tool, and the properties of the component are of major importance. There are other pertinent factors affecting any machining problem, such as production and cost requirements, personnel, available equipment, and plant layout.

Hot Machining. In machining metals emphasis has generally been placed on work at room temperatures. Recently interest has developed in the subject of hot machining, in which the metal being machined is maintained at an elevated temperature. While this research is far from complete, certain general statements can be made. Among them is the fact that length of tool life may either increase or decrease as workpiece temperature is raised. A metal that machines well at room temperature will deliver lowered tool life when machined at elevated temperatures. On the other hand, materials that are unmachinable, such as high-temperature alloys used in jet engine blades, give improved tool life when machined at an elevated temperature. This behavior is explained in the same manner as machining at normal temperatures.

Tool Cutting Action

The generally held belief that a cutting tool working in metal acts similarly to a wedge used in splitting wood has been shown to be inaccurate as a result of research studies by Hans Ernst.[1]   In place of the so-named theory of splitting, the concept of metal shear has been evolved. To make it possible for the cutting edge of the tool to enter the metal being machined, a force needs to be applied along that edge which is equal to the forces tending to hold the crystals within the metal together. With the application of this force, the metal ahead of the cutting edge is placed in shear.   This shear stress reaches a maximum value along a shear plane that is approximately perpendicular to the face of the tool. The location of the shear plane varies as does its size or the shear area. Among the pertinent factors are the shape and geometry of the cutting tool.   Careful attention must be given to the grinding of a cutting tool in order to obtain optimum performance both as to metal removal and as to finish on the component being machined.   The physical characteristics of the component also exert a profound effect on the final machining results.

A further factor is that of friction between the chip and the face of the cutting tool.   Friction can be lessened with light cuts that yield thin chips; however, that is not an efficient procedure for maximum metal removal.   In like manner, a low relative velocity between the chip and the face of the cutting tool is inefficient when viewed from the standpoint of metal removal.   Two alternatives remain—the use of a lubricant between the chip and the tool face and the improvement of quality of the surface on the cutting tool face.   Insofar as the former is concerned, it is apparent that a cutting fluid should be selected with extreme care, since it serves the dual function of coolant and lubricant.   The surface condition of a cutting tool will change with use.   It may be honed to a smooth finish but as a result of chip abrasion the surface soon roughens in service.

Another approach to the reduction of friction between chip and tool is that of additives in the metal being machined.   The free-machining steels feature the inclusion of sulfides—and in remote cases of lead—as a means of lowering the friction coefficient between the workpiece and the tool.   Obviously, lower power requirements parallel lower frictional forces.   In addition, better surface quality is obtained on the workpiece, since greater freedom from built-up tool edge is a natural result.

Coolants.   The practice of using a coolant in machining operations is standard procedure.   The array of coolants extends from water through the soluble oils.   Included among the latter are many proprietary compounds as well as oils of both animal and mineral base.   Con-

[1] "Physics of Metal Cutting," American Society for Metals, Cleveland, 1938.

tinuing research is yielding important new developments in this field. A newcomer is the use of wax as a coolant. It is suggested that the individual operation be carefully studied in order that proper coolant selection can be made. The selection of an improper material for this important application can prove distressing from the standpoint of cost as well as of end product.

CHIP FORMATION

The science of metal cutting has developed the facts on chip formation to the point where three basic types are classified; these classifications

Fig. 25-1. Type 1 chip: discontinuous, or segmented, chip. (*Courtesy of Cincinnati Milling and Grinding Machines Co., Cincinnati.*)

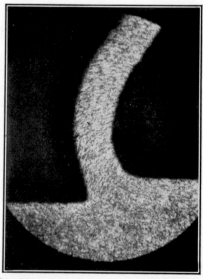

Fig. 25-2. Type 2 chip: continuous chip without built-up tool edge. (*Courtesy of Cincinnati Milling and Grinding Machines Co., Cincinnati.*)

are recorded in the literature[1] and are accepted as basic, irrespective of the type of machining operation used—broaching, drilling, milling, turning, or any other.

Type 1 Chip. This type, termed the discontinuous, or segmented, chip (Fig. 25-1), is commonly found in the machining of brittle metals such as gray cast iron. The chip consists of individual segments of varying size, which may or may not adhere to each other, and may leave the tool in the form of particles. Segments result from the actual fracturing of the metal ahead of the tool cutting edge. The surface quality on the workpiece is usually fair; long tool life and low power consumption

[1] Ernst, Hans, and M. E. Merchant: "Chip Formation, Friction and Finish," Cincinnati Milling Machine Co., Cincinnati.

are further characteristics. This chip type can also be obtained when ductile materials are machined at low speeds; such procedure is not conducive to long tool life, and a poor surface quality results.

Type 2 Chip. This classification refers to the continuous chip without built-up tool edge (Fig. 25-2). It is the ideal chip to obtain when machining ductile metals. The chip is formed by the continuing deformation of the metal ahead of the tool without fracture and is accompanied by smooth flow of the chip over the tool face. It results in an excellent surface on the workpiece. This chip is best obtained when machining at high speeds. On brass, this chip can be obtained at practically any cutting speed. It does pose the problem of chip disposal; this drawback can be overcome by grinding a groove, termed a chip breaker, on the face of the cutting tool. Attention must be given to this detail as a safety precaution for the operator.

Type 3 Chip. The basic characteristic in this classification is a continuous chip formed with built-up tool edge (Fig. 25-3). In effect this chip is similar to type 2 except for the built-up tool edge, which is a mass of metal that adheres to the tool face. This mass is formed as the result of high resistance to sliding of the chip along the tool face. The mass increases in size until it becomes unstable under the influence of the cutting pressure, when a part or all of the mass may break away. A part of the broken-off built-up edge may pass over the cutting edge

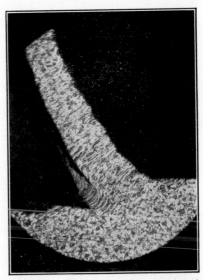

Fig. 25-3. Type 3 chip: continuous chip with built-up tool edge. (*Courtesy of Cincinnati Milling and Grinding Machines Co., Cincinnati.*)

into the work, resulting in a rough surface. It is conceded that the chief cause of surface roughness can be traced to built-up edge effect. The elimination of this difficulty is achieved by reducing the high frictional resistance between the chip and the tool edge. Regardless of chip classification, the fundamental mechanism of metal cutting in machining is the same; differing results are traceable to material composition and to tool behavior in the given job.

Single-point Tools

A single-point tool is a cutting tool for use in a lathe, turret lathe, planer, shaper, boring mill, or other machine having one face and one continuous cutting edge which produces the machined surface.[1] Such a tool can either be made in one piece, with the cutting edge an extension of the shank, or it may be in the form of a bit that is clamped in a toolholder. In either case the actual cutting face may be in the form of an inserted tip; in some special cases the cutting tip may be built up by welding through the use of a weld rod of desired composition. Tool bits offer the advantage of ease of interchangeability and low cost.

Tool bits are clamped in a toolholder which is designed to accommodate a given cross section. Toolholders are available in a wide range of styles and shapes. The usual set employed with a lathe consists of three holders, one right bent, one left bent, and a straight one. Clamping is usually accomplished with a setscrew that seats on the bit, although wedging devices have also been developed for this purpose.

Single-point Tool Designations. A single-point tool is ground to perform a specific metal-cutting operation. There is diversity of opinion in regard to nomenclature; in the interest of uniformity Fig. 25-4 is inserted here to show standard terminology. Adoption of this method of designation will do much to eliminate the misunderstandings that frequently occur in tool design. The tool bit shown is a right-cut one suitable for turning soft steel. The magnitude of the elements of the tool bit as shown in the key are established for a particular usage. The functions of these elements are outlined in the following paragraphs.

Rake Angles. These angles include the back rake and side rake ones. The back rake angle lies between the face of a tool and a line parallel to the base of the holder measured in a plane parallel to the center line of the point and at right angles to the base. Positive rake exists when the face slopes downward from the point toward the shank; if the slope is reversed, the tool has negative back rake. The side rake angle lies between the face of the tool and a line parallel to its base.

The rake angles exert a greater effect on the cutting efficiency of a metal-cutting tool than any other angles. Their combined effect is to facilitate the flow of the chip over the face of the tool and also to influence the shear angle. Rake angles for cemented carbide tools are generally of lower magnitude than high-speed-steel cutting tools. The brittle nature of cemented carbides necessitates rigid support for the cutting edge. Negative back rake tends to absorb impact loads resulting from interrupted cuts. For most machining requirements the back rake angle is positive for best cutting action.

Relief Angles. Relief angles provide the necessary clearance to permit the tool to enter the work. In the absence of relief angles, the tool would merely abrade the workpiece. The end relief angle is the one

[1] American Standard B5.22—1950, American Society of Mechanical Engineers, New York.

between the portion of the end flank immediately below the cutting edge
and a line drawn through that cutting edge perpendicular to the base.
Relief angles should be held to a minimum in order to prevent weakening
the cutting edge. Generally speaking, relief angles from 5 to 10° are
satisfactory; the exact amount depends on the diameter of the workpiece
as well as the feed.

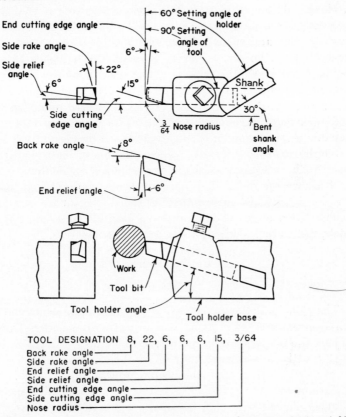

Fig. 25-4. Single-point tool designations showing a tool bit in a 30° left-bent shank and 15°
tool-bit angle toolholder. (*From American Standard B5.22—1950, American Society of Mechanical
Engineers, New York.*)

End Cutting Edge Angle. This angle is measured between the cutting
edge on the end of the tool and a line normal to the side edge of the
straight portion of the tool shank. It should be held to a minimum in
order to support the nose of the tool and conduct the heat from the
critical cutting area. The magnitude of these angles ranges between 8
and 15°. Chattering usually results from having the end cutting edge
angle either too small or too large. For plunge cutting, a large end cutting edge angle is a necessity.

Side Cutting Edge Angle. The side cutting edge angle on a single-point tool used for turning acts to absorb the initial load, thereby relieving the nose, which is the weakest part of the tool, of this shock.   Chip thickness is controlled by the side cutting edge angle, and chip distribution over the entire edge is also effected.   This angle is measured between the straight side cutting edge and the side of the tool shank.

Nose.   The nose of a single-point cutting tool is critical, since it is generally the weakest part of the tool.   It is actually an extension of the cutting edge and as such is called upon to dissipate much of the heat generated by the cut.   Since it is small, the tendency to overheat and break down is always present.   The quality of the finished surface is largely dependent upon the shape of the tool nose.   In some instances a sharp point is desirable because of its ability to minimize chatter.   On the other hand, a rounded nose makes for a stronger tool and one more capable of withstanding the heat generated by the cutting action.

Single-point Tool Types.   There are many classifications of single-point tools, based on tool shape or specialized application.   Among those best known are radial tools, straight tools, goose-necked tools, roughing and finishing tools, curved cutting edge tools, square-nosed tools, dovetailing tools, cutoff or parting tools, boring tools, knurling tools, form tools, radius tools, skiving tools, and recessing tools.

Cutting Tool Materials

HIGH-SPEED STEEL

The principal alloying elements are tungsten and molybdenum, along with chromium, vanadium, and sometimes cobalt.   These elements impart the property of red-hardness, which means that when these steels are correctly heat-treated, they retain their original hardness at temperatures at which they approach visible redness.

Carbon content governs the initial hardness of high-speed steel; the alloying elements develop properties other than hardness.   A range of from 0.65 to 0.80 per cent carbon gives the best combination of hardness, cutting ability, and resistance to shock.   Shock resistance is best met with lower carbon contents; dies, punches, and similar impact-type tools are made from such steels.   Cutting tools requiring high hardness, such as tool bits used where length of tool life and cutting ability are of paramount importance, are made from high-carbon, high-speed steels.

Designations.   High-speed steels are generally designated by a ratio, as 18:4:1; the analysis corresponding to this ratio is 17 to 19 per cent tungsten, 3.5 to 4.5 per cent chromium, and 0.75 to 1.25 per cent vanadium.   This particular type, along with 18:4:2 and 14:4:2, is most popular when tungsten is in ample supply.   Our vulnerability in regard to the latter material caused research work on substitute materials to be undertaken. Molybdenum emerged from these studies as an element approximately twice as effective as tungsten in imparting red-hardness properties to high-speed steel. In consequence, a second series of high-speed steels featuring molybdenum has been developed. Steels containing 0.80 per cent C, 1.50 per cent W, 4.00 per cent Cr, 1.00 per cent V, and 8.00 per cent Mo or 0.80 per cent C, 6.00 per cent W, 4.00 per cent Cr, 1.75 per cent V, and 5.00 per cent Mo are representative of this latter group.

A further departure in high-speed steel compositions comprises those that include cobalt as a major alloying element. These steels are somewhat higher in red-hardness than are the tungsten types; however, they are more difficult to forge and are more brittle. A typical cobalt type has the following analysis: 0.75 per cent C, 19.00 per cent W, 4.00 per cent Cr, 1.00 per cent V, and 5.00 per cent Co.

High-speed tool steels are being designated by code numbers sponsored by the Joint Industry Conference, known as the JIC. With this codification, analyses can be expected to follow rather definite patterns. It is possible, for example, by using the JIC code number, to specify cobalt-tungsten 18-4-2-8 as T-5, which represents a decided simplification.

High-speed Steel Tools. Every category of cutting tool used in the machine shop is obtainable in high-speed steel. The range extends from taps to broaches and from tool bits to hobs. Such tools are purchased ready for use, although high-speed steel is also obtainable as bar stock and blanks. Bar stock can be forged and is used principally for making solid-type single-point tools. Fully heat-treated high-speed steel will show a working hardness of Rockwell C 62-65 and a compressive stress approximating 400,000 psi.

CAST ALLOYS

There are a series of materials employed for metal-cutting tools that are produced by casting. There is no forging or machining performed on these materials, which are merely cast and ground prior to use. They are nonferrous materials in the true meaning of that term, and are on occasion referred to entirely by composition. The range of analysis includes: 25 to 35 per cent Cr, 4 to 25 per cent W, 6 to 20 per cent Mo, 1 to 3 per cent C; Mn and Si are always present as deoxidizers. Additives such as Va, B, Ta, and Co are present in some types. Ni is regarded as an impurity except in those cases where it is added for toughening.

Considerable interest is being displayed in tool bits of these cast-alloy tools, which are available in ground bit and ground tipped tool types. They have strengths above the high-speed steels, and a hardness of Rockwell C 60-62. Such tools are, generally speaking, intermediate between high-speed steels and cemented carbides in application as well as initial cost. An example of the application of cast-alloy tool bits is shown in Fig. 25-5.

Fig. 25-5.   Turning steel with cast-alloy cutting tools.   (*Courtesy of Crucible Steel Company of America, New York.*)

CEMENTED CARBIDES

A most significant development in cutting tool materials has been cemented, or sintered, carbides.   These materials were originally developed for use in drawing lamp filament wire where diamond dies had previously been used.   This development occurred between 1920 and 1930; improved compositions and manufacturing methods have continued to broaden the scope of cemented carbide applications (Fig. 25-6).   The use of cemented carbides is not confined to cutting tools but holds interest in the machine shop for components requiring extreme hardness and wear resistance, such as lathe centers, micrometer anvils, gage points, and others.   Cemented carbides fit into two broad classifications on the basis of composition and application.

Group I.   The cemented carbides in this group are composed of tungsten carbide and cobalt.   They are used in tools for machining cast iron, nonferrous metals and nonmetallic materials; other applications include dies and wear-resisting machinery parts.

Group II.   This grouping features more complex compositions in which tungsten carbide predominates, with additions of tantalum carbide or titanium carbide or both. In addition, columbian carbides may also be present with any or all the others—cobalt is included regardless of the carbide types used. The carbides added in this grouping serve the purpose of increasing resistance of the cutting tip to "cratering," which results from the action of the heated chips during the machining operation. Cemented carbides in this grouping are employed in tools for machining steel.

Processing. The manufacture of cemented carbides is essentially the same for all types. The carbides are generally formed by heating a mixture of tungsten oxide or powder with a measured amount of carbon

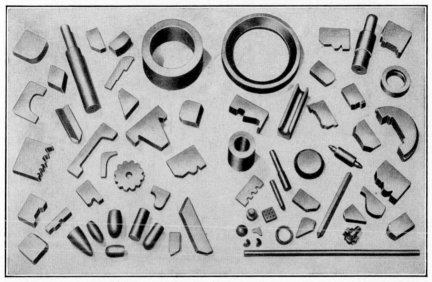

Fig. 25-6. A diversity of cemented carbide components. (*Courtesy of Carboloy Company, Detroit.*)

powder, such as lampblack, in a hydrogen atmosphere; there are other methods of forming carbides as well. The carbides are then crushed, milled, and screened in powdered form. The cobalt constituent, which is the binder material, is likewise prepared as a powder. The carbide and cobalt powders are mixed in carefully calculated proportions prior to shaping. The processing of the final product follows several different methods.

Cold pressing is the most used process. The powders are placed in a die and then are subjected to pressures ranging from 5 to 30 tons. The resulting blank is relatively soft and is similar in appearance to a pencil lead. A shrinkage allowance of approximately 15 per cent is compensated in the pressing die dimensions. The blank is next sintered for an hour at a temperature range of 2550 to 2700°F in a protective hydrogen atmosphere or in a vacuum. Final properties are established in the sintering operation and the cooled blank is ready for final use. Another processing method consists of combining the pressing and sintering operations into one.

A development of extrusion processing has recently been perfected (Fig. 25-7). A plasticizer is mixed with the carbide powders in controlled amounts. The extruded products are baked at a relatively low temperature, followed by pre-sintering and final sintering operations. Since extruded products are practically unlimited as to cross section, such items

Fig. 25-7.   Extruding cemented carbide shapes.   (*Courtesy of Carboloy Company, Detroit.*)

as tubes, bars, shapes, and twist drill bodies can be made from sintered carbides.

Cemented Carbide Cutting Tools. Cemented carbide tipped tool bits are so generally used that the insert blanks, or tips, have been standardized.[1] This standard recognizes six styles or shapes of sintered tips, known as the 1000, 2000, 3000, 4000, 5000, and 6000 series, respectively. All manufacturers of sintered carbide tips for single-point cutting tools have adopted these standard sizes. Sintered tips are generally brazed to suitable tool-bit shanks (Fig. 25-8). However, this procedure is not limited to such tools; milling cutters, twist drills and broaches are built in a similar manner. Copper is frequently used as a

[1] American Standard B5.22—1950, American Society of Mechanical Engineers, New York.

Fig. 25-8. Cemented-carbide-tipped lathe tool bits of various styles. (*Courtesy of Kennametal Inc., Latrobe, Pa.*)

Fig. 25-9. Cemented carbide inserts mechanically clamped in accommodating toolholders. (*Courtesy of Norton Company, Worcester, Mass.*)

braze metal because of its relatively high melting point. If a braze metal of low flowing temperature is used, there is the danger of the tips loosening under the heat caused by the machining operation.

Another method of using cemented carbides for single-point tools is that of clamping the blanks mechanically instead of brazing. A further departure is eliminating the tool bit, as such, and clamping the carbide pieces directly in a specially designed holder (Fig. 25-9), of which there are several types.   There are several advantages connected with this method of holding the carbide.   No machining is necessary for fitting the insert to the shank, nor is a brazing operation required.   A saving in grinding time is realized with clamped tools because the carbide alone is ground.   Grinding is done less frequently, since the carbide inserts can be indexed several times before regrinding is necessary.   Those metal-cutting tools featuring mechanically held cemented carbide cutting elements are sometimes referred to as ejector, or insert, tools.

DIAMOND-TIPPED TOOLS

Because of their extreme hardness, diamonds are used to advantage as specialized metal-cutting tools.   They are difficult to mount and will chip or fracture under certain conditions of interrupted cutting.   Their outstanding ability to hold size and finish for an extended production run makes them especially valuable for boring and finishing nonferrous and nonmetallic engineering materials.

Machining Performance

Research on chip formation has resulted in shifting the machining of metal from an art to a science.   Continuing study is providing further knowledge of machining fundamentals.   In order to secure the best possible results in machining, it is imperative that the cutting element (tool) be correctly ground both as to keenness and surface finish, and that it be rigidly supported in its machine.   Heat generated by the machining action must be minimized and dissipated rapidly.

Survey Questions

25-1. Give the definition of a cutting tool.

25-2. When was the first research of metal cutting made in America?

25-3. Why was the Taylor-White process significant to metal cutting?

25-4. What are coolants?

25-5. Explain the theory of metal-cutting tool action.

25-6. Wherein are free machining steels distinctive?

25-7. Where is hot machining of especial interest?

25-8. Describe the type 1 chip.

25-9. For machining what metals is the type 2 chip superior?

25-10. Name one important cause for surface roughness in machining.

25-11. List the machine tools that are equipped with single-point tools.

25-12. What are tool bits?

25-13. How many lathe toolholders comprise a normal set?

25-14. Name and describe the rake angles of a lathe tool bit.

25-15. Is negative back rake ever specified?

25-16. Will a lathe tool bit function in the absence of relief angles?

25-17. Does a round-nose cutting tool have any advantages over a pointed-nose type?

25-18. Wherein does the behavior of high-speed steels differ from high-carbon steels in metal cutting?

25-19. Make a listing of the different tool types that are obtainable in high-speed steel.

25-20. Do cast-alloy tool bits offer any advantages over steel types?

25-21. How are cemented carbides made?

25-22. Classify the cemented carbide tools as to composition.

25-23. What are extruded carbides?

25-24. Under what engineering standard are carbide tips and blank designs controlled?

25-25. How are carbide tips joined to the tool shanks or bodies?

25-26. Are carbide tools used as separates?

25-27. Where are diamonds used in metal cutting?

25-28. Make a comprehensive listing of all of the materials that are used for metal-cutting tools.

REFERENCES

Boston, O. W.: "Metal Processing," John Wiley & Sons, Inc., New York, 1941.

Chao, B. T., and K. J. Trigger: "Cutting Temperatures and Metal-cutting Phenomena," American Society of Mechanical Engineers, New York, 1951.

Donaldson, Cyril, and George H. LeCain: "Tool Design," Harper & Brothers, New York, 1943.

Ernst, Hans: "Physics of Metal Cutting," American Society for Metals, Cleveland, 1938.

Ernst, Hans, and M. Eugene Merchant: "Chip Formation, Friction and Finish," Cincinnati Milling Machine Co., Cincinnati, 1940.

"Machining of Metals: A Symposium," American Society for Metals, Cleveland, 1938.

"Metals Handbook," American Society for Metals, Cleveland, 1948.

"Powder Metallurgy," Chaps. 39 and 40, American Society for Metals, Cleveland, 1942.

Samans, Carl H.: "Engineering Metals and Their Alloys," The Macmillan Company, New York, 1949.

Schmidt, A. O., and J. R. Roubik: "Milling Hot Workpieces," American Society of Tool Engineers, Detroit, 1949.

"Single Point Tools and Tool Posts," American Standard B5.22—1950, American Society of Mechanical Engineers, New York, 1950.

Taylor, Frederick W., On the Art of Cutting Metals, *Trans. ASME*, Vol. 28, New York, 1907.

"Tool Engineers' Handbook," McGraw-Hill Book Company, Inc., New York, 1949.

CHAPTER 26

MEASURING

The objective of every machining operation is that of bringing an end product to dimension or to a desired surface condition or to both. A finished machined component is one that meets specifications as to dimensions and surface quality alike. Surface quality was taken up in Chap. 22; measurements will be surveyed here.

It is the duty of the design department to establish the desired degree of accuracy and to convey the requirements to the production department. The best means of securing the objective of accuracy is coordination between these departments. There is no point in specifying accuracy that is either impossible or too costly to achieve. Frequently the machine tool equipment necessary to produce the requested accuracy is not available; then, too, the specified precision may be beyond the requirements of the end product, resulting in unnecessarily high cost. With the increased use of standards for fits, surfaces, and quality, carelessness in dimension design should be eliminated. In this connection it is suggested that "Limits and Fits for Engineering and Manufacturing"[1] be consulted for standard dimensioning procedures in order to develop uniform practices throughout the engineering industries. If such uniformity were achieved, much of the confusion that inevitably accompanies contract manufacturing would be eliminated and absolute interchangeability of competitively manufactured products would be established.

Variability. There can be no such thing as an absolute dimension in manufacturing. In recognition of this situation, tolerances are, or should be, included in every precision measurement. Tolerances are necessary to overcome the variability that is inherent in all phases of manufacturing. Materials vary in composition and properties; machine tools are subject to the vagaries resulting from temperature changes during prolonged operation as well as to deterioration from usage. Cutting tool behavior is the greatest single source of dimension variability, since tool wear and tool slippage are constant occurrences. Obviously, artisanship is a variable quality. Regardless of how well a design is conceived

[1] American Standard B4.1—1947, American Standards Association, New York.

and prepared, it must be processed, and therein lie the problems of manufacturing.

Measurement Levels. The degree of precision that is necessary for the proper functioning of a particular component must be recognized by the designer. There are several approaches to, or available means of, making measurements. It is desirable to establish some arbitrary classifications in order that measuring instruments, equipment, and tools can be studied. Common usage divides measurements at three levels, viz., non-precision, semi-precision, and precision.

Another classification of dimensional measuring is a grouping by method; a distinction is made as between direct measurements on the one hand and comparative measurements on the other. Direct measurements are made on the workpiece in order to determine its actual dimensions and size. A direct measurement involves the human equation, since the recorded result is obtained by reading or interpretation.

Comparative measurement means that the dimension under consideration is compared with a standard. This method of measurement is highly regarded for inspection purposes in production manufacture. Comparative measurement is capable of producing accurate results provided the measuring equipment is maintained at a high level of precision: any comparison is only as trustworthy as the accuracy of the standard of comparison.

Emphasis is necessary in the matter of the accuracy of the measuring equipment. *Never take the accuracy of any measuring equipment for granted.* It is always sound procedure to check the zero reading, or similar features, of any measuring equipment prior to employing it for dimensional measuring. The higher the level of precision desired, the more important this precaution becomes. That industry recognizes this necessity is shown by the use of such devices as periodic checking against standards and of constant-temperature workrooms, where precision fits for guaranteed interchangeability are produced. Gaging rooms are held at constant temperature and humidity conditions as a means of eliminating variability and of increasing precision.

Direct Measurements

Every toolmaker and machinist equips himself with a complement of precision measuring tools as his "tools of the trade." The elaborateness of this tool collection is usually in direct proportion to his skill, since as his ability grows he is called upon for an increasing diversity of performance. In recognition of this situation, a wide range of standard and special measuring equipment is available. This diversification has reached such proportions that only a current tool catalog can do justice to the subject. However, some of the basic types will be reviewed here because a knowledge of their uses is fundamental to the student of engineering manufacture.

Steel Rules. The basic measuring tool is a steel rule, frequently termed a scale. Rules are available in individual lengths from 1 to 72 in. The face of the rule is marked with graduations along each of its four edges. Graduation marks varying from 0.0005 to 0.010 in. in width are either etched or milled into the rule, which is made of heat-treated steel. The four scales on a steel rule follow a series of graduation designations. A rule equipped with no. 4 graduation means that the scales on that rule are graduated into 64ths, 32ds, 16ths, and 8ths of an inch, respectively. Many combinations are available, including fractions and hundredths in addition to metric scales.

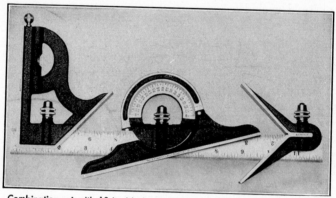

Fig. 26-1. Combination set with 12-in. blade, combination stock, center head, and reversible protractor head. (*Courtesy of The L. S. Starrett Co., Athol, Mass.*)

Steel rules are available in several designs including flexible, stainless, end graduated, shrink, pocket, hook, and others. A favorite type for general shop measurements is one that is grooved longitudinally on one face. This groove is used as a guide for the several heads that can be clamped to the rule, which acts as a blade (Fig. 26-1). The most versatile of these accessories is the combination head, which when clamped to the blade forms a square. The other leg of the head provides a 45° angle and the head also has a level that can be used for checking vertical as well as horizontal surfaces. The combination head can be clamped at a graduation to mark off a fixed distance for gaging purposes when setting an inside caliper. Another accessory shown in Fig. 26-1 is termed a center head. It is used to locate the center of round bar stock on any relatively true circular workpiece. The legs of the head are tangent to the circle and, since the blade bisects the leg angle, its edge passes through the center of the circle. It is only necessary to scribe two lines on the circle at different positions; their intersection is the center of that circle.   A reversible protractor accessory is also available for clamping to the blade, to make possible angular measurements.   Double protractors and inclinometers are other useful accessories.   However, the conventional combination set consists of a combination head, or stock, a center head, and a reversible protractor head.   This set is indispensable for layout work in the toolroom or die shop, as it is for direct measurements in machining operations.

Calipers.   An outside caliper measures outside diameters, while the inside type is used for measuring bores and hole diameters.   Such calipers are usually made with a spring joint (Fig. 26-2), but there are two addi-

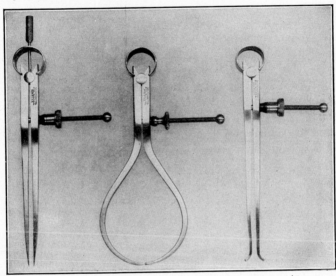

Fig. 26-2.   Spring divider, outside spring caliper, and inside spring caliper.   (*Courtesy of The L. S. Starrett Co., Athol, Mass.*)

tional styles, known as the firm-joint (in this, friction holds the caliper setting) and the lock-joint (held by means of a locking screw).   There is considerable skill required to make an accurate reading with a spring-joint caliper.   The user must develop a "feel" for the caliper.   Since the joint has a spring and the caliper legs are not stiff, it is possible to force a caliper over a workpiece even though its setting is too small.   The setting should be such that the weight of the caliper will just carry its points over the workpiece without any effort on the part of the mechanic.   An outside caliper is read by placing one leg against the end of an accurate steel rule and reading the rule graduation at the other leg point.

Inside calipers are distinguished by the fact that their leg points face outward.   They are inserted in the bore or hole and the adjusting nut is loosened until the leg points contact the wall.   Here again a delicate sense of feel is necessary for accurate measurement. After a caliper has been adjusted to the hole diameter, its setting is read by placing it on a steel rule. Both rule and caliper leg can be placed against a finished surface as a means of alignment, or the combination stock can be set at a full inch blade graduation, one caliper point placed against it, and the measurement read at the other caliper leg point.

A workpiece should never be calipered while it is rotating; inaccurate readings will result, and there is danger of accident. Another precaution is that of placing the caliper exactly normal to the workpiece surface. If a caliper is accidentally dropped, its setting should be rechecked immediately.

Several other styles of calipers are available, including thread, Yankee thread, keyhole, transfer type, forging, double, and hermaphrodite—the last with one leg as a divider point and the other resembling an inside caliper leg. Dividers are generally included as a tool related to calipers. All the calipers mentioned thus far depend upon the ability of the user for accuracy of measurement and are not considered precision measuring instruments.

Micrometer Calipers. The best known and most generally used precision direct-measuring tool is the micrometer caliper. It is available in many styles and also in outside and inside types. The measuring principle is the same for all. They are graduated to give readings in one-thousandths of an inch; when equipped with a vernier, readings are made to ten-thousandths.

Outside micrometer calipers are generally made to cover a range of 1 in. (Fig. 26-3). The small size reads from 0 to 1 in. and the next size from 1 to 2 in., which means that the zero reading for the 1- to 2-in. size is at 1 in. An exception to this design is the tubular frame micrometer caliper. It has several spindles that can be inserted to cover a wide range of diameters.

The micrometer principle of measuring has been in use for approximately a century. The micrometer caliper is almost universally referred to as a "mike." This instrument consists of a C frame that is usually a forging. The fixed measuring surface, termed the anvil, is located inside the outer frame end. The movable measuring surface is the end of the spindle, which is threaded at its opposite end and attached to the thimble. The micrometer barrel has graduations on its outer surface and is equipped with a spindle nut in its bore. As the thimble is turned, the spindle advances or retracts, depending on the direction of thimble rotation.

The principle of measurement is based on the fact that the spindle thread has a pitch of $\frac{1}{40}$ in., which equals the decimal fraction of 0.025 in. Turning the thimble one revolution advances the spindle 0.025 in. The barrel is graduated with each mark thereon representing one revolution of the thimble, *i.e.*, 0.025 in.   Every fourth graduation, 0.025 × 4 = 0.100 in., carries a digit starting from zero.   The micrometer reading in *tenths* can be made by noting the highest digit uncovered on the barrel.   Each uncovered graduation beyond the digit equals 0.025 in.   If three graduations are uncovered, for example, the reading equals the number of tenths plus 3 × 0.025 in. = 0.075 in.   However, a

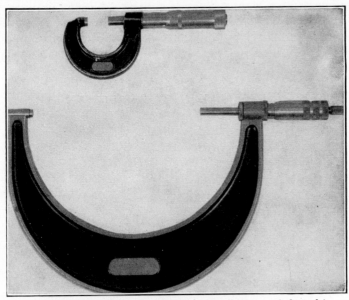

Fig. 26-3.   Outside micrometer calipers.   Upper view shows caliper with 0- to 1-in. range while lower one has a 5- to 6-in. range and is equipped with ratchet stop.

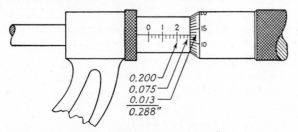

Fig. 26-4.   Micrometer caliper reading.

full space graduation is rarely encountered; usually a fractional space results.   This is read directly from the thimble edge, whose periphery is divided into 25 equal spaces, each one equaling 0.001 in.   In order, therefore, to make a micrometer reading, it is necessary to read the highest full number uncovered on the barrel scale, add the number of *full* spaces between that number and the thimble edge, and finally add the number of spaces on the thimble scale for the total reading (Fig. 26-4).

There is room for error, since varying tension can be applied when bringing the spindle into contact with the workpiece. This difficulty is solved by placing a ratchet at the outer end of the spindle. Another design that provides accurate readings is shown in Fig. 26-5. This micrometer caliper employs a built-in dial indicator as a means of eliminating human error and pressure variations. The micrometer shown is also equipped with a vernier, thereby giving readings accurate to within 0.0001 in. Regardless of type or style, a micrometer caliper will only read accurately when it is in proper adjustment. Prior to using a micrometer *always check its zero reading with a gage block or other standard measure.*

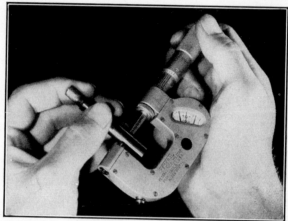

Fig. 26-5. Indicating micrometer caliper. (*Courtesy of Federal Products Corp., Providence.*)

Types of Micrometer Calipers. Because of its precision, the micrometer caliper has been adapted to fit many varied applications. Thread micrometers are commonly used for measuring screw threads. Some of the specialized ones include hub, tube, paper gage, sheet metal, inspector's gage, and depth types. Micrometer calipers are also available in direct reading styles.

Vernier Calipers. Vernier tools are precision measuring instruments capable of a degree of accuracy on the order of 0.001 in. The vernier is named after Pierre Vernier, by whom it was invented, in 1631. The vernier caliper (Fig. 26-6) is not as commonly used in America as it is in Europe, since the micrometer has greater appeal here. The vernier is used with a scale that is graduated into 40ths or 0.025ths of an inch. The vernier has 25 divisions which are numbered at every fifth division and which equal, in extreme length, 24 divisions on the scale or 24 × 0.025 in. = 0.600 in. Therefore, one division on the vernier equals $\frac{1}{25}$ of

0.600 in. = 0.024 in. This results in a difference of 0.001 in. between a division on the vernier and a division on the scale.

Dial Gages. Dial gages are direct reading instruments whose application is always associated with precision measurements. Dial gages are

Fig. 26-6.   Vernier caliper graduated for English measure.

used in a great variety of indicators and other instruments for measuring and checking. In order to meet these varied requirements, dial gages are built in several styles (Fig. 26-7) and in different calibrations. Dial gages carry either 0.001-, 0.0005-, or 0.0001-in. calibrations. The scales on the dials can be had in various styles and arrangements, and it is

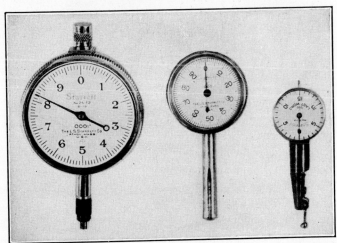

Fig. 26-7.   Dial gages and dial indicators of different styles and calibrations.

usual to have movable dials which permit zero alignment. The utility of dial gages is not limited to measurement, since they are reliable for checking workpiece setups and alignment. A further application is that of checking the accuracy of machine tools on spindle concentricity and bed-way alignment.

Comparative Measurements

Precision and high-precision measurements are usually made by comparative means. The actual measurement resolves itself into a deviation from the selected standard measure. For genuine interchangeability, the same basic standard should be employed throughout all industry. The lack of this fundamental standardization has proved costly, especially in wartime, when production was divided among several subcontractors.

Gage Blocks. The idea of a gage block, as a precision standard, was conceived by C. E. Johansson, who produced the first set in Sweden in

Fig. 26-8. A set of Johansson gage blocks containing 81 individual blocks. (*Courtesy of Brown & Sharpe Mfg. Co., Providence.*)

1896. The individual blocks that comprise a set (Fig. 26-8) are made from steel that has been suitably finished, hardened, and stabilized. An innovation is the production of gage blocks of solid carbide. This construction is said to make the life of the block longer than that of the older types.

Gage blocks, frequently termed jo-blocks, are produced by several sources, many of which have introduced design and manufacturing innovations. Gage blocks are generally made in decimal sizes, but there are fractional sizes available. The degree of precision varies with the different classifications; yet at 68°F, class AA blocks have a tolerance of only ±0.000002 in. When such gage blocks are carefully wrung together, their cohesion is said to be more than thirty times that ascribable to atmospheric pressure.

Cylindrical Plug and Ring Gages. It is desirable to have standard gages for circular measurements, since they will facilitate checking the working gages. In common with other precision gages, these are stabilized and have a high degree of accuracy at a working temperature of 68°F. The plug gage is used for gaging holes and bores, while the ring gage is for checking outside diameters.

Plug and ring gages are conventional inspection tools. Formerly they were universally made of steel and suitably heat-treated and finished; for protection against hard usage or measurable wear, steel gages are frequently chromium-plated. An interesting innovation has been that of making the gaging members of glass (Fig. 26-9). The plug gage shown has both "go" and "not-go" gaging members fitted with tapers in a

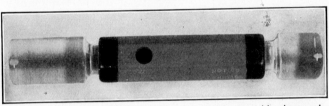

Fig. 26-9. Plug gage of "go" and "not-go" type equipped with removable glass gaging members.

plastic holder to make possible the replacement or renewal of the gaging members. The go and not-go members are ground to meet the upper and lower tolerance limits.

Snap Gages. A snap gage has two sets of gaging points in tandem, so that it is possible to gage an outside diameter with a single motion of the hand, in contrast to the procedure with a plug gage, whose ends must be reversed. Snap gages are usually single styles so designed that the gaging points have a range of adjustment. Snap gages of this type are set by gage blocks to the sizes desired. There are fixed snap gages that do not have the adjustable anvil feature. Design changes and innovations include a snap gage with dial attachment for reading exact diameters within the tolerance range.

Supermicrometers. This instrument is, in effect, a gaging machine of precision on the order of 0.0001 in. at 68°F (Fig. 26-10). It has a capacity range that permits the checking of components and gages in the range from 0 to 10 in. The gaging anvils are set by means of individual gages, as shown in Fig. 26-10.

Visual Gages. There are numerous visual gage designs that are used principally for parts inspection. The principle of operation varies with different design types. These instruments are commonly referred to as

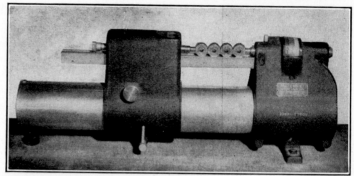

Fig. 26-10. Supermicrometer with four 1-in. circular gages in position. (Courtesy of University of Washington Gaging Laboratory.)

comparators. In the one shown in Fig. 26-11 the upper gage point is

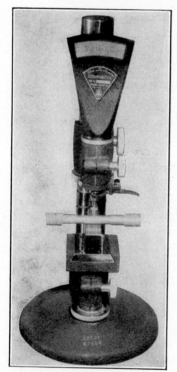

lowered onto the part manually and the size deviation is read on the dial, which is graduated for both plus and minus tolerances. The basic dimension is set by means of standard gages. Another type of visual comparator employs a lighted scale for the readings. Instruments of this design are frequently termed electro-limit gages.

Multiple Electric Contact Gages. The gages in this classification have been developed for inspection work in mass-production industries. The basic feature of these gages is their capacity to inspect several dimensions simultaneously. There is some difference in their operating details as between different makes; however, as a rule, green and red lights are arranged to flash a go and not-go signal. Gages of this classification are especially well adapted for inspecting projectiles in ordnance work. Automotive pistons can be gaged for ring-groove and land diameters in a single operation with multiple electric contact gages (Fig. 26-12).

Fig. 26-11. Visual comparator gaging the diameter of a tension test bar. (Courtesy of University of Washington Gaging Laboratory.)

Air Gages. Compressed air is employed in a series of gage designs that operate on two basic principles. One, known as the pressure type, is based on the idea of varying air pressures, while the other one, termed the flow type, operates with varying air velocities at constant pressure. The latter principle has proved most adaptable owing to inherent advantages. When a column of air flows under constant pressure, it will have the same velocity at every point in its length. This feature gives this

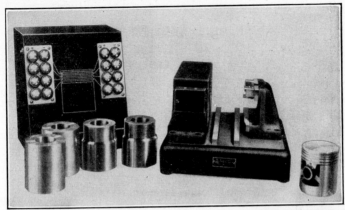

Fig. 26-12.   Multiple electric contact gage that measures several diameters simultaneously.   (Courtesy of Pratt & Whitney, Division Niles-Bement-Pond Co., West Hartford, Conn.)

Fig. 26-13.   Checking connecting rod bores with a flow-type air gage.   (Courtesy of The Sheffield Corporation, Dayton, Ohio.)

gage great flexibility, since the distance of the gaging spindle from the instrument is of no consequence.

Air gages have been expanded from the single unit for measuring bores to multiple units capable of several simultaneous measurements. In addition, gages of this design are used for checking straightness, square-ness, parallelism, concentricity, bell mouthing, and other conditions. Their operation is fully automatic, and the readings are instantaneous (Fig. 26-13). The scale arrangement lends itself to a variety of treat-ments, including amplification of any desired magnitude.

Precision Measurements

The necessity for accuracy in gages is fundamental to the program of interchangeability of parts manufacture. A master standard should be adopted by management, and all essential measuring tools, gages, and instruments should be calibrated to the established master standard. Such calibration is not difficult since it can readily be done by measure-ment with light rays through the use of optical flats in combination with a monochromatic light source.

Measurement with Light Rays. The equipment necessary for measur-ing with light rays consists of a set of optical flats, a set of master reference gages, and a source of monochromatic light. It is desirable to have a steel working flat available since it can be used for checking gages other than gage blocks, thereby preserving the optical flats.

Optical flats are flat disks made from fused quartz, pyrex, or clear white glass in a variety of diameters and thicknesses. The best thermal stability and wearing properties can be attained in the fused quartz flats. Only one face of the flat need be accurately flat, although the opposite face is made approximately parallel. Optical flats should be given extreme care both in use and storage in order to prevent scratches and nicks.

The light source used in this measuring method must be one of a single wave length. A light bulb shielded by a special selenium diffusion glass is frequently used. The diffusion glass serves to cut out all of the wave lengths of the violet, blue, green, yellow, and orange light. It transmits a red wave length whose equivalent measuring unit is 12.5 millionths of an inch per dark band, which equals 8 bands to the ten-thousandths inch.

The monochromatic light source is passed through an optical flat resting on a surface whose flatness is to be checked. When a deviation from absolute parallelism exists between the surface being checked and the optical flat, there will be interference between the light bands that will show as alternate light and dark spaces. The number and shape of these alternate spaces accurately show the nature of the surface being examined.

When plug gages, for example, are checked, they are placed with a master standard of the desired dimension on a working flat. They are then covered with an optical flat and placed in the monochromatic light source for checking interference bands. The number of these bands is an accurate measure of the gage deviation from the master standard. Measurements made by this method are read in millionths of an inch. Temperature conditions must be constant at 68°F for effective control.

Spectroscopy. The accuracy of light-wave measurements in millionths of an inch can be exceeded. Developments indicate that the unit of measurement has been extended to angstroms. Since an angstrom unit is slightly less than 4 billionths of an inch, it is obvious that new concepts of precision are possible. The atomic pile has contributed a minute amount of special mercury that, when combined with a spectroscope and an interferometer, can measure to less than a billionth of an inch. This scientific development gives new and fuller meaning to precision measurements.

Survey Questions

26-1. Should engineering or production specify the degree of accuracy?

26-2. How can accuracy requirements affect production costs?

26-3. From what sources does variability arise?

26-4. List the three levels of precision and give an example of each.

26-5. Fundamentally, what are comparative measurements?

26-6. How many scales are there on a steel rule? Are these always of the same graduations?

26-7. Give some applications for a combination head.

26-8. Is an outside spring caliper capable of making accurate measurements?

26-9. How best can an inside spring caliper measurement be read?

26-10. On what principle does a micrometer caliper function?

26-11. How can the accuracy of a mike be checked?

26-12. What is the function of the ratchet stop?

26-13. Do Vernier calipers function on the same principle as micrometer calipers?

26-14. How can a dial gage be used with a lathe?

26-15. Distinguish between direct and comparative measurements.

26-16. What degree of precision is available in gage blocks?

26-17. Give some specific applications for gage blocks.

26-18. Why should gaging be done under constant temperature conditions?

26-19. Is a plug gage regarded as a flexible measuring tool?

26-20. How does the "go" and "not-go" theory function?

26-21. Where are snap gages especially adaptable?

26-22. What is a supermicrometer?

26-23. Are visual gages suited best to production or inspection?

26-24. To what type of work are air gages suited?

26-25. As a general rule, are the same tools or instruments used for both production and inspection?

26-26. How can the dimensional accuracy of a gage block be checked?

REFERENCES

"Dimensional Control," The Sheffield Corporation, Dayton, 1942.

"Kent's Mechanical Engineers' Handbook," 12th ed., John Wiley & Sons, Inc., New York, 1950.

Michelson, Leno C.: "Industrial Inspection Methods," rev. ed., Harper & Brothers, New York, 1950.

"Tool Engineers' Handbook," McGraw-Hill Book Company, Inc., New York, 1949.

CHAPTER 27

WELDING BASICS

The welding of metal through employing elevated temperatures complemented by pressure has been practiced since antiquity. There appears to be no definitely known date of origin for any of the basic welding processes. The Dura wrought-iron objects which were found in Syria by the Fine Arts Department of Yale University in cooperation with the French Académie des Sciences, as a result of their excavations in the early 1930's, included specimens of welded rings. These discoveries indicate that hammer welding was known as early as the second century A.D.[1] The carved iron pillar at Delhi, India, whose total height is 23 ft 8 in. and whose outside diameter varies from 16.4 to 12.05 in., Thomas Turner states, "consists of malleable iron of great purity, and was made about A.D. 400, by welding together discs of metal."[2]

It was in 1778 that Peter Townsend was commissioned to make, for the sum of £5,000, a chain that would reach across, in the Hudson River, from Constitution Island to West Point and would act as a barrier against the British fleet. This chain was made from $2\frac{1}{2}$ in. square wrought-iron bars at the Stirling Iron Works located at Chester, Orange County, N.Y. Each link was approximately 2 to 3 ft in length and weighed upward of 140 lb; the total weight with fastenings was about 180 tons. The chain was made by using 17 forges continuously, employing 60 men in an operation that could well be termed the first mass-production metal-manufacturing job in the United States. The chain was hauled in sections to the assembly site, where it was joined by further welding, supplemented by clevises.

The necessary buoyancy was imparted to the chain by attaching it to supporting logs that were, in turn, held against the current by suitable anchors. There are links of this chain displayed at Raynham Hall, Oyster Bay, N.Y., and at the U.S. Military Academy at West Point, as well as at various museums (Fig. 27-1).

[1] Higgins, John W.: The Iron Age of Dura Craftsmanship, *The Iron Age*, Vol. 135, No. 2, pp. 13–15, 75, Jan. 10, 1935.
[2] "Metallurgy of Iron," 2d ed., p. 4, Charles Griffin & Co., Ltd., London, 1900.

There is considerable uncertainty about the origin of arc welding. The consensus of historians on this subject is, however, that electric arc welding was originated in Europe.   It is known that the Russian scientist N. Benardos welded boiler tubes with a carbon arc as early as 1881 (Fig. 27-2).   On May 17, 1887, this scientist, in collaboration with S. Olszewski, obtained American patent no. 363,320 on a process and apparatus for welding with the electric arc.   The sketch in Fig. 27-3 was copied from the patent drawings issued on that date.

Another Russian inventor, N. Slavianov, is credited with originating the idea of metallic arc welding, a revision of the Benardos carbon arc

Fig. 27-1.   Section of the great chain, 1,700 feet long, which was stretched across the Hudson River. (*Courtesy of United States Military Academy, West Point, N.Y.   Department of the Army photograph.*)

method.   Slavianov was given an award at the Chicago world's fair in 1893 for an exhibit of a "Process of Electric Welding."   This award was granted, according to the citation, "For the ingenuity and efficiency of the process and the strength secured at the point of welding."   Prominent among other early investigators in the field of electric arc welding was Sir Humphry Davy in England.

The development of oxyacetylene welding was hampered by a lack of knowledge of the behavior of these gaseous mixtures.   The explosive potential of acetylene when mixed with air or oxygen retarded the development of suitable apparatus.   Edmond Fouché was granted a patent in the United States on November 11, 1902, covering a welding blowpipe; Fig. 27-4 is taken from a copy of this patent.   Fouché was associated with Émile Picard and Eugene Bournonville in the Société Acétylène

Fig. 27-2.   One of the earliest examples on record of arc welding, showing N. Benardos welding boiler tubes.

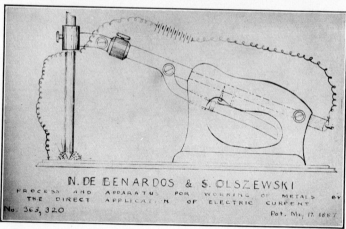

Fig. 27-3.   Patent drawing of semiautomatic arc welding apparatus of N. Benardos and Olszewski.

Dissous in France.   It was in 1901 that Bournonville installed the first plant in America for generating and compressing acetylene gas in portable cylinders as dissolved acetylene.

The original work in electric resistance welding was done in America by Elihu Thomson.   His experiments, dating as early as 1883, were referred to by himself as dealing with the "art or process of electric welding."   A

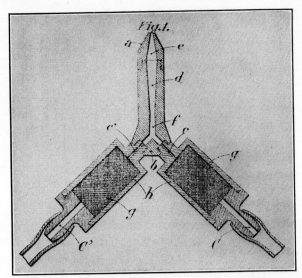

Fig. 27-4.   Fouché blowpipe taken from patent drawing.

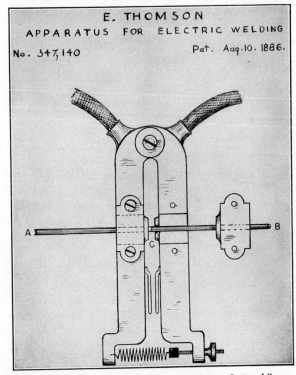

Fig. 27-5.   Original patent of electric resistance butt welding.

sketch of his apparatus, patented on August 10, 1886, is shown in Fig. 27-5. This equipment was used for butt-welding the wires shown as *A* and *B*, with the resultant weld located at *C*.

This brief historical sketch of the early developments in welding would be incomplete without mention of the achievements of Dr. Hans Goldschmidt. It was in 1895 that he succeeded with his experiments in Thermit welding. His discovery was based on the reduction of iron oxide into metallic iron by aluminum. However it was not until 1897 that a patent was granted, and the process was introduced into America in 1902.

Welding Nomenclature

There are many variables entering into the concept of welding. By way of example, welding processes can be assessed from the metallurgical viewpoint or from the viewpoint of the heat source. Techniques, methods, and procedures have all formed the basis for segments of welding terminology. Continued usage of a welding expression has, on occasion, resulted in a traditional inference. The case of the term fusion welding is an illustration. Even though the term fusion welding has been recognized over the years as designating a basic process, it is no longer accepted.

Standardization of Nomenclature. The desirability and advantages of uniform terminology in welding have been recognized by engineering and manufacturing alike. Lack of standardization in this regard has led to the introduction of expedients. This has been the normal result of the rapid expansion of welding both as to process development and as to applications.

The American Welding Society from time to time issues standards covering welding nomenclature. A study of these standards reveals the fact that their revision has always been in the direction of greater clarity and simplification. The latest revision, the work of the Committee on Definitions and Charts, has been embodied in two standards:

1. "Master Chart of Welding Processes and Process Charts" (A3.0-49)

2. "Standard Welding Terms and Their Definitions" (A3.1-49)

The Master Chart of Welding Processes is presented here as Fig. 27-6. This chart diagrams all the currently used welding processes in one concise, logical arrangement. The method used in developing these standards is explained in an article entitled Welding Nomenclature and Definitions by W. L. Warner.[1] The standard that includes the Master

---

[1] *The Welding Journal*, Vol. 28, No. 5, pp. 427–434, May, 1949. These standards are available as separate publications; they also appear in Chap. I of the 3d edition of "The Welding Handbook," American Welding Society, New York, 1950.

Chart has three appended pages devoted to Process Charts. The first of these pages of Process Charts covers forge, flow, gas, induction, and Thermit welding, the second deals with arc welding, and the final one is

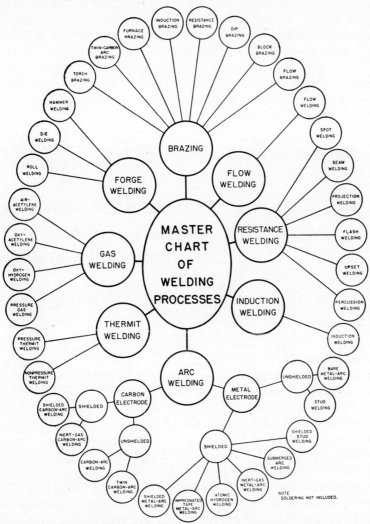

Fig. 27-6. Master Chart of Welding Processes. (American Standard A3.1-49, American Welding Society, New York, 1949.)

devoted to resistance welding processes. The charts interpret the characteristics of each process under twenty-four headings.

The Process Charts omit brazing, which appears on the Master Chart. This situation raises the question of the fundamental concept of brazing; this process is considered to be predicated on capillary action and, except for processing temperature range, is similar to soldering. The demarcation temperature between brazing and soldering has been established at 800°F by this standard. The other processes on the Master Chart are established primarily by the manner of heating.

Cold Weld. There has been considerable divergence of opinion in connection with the formal definition of the term weld. While it has always been assumed that a weld is made at an elevated temperature, it is a known fact that some pure metals can be joined while at room temperature through the use of pressure alone. Recently there has been some interest displayed in welding certain of the aluminum alloys in this manner. The specimens of cold welding pictured in Fig. 27-7 are typical.

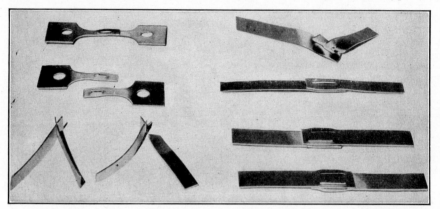

Fig. 27-7. Examples of cold welding. (*Courtesy of The General Electric Company, Ltd., of England.*)

The processing consists of cleaning the faying surfaces thoroughly with a scratch brush and, after lapping them, applying pressure in a power press. When the work is correctly done, the resulting joint is sufficiently strong to cause a "button" to pull out in destructive testing. Considerable development work has been done in England,[1] where the term cold welding was first applied to this type of metal joining.

Definition of a Weld. The standard definition for the term weld is: "A localized coalescence of metals wherein coalescence is produced by heating to suitable temperatures, with or without the application of pressure, and with or without the use of filler metal. The filler metal either has a melting point approximately the same as the base metal or has a melting point below that of the base metal but above 800°F."[2] It should be noted that the expressions pressure weld and non-pressure weld have been rendered obsolete by this revised standard definition.

[1] Sowter, A. B.: Metals Joined by New Cold Welding Process, *The Welding Journal*, Vol. 28, No. 2, pp. 149–152, February, 1949.

[2] "Standard Welding Terms and Their Definitions," American Standard A3.0-49, American Welding Society, New York, 1949.

Welder or Weldor. Some clarification is necessary of the terms used when referring to the worker who actually makes a weld, especially since the terminology used in labor contracts has been indefinite to the point of becoming controversial. There is some sentiment in favor of the use of the term *weldor* in preference to *welder*. The reasoning behind this trend is that the term welder can, according to some interpretations, refer either to the worker or to the welding machine.

The standards definition considers the terms synonymous, defining them as "one who is capable of performing a manual of semiautomatic welding operations." A *welding operator*, on the other hand, is understood to be one who operates machine or automatic welding equipment.

Welding Processes

The Master Chart (Fig. 27-6) recognizes eight fundamental welding processes, each of which has one or more subdivisions. Those represented by one or only a few modifications will be discussed here, while each of the more diversified processes will be the subject of a subsequent chapter. The sequence of the welding processes in the treatment that follows has no significance beyond being a convenient alphabetical arrangement.

The point has repeatedly been made in earlier chapters that metal products are produced by casting or by mechanical work; in other words, they are either cast or wrought. This must be kept in mind when welding either cast or wrought products, since in some welding processes the resultant weld metal is actually a casting, while in those welds where pressure of impact is used in the welding procedure a modification of the cast structure of the weld results (Fig. 27-8). There is the difference, however, that the deposited weld metal has a higher cooling rate than a sand casting, and modified cast structure results.

Welding processes cannot be divided on the basis of their application either to cast products on the one hand or wrought products on the other. Some processes do fall into one or the other division, others have but minor use in the one field and major applications in the other, while gas and arc welding as well as brazing are commonly used on both categories of metal products. In fact, brazing was the only method that could be used universally until the comparatively recent development of torch and arc welding.

Flow Welding. Castings were formerly repaired through the expedient of bolted or riveted straps or patches. A repair of this kind required skill and ingenuity of a high order. The author remembers seeing a repair on a broken cast-iron automobile crankcase that involved affixing some 40 assorted pieces to a copper plate, which was in turn fashioned and riveted to the remainder of the crankcase in a manner that resulted in an oil-tight job!

A different approach to repairing castings was by the method of burning on—a job that was generally assigned to the foundry. Burning-on was the method from which flow welding was developed; these two terms are used interchangeably.

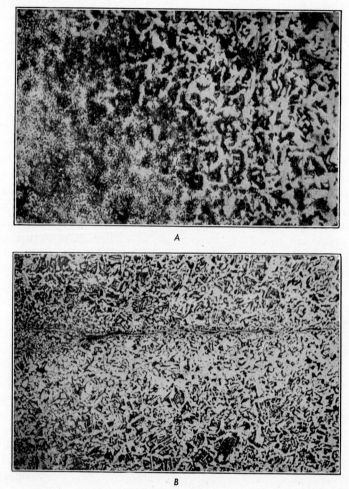

Fig. 27-8. A, metallic arc weld in mild steel with E4510 electrode, × 112. B, forge weld in mild steel, × 80.

The technique used in flow welding is that of imbedding the broken parts, properly aligned, in molding sand or other suitable investment. Provisions for flowing molten metal around the fracture are included in the mold. The actual welding operation consists of pouring molten metal, whose flow is directed through suitable gating arrangements, past the casting fracture. After an interval sufficiently great to bring both edges of the break to fluidity, the stream of molten metal is stopped off. The casting is permitted to cool prior to its removal from the mold. Chipping and grinding follow, to smooth the weld to shape.

Flow welding is also used for repairing mis-run castings that would be difficult or expensive to reclaim by any other process. Entire sections of castings are "flowed in" by this method. There are occasions where the filler metal is of a lower fusion point than the base metal in flow welding; in such cases, the base metal is merely heated by the molten filler metal, as in brazing.

Forge Welding. One of the most beloved poems in American literature is "The Village Blacksmith," in which Longfellow so graphically portrays one of the artisans by whose skillful hands forgings and weldments have been wrought throughout the ages of civilization. Forge welding must be accorded the honor of being the first welding process.

The shortcomings of forge welding are its relatively narrow field of application and its lack of adaptability. Forge welding enjoyed its greatest popularity in producing wrought iron and mild steel weldments. It has been responsible for some remarkable achievements, notable both for magnitude and for complicated shape. Interesting examples are to be found in shipbuilding, ordnance, ship's fittings, and mechanical devices generally.

The technique of making a forge weld depends somewhat upon the type of joint. For the most part, a lap joint is used for forge welding. The two bars to be welded are first scarfed (tapered) in a manner that will result in a normal thickness throughout the length of the welded section. After scarfing and fitting, the faying surfaces are heated to pronounced redness, when they are momentarily withdrawn from the forge fire and sprinkled with or dipped in flux. The flux is in powdered form, primarily a borax or a silica base which melts on heating. It acts as a solvent of any oxides present and protects the surfaces from further oxidation by the forge blast. The pieces are then replaced in the forge fire and the air blast is opened to develop rapid heating to welding temperature.

The blacksmith gages proper welding temperature by the appearance of the scarfed surfaces. When these surfaces are just below the point of flowing, corresponding to a high state of plasticity, he shuts off the forge air blast and rapidly removes the pieces from the fire. The parts are struck violently against the anvil in order to free the scarfs of adhering scale. The parts are placed on the anvil with the scarfs mating. Once the scarfs have been matched, the smith grasps his hammer and rains light, rapid blows on the joint, to be followed by blows of increasing intensity until the weld is completed. Figure 27-9 shows a forge weld nearing completion.   The forge used for this weld is shown in the right background.

In addition to the manual method of forge welding, other modifications of this basic process include the use of power hammers, presses, or rolls; these are especially useful as the size of the weldments increase.   Heating furnaces replace the forge for reasons of both capacity and control.   On repetitive work, dies are used in a power hammer much as they are used in the production of drop forgings.

Among the modifications of forge welding butt-welded pipe deserves particular mention.   The skelp, from which the pipe is to be made, is

Fig. 27-9.   Finishing manual forge weld.   *(Courtesy of Mendota Manufacturing & Transfer Company, Mendota, Ill.)*

sheared to form a tong hold on the skelp end.   Skelp is charged into a furnace, where it is brought to welding temperature.   A device similar to a drawbench is located on the delivery end of the furnace.   The actual welding of the skelp into pipe is accomplished by drawing the skelp through a collar known as a welding bell; this operation forces the edges together into a butt weld (Fig. 27-10).   The welding bell is slipped over a pair of tongs which grip and pull the skelp from the furnace by dropping the handle end of the tongs into the moving drawbench chain. The entire operation is speedily done with production of 1-in. pipe approaching 700 20-ft lengths per hour.

Induction Welding.   This welding process derives its name from the heating source used.   Limitations are placed on broader use of induction welding because of the relative scarcity of induction heating installations in manufactories generally. Potentially rapid processing is a favorable factor that should develop increasing interest in induction welding.

Thermit Welding. Although the Master Chart shows both pressure and nonpressure Thermit welds, there is evidence to indicate that the pressure method can now be considered obsolete.[1] In view of this development, the following discussion will be confined entirely to nonpressure Thermit welding.

Fundamentally, Thermit is a mechanical mixture of powdered aluminum and iron oxide. In order to develop desired characteristics in the final weld metal, various elements, such as manganese, nickel, molybdenum, and carbon, are added to the Thermit mixture in varying

Fig. 27-10. Skelp drawn through welding bell to form longitudinal weld in pipe. (*Courtesy of Carnegie-Illinois Steel Corporation, Pittsburgh.*)

combinations. This mixture is ignited by means of a magnesium fuse or powder. The resulting chemical reaction

$$8Al + 3Fe_3O_4 = 9Fe + 4Al_2O_3$$

is of about 30 sec duration, regardless of the quantity of Thermit used, and develops a temperature approximating 5000°F.

The Thermit welding operation is not unlike flow welding, the Thermit reaction supplying the required molten weld metal. The parts to be welded are given proper joint preparation by chipping, flame cutting, or grinding. The joint must be open throughout its entire area. The pieces are placed in alignment and secured to prevent movement prior to and during welding. The joint opening is filled with wax and a reinforcing wax band is built to the shape desired by the weld metal. When the wax has been worked to proper shape, a mold box is placed around the wax pattern. The box is then filled and rammed with molding material similar to steel molding sand.

As the mold is made, suitable gates and risers are placed in position. These are withdrawn upon completion of the mold, and heating torches, for drying the mold and melting out the wax, are brought into play. Preheating is continued until the casting weld faces reach full redness.

[1] Private communication from the Metal & Thermit Corporation, New York.

The Thermit mixture, held in a conically shaped crucible equipped with a tapping pin at its apex, is ignited and upon completion of the reaction the crucible is tapped, which permits the molten metal to flow into and fill the mold. A typical Thermit welding operation is pictured in Fig. 27-11.

Thermit welding is applied to fabrication and repair of heavy sections. An outstanding achievement was the welding of stern frame castings for

Fig. 27-11. Tapping the crucible during a Thermit welding operation. (*Courtesy of Metal & Thermit Corporation, New York.*)

aircraft carriers and other craft. Stern frames were cast in sections and welded; some of these welds were made in cross sections reaching to 40 in. in one dimension.

WELDING SYMBOLS

With the increased application of welding, the necessity for standardized design has arisen, and this has led to the development of welding symbols. The American Welding Society has sponsored the symbols shown in Fig. 27-12. These symbols are used throughout the designing and welding industry in America. They are not used universally as yet, but revisions are being considered whereby welding symbols for both the United States and Great Britain would be standardized.

There have been several revisions of the welding symbol code, and to avoid confusion, only the current code should be used. The student is urged to become familiar with the basic elements in the welding symbol code.

Survey Questions

27-1. Classify the early type of welding.

27-2. Where was metal arc welding originated?

27-3. To whom was the first welding blowpipe patent issued?

27-4. How is Elihu Thomson connected with welding development?

27-5. Give the principal welding methods appearing on the Master Chart.

27-6. Wherein does cold welding differ from the formal definition of welding?

27-7. Are the terms "weldor" and "welding operator" synonymous?

27-8. Is flow welding an obsolete process?

27-9. Mention some modifications of forge welding that apply to manufacturing.

27-10. Where is skelp used?

27-11. What is the heat source for induction welding?

27-12. Is Thermit welding considered as a production method?

27-13. Why will the metallurgical structure of an arc weld and a forge weld in the same steel be different?

27-14. Will the structure of a forge weld and an electrical resistance weld be similar?

27-15. Can the weld metal deposited by either torch or arc be regarded as a casting?

27-16. What are welding symbols?

27-17. By whom are welding symbols standardized?

27-18. Name the four types of grooves covered by welding symbols.

27-19. Do welding symbols apply to resistance welding?

27-20. Is it correct procedure to show weld metal on a drawing?

REFERENCES

Khrenov, Dr. K. K., and V. I. Yarkho: "Technology of Electric Arc Welding," State Publishing House of the Literature on Mechanical Engineering, Moscow and Leningrad, U.S.S.R., 1940.

"Master Chart of Welding Processes and Process Charts," American Standard A3.1-49, American Welding Society, New York, 1949.

"Standard Welding Terms and Their Definitions," American Standard A3.0-49, American Welding Society, New York, 1949.

"The Welding Encyclopedia," 11th ed., The Welding Engineer Publishing Company, Chicago, 1943.

The Welding Engineer, McGraw-Hill Publishing Company, Inc., New York.

"The Welding Handbook," 3d ed., American Welding Society, New York, 1950.

The Welding Journal, American Welding Society, New York.

CHAPTER 28

ARC WELDING

Direct Current

Arc welding is defined as "a group of welding processes wherein coalescence is produced by heating with an electric arc or arcs, with or without the application of pressure and with or without the use of filler metal."[1] The approach to applied arc welding—and the terminology most commonly heard—is based on type of current and method of manipulation. Both direct current and alternating current are used. Arc welding methods have been developed in which both d-c and a-c arcs are used, to complement each other. The manner of manipulating the arc during welding may be manual, semiautomatic, or fully automatic. Manual arc welding equipment is divided between single-operator and multiple-operator sets.

Direct-current Sources. The majority of d-c welding uses motor-generator sets as a means of converting power-line alternating current of high voltage and low amperage into direct current of suitable characteristics for arc welding. A typical arc welding machine, in which the d-c welding generator is driven by an a-c motor, is shown in Fig. 28-1. There are some welding machines equipped with d-c motors, but such equipment is rare.

For field work and in those instances where a satisfactory power-line source is unavailable, d-c welding generators are equipped with gas engines or Diesel motors. The load on these motors is such that they must have ample reserve power, coupled with the ability to respond quickly to fluctuating power demands. An example of this equipment is shown in Fig. 28-2.

There is some d-c arc welding equipment that utilizes rectifiers in place of a generator. One such design features electronic tubes of a mercury arc type so designed that the tubes can be connected in banks for increasing output. Close regulation of the welding current is achieved by

---

[1] "Standard Welding Terms and Their Definitions," American Standard A3.0-49, American Welding Society, New York, 1949.

introducing a resistance into the welding circuit, making possible the lowering of the welding current to 5 amp.

Direct-current welding equipment featuring a three-phase current supply connected to a transformer is available. The secondary current

Fig. 28-1. A portable motor-generator welding machine, d-c type. (*Courtesy of Air Reduction Sales Company, New York.*)

Fig. 28-2. Portable gas-driven d-c welding generator. (*Courtesy of Westinghouse Electric Corporation, Buffalo.*)

from the transformer is then changed to direct current by a selenium cell rectifier.

Direct-current Generators. Welding literature contains many articles on d-c generator design. The development of the metal electrode has shifted the emphasis in generator characteristics. Formerly there was considerable interest in voltage recovery time from the dead short resulting from arc starting, but now that electrode shieldings are capable of residual ironization, there seems less necessity for instantaneous voltage recovery.

There are a few fundamental considerations in connection with the operating characteristics of a welding generator that should be mentioned.

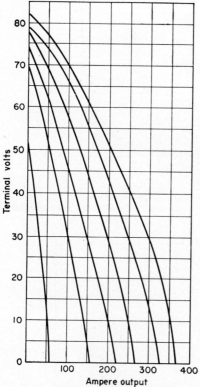

There is a psychological factor that is very important. A blindfold test of five different welding machines revealed practically no major advantage inherent in any one make. Obviously this means that personal preference is the main consideration and that electrical characteristics are secondary.

Direct-current welding generators are designed to produce "drooping characteristics" for the static va curve plotted for an individual design. These curves, of which Fig. 28-3 is an example, show the relation between voltage and amperage for a given terminal voltage. It is of interest to note the degree of change in current values (amp) for any change in arc voltage. If 25 v is taken as a representative value for a welding arc, it can readily be seen that when the arc shorts (zero voltage) there is but a very slight increase in amperage. This is of practical importance, since the arc length, which controls the voltage, is continually varying.

Fig. 28-3. Typical volt-ampere curves for a d-c welding generator. (*Courtesy of Harnischfeger Corporation, Milwaukee.*)

This variation in arc length is due to a combination of manipulations plus the conditions in the arc stream of metal globules. The steeper the va curve, the less will be the amperage fluctuation during welding.

The above explanation refers to the *static* characteristics of the welding generator. When this generator is welding, the results encountered are not actually those of the curve. However there is enough evidence at hand to indicate that the static curve characteristics point the way to the performance that can be expected under operating conditions.

A further check on operating performance can be had by photographing the transients of the welding circuit during operation. For this purpose an oscillograph is connected into the welding circuit. In order to obtain reliable comparative results, test conditions should be identical; the same electrode should be used. Figure 28-4 is an oscillogram of a welding circuit in the University of Washington welding laboratory, taken as one of a series in an investigation of electrode shielding behavior.

Welding generators can be designed to deliver a wide range of characteristics, for example, arc voltage remaining constant while current varies, or the reverse. The type of excitation used can be an external source, cross field, or third brush. Of greater practical importance is

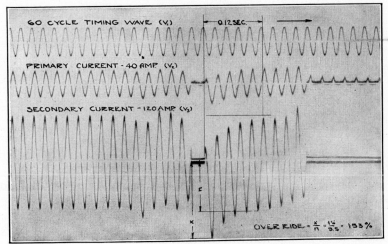

Fig. 28-4. Oscillogram of a motor-generator welding generator.

the matter of control of the welding current. The two best-known systems are the single control, in which the welder manipulates one knob, and the dual control, which offers individual regulation of both open circuit voltage and current.

Polarity. The outstanding feature of d-c welding equipment is its unidirectional current flow. The terminals on the welding current circuit are positive (anode) and negative (cathode) respectively. As a result the welding circuit can be connected with the electrode negative or positive, depending on the procedure requirements. Straight polarity means that the work is positive (electrode negative). Reverse polarity is the opposite connection, or the one in which the work is negative (electrode positive). The polarity connections are sketched in Fig. 28-5.

The significance attached to polarity arises from the fact that in an arc composed primarily of iron (unshielded electrodes), greater heat is liberated at the anode.   This preponderance of heat at the anode is attributed to the electrons flowing at high speed from their cathode source, bombarding the anode area.   The ratio of heat distribution is generally considered to be 2:3 at the anode to 1:3 at the cathode.   Consequently the base metal, being of greater volume, is connected at the anode in order to give it the benefit of greater heat input.   When shielded

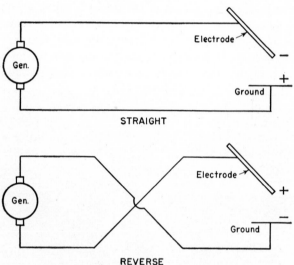

Fig. 28-5.   Schematic drawing of straight and reverse polarity connections for a d-c welding generator.

electrodes are used, this situation may be altered by reason of the action of certain of the components in the shielding.

CARBON ARC WELDING

Arc welding began with the use of carbon electrodes.   There remain some applications in which carbon arc welding is preferred, but the continuing development of metal electrodes is offering serious competition even in the remaining applications, which are primarily among the nonferrous metals.

Carbon arc welding features a carbon or graphite electrode that is used in either a shielded or an unshielded manner.   The differences between the graphite and the carbon electrode are that the former has a higher current-carrying capacity, while the latter is harder and somewhat lower in cost.

The arc is struck between the carbon electrode and the base metal. The welding circuit is d-c straight polarity.   Reverse polarity causes a very unstable arc condition, rapid electrode burn-off, and, in the welding of steel, carbon pickup.   The carbon arc acts as a torch, serving as a source of heat; weld metal must be provided from an outside source or from the base metal, as in the case of a flange weld.

In the *twin* carbon arc welding method, the electrode holder accommodates two carbon electrodes, so arranged that the arc is drawn between them; the arc is established and maintained entirely independently of the base metal. This method can be used with either direct or alternating current. Welds made by unshielded carbon arc welding tend toward brittleness. This can be remedied by the introduction of a shielding method such as painting the surface to be welded with a suitable flux.

Manual carbon arc welding is used on light-gage steel and on coated steels such as galvanized sheet; it is especially favored for welding copper and its alloys. Repair welding of cast iron is another application in which carbon arc welding has proved itself.

Alternating Current

The use of alternating current for welding is not a recent development. C. J. Holslag,[1] among others, championed this system with enthusiasm. It failed of general acceptance because of the practical operating difficulties of both striking and maintaining an arc when only bare or lightly coated electrodes were available. The introduction of shielded electrodes and their subsequent and continuing functional improvement have caused an increasing interest in a-c welding, to the point where this method has surpassed the d-c method for steel production welding.

Welding Transformers. Alternating-current welding installations generally employ a welding transformer as the source of current. A representative welding transformer is pictured in Fig. 28-6. Regulation of welding current output is obtained by the dial knob shown in the center of the transformer. Essentially the

Fig. 28-6. Transformer-type a-c welding equipment. (*Courtesy of Harnischfeger Corporation, Milwaukee.*)

a-c welding transformer is designed to receive single-phase power of line voltage and transform it into welding current of relatively lower voltage

[1] "Arc Welding Handbook," McGraw-Hill Book Company, Inc., New York, 1924.

and stepped-up amperage. Provision for adjusting the welding current is a feature of all welding transformers. The design of this feature varies with different manufacturers; such ideas as taps taken from the windings, movable coils or cores, and combinations of these are incorporated. Built-in power factor correction and a cooling fan are other features of the welding transformer.

Alternating-current Welding Generators. Prior to the general acceptance of a-c welding transformers, there were some generators built for this method of welding. Such generators were in effect frequency changers. One type was designed as a vertical unit in which the alternating current was stepped up from 60 to 180 cycles. This welding machine consisted of an a-c motor operating from a power line of three-phase, 60-cycle current, driving an a-c generator delivering single-phase, 180-cycle welding current. Increasing the number of alternations from 60 to 180 divided the interval at zero voltage by 3; consequently, less difficulty was experienced in maintaining the arc.

Alternating-current Welding. The characteristics of welding current from an a-c source are different from those of the d-c type. In a-c welding there is a reversal from positive to negative equal to the number of cycles of that current; there is no difference in heat distribution as between the terminals of the welding circuit. A further feature is that alternating current does not build up a magnetic field surrounding the electrode (conductor) to the degree that this phenomenon occurs in a d-c welding circuit. As a result, a-c welding is relatively free of the magnetic disturbance, or arc blow, that proves so annoying in d-c welding, especially where high amperage is needed or where weldment design requires the placing of metal in a position causing magnetic disturbance in the welding arc.

DIRECT- AND ALTERNATING-CURRENT WELDING COMPARED

The outstanding feature of d-c welding is its polarity system. This is especially important in the welding of nonferrous alloys, and also in many applications of the carbon arc. Further advantages claimed for direct current are arc stability and ease of manipulation. It is also noteworthy that on motor-generator sets a much better line-load situation is obtained from a three-phase motor, which makes the set more desirable than in the case of the transformer.

One of the criticisms directed against motor-generator sets for d-c welding is that the rotating members, commutators, and other rotating parts create a maintenance problem. When the weldor is changing electrodes or is taking care of other tasks, the machine is running and power is being consumed in overcoming the friction load of the set, resulting in added over-all cost of operation.

Alternating-current transformers, when they are equipped with proper power factor correction, are the most efficient of the arc welding current sources. This equipment costs considerably less per unit than does direct current. It requires less floor space and is lighter in weight and more easily moved. The major advantage of a-c welding arises from insignificant arc blow. Because of this, heavier welding currents are used and more rapid welding is obtained.

An undesirable feature of a-c welding is the possibility of power-line unbalance occasioned by single-phase load. This situation can be improved by the installation of other motor-driven equipment to afford a balanced line load. The former objection to a-c welding with its high arc striking voltage has been almost entirely overcome through the introduction of suitable shielded electrodes.

Fig. 28-6a.   Diesel-electric freight locomotive built largely by arc welding.   (*Courtesy of Electro-Motive Corp., La Grange, Ill.*)

Metal Electrode Welding

Replacement of the carbon electrode by a metal one is the basis of the preponderant use of arc welding systems. Metal electrodes originally were lengths of bare wire; these proved difficult to use because of arc instability. Remedial measures included dipping, dusting, or painting the wire with a thin coating of ferric or calcium compounds. These electrodes were known as light-coated or sul-coated and were used with d-c straight polarity. They were unsatisfactory for a-c welding. Welds made with this electrode do not have a heavy slag coating—rather there is a light oxide deposit that is readily removed by brushing. The absence of a slag deposit has proved of value in those applications where freedom from slag inclusions is critical. Light-coated electrodes are used to a considerable extent in automatic arc welding.

SHIELDED METAL ELECTRODES

Although shielded or heavy-coated electrodes have come into general use in comparatively recent years, the basic idea is not new. Benardos

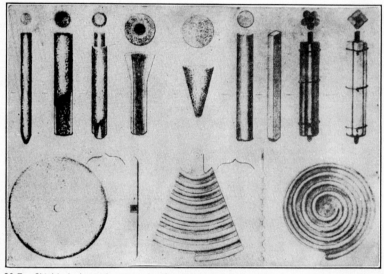

Fig. 28-7. Shielded electrode types developed by Benardos in the latter part of the nineteenth century.

introduced electrodes of various shapes and with various types of shielding before the turn of the century; some of his electrodes are shown in Fig. 28-7.

Specifications covering shielded electrodes have been developed by the American Welding Society in cooperation with the American Society for Testing Materials. These specifications carry the following designations: mild steel arc-welding electrodes (AWS A5.1—48T; ASTM A233—48T), low alloy steel arc-welding electrodes (AWS A5.5—48T; ASTM A316—48T), corrosion-resistant chromium and chromium-nickel steel welding electrodes (AWS A5.4—48T; ASTM A298—48T), copper and copper-alloy metal-arc-welding electrodes (AWS A5.6—48T; ASTM A225—48T). These specifications give the information on electrode classification, mechanical properties, and welding current in addition to some data on shielding materials.

TABLE 28-1. ELECTRODE CLASSIFICATION*

Electrode classification no.	Type of coating or covering	Capable of producing satisfactory welds in position shown†	Type of current
E45 Series.—Minimum Tensile Strength of Deposited Metal in Non-stress-relieved Condition 45,000 Psi			
E4510 E4520	Sulcoated or light-coated	F, V, OH, H H-fillets, F	Not specified, but generally d-c, straight polarity (electrode negative)
E60 Series.—Minimum Tensile Strength of Deposited Metal in Non-stress-relieved Condition 62,000 Psi or Higher			
E6010	High cellulose sodium	F, V, OH, H	For use with d-c, reversed polarity (electrode positive) only
E6011	High cellulose potassium	F, V, OH, H	For use with a-c or d-c, reversed polarity (electrode positive)
E6012	High titania sodium	F, V, OH, H	For use with d-c straight polarity (electrode negative), or a-c
E6013	High titania potassium	F, V, OH, H	For use with a-c or d-c, straight polarity (electrode negative)
E6015	Low hydrogen sodium	F, V, OH, H	For use with d-c, reversed polarity (electrode positive), only
E6016	Low hydrogen potassium	F, V, OH, H	For use with a-c or d-c, reversed polarity (electrode positive)
E6020	High iron oxide	H-fillets, F	For use with d-c, straight polarity (electrode negative), or a-c for horizontal fillet welds; and d-c, either polarity, or a-c, for flat-position welding
E6030	High iron oxide	F	For use with d-c, either polarity, or a-c

* Abstracted from "Tentative Specifications for Mild Steel Arc-welding Electrodes," American Welding Society and American Society of Testing Materials, 1948.

† The abbreviations F, H, V, OH, and H-fillets indicate welding positions as follows: F, flat; V, vertical; H, horizontal; OH, overhead; H-fillets, horizontal fillets. For electrodes $\frac{3}{16}$ in. and under except in classification E6015 and E6016, $\frac{5}{32}$ in. and under.

The classification number is devised in such a manner that the first two digits indicate the minimum tensile strength of the weld metal in pounds per square inch.   For example, electrode E6010 specifies a tensile strength of 62,000 to 70,000 psi with a yield of 52,000 to 58,000 psi.   The entire series of electrodes in the E60 classification is for mild steel welding and specifies a minimum tensile strength of deposited weld metal in non-stress-relieved condition of 62,000 psi.

The types of shielding used on these various electrodes, together with the welding position in which they are to be used, are shown in Table 28-1.   The shielding materials used by the various manufacturers for the electrode classifications given above are not a matter of general knowledge; however, an indication of the materials most commonly used is given in Table 28-2, which supplies the material formula as well as the shielding composition after baking.

TABLE 28-2.   COVERINGS FOR PLAIN CARBON OR LOW-ALLOY STEEL*
Material Formulas, Parts by Weight

Gas shielded (E6010)		Gas-slag shielded (E6012)		Slag shielded (E6020)	
Cellulose	35	Cellulose	5	Iron oxide	30
Asbestos	20	Rutile	55	Rutile	20
Titania	12	Asbestos	10	Clay	5
Sod. Sil.	80	Clay	10	Asbestos	15
		Iron oxide	1	Sod. Sil.	70
		Sod. Sil.	40		

Chemical Composition, Per Cent (after Baking)

(E6010)		(E6012)		(E6020)	
SiO_2	50.0	SiO_2	29.6	SiO_2	44.0
TiO_2	10.1	TiO_2	49.0	TiO_2	16.4
FeO	1.6	FeO	7.0	FeO	30.7
MgO	3.2	MgO	2.0	MgO	2.8
Na_2O	5.1	Na_2O	2.4	Na_2O	3.8
Volatile matter	30.0	Al_2O_3	5.0	Al_2O_3	2.3
		Volatile matter	5.0		

* "Welding Metallurgy," 2d ed., American Welding Society, New York, 1949.

Electrode shieldings serve a multiple function.   First, they are used to prevent atmospheric contamination of the arc stream.   Second, by depositing a slag on the weld bead they shield the freshly made weld from the atmosphere.   Third, the generation of combustion products in the arc aids in penetration of the weld.   Finally, ingredients in the coating act as ionizing agents in the arc stream.   This last feature is of especial importance with electrodes used for a-c welding.   Alloying elements can be introduced into the weld metal from the shielding.

It will be noted (Table 28-1) that shieldings are, roughly, of four types, viz., cellulose or gaseous, titania or mineral, low hydrogen, and iron oxide or heavy slag.

Coating of Electrodes. The shielding materials are compounded dry and then mixed with some type of liquid binder, generally sodium silicate. This mixture is worked in a pugmill or similar mechanical mixer. When the coating material reaches the consistency of stiff mud, it is transferred to the electrode coating machine for extrusion onto the base wire.

The wire used for the various electrodes does not vary in chemical composition. The electrode core wire is produced in the wire mill in the form of coils. These coils are straightened and cut to lengths which vary with the diameter. The core wires are then transferred to the

Fig. 28-8. Extruding shielding on core wire in the production of shielded electrodes. (*Courtesy of The Hydraulic Press Manufacturing Co., Mount Gilead, Ohio.*)

extrusion press, where the coating is extruded onto them. Among the necessary precautions is making sure that the coating is concentric with the wire. Shielding material should not cause extensive die erosion. Figure 28-8 shows one type of electrode extrusion press in operation. It should be noted that the coating is extruded over the entire length of the electrode. As the electrode travels toward the oven, the coating is brushed off the end for holder gripping. Extrusion material is also removed from the opposite end of the electrode in order to present a clean metal contact there.

The method of producing shielded electrodes varies with different manufacturers. In some cases electrodes are extruded to double length, being cut in half later. The general practice, however, is to extrude the electrode to length (Fig. 28-8). The rate of production of electrodes is a function of the type of extrusion press used. Production rates in excess of 900 electrodes per minute have been reported.[1] Prior to World War II, there was in Europe some interest in electrodes that carried the shielding in the center rather than on the surface.

Electrode Color Code. A color code for distinguishing between electrodes has been developed and published as a specification entitled "Standard for Color Markings for Electrode Identifications."[2] The color markings occur in two places on the electrode: at the end (this is known as the primary color) and on the electrode grip (this is referred to as the secondary color). Some electrodes are marked in one place, some in both.

Burn-off Characteristics. The metal electrode is consumed in arc welding because of the heat of the arc, which causes it to melt and transfer across the arc to the base metal. Here it unites with the melted base metal to form the molten pool of weld metal. Transference across the arc is characterized by various-sized globules, particles, and vaporized metal. The phenomenon of metal transfer is influenced considerably by the rate at which the electrode tip melts or burns off. Variability in burn-off will give nonuniform results in the weld deposit. Welding speed is an equally pertinent consideration: faster burn-off means higher rates of weld metal deposition.

Burn-off rates vary with the different electrode classifications, and there are variations between electrodes within a given classification. It seems established that the method of manufacture of the steel core wire contributes to this situation. Electrode shieldings also modify burn-off rates.[3]

Manual Arc Welding Techniques

Preliminaries. Before striking the arc, certain precautionary measures should be taken. The weldor needs to be equipped with suitable clothing to protect him from the rays and the heat emitted by the arc. Proper eye protection must be provided; welding face shields and hoods must be equipped with filter lenses that are free of cracks. Cover glasses should be free of spatter. Ventilation of the welding area should be adequate.

The welding equipment also requires attention. The leads from the welding machine must be fully insulated against current leakage; this

---

[1] Mr. Lincoln's Formula, *Fortune*, Vol. 29, No. 2, February, 1944.

[2] Pub. No. EW2-1950, National Electrical Manufacturers' Association, New York.

[3] Martin, D. C., P. J. Rieppel, and C. B. Voldrich: "Burn-off Characteristics of Steel Welding Electrodes," Welding Research Council Bulletin No. 3, May, 1949.

important consideration is too frequently overlooked. Ground connections should give solid contact to eliminate resistance, thereby ensuring maximum welding current flow. The electrode holder should be free of weld spatter and should be constructed so as to give firm contact with the electrode. Machine settings should be checked prior to striking the arc.

Striking the Arc. The arc is established by contacting the electrode with the work and promptly separating it from the work by a distance equal to the desired arc length; this maneuver closes the welding circuit and establishes the current flow. A straight vertical movement is difficult to master, since hesitation on contact will cause the electrode to freeze or to stick to the base metal. Should sticking occur, a sharp sidewise twist of the electrode will break it free. On the other hand, a too vigorous withdrawal of the electrode from its initial contact will draw out and extinguish the arc.

A second method of arc striking is to move the electrode as if striking a match, drawing the electrode across the base metal. There is less possibility of a stuck electrode when the scratching method is employed. Once the arc is kindled, it can readily be guided to its required position.

Maintenance of a proper arc length is dependent upon a continuing downward movement of the electrode as compensation for the melting of its tip by the arc. Failure to follow this procedure will result in an increasing arc length and, ultimately, no arc at all. The electrode is consumed by this downward movement into the arc until it becomes too short for further welding. The remainder of the electrode, called the stub, is removed from the electrode holder and replaced by another electrode.

Once the arc is established, the base metal becomes fused in the actual welding operation. The electrode is held at an inclination to the work in the direction of weld travel. The behavior of the arc is diagramed in Fig. 28-9. The electrode is moved along the line of welding at a speed that will give a smooth uniform weld deposit. Electrode movement will vary with the position of welding, *i.e.*, flat (down-hand), horizontal, vertical, or overhead (Table 28-1). The practice of weaving the electrode is generally followed; however, there is considerable divergence of opinion on the pattern such movements should take. Procedures should be definitely established in order to remove this important feature of welding from the sphere of the weldor's discretion.

Restriking the Arc. The arc can be broken through faulty technique, wind interference, or accident. The arc must be broken when the electrode has been consumed. A satisfactory procedure for restriking the arc is to kindle it at the forward end of the weld crater, following this by a movement back across the crater, and forward again as welding

continues.   If the interval during which the arc is extinguished is sufficiently great to permit the slag to congeal, welding must be stopped until
the slag has been removed in order to prevent the possibility of slag
inclusion.

Breaking the Arc—There are two accepted methods of breaking an
arc.   When the electrode is to be changed and the weld continued from
the crater, it is customary to shorten the arc and move the electrode
rapidly sidewise out of the weld crater.   The second method of breaking
the arc consists of holding the electrode stationary until the crater
becomes filled, following this by a gradual withdrawal of the electrode.

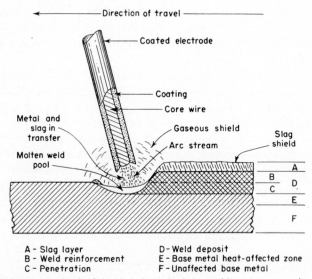

Fig. 28-9.   Diagrammatic sketch of shielded electrode during welding operation.   (*From "Welding Metallurgy,"* 2d ed., American Welding Society, New York, 1949.)

Arc Length.   The maintenance of correct arc length is a major consideration in metal arc welding.   A long arc promotes oxidation and
porosity in the weld metal; it also is a contributing factor to undercutting
—a serious weld defect.   Proper penetration is necessary for making
sound, strong welds.   Here again arc length is a controlling factor.
Metal deposition rate and the elimination of spatter are promoted by
shortness of the arc.

Maintenance of the desired arc length depends upon the skill of the
weldor.   This skill is acquired from long experience and cannot be gained
through shortcuts.   The arc-length monitor pictured in Fig. 28-10 has
proved invaluable in weldor training as it has in aiding the experienced
weldor.   The instrument is set to the desired arc voltage after it has been

connected both to the welding circuit and to the weldor's hood.   There are two small pilot lights on the face of the monitor as well as one below each eye location in the hood.   When welding is proceeding with the

desired arc length, neither light burns; if the arc is too short, one light comes on, while if the arc is too long, the other one lights up. The weldor, equipped with this apparatus, concentrates on keeping both lights extinguished, since this assures him that proper arc length is being maintained.

Arc length requires variation with the position of welding. Both overhead and vertical welding are best performed with a short arc, whereas down-hand

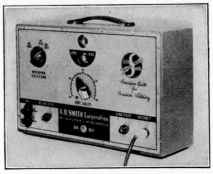

Fig. 28-10. Arc-length monitor. (Courtesy of A. O. Smith Corp., Milwaukee.)

welding offers greater latitude in choice of arc length.   In any event, a short arc yields more satisfactory welding results than a long one.

Survey Questions

28-1. Is manual arc welding adaptable to mass production?

28-2. In d-c welding, what is the major current source?

28-3. Are rectifiers used for producing d-c welding current?

28-4. How have electrode developments affected welding generator design?

28-5. What is meant by straight polarity?

28-6. Why is arc polarity of importance?

28-7. Why was the acceptance of a-c arc welding retarded?

28-8. From what equipment source is a-c welding current usually obtained?

28-9. Explain the outstanding advantage of a-c arc welding.

28-10. In production welding, which is predominant, d-c or a-c type?

28-11. Is there a favorable cost increment of a-c over d-c, or the reverse?

28-12. Does carbon arc welding require the use of a filler rod?

28-13. Mention some specific applications for carbon arc welding.

28-14. What are shielded electrodes?

28-15. How does the shielding function?

28-16. In electrode specifications, what do the numerals immediately following the letter "E" signify?

28-17. How is the shielding material applied to the electrode?

28-18. Where are the color identification marks placed on an electrode?

28-19. What is the meaning of burn-off rate?

28-20. Explain manipulation necessary to striking an arc.

28-21. Why is arc length important?

28-22. How does horizontal welding differ from the flat position?

28-23. What is "weaving" in metal arc welding?

28-24. Where should the arc be rekindled with respect to the deposited metal?

REFERENCES

Andrews, W.: Binding Agents for Flux Coatings: Their Composition and Production, *The Welding Journal*, Vol. 24, No. 12, December, 1945.

Bardtke, P.: "Technique of Modern Welding," Blackie & Son, Ltd., Glasgow, 1935.

Brooking, W. J.: "Arc Welding Engineering and Production Control,"McGraw-Hill Book Company, Inc., New York, 1944.

"Flexarc Engineering Data Book," Westinghouse Corporation, Inc., Buffalo, 1946.

"Handbook for Electric Welders," Murex Welding Processes, Ltd., Waltham Cross, Herts., England, 1946.

Henry, O. H., and G. E. Claussen: "Welding Metallurgy," 2d ed., rev. by G. E. Linnert, American Welding Society, New York, 1949.

Holslag, C. J.: "Arc Welding Handbook," McGraw-Hill Book Company, Inc., New York, 1925.

"Master Chart of Welding Processes and Process Charts," American Standard A3.1-49, American Welding Society, New York, 1949.

"Procedure Handbook of Arc Welding Design and Practice," 8th ed., Lincoln Electric Company, Cleveland, 1945.

Spraragen, W., and G. E. Claussen: "Coatings and Fluxes in the Welding of Steel," supplement to *The Welding Journal*, Vol. IV, No. 5, May, 1939.

"The Welding Encyclopedia," 11th ed., The Welding Engineer Publishing Company, Chicago, 1943.

"The Welding Handbook," 3d ed., American Welding Society, New York, 1950.

CHAPTER 29

GAS WELDING

Gas welding is the name applied to those processes in which the necessary heat for coalescence is provided by a gas flame or flames. The requisite gases are mixed in a blowpipe, also termed torch, whence they issue as a combustible gaseous mixture; this, upon ignition, supplies the welding heat. There are always two gases in the mixture; one is combustible and the other serves to speed and support combustion, thus promoting high flame temperature. Since by far the major part of gas welding is performed by the oxyacetylene process, it seems desirable to consider its components and interpret its significance.

Oxyacetylene Fundamentals

Oxyacetylene welding was presented by Le Châtelier in 1895 in a paper read before the Académie des Sciences in Paris; he stated that the combustion of a gaseous mixture composed of equal volumes of acetylene and oxygen exceeded by 1000°C the temperature of the oxyhydrogen flames. Another fundamental contribution to the oxyacetylene process was the invention by Thomas L. Willson, in 1892, of a commercial method for manufacturing calcium carbide as a raw material for the production of acetylene.

Calcium Carbide. The electrochemical industry is the parent of calcium carbide. This material, referred to in the trade as carbide, is dark gray in color and of a stonelike consistency. It is produced in an electric arc furnace, of the type shown in Fig. 29-1, from a basic charge consisting of lime and coke. The temperature within the furnace is sufficiently high to cause the following reaction between these materials:

$$CaO + 3C = CaC_2 + CO$$

The purity of the raw materials in the charge is of extreme importance, since only high-grade calcium carbide will produce acetylene gas of superior quality.

The molten calcium carbide is tapped from the furnace and permitted to cool and solidify. It is then broken for screening and grading, in accordance with such designations as lump, egg, nut, etc. (the nut size is $1\frac{1}{4}$ by $\frac{3}{8}$ in.). After grading, it is packed in sheet steel drums for storage or shipment. The drums must be tightly sealed to guard against moisture penetration.

Calcium carbide is a safe material to store or transport. It will not burn nor will it deteriorate. It will not explode. All these statements hold only if the material is kept moisture-free. A violent-action occurs when calcium carbide is mixed with water. This reaction is accompanied by the evolution of acetylene gas, which has a characteristic

Fig. 29-1. Example of an arc furnace used for the production of calcium carbide. (*Courtesy of Pittsburgh Lectromelt Furnace Corporation, Pittsburgh.*)

odor. Calcium carbide, on the other hand, is an odorless substance. If, then, an odor is noted in the vicinity of carbide storage, it should act as a warning that acetylene gas is present.

Acetylene Gas. Acetylene gas, C_2H_2, is one of a number of hydrocarbon gases. As has been said, it is produced by the action of water on calcium carbide. The chemical equation for this reaction is the following:

$$CaC_2 + 2H_2O = C_2H_2 + Ca(OH)_2$$

Acetylene is composed of 92.3 per cent C and 7.7 per cent H by weight. A distinctive feature of acetylene gas is its endothermic property, which is equal to 228 Btu/cu ft.

Generation of Acetylene. Acetylene gas for welding is produced in acetylene generator equipment. Generators are of two basic designs.

The least-used method is that in which water is dripped onto a large volume of carbide. The term drip generator has been applied to this design, which is used primarily for small lamp applications. The difficulty encountered in this type is that as the water is added to the carbide, considerable quantities of heat are developed. The heat, in turn, acts to increase the temperature of the carbide, which may become high enough to cause dissociation of the acetylene into its components, with further release of heat.

The heat difficulty was overcome by building a generator on the principle of dropping carbide into a large volume of water, so that reaction temperatures could be controlled. A generator of this design is shown in Fig. 29-2. Charging is regulated in order to maintain a constant pressure of acetylene independent of the volume being withdrawn from the generator.

The National Board of Fire Underwriters exercises a strict jurisdictional control over the design and manufacture of acetylene generators. Capacities for water and carbide are specified, as are other constructional features including gas withdrawal rate and safety devices. Generators are further divided, as to operation, between low- and medium-pressure systems. Portable generators are popular where small volumes of acetylene are used, while large industrial establishments have permanent installations.

Compressed Acetylene. Inasmuch as many users of acetylene gas do not require a volume sufficient to warrant the installation of generator equipment, they find it expedient to purchase the gas rather than to produce it. In the early years of the industry, the term dissolved acetylene was widely used. This expression originated from the construction of the acetylene cylinders, wherein the gas is actually held in solution in acetone (CH_3—CO—CH_3). Claude and Hess[1] discovered that at pressures exceeding 24 psi, dissociation starts at one point in the gas volume and spreads very rapidly through the entire volume, causing a complete breakdown of the acetylene accompanied by a tremendous increase in temperature and pressure.

The practice of diluting acetylene with an exothermic gas was conceived of as a means of compressing it. In 1896 basic patents were granted on the revolutionary idea of compressing acetylene in the small voids that result from inserting a porous filler in the acetylene storage cylinder. In a later development, acetone was poured into the porous lining in order to fill all voids. Acetone has the property of dissolving approximately twenty-four times its own volume of acetylene for each atmosphere of pressure.

[1] Claude, Georges, and Albert Hess: "Sur un nouveau mode d'emmagasinement de l'acétylène," Académie des Sciences, Paris, 1897.

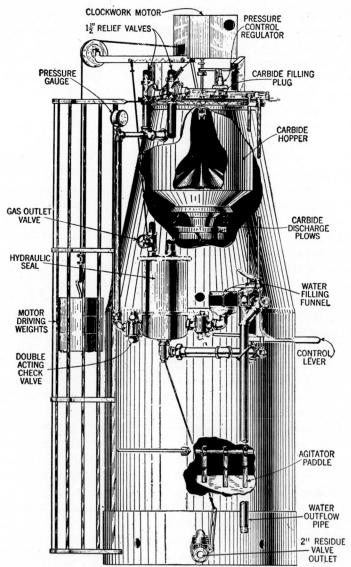

Fig. 29-2. Sketch of an acetylene generator of the type found in large industrial installations. (*Courtesy of Air Reduction Sales Company, New York.*)

Acetylene Cylinders. The construction of acetylene cylinders is governed by regulations of the Interstate Commerce Commission. The cylinders in most common use for welding have an acetylene capacity of approximately 275 cu ft at 250 psi pressure at 70°F. Cylinders are varied as to physical form, both domed- and recessed-head types being

used.   There is a base band encircling the bottom of the cylinder as a
protective device for safety in handling.   Several fusible plugs that
melt at 220°F are located in both the top and the bottom of the cylinder
as an additional protective measure.   Regulations do not generally
permit the use of a valve handwheel; instead a wrench is necessary to
open the cylinder—a precaution
against tampering.   A safety link
is usually provided in the valve
stem as a means of preventing valve
damage from rough treatment.

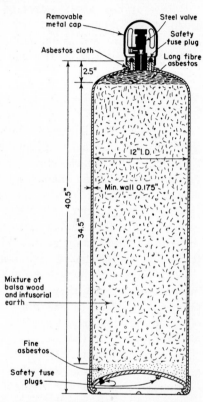

The cylinder contains some type
of porous filler material to provide
the cells which hold the acetone.
There are several classifications of
filler materials—loose fillers, semi-
supported fillers, and self-supporting fillers.   Examples of loose fillers
are raw silk, kapok, granulated
charcoal, and infusorial earth mixed
with treated wood chips.   Loose
fillers lack adhesive properties and
are forced into the cylinders in a
predetermined amount.   Asbestos
blocks constitute the leading type
of semi-supported filler.

Self-supporting fillers are composed of grains or fibers, or both,
joined together by binding agents
into a monolithic, porous body.
Charcoal, infusorial earth with
asbestos fibers bound together with
zinc or oxychloride cement are examples of this type of filler (Fig.
29-3).   Inasmuch as the acetylene
gas in a cylinder is dissolved in
acetone, the pressure gage is in-

Fig. 29-3.   Diagram of the cross section of a
conventional acetylene cylinder. Acetylene
capacity approximately 275 cu ft at 250 lb per
sq in. pressure and 70°F water capacity
approximately 4,021 cu in. (*Courtesy of Air
Reduction Sales Company, New York.*)

adequate for showing gas content.   The gas volume is determined by
weight, using a constant of 14.5 cu ft/lb. at 70°F.

Precautions.   Regulations forbid any but the supplier to fill acetylene
cylinders.

One cylinder should never be filled from another for any reason what-
soever.

Open flame should be kept away from acetylene cylinders.

Acetylene cylinders can only provide gas in a volume that the acetone will yield; therefore the valve should be opened only partially. Failure to observe this precaution will result in drawing liquid acetone into the welding apparatus, causing it to foul. Cylinders should always be used in an upright position.

Copper tubing should never be used as an acetylene line. Brass or a copper-base alloy is the proper material. Iron or steel pipe is entirely satisfactory for distribution mains and laterals.

Acetylene gas mixed with air in volumes from 3 per cent upward forms an explosive mixture.

OXYGEN

This gas is a familiar one to the student. It is obtained for welding by the fractional distillation of liquid air, of which it forms about 20 per cent by volume. Other processes for obtaining oxygen have been used at various times, among them (a) the ignition of niter, (b) the heating of manganese dioxide, (c) the electrolysis of water, which provides both hydrogen and oxygen. This last process had rather wide application until well after World War I.

Practically all the oxygen used in gas welding is now produced by the fractional distillation of liquid air. The boiling point of oxygen is $-297.2°F$, while nitrogen boils at $-320.5°F$. When two liquids are mechanically mixed, they can be separated by reaching and holding the temperature at which one will vaporize. This process forms the basis of oxygen production. Oxygen is compressed in cylinders for industrial distribution.

Oxygen Cylinders. Cylinders for the distribution of oxygen are manufactured and maintained under the regulations of the Interstate Commerce Commission. Cylinders are of various sizes; the most common size in the gas welding shop has a capacity of 220 cu ft at 2,000 psi pressure at 70°F. The cylinders are of one-piece construction, being produced by piercing a billet section, as shown in Fig. 29-4.

Every oxygen cylinder has a series of numbers and letters stamped on its dome. The inscription ICC-3A refers to Interstate Commerce Commission regulation 3A governing the manufacture and maintenance of cylinders. The serial number and the initials of the owning company are then given. The series of figures below these are the date of manufacture and the dates of testing. Each cylinder must be tested at five-year intervals as a precautionary measure, and the month and year of each test are stamped on the cylinder.

Oxygen cylinders are equipped with valves designed to be opened fully when in service. Many designs have an upper seat which acts to prevent leakage along the stem when the valve is fully open. The valve body

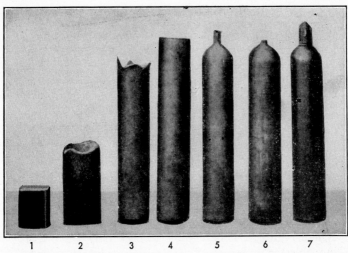

Fig. 29-4. Successive operations in the production of a standard oxygen cylinder. 1, slug from billet; 2, pierced cup; 3, shell after first draw; 4, shell after second draw; 5, necked cylinder; 6, cylinder cut to length and tapped; 7, finished cylinder. (*Courtesy of Taylor-Wharton Iron & Steel Company, Easton, Pa.*)

has a frangible disk designed to release the contents of the cylinder in case excessive pressures should be built up, as in the event of a fire. A protective cap covers the valve and prevents damage to this vital part of the cylinder assembly.

Gas Welding Equipment

Regulators. The pressure of a full oxygen cylinder at room temperature is 2,200 psi, while the acetylene cylinder carries a pressure of 250 psi. These pressures are too high for any welding operation. In order to reduce the pressures to a usable amount, a piece of equipment known as a regulator is attached directly to the gas cylinder. Figure 29-5 shows representative oxygen regulator equipment.

Regulators are obtainable for acetylene as well as oxygen. However, regulators are not the same for the two gases, since cylinder pressure for oxygen is almost ten times that for acetylene. Regulators can be distinguished between by noting the

Fig. 29-5. Cutaway view of a single-stage regulator. (*Courtesy of Victor Equipment Company, San Francisco.*)

scale on the gages of the regulators or by checking the threads for the hose connection (see page 504).

A regulator is a reduction valve operating on the diaphragm principle. The regulator has a T handle which, when turned clockwise, loads a spring as desired by the weldor. The spring pressure is such that the diaphragm reacting against it will permit gas of the predetermined pressure to pass through to the hose.

Insofar as the design of the regulators is concerned, there are two general types. The one described above is known as a single-stage regulator; a more recent development is the double, or two-stage, regulator. The advantage of the two-stage regulator is that it makes a more accurate compensation for pressure loss in the cylinder resulting from gas consumption. In this design the first stage is generally an automatic one, while the second stage is controlled by the aforementioned T handle.

Another respect in which regulator design offers two alternatives is the gage; some designs use a single gauge, while others use two. With the single-gage regulator it is possible to read only the pressure on the welding line; there is no means of determining cylinder pressure. When there are two gages on the regulator, one gage shows the cylinder pressure and the other one will read at zero until the desired gas pressure has been established by turning the T handle. It must be remembered that as the volume of gas in the cylinder is consumed, cylinder pressures drop, which may, in the case of a single-stage regulator, make it necessary for the weldor to readjust the regulator to maintain desired line pressure.

Before a regulator is attached to a cylinder, the cylinder valve, with the opening facing away from the weldor, should be "cracked," *i.e.*, opened slightly and immediately closed. This is done in order to free the regulator attachment seat of any foreign matter. The regulator is attached by means of a union nut, which should be drawn up snugly.

Welding Hose. The gases are conducted from the regulators to the torch by means of hoses specially made for this purpose. As a warning, the hose on the acetylene cylinder is red, indicating inflammable gas. The hose used for oxygen is either dark green or black. There is also available a twin hose in which both hoses are bound into one. Hose connections are arranged with a connecting nut on each end of the hose. In order to prevent a crossover on hose connections, the acetylene hose is always equipped with a left-hand thread, while the oxygen hose has a right-hand thread. As a further distinguishing characteristic, the acetylene hose nut has a groove machined in it, whereas the oxygen one is plain.

TORCHES

The construction of the welding torch and all its features vary with different manufacturers (Fig. 29-6). Essentially a torch consists of the base or butt, of which the gas connections are an integral part. Gas flow is regulated by a needle valve on each gas inlet. The base of the torch is joined permanently to the body, which serves as the handle and contains single passages for oxygen and acetylene.

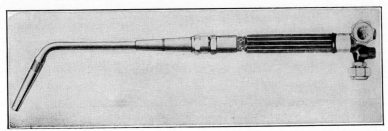

Fig. 29-6. Conventional oxyacetylene welding torch. (*Courtesy of Bastian-Blessing Company, Chicago.*)

The torch head houses the mixing chamber, in which the two entering gases are blended into the oxyacetylene mixture that issues from the torch tip, where combustion occurs. The tips are of different design and construction insofar as appearance and mechanical details are concerned. Each tip has an appropriate gradation based on the size of the orifice

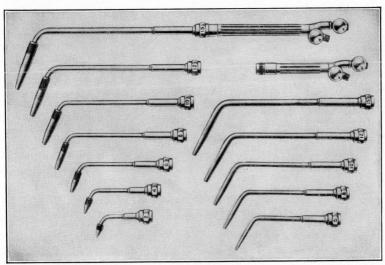

Fig. 29-7. Oxyacetylene welding torch and interchangeable tips. (*Courtesy of Harris Calorific Company, Cleveland.*)

at its open end (Fig. 29-7). A given tip is designed to weld a joint of specific thickness; correct choice of tip is essential to proper welding results. The employment of a tip that is too small or one that is too large will result in improper welding conditions and prove costly in both gas and labor.

Basic Torch Design. Welding torches are designed either for *low-pressure* or for *medium-pressure* operation. Design details for these two types of operation are different. There are no high-pressure welding torches; in the early period of oxyacetylene welding these proved too dangerous and were discarded. There is one torch designed to function on both the low- and the medium-pressure system. An acetylene generator or torch which operates at a pressure below 1 psi is of the low-pressure type, whereas those operating at pressures up to 15 psi are in the medium-pressure category.

The low-pressure torch employs a low acetylene pressure. The oxygen pressure is considerably higher and functions like an injector. The low-pressure torch, uses the oxygen pressure to aspirate the acetylene in an action similar to that of a Bunsen burner.

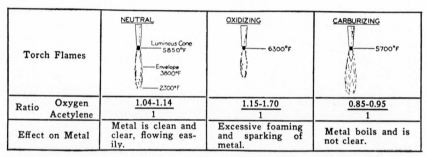

Torch Flames	NEUTRAL	OXIDIZING	CARBURIZING
Ratio Oxygen Acetylene	$\dfrac{1.04\text{-}1.14}{1}$	$\dfrac{1.15\text{-}1.70}{1}$	$\dfrac{0.85\text{-}0.95}{1}$
Effect on Metal	Metal is clean and clear, flowing easily.	Excessive foaming and sparking of metal.	Metal boils and is not clear.

Fig. 29-8. Oxyacetylene flame characteristics under different gas ratios. (*Courtesy of Air Reduction Sales Company, New York.*)

The medium-pressure torch, on occasion referred to as an equal-pressure torch, operates with both gases at the same pressure. The gas pressure is relied upon to cause flow of the combustible mixture through the tip. Pressures vary with tip sizes—each different tip size requires pressure adjustment for that particular size. Manufacturers' recommendations should be followed as to tip sizes and pressures.

Oxyacetylene Welding Flames. Since there are two gases combined in the combustion mixture in the torch, three flame conditions are possible:

1. Neutral or normal flame (gases correctly proportioned)
2. Carburizing or reducing flame (excess acetylene in mixture)
3. Oxidizing or cutting flame (excess oxygen in mixture)

These three flames are distinctive in appearance, in sound of operation, and in temperature (Fig. 29-8). For most welding applications the neutral flame is best, although both of the other types are employed in specific instances. Chart 29-1 embodies the recommendations of the International Acetylene Association.

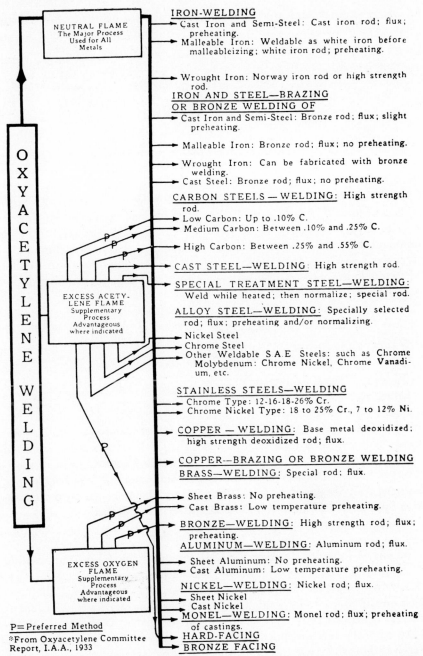

IRON-WELDING
Cast Iron and Semi-Steel: Cast iron rod; flux; preheating.
Malleable Iron: Weldable as white iron before malleableizing; white iron rod; preheating.

Wrought Iron: Norway iron rod or high strength rod.
IRON AND STEEL—BRAZING OR BRONZE WELDING OF
Cast Iron and Semi-Steel: Bronze rod; flux; slight preheating.

Malleable Iron: Bronze rod; flux; no preheating.

Wrought Iron: Can be fabricated with bronze welding.
Cast Steel: Bronze rod; flux; no preheating.
CARBON STEELS — WELDING: High strength rod.
Low Carbon: Up to .10% C.
Medium Carbon: Between .10% and .25% C.

High Carbon: Between .25% and .55% C.

CAST STEEL—WELDING: High strength rod.

SPECIAL TREATMENT STEEL—WELDING: Weld while heated; then normalize; special rod.

ALLOY STEEL—WELDING: Specially selected rod; flux; preheating and/or normalizing.
Nickel Steel
Chrome Steel
Other Weldable S A E Steels: such as Chrome Molybdenum: Chrome Nickel, Chrome Vanadium, etc.

STAINLESS STEELS—WELDING
Chrome Type: 12-16-18-26% Cr.
Chrome Nickel Type: 18 to 25% Cr., 7 to 12% Ni.

COPPER — WELDING: Base metal deoxidized; high strength deoxidized rod; flux.

COPPER—BRAZING OR BRONZE WELDING
BRASS—WELDING: Special rod; flux.

Sheet Brass: No preheating.
Cast Brass: Low temperature preheating.

BRONZE—WELDING: High strength rod; flux; preheating.
ALUMINUM—WELDING: Aluminum rod; flux.

Sheet Aluminum: No preheating.
Cast Aluminum: Low temperature preheating.

NICKEL—WELDING: Nickel rod; flux.
Sheet Nickel
Cast Nickel
MONEL—WELDING: Monel rod; flux; preheating of castings.
HARD-FACING
BRONZE FACING

NEUTRAL FLAME
The Major Process Used for All Metals

EXCESS ACETYLENE FLAME
Supplementary Process Advantageous where indicated

EXCESS OXYGEN FLAME
Supplementary Process Advantageous where indicated

OXYACETYLENE WELDING

P= Preferred Method
*From Oxyacetylene Committee Report, I.A.A., 1933

Chart 29-1. Oxyacetylene welding applications. (Courtesy of International Acetylene Association, New York.)

The chemistry and heat balance of the neutral oxyacetylene welding flame are as follows:

		Btu per cu ft
Primary combustion	$C_2H_2 + O_2 = 2CO + H_2 =$	287
Secondary combustion	$2CO + O_2 = 2CO_2 =$	641
	$H_2 + \tfrac{1}{2}O_2 = H_2O =$	277
Endothermic		228
		1433

Primary combustion employs one volume each of C_2H_2 and O_2; these gases are supplied directly from the cylinders or gas lines. Their combustion represents the inner core of the flame (Fig. 29-8). The highest flame temperature occurs at the tip of the inner cone, hence the tip of this cone should be held just off the metal for best results in welding.

The oxygen necessary for secondary combustion is obtained from the ambient atmosphere and totals $1\tfrac{1}{2}$ volumes. Secondary combustion is present as the outer or enveloping flame. Its importance in welding is twofold: it acts as a preheating medium and also prevents oxidation of the weld, since it consumes the oxygen of the surrounding air. Correct flame adjustment, coupled with proper torch manipulation and welding techniques, delivers the high type of work of which gas welding is capable.

WELD RODS

In some types of joints, such as edged or flange-edged, or flange joints, welding can proceed without addition of an external source of weld metal. Gas welds made without the addition of weld metal were formerly termed autogenous welds. When, however, a veed or similar joint is to be welded, it is necessary to add weld metal from a source referred to as a welding rod. Information on gas welding rods is given in specification A251-42T issued jointly in 1942 by the American Welding Society and the American Society for Testing Materials under the title "Tentative Specifications for Iron and Steel Gas-Welding Rods."

Applied Gas Welding

It is not intended to give a detailed explanation of actual welding techniques in this chapter; however, a brief presentation seems in order. The groundwork for making a gas weld consists of proper joint preparation on the metal to be welded. The weldor then selects the tip that is correct in size for the joint and adjusts the regulator pressures in accordance with the recommended values for the particular tip chosen. The torch is lighted by opening the acetylene valve very slightly. After the acetylene gas is ignited, greater volume is turned on until the acetylene flame, which is a very deep yellow, just leaves the tip of the torch. The oxygen valve on the torch is then opened and oxygen is fed into the flame until the desired flame has been achieved.

The actual welding operation consists of heating the base metal until a molten pool forms. The welding rod is immersed in the pool and thus melted. The flame should bring the edges of the joint to a molten state ahead of the puddle. The weldor moves the torch from side to side in a rippling motion.

Gas welding can be performed with either the forehand or the backhand method. In the case of a right-handed weldor, using the forehand method means that the weld will start on the right and progress toward the left. This procedure results in the torch flame pointing in the direction of welding, thereby giving considerable preheat to the joint. Backhand welding is just the reverse. The welding starts at the left end of the joint and proceeds toward the right. Steel is welded without the use of flux; cast iron, brass, and aluminum require flux. Flux is added by heating the weld rod and dipping it into the flux, or by sprinkling flux onto the joint, or, as is frequently done in the case of nonferrous metals, the flux is made into a liquid paste that is brushed on both the weld rod and the joint. The addition of flux serves the purpose of removing oxides and preventing their formation. It also aids in some instances by giving a "wetting" action to the molten weld metal. Gas weld rods containing flux in their interior are reported by H. Danhier.[1] Cast-iron weld rods with flux coatings have had some applications.

OXYHYDROGEN WELDING

The Master Chart of Welding Processes shows that oxyhydrogen is a significant gas welding process. Hydrogen, when burned with oxygen, delivers a flame temperature of 4622°F, which is considerably below that of the oxyacetylene flame. Because of low flame temperature, oxyhydrogen welding is applied primarily to low-fusion-point metals. There have been instances where this flame was desirable because of the absence of any carburizing action such as can result from an improperly adjusted oxyacetylene flame.

PRESSURE GAS WELDING

Employment of a gas torch flame, or flames, for heating the base metal to plasticity or coalescence, with either simultaneous or subsequent application of pressure in order to complete the weld, is the salient feature of pressure gas welding. There may be some question about the interpretation of the term pressure gas welding, since this expression is, on occasion interpreted to cover only solid phase welding. This is the

---

[1] New Flux-cored Filler Rods for Torch Welding, *Welding Journal Research Supplement*, April, 1947.

method in which heat and pressure are applied to a joint, causing a weld to be formed without any of the metal attaining fusion. However, there seems justification for including in pressure gas welding the second category, wherein coalescence takes place prior to pressure application and the latter is essential to weld completion.

Actually, solid phase welding is performed either by gas torch or by induction coil. In this method of welding, the abutting faces of the joint are placed under compression during the heating period, with the result that the weld is made at a temperature below the melting point

Fig. 29-9. Tube welding machines employing oxyacetylene pressure welding. (*Courtesy of Kawneer Manufacturing Company, Niles, Mich.*)

of the metal. A detailed dissertation on "Solid Phase Welding" was presented by A. B. Kinzel as the Adams Lecture before the annual meeting of the American Welding Society.[1]

The other category of gas pressure welding, in which melting of the base metal occurs, has been practicable almost since the beginning of gas welding. Davis Bournville conducted experiments as early as 1908 applying this method to the manufacture of tubing.[2] The Kawneer Mfg. Co. of Niles, Michigan, produced welded tubing by this method just prior to World War I. The welding machines designed by Kawneer featured the use of a four-flame, water-cooled torch (Fig. 29-9). Both round and square tubing were produced on this equipment. The tubing

[1] Published in *The Welding Journal*, Vol. 23, No. 12, December, 1944.
[2] Jones, H. O.: High-Speed Oxyacetylene Tube Welding, *The Welding Journal*, January, 1948.

was rolled cold in a rolling machine and then fed into the welder, where suitably designed rolls held the edges in proper relation for heating. After the tubing passed under the torch flames, it entered a pair of rolls that applied pressure in such a manner that no welding joint was discernible on the surface. Pressure gas welding has recently found favor

Fig. 29-10. Heating and pressure are maintained on tube sections until a predetermined amount of upsetting occurs. The beginning of such upset is shown here. (*Courtesy of Linde Air Products Co., New York.*)

for end welding pipe (Fig. 29-10) and railroad rails, as it has for welding longitudinal seams.

MANIFOLDS AND DISTRIBUTING SYSTEMS

Portable oxygen and acetylene cylinders are used primarily in jobbing-type welding. The volume of gas available from a single cylinder is limited for a given time interval. Production welding frequently requires gas in considerable volume because of the number of torches operating simultaneously. In order to supply this demand it is customary to connect several cylinders to a common line. Essentially these lines are headers equipped with requisite threaded connections and valved to permit adding or closing off the connected gas cylinders as circumstances demand. These headers, together with their accompanying valves and gages, are known as manifolds.

Acetylene manifolds are connected to flash-back arresters, which in turn lead to the distribution system. Large users of acetylene employ generators as the gas source; however, the oxygen is supplied from manifolded cylinders. The welding stations are equipped with single-gage regulators, inasmuch as line pressures established at the manifolds are usually above torch needs. The piping comprising welding gas distribution systems should have welded joints and should be painted in colors to meet safety regulations. There is some portable equipment used in which an acetylene generator is placed on a truck together with an oxygen cylinder (Fig. 29-11).

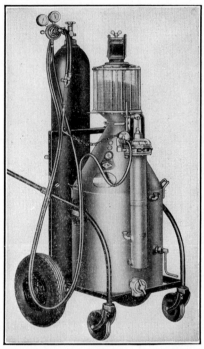

Fig. 29-11. Portable acetylene generator (*Courtesy of The Sight Feed Generator Company, West Alexandria, Ohio.*)

Survey Questions

29-1. How many gases are necessary to a welding flame?

29-2. Give the function of each gas in the flame.

29-3. In what equipment and from what ingredients is calcium carbide made?

29-4. Write the equation that governs the formation of acetylene gas.

29-5. On what two basic designs are acetylene generators built?

29-6. What national authority has jurisdiction over the construction of compressed acetylene cylinders?

29-7. List the types of fillers used in compressed acetylene cylinders.

29-8. How is the oxygen used for welding obtained?

29-9. What is the meaning of the figures and letters stamped into the upper end of an oxygen cylinder?

29-10. Why are welding gas regulators equipped with gages?

29-11. How can an oxygen regulator be distinguished from an acetylene one?

29-12. What design feature insures correct gas-hose connections?

29-13. On what two principles are welding torches built?

29-14. Is a welding torch equipped with a single tip?

29-15. State the different flame conditions available to the oxyacetylene welding torch.

29-16. Which of the above is most generally used for welding?

29-17. What is the meaning of secondary combustion?

29-18. Are welding rods and welding electrodes the same thing?

29-19. Describe correct procedure necessary to lighting a welding-torch flame.

29-20. Are there any advantages for oxyhydrogen welding?

29-21. How are solid-phase welds made?

29-22. Why are flash-back arresters installed in acetylene distribution systems?

29-23. Is it possible to distinguish a torch weld from an arc weld by visual inspection?

29-24. How does the term "forehand welding" apply to torch manipulation?

REFERENCES

Cuke, N. H.: Multiple Flame Pressure Welding Process, *The Welding Journal*, Vol. 27, No. 1, January, 1948.

Henry, O. H., and G. E. Claussen: "Welding Metallurgy," 2d ed., rev. by G. E. Linnert, American Welding Society, New York, 1949.

"Instructions in Oxyacetylene Welding and Cutting Processes," Air Reduction Company, New York, 1940.

International Acetylene Association: *Official Proceedings* and *Oxy-Acetylene Committee Publications*, various titles and dates, New York.

"Master Chart of Welding Processes and Process Charts," American Standard A3.1-49, American Welding Society, New York, 1949.

Ness, Charles: The Acetylene Cylinder—Industry's Unique Container, *The Welding Journal*, Vol. 27, No. 6, June, 1948.

"The Oxy-Acetylene Handbook," The Linde Air Products Company, New York, 1943.

Plumley, Stuart: "Oxy-Acetylene and Arc Welding," 3d ed., University Printing Co., Minneapolis, 1939.

"Victorgram," Victor Equipment Co., San Francisco, 1939.

"Welding and Cutting Manual," The Linde Air Products Company, New York, 1949.

"The Welding Encyclopedia," 11th ed., The Welding Engineer Publishing Company, Chicago, 1943.

"The Welding Handbook," 3d ed., American Welding Society, New York, 1950.

CHAPTER 30

BRAZING AND BRAZE WELDING

The joining of ferrous metals as well as the copper-base alloys by a nonferrous filler metal was undoubtedly one of the earliest welding processes. The nomenclature applied to these processes has largely grown out of custom. Under the specification "Standard Welding Terms and Their Definitions,"[1] terminology has been adopted to include all the metals that lend themselves to this type of joining. Brazing is defined in this standard as "a group of welding processes wherein coalescence is produced by heating to suitable temperatures above 800°F and by using a non-ferrous filler metal, having a melting point below that of the base metals. The filler metal is distributed between the closely fitted surfaces of the joint by capillary attraction."

Braze welding is defined in the same standard as "a method of welding whereby a groove, fillet, plug or slot weld is made using a non-ferrous filler metal, having a melting point below that of the base metals but above 800°F. The filler metal is *not* distributed in the joint by capillary attraction. (Bronze Welding, formerly used, is a misnomer for this term.)" Note that the parenthetical sentence is part of the standard definition. These definitions are given in order to clarify the terms as used in this chapter.

Brazing

Brazing is classified into eight types on the Master Chart of Welding Processes.[2] Each of these types refers primarily to a heating method. Other classifications can be made on the basis of filler metal and, to a lesser extent, of base metal. Again, brazing processes are, on occasion, catalogued as high-temperature or low-temperature.

The use of the word brazing can be misleading. Originally it may have been derived from the idea of using pulverized brass or brass spelter, a practice that has been followed for a long time. This limitation is no longer valid, since copper and copper-base alloys do not monopolize the

[1] American Standard A3.0-49, American Welding Society, New York, 1949.
[2] American Standard A3.1-49, American Welding Society, New York, 1949.

field of braze filler metals.   A newcomer is the group of aluminum alloys, and the silver-base alloys are also well known.

The Bond.   A brazed joint is one that is processed by employing a temperature which is at least 100°F below the melting point of the base metal.   The base metal is not brought to fusion where it could form an alloy with the molten braze metal.   Conjecture arises at once over the exact nature of bond.   This question is best answered by a microscopic examination of the area (Fig. 30-1).   The example shown displays some diffusion at the interface of the brazing and base metal resulting in a narrow area of intermediate composition.   The braze metals are chosen for their affinity to the base metal.   Braze metals must diffuse rapidly into the base metal, thereby creating an alloy of a relatively low melting

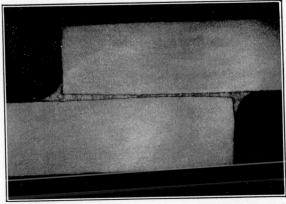

Fig. 30–1.   Micrograph of brazed bond in steel.   (Courtesy of American Brass Company, Waterbury, Conn.)

point.   The success or failure of a brazed joint is dependent upon the proper interbonding between the metals composing the joint.

Braze Metals.   The braze metals employed with ferrous materials are primarily of copper or silver base.   The copper-base brazing alloys have higher melting points than those containing silver.   Commercially pure copper is used as a brazing alloy even though temperature has to reach 2050°F; this is the highest temperature for any brazing operation. There are many copper-base brazing compositions; some meet the standard specifications, while others have been developed on an individual basis.   A representative listing of copper-base brazing alloys is given in Table 30-1.

The second classification of braze metal used in joining ferrous materials of all types, whether the join is of the same or dissimilar metals, comprises the silver-base alloys.   These materials are receiving deserved attention on a broad scale as they become better known and their poten-

TABLE 30-1. BRASS, NICKEL SILVER, AND COPPER BRAZING ALLOYS*

Brazing alloys	Melting range, °F	Composition, per cent			Form
		Copper	Zinc	Others	
ASTM 50-50....	1595–1620	50–53	Remainder	0.50 lead, max. ⎫	Common spelter solders, brass yellow color, in granulated form for general brazing
ASTM 52-48....	1600–1620	52–53	Remainder	0.50 lead, max. ⎭	
Spelter bronze..	1575	Remainder	45	3–5 tin	Pale yellow in granulated or lump form for special work. Harder than ASTM grades
Nickel braze....	1600	Remainder	55–69	7–9 nickel	White, granulated form, match for nickel silver, cupro-nickel and the like
Phos-copper....	1304–1526	93	Remainder	Phosphorus	Rod or strip for self-fluxing brazes on copper. Gray color
Copper.........	1981–2050	99.9	....	....	Tough-pitch or deoxidized copper in wire, granulated, or electrodeposited on steel for brazing in a hydrogen atmosphere

* Abstracted and revised from "Metals Handbook," American Society for Metals, Cleveland, 1948.

TABLE 30-2. SILVER BRAZING ALLOYS: COMPOSITION AND PHYSICAL PROPERTIES*

Grade	Chemical composition, per cent					Melting point, °F	Flow point, °F	Specific gravity as cast	Electrical conductivity Cu = 100%
	Ag	Cu	Zn	Cd	P				
1	10	52	38	....	..	1510	1600	8.55	20.5†
2	20	45	30	5	..	1430	1500	8.80	24.4†
3	30	38	32	....	..	1370	1410	8.86	
4	40	36	24	....	..	1330	1445	9.11	
5	45	30	25	....	..	1250	1370	9.15	†
6	50	34	16	....	..	1280	1425	9.37	24.4†
7	60	25	15	....	..	1260	1325	9.52	
8	70	20	10	....	..	1335	1390	9.76	26.7†
9	72	28	....	....	..	1435	1435	9.95	77.1
10	80	16	4	....	..	1360	1460	10.05	46†
11	15	80	....	....	5	1190	1300	8.45	14‡
12	50	15.5	16.5	18.0	..	1160	1175	9.49	23.9‡

* Abstracted from "Welding Handbook," 2d ed., American Welding Society, New York, 1942.
† ASTM standard specifications for silver brazing.
‡ Proprietary alloys.

tialities are better understood. One deterrent to wider acceptance is the belief that because they contain silver they are too costly to use in engineering manufacture. Actually the reverse is true when silver brazing alloys are specified and correct procedures are established. These alloys have a flow point range between 1175 and 1600°F. These braze metals find greater acceptance in joining stainless steels than do the copper braze ones. A listing of the better-known silver brazing alloys is given in Table 30-2.

The alloys in Table 30-2 are procurable in the form of sheet, strip, wire, and powder or granules. Sheet that is only a few thousandths of an inch thick is available as a standard commercial product. A desirable procedure is to place thin braze metal sheet or rings in a joint as a means of proper distribution. The use of wire for ringing a circular joint is also common practice.

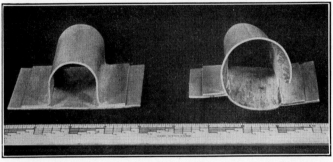

Fig. 30-2. Aluminum brazed specimen using brazing sheet before and after destructive testing. (*Courtesy of Welding Laboratory, University of Washington.*)

A third class of brazing alloys comprises those used in brazing aluminum alloys. Brazing aluminum alloys differs from other brazing applications only in the choice of braze metal. Some alloys have been developed specifically for this purpose. The chief one is 43S, also specified as ASTM B85-49T; this alloy is composed of 5 per cent Si and the balance Al. It has a flow range between 1070 and 1165°F. Other aluminum brazing alloys are 711 and 713 brazing sheet, and 718 brazing wire. An interesting development of Al brazing is that sheet is procurable that has an integral braze metal surface. The use of this composite sheet greatly simplifies brazing procedures. Figure 30-2 shows a braze made with such a sheet, bent in U shape, to a plain sheet of 3S Al alloy. Information on aluminum brazing is listed in Table 30-3.

Brazing Paste. The major part of copper brazing is done in furnaces. Brazing copper is generally supplied in the form of rings, foil, slugs, metalizing, or electroplate. Another means for supplying the copper braze metal is brazing paste. It is maintained that the ease with which

TABLE 30-3. ALCOA BRAZING MATERIALS*

Material being brazed	Filler material	Form	Use
2S or 3S..........	No. 718 brazing wire	Wire and shims	General use
	43S	Wire	Limited use—torch brazing only
4S or 52S.........	No. 718 brazing wire	Wire and shims	Limited use—short joints—torch brazing only
53S, 61S, or 63S....	No. 718 brazing wire	Wire and shims	General use
No. 1 or 2† brazing sheet	No. 718 brazing wire	Wire and shims	General use
	No. 711 brazing sheet†	Shims	
	43S	Wire	Limited use—torch brazing only
No. 11 or 12‡ brazing sheet	No. 718 brazing wire	Wire and shims	General use
	No. 713 brazing sheet†	Shims	
No. 21 or 22‡ brazing sheet	No. 718 brazing wire	Wire and shims	General use
	No. 713 brazing sheet†	Shims	

* Abstracted from "Welding and Brazing Alcoa Aluminum," Aluminum Company of America, 1948.

† Same composition as brazing coating.

‡ Even-numbered brazing sheet is coated on two sides with brazing metal. Odd-numbered brazing sheet is coated on one side with brazing metal.

the paste can be applied simplifies the entire brazing operation. Applicator units have been developed which permit the paste to be extruded in a number of forms, such as rounds, ribbons, flats, etc., thereby facilitating its placement at the desired location in the joint.

Fluxes. The use of flux on a brazed joint is mandatory inasmuch as the necessity of protecting the base metal from oxidation at brazing temperatures is always present. Flux must dissolve any oxides which are present and also prevent the formation of oxides. It must also be liquid at brazing temperatures in order to flow over the joint surface.

Fluxes used for brazing are of various compositions, since their behavior is a combination of chemical and mechanical action. Common borax has long been a stand-by in forge welding. It has some application in brazing, but its application is limited because it does not/have the property of dissolving the oxides of aluminum, chromium, or beryllium. When borax is used as a flux, it should be made into a paste by dissolving it in alcohol; water is useless for this purpose, since it will evaporate at operating temperatures, leaving crystalline borax.

The composition of brazing fluxes can be quite complex. Some of the ingredients used are boric acid, phosphates, and halogen salts. Fluorides are generally present in fluxes used for brazing aluminum. Fluxes are available as powder, as paste, and as liquid. Flux is usually painted on the surfaces to be brazed, since this results both in full coverage and in even distribution.

The possibility of entrapped flux on large areas is always present. A research project on this problem was undertaken at the University of Washington.[1] The specimens used in this project were $\frac{7}{8}$-in.-diameter C1035 cold-drawn steel. After brazing, the specimens were machined

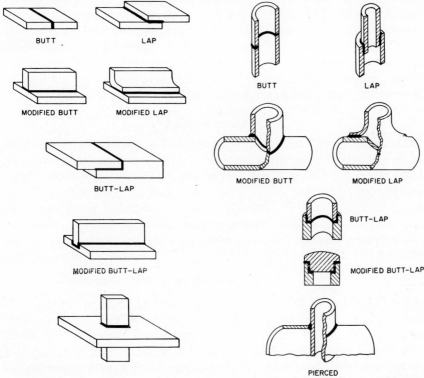

Chart 30-1.   Basic development of joint designs common to brazing.   (*Courtesy of Handy & Harman, New York.*)

to standard 0.505-in. tensile test bars and subjected to the tensile test. The brazed joints proved unsound because of flux inclusions. A solution to this problem was found by vibrating the joint to eliminate entrapped flux.

Joint Design.   Since brazing depends on capillary attraction for its success, joint clearance should be designed to promote this action. The general principle governing braze joint design is that of having the smallest possible clearance in the joint. Experience gained on many

[1] Crane, C. H., and T. J. Bauer: "Silver Brazed Joints," graduation thesis in Mechanical Engineering, 1946.

brazing specimens indicates that with grade 12 alloy (Table 30-2), there was little difference in joint strengths, when loaded in tension, so long as the clearance in the joint did not exceed 0.015 in.   Above that value, joint strengths lessened in direct proportion to joint clearance.

Shear-type joints are preferable, since they permit variation in joint surface area to meet design requirements.   They have also proved superior from the standpoint of corrosion resistance.   A joint design that permits the use of pressure during the brazing operation will give superior results.   Joint design means little if the ordinary precautions of surface cleansing and surface finish are overlooked.   The use of carbon tetrachloride on the joint surface prior to flux application will remove oil, grease, and foreign matter and provide a clean surface for subsequent processing.   Examples of joint designs are shown in Chart 30-1.

Brazing Method

There are several methods of applying heat for brazing.   The selection of the method to be used will be dependent on such factors as base metal, braze metal, joint design, part size, and production requirements.   Most satisfactory results are achieved by assembling the joint with the braze metal in place prior to heating.   This recommended procedure often requires the use of holding fixtures or other clamping devices.   However, the pressure that such devices exert on the joint contributes to the superior results that are obtained.

TORCH BRAZING

Torch brazing involves the use of a gas torch as the source of heat.   A welding torch is commonly used because of flexibility.   Braze metal is added in the form of wire where such procedure is desirable (Fig. 30-3).

A second application of torch brazing is shown in Fig. 30-4.   In this setup, multiple-flame torches are used.   These form a permanent installation into which the product to be brazed is moved.   On this particular job the flame time of 45 sec is controlled by a timing device that shuts off the gas.   There are 32 joints brazed simultaneously in this operation.

INDUCTION BRAZING

The principle of induction heating is being applied to brazing where the product is produced in quantity.   Where induction brazing is employed, it is necessary to develop heating coil equipment of a shape and size to accommodate the piece to be brazed.   It is for this reason that induction brazing does not offer the versatility of the torch system; however, when an installation has been properly made, much more accurate control can be had by induction brazing.   An example of induction brazing is shown in Fig. 30-5; in effect this is a double brazing operation.   The braze

Fig. 30-3. Manual torch brazing of heat exchanger member. (*Courtesy of Handy & Harman, New York.*)

Fig. 30-4. Stationary torch brazing of heat exchanger parts. (*Courtesy of Handy & Harman, New York.*)

metal can be noted on the bench at the operator's right hand; the square pieces of braze metal are used for brazing the blades to the stem. This constitutes the first operation. The second operation is that of brazing the dough guard, which is done with the rings of braze metal shown.

Fig. 30-5. Work place used for induction brazing electric mixer parts. (*Courtesy of Handy & Harman, New York.*)

The equipment is operated by means of a foot switch, and through electronic controls the time and temperature are held within close limits.

FURNACE BRAZING

Furnace brazing is employed on assemblies, and the entire operation is frequently mechanized by using a conveyor-type furnace. The sections to be joined are assembled with the braze metal in position. Clamping fixtures may or may not be necessary, depending upon the individual job.

There is a considerable amount of copper hydrogen furnace brazing. The hydrogen atmosphere maintained within the furnace eliminates the use of flux. This system of brazing has had a great deal to do with the development of carbide-tipped tools, the single-point as well as the more elaborate types. When a single-point tool is being tipped with a carbide insert, the tool material is milled out to accommodate the insert. The braze metal is then placed between the carbide piece and the tool and wired into position. This assembly is placed in the controlled hydrogen atmosphere of the furnace and brazing is completed. Brazing alloys used for such work are either silver-base or copper-base.

DIP BRAZING

The idea of using a molten bath as a source of heat for brazing has two aspects. In one instance the bath is composed of some type of salts, which serve merely as a source of heat. The advantage, of course, is that any assembly immersed in the molten salt bath will attain a uniform temperature.

In the other system of dip brazing, the molten bath is composed of filler metal. The part to be brazed, having previously been fluxed, is dipped into the molten bath and the filler metal enters the joint, thereby completing the brazing operation. This system is used for such specialties as joining wire ends and is not employed on parts of any size.

Braze Welding

Braze welding consists of a gas torch welding operation in which the weld rod is of copper base, although copper-base electrodes are available for arc use. The composition of the weld rod is such that its melting point is well below that of the material on which it is used. By way of example, one of the well-regarded braze weld rods has a melting temperature of 1650°F. When this is used in connection with a ferrous metal, savings can obviously be effected, since welding time is shortened and less heat is required.

There are some instances in which ferrous materials have been braze-welded in construction. There have been some cast-iron pipe lines assembled with braze-welded joints. Galvanized sheet steel can be braze welded with ease and at the same time retain the corrosion resistance of the original sheet. Examples can be found in motorcar construction, where sheet steel stampings are joined by braze welding.

Braze welding is of greatest utility in connection with reclamation and repair. The soundest procedure for reclaiming a broken malleable cast-iron part is braze welding. This is true both from the metallurgical and from the mechanical standpoint. Cast-iron parts are frequently repaired with braze welding. This method has become so general in the repair shop that steel parts are also being braze-welded.

APPLIED BRAZE WELDING

Joint surfaces must be clean and free of grease. They should then be placed in proper alignment prior to heat application. An important consideration for making a sound braze weld is the careful fluxing of the joint. Fluxes are generally in powdered form. They are added to the braze weld by sprinkling on the surface, both before and during the welding operation. Further flux can be added by heating the weld rod and dipping it into the flux, causing the latter to flow and form a coating on the weld rod.

Heating of the base metal is most generally done with the gas torch. The chief precaution is to see to it that the base metal is not overheated and at the same time receives sufficient heat. The temperature should be such that the braze weld rod will melt and flow when it is rubbed against the heated base metal.

The best way of making a braze weld is to coat the surface of the joint with braze metal in a procedure referred to as tinning. This is merely a

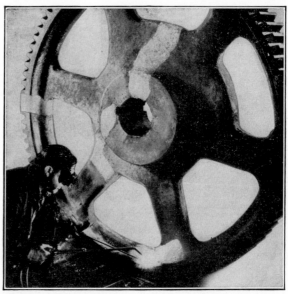

Fig. 30-6.   Repair of large broken cast-iron gear by braze welding, using copper-base filler rod. (Courtesy of American Brass Company, Waterbury, Conn.)

very light or thin coat of braze metal. When tinning is done correctly, the braze welding operation becomes a very simple one. One difficulty, especially in braze welding cast iron, is that of preventing the formation of "whirlpools" in the molten weld metal. When these do appear, their cause can usually be traced to the presence of scale or slag inclusions. It is then necessary to heat that area and puddle the metal with a weld rod freeing the inclusion so that it can float to the surface.

Braze welding is frequently the preferred method for repairing broken cast parts (Fig. 30-6). Welds can be made relatively quickly, and owing to the high ductility of the braze metal the finished braze-welded joint is stronger and generally better in mechanical properties.

EFFECTING ECONOMIES THROUGH BRAZING

Brazing or braze welding can be a decided step in the direction of lowered production costs. These processes have for the most part been regarded as a specialty associated primarily with joining small, light-gage metal parts. The potentialities of these processes for lowering production costs on heavier members has frequently been overlooked. The design shown in Fig. 30-7 is but one example of the possibility of

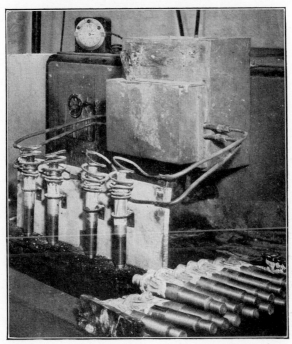

Fig. 30-7. Induction brazing shaft assembly used in brazing collar to shaft. (*Courtesy of Handy & Harmon, New York.*)

breaking down a member into smaller components that will be the basis of a brazed assembly. Smaller components are made with less material and frequently with a substantial saving in labor and material costs.

The problem of producing a crankshaft for a 2 by 2-in. air compressor was solved in a satisfactory manner by a brazed assembly. Samples of crankshafts so produced were tested in torsion and the results were well above design values. Another important saving resulted from the elimination of substantial investment in forging dies and forging equipment. The brazed design offered flexibility without the risk of obsolescence of expensive tooling.

The heat exchanger tube shown in Fig. 30-8 is another example of production brazing. This tube is made by winding the radiating fin metal as a helix on the base tube. The junction between them is brazed to give a solid joint with high heat conductivity. An example of the reclamation of broken tools is shown in Fig. 30-9. It is evident that such repair work can effect considerable economies both through the

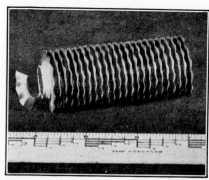

Fig. 30-8.   Heat exchanger tube with radiating fins brazed to main tube.

Fig. 30-9.   Milling cutter repaired by the use of silver brazing. (*Courtesy of Handy & Harman, New York.*)

reuse of the tool and through the saving that can be realized by reducing lost time in the shop.

Survey Questions

30-1. How is the filler metal distributed in brazing?

30-2. Is joint design similar for both brazing and braze welding?

30-3. On what characteristic are brazing methods classified?

30-4. Explain the bonding action in a brazed joint.

30-5. Mention the methods whereby copper braze metal can be placed in a joint.

30-6. Is all brazing done with copper or copper-base alloys?

30-7. Can aluminum alloys be joined by brazing? If so, what braze metal is used?

30-8. Why is the use of brazing flux mandatory?

30-9. Can the entrapment of brazing flux in a joint be eliminated?

30-10. What type of loading is preferred for brazed joints?

30-11. When brazing is used for mass production, what are the preferred heating methods?

30-12. Why is a hydrogen furnace atmosphere used with copper brazing?

30-13. In dip brazing, what is the heating medium?

30-14. Where is braze welding mostly used?

30-15. How does "tinning" apply to braze welding?

30-16. What is the usual heat source for braze welding?

30-17. Can steel be welded to cast iron?

30-18. How can a broken cast-iron component be salvaged most economically?

30-19. Cite an example of production economy resulting from brazing.

30-20. Need braze welding be confined to small parts?

30-21. How are carbide tips joined to cutting tools?   Give some details.

REFERENCES

Henry, O. H., and G. E. Claussen: "Welding Metallurgy," 2d ed., rev. by G. E. Linnert, American Welding Society, New York, 1949.

"Master Chart of Welding Processes and Process Charts," American Standard A3.1-49, American Welding Society, New York, 1949.

"Metals Handbook," American Society for Metals, Cleveland, 1948.

"The Welding Encyclopedia," 11th ed., The Welding Engineer Publishing Company, Chicago, 1943.

"The Welding Handbook," 3d ed., American Welding Society, New York, 1950.

CHAPTER 31

RESISTANCE WELDING

Fundamental Factors

Resistance welding is defined as "a group of welding processes wherein coalescence is produced by the heat obtained from the resistance of the work to the flow of electric current in a circuit of which the work is a part, and by the application of pressure."[1] A feature of resistance welding is that all the welding covered by this term involves the use of pressure. From this it is obvious that there is no such thing as manual resistance welding; on the contrary, all resistance welding is done in some type of resistance welding machine. There is some portable equipment; however, the work done by this equipment is not analogous to manual welding by other methods.

Since welding machines are necessary to resistance welding, the range of work that can be resistance welded is narrow. Resistance welding is thought of primarily as a process for joining comparatively light gage metal parts. An exception is the flash butt welding of sections attaining diameters of several inches.

Heat Origin and Distribution. Heat used in these welding methods is generated by the resistance of the parts to be welded to the passage of the electric current supplied by the welding machine. The heat for resistance welding is expressed by the formula

$$W = I^2Rt$$

where W is heat in watt-seconds, I is the amperes flowing through the weld, R resistance in ohms, and t is the time in seconds.

The salient features of a typical spot welder are shown in Fig. 31-1. The pieces to be welded are lapped and in position under the electrodes of the welding machine. Power supply is brought in through a timer, then passes through a transformer equipped with current regulator; provision for applying pressure to the electrodes is also included.

[1] "Standard Welding Terms and Their Definitions," American Standard A3.0-49, American Welding Society, New York, 1949.

The temperature gradient on a spot-welding operation is shown in Fig. 31-2. The temperature varies considerably through the weld section. The flow of heat in a resistance weld is affected by several factors; prominent among them is the electrical resistance of the materials being welded. This means that materials of high heat and electrical conductivity will be

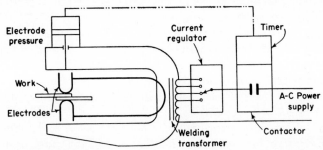

Fig. 31-1. Diagrammatic sketch of spot welder circuit. (*From Resistance Welding Fundamentals, The Welding Journal, August, 1945.*)

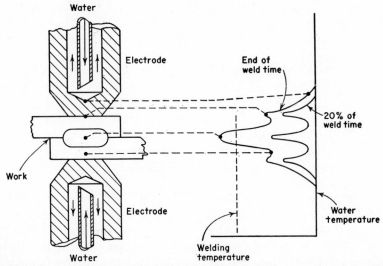

Fig. 31-2. Temperature gradient diagram for a spot welding operation. (*From Resistance Welding Fundamentals, The Welding Journal, August, 1945.*)

difficult to weld in that they will require high welding currents. They also make it necessary to provide electrode material capable of carrying the required currents. Silver and copper are not readily welded, yet certain of their alloys present no difficulty because of their lower conductivity. Aluminum, whose conductivity is about 60 per cent of that of annealed copper, is readily welded but current requirements are high. The high-strength aluminum alloys, prominent in aircraft construction, have a conductivity equal to about one-half that of commercially pure aluminum, a fact that makes them well adapted to resistance welding. Other commonly used engineering materials—such as nickel alloys, steel, magnesium, and, especially, stainless steels—require relatively low current values.

The contact resistance at the faying surfaces is a critical consideration, since it is influenced to a marked degree by surface conditions. Procedures for resistance welding always carry instructions on surface preparation. Mild steel has mill scale, which may or may not be aggravated by rusting, that must be removed prior to welding. When surface preparation is faulty or is omitted, sound welds are impossible. There have been many cases of weld failure in which the difficulty was caused by neglect of surface preparation.

Welding electrodes require care in both selection and maintenance; contact resistance between them and the weldment must be held to a minimum. The tendency for the electrode contact surface to pick up metal from the weldment is always present. The degree of pickup is governed by such factors as composition, temperature, surface condition, and pressure. Strict attention to shape and surface condition of electrode tips is mandatory if excessive resistance is to be avoided at the outer contact surfaces.

Heat losses in resistance welding vary in proportion to the heat conductivity of the weldment metal. Metal of high heat conductivity will remove heat from the local weld area at a rate detrimental to the operation. It is for this reason that high current values are invariably accompanied by short welding times. Another heat loss arises from cooling water circulated in the electrodes. If they were permitted to operate without cooling, their temperatures would increase rapidly and electrical conductivity would drop.

Heat distribution across the weld is important for proper welding results. In a weldment consisting of two or more pieces, they should arrive at their respective welding temperatures simultaneously. This requisite is the same as in any welding operation. When this desired condition is fulfilled, there will be mutual diffusion, as between the weldment parts, and a sound weld will be formed. It is readily understandable that welding dissimilar metals is an extremely difficult matter, since with different fusion points, differing heating periods are indicated.

Power Supply. The unbalance in the power line caused by the operation of conventional single-phase resistance welding equipment (Fig. 31-3) has become a source of concern. The difficulty arises from the fact that a conventional single-phase welder operates at a low power factor, usually below 30 per cent, and has a high kva demand that is of short duration. A single-phase load connected to a three-phase power line causes unbalanced conditions in the latter which result in voltage disturbance in all three phases. One result of this unbalance is the flickering of lights when the welder is operating.

Another shortcoming in the operation of single-phase resistance welding equipment, of the spot welder type, arises from the introduction of the material to be welded into the throat of the machine. When material is thus placed, impedance is increased and the current passing through the secondary circuit is decreased. In procedures where spot welds follow along a welded joint, causing the weldment to move into the

Fig. 31-3. Foot-operated, single-phase, conventional-type spot welder. (*Courtesy of The Taylor-Winfield Corp., Warren, Ohio.*)

throat, each succeeding weld is made with decreasing heat because of the increasing impedance. Current compensating devices can be installed to maintain a constant current in the welding circuit; however, such further installations increase the amount of the original investment and tend, in a measure, to complicate the operation.

Storage Battery Welders. The difficulties of line unbalance occasioned by single-phase equipment are capable of a variety of solutions. All of these embrace problems in electrical circuit design. A simple solution is to use storage batteries as the source of welding current. Electrochemical equipment of substantial capacity and built for portability is proving itself in industry. There is much to recommend this equipment for production line welding where machines are in fixed positions and lack the flexibility required by this type of manufacture.

Alternating-current Heat Control. Since the welding current in a single-phase a-c circuit is equal to the secondary voltage of the welding transformer divided by the impedance of the secondary circuit, it can be changed by varying either of these values. As has been explained, impedance cannot be readily changed because its value depends on the dimensions of the secondary loop circuit coupled with the resistance of the weldment in the circuit and the resistance of the secondary leads. Varying the secondary voltage offers a better and more exact means of controlling the welding current. A simple means for varying secondary voltage is the use of taps, controlled by a tap switch, on the primary winding.

Equipment is available for changing the voltage to the primary of the welding transformer. The autotransformer is equipped with taps whereby its output voltage is varied. This output is connected to the tapless primary of the welding transformer; the resultant hookup is capable of modifying the secondary transformer welding voltage and thus of varying the heat in the welding circuit.

Electronic Control. Heat control is also possible through the installation of gas-filled vacuum tubes in the circuit ahead of the welding transformer. The two types of tubes used for this purpose are the ignitron and the thyratron. The ignitron tube is of the mercury vapor type equipped with an ignitor and a mercury pool cathode. These tubes, when connected in pairs, function as a contactor or inertia-less switch controlling the flow of current to the welding transformer. When current is permitted to flow, voltage is applied to the primary and the secondary of the welding transformer; when, on the other hand, no current is permitted to flow, welding voltage is also shut off.

A further function of electronic gas-filled tubes is the effect that the timing of the welding current has on the effective voltage. Delaying the current start at each half cycle results in the current becoming discontinuous, and the current wave is an interrupted sinusoidal one. The range of current control, where this method is used, is governed by the power-line voltage as well as the type of tubes used in the control unit. Thyratrons are capable of full-range control from 0 to 100 per cent current value. The heat control described here is termed the phase-shift method.

Three-phase Balanced Load Designs

The practical disadvantages resulting from connecting single-phase resistance welding machines to three-phase power circuits have resulted in the development of means for overcoming these difficulties. The expedient of using a motor-generator set seems attractive until costs and operating features are evaluated. A more feasible approach to the solution of this problem has been that of the storage of electrical energy. The three possibilities for stored energy are the electrochemical, or battery type, the electrostatic type, and the electromagnetic type.

In general the characteristics of resistance welding machines using stored energy embody much lower kva demand, hence appreciably lower welding costs. These welding machines are capable of discharging very high current values in short intervals of time. Stored-energy welders

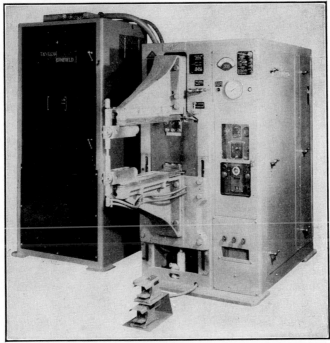

Fig. 31-4. Condenser-discharge-type spot welder. (*Courtesy of The Taylor-Winfield Corp., Warren, Ohio.*)

are of greatest interest for welding materials of high electrical and heat conductivity, for example, aluminum alloys.

Electrostatic Type. The principal features of this type include current rectifiers, capacitor bank, means of charging the capacitor to a predetermined voltage, and means of discharging the capacitor-stored energy through a welding transformer. The chief advantage of a capacitor type is that the shape of the welding current wave can be adjusted to almost any desired form. The rates of current rise and decay are functions of capacitor rating. The number of capacitors used governs the power that such equipment can deliver. This imparts a wide range of welding currents, which enables such resistance welders to perform successfully on a great variety of materials. The resistance welding machine embodying the condenser discharge principle is about the same in appearance (Fig. 31-4) as the conventional spot welder.

Electromagnetic Type. The energy-storage feature here is the sending of direct current through the primary of a welding transformer. When the direct current sustaining the magnetic field is interrupted, the field collapses and the energy stored in that field is transmitted to the welding transformer, where it becomes the welding current. When current is being established in the primary of the welding transformer, there will be a current flow in the secondary. The latter is frequently referred to

Fig. 31-5. Electromagnetic stored-energy spot welder. (*Courtesy of Sciaky Bros., Chicago.*)

as a preheating current; as such, it is of value in welding certain classes of materials.

The electromagnetic method has simplicity on its side: there is little in the equipment to cause difficulty or to require undue maintenance. There are limitations of the secondary current and there is also an inflexible wave shape. Welding results are excellent when requisite capacity equipment is used for welding material especially adapted to the available wave shape of the secondary discharge current. These welding machines have developed fine records in aircraft plants for welding aluminum alloys. In appearance these machines (Fig. 31-5) are also similar to conventional spot welders.

Three-phase Single-phase System. The three-phase power supply is brought through a transformer whose secondary feeds through a double six-tube rectifier. The current then passes through a control circuit arranged so that it is reversed, which, in effect, results in a sinusoidal wave. The frequency caused by the reversal of the welding current is low, a condition that is said to be desirable for welding steel. The basic idea is that of reversing a direct current in a pattern which bears some resemblance to alternating-current. The advantages of this system are substantially lowered power requirements and balanced demand from the power supply lines.

Controls and Electrodes on Resistance Welders

Time Controls. The importance of proper timing is seen indicated by the fundamental heat equation, in which the time t is a factor. The methods used for timing control are varied to suit the particular welding job. In spot welding, the timing allows for a continuous flow of current for a given interval which is repeated with each spot weld made. The timing interval is commonly expressed in cycles of the basic frequency, as: 5 cycles of a 60-cycle current.

Seam welding presents a different problem, since a continuity pattern is essential. The electrodes for seam welders are in the form of disks which contact the work continuously. Welding current is timed by adjusting both "on" time and "off" time as the seam proceeds through the welding disks. The welding current is interrupted even though the initiating switch is closed.

Still another basic timer is used in connection with pulsation welding, a process in the spot weld category which consists of repeated heating and cooling periods. The number of repetitions depends primarily on the type of material being welded and its thickness. When a sequence has been developed as to "on" and "off" times, this sequence is repeated for each similar weld. The timing device must, therefore, control three elements, viz., on time, off time, and number of repetitions.

Resistance welding procedures which are directed toward the heat-treatment of the weld call for a timing sequence that is variable. There are "on," or heat, times of differing lengths with subsequent "off," or cool, times also of variable lengths. Such timing devices are assembled from available standard timers.

Timing devices are classified as synchronous and nonsynchronous. The former operate in conformity with the current of the primary of the welding transformer, while the latter are of a random pattern insofar as stopping current flow on the primary wave is concerned. There are several available types of each classification. Synchronous timers of a high degree of accuracy are based on electronic tube controls.

Pressure Controls. The conventional spot welder is equipped with a treadle or a manually operated lever as the pressure device. The total resistance R in the fundamental heat equation is composed of several factors. The specific resistance of the material being welded, the contact resistance between electrode and work, and the contact resistance at the faying surfaces, taken together, add up to the R factor. The specific resistance of the material is an inherent physical property that is unaffected by pressure; however, the remaining two resistances are influenced by the pressure applied to the electrode. A high pressure will tend to compact the weld pile, with the result that resistance will be lowered and greater current will flow. It would appear desirable to use a low pressure and thus gain increased resistance. Practical results do not bear out this reasoning, for sparking and electrode sticking develop when low pressure is used. Electrode deterioration and poor welding generally are other results of too low pressure.

Applied pressure is of importance, yet when any appreciable dwell time is incorporated in the sequence, the actual contact resistance decreases. The phenomena involved in this situation are traceable to such sources as metal film behavior and even plastic flow as well as other physical properties of the weldment metal. Pressure is included in some resistance welding sequences as a post- or forging treatment of the completed weld. There are instances where surface irregularities are ironed out by electrode pressure.

Manual Pressure Devices. Foot-pedal mechanisms are an ideal solution, since they permit freedom of movement to both hands for guiding the weldment materials. Many existing designs employ some principle of mechanical advantage as a means of multiplying the actual foot pressure. The rocker arm type, in which the upper electrode moves in an arc is a widely used design; spring action is built into these linkages for flexibility of movement. The pressure potential of foot-operated mechanisms is relatively low and they are not generally found on production equipment.

Mechanical Pressure. Closer pressure control and lessened operator fatigue are achieved by the substitution of power for manual pressure operation. Motorized pressure mechanisms are also capable of higher pressures and for that reason offer an advantageous production potential. Design details of these types feature the use of a cam system for actuating the rocker arm of the resistance welding machine.

Hydraulic Pressure Systems. As the capacity and size of resistance welding machines increase, it is to be expected that design features will follow those found satisfactory in related equipment. Hydraulic controls are becoming more common on large resistance welders in which a multiplicity of electrodes are incorporated. Resistance welding machines of the type considered here are specialized production equipment in that they are designed for single-purpose application.

Hydraulic cylinders are located to permit the mounting of the electrodes directly in the piston rods. The pressure potentials are high, and close control is possible.

Pneumatic Pressure Systems. The introduction of air-operated pressure applications has fostered the development of a resistance welding machine known as a press welder. The unique feature of this design is that the movable electrode holder travels in a vertical slide, thereby causing straight-line motion instead of the arc travel of the rocker arm types. This design feature results in close electrode alignment.

Air-operated pistons are capable of flexible pressure control through suitable valves and air-line pressures. Electrodes are advanced and retracted by introducing air pressure on alternate ends of the piston. Cushioning of electrode impact is another feature of air-operated pressure systems. Air operation is used on rocker arm welders in a variety of arrangements.

Electrodes for Resistance Welding. The importance of proper electrode selection and application can be gathered from the standard specifications that have been developed for guidance in their selecting. The Resistance Welder Manufacturing Association (RWMA) has sponsored electrode specifications in which group A covers the copper-base alloys and group B the copper-tungsten alloys. Each group is subdivided into classes which define application in respect to equipment use as well as weldment material.

Both the physical and the electrical requirements of electrodes vary with the type of materials to be welded, as they do with the welding machines in which they are to be used. Spot welders predominate, with the result that standardization has been introduced. These electrodes are made with no. 1 or no. 2 Morse tapers for friction fit in the electrode holder. The electrodes are equipped with a blind hole for water cooling. Electrode operating temperatures profoundly affect performance, since electrical conductivity is a function of temperature as it is of composition. Cool electrodes promote sound welds and reduce the tendency to foul the contact surfaces. The choice of electrode shape and material depends on the work to be welded. Material of high conductivity requires high current and electrodes capable of delivering that current.

Composite, or faced, electrodes are available for meeting specific welding conditions. The facing may cover the entire welding tip, or inserts may be used. Copper-tungsten alloys are favorite facing materials for welding stainless steels and brass. The facings are brazed to copper backing, with the latter forming the electrode body. Electrode contours carry such designations as pointed, dome, flat and offset. Electrode point dimensions are critical, since if a $\frac{3}{16}$-in.-diameter point is permitted to wear to $\frac{1}{4}$-in. diameter, the weld area will be almost doubled, requiring a substantial increase in welding current.

Electrodes of a variety of shapes are available to meet clearances and seam locations.   Electrode holders are influenced by similar considera-

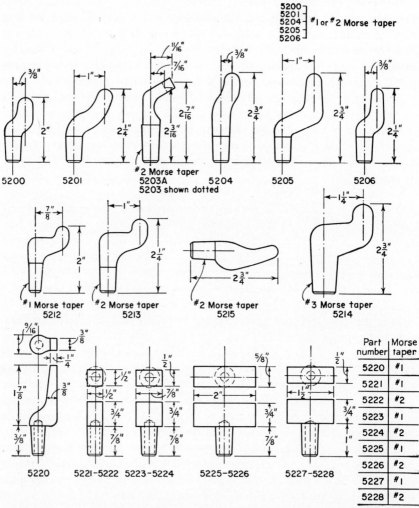

Fig. 31-6. Typical spot welding electrode designs. (*Courtesy of SMS Corporation, Detroit.*)

tions, to the point where straight and offset holders have been standardized.   The fit, or seating, between electrodes and their holders must be of the best to provide proper electrical contact and water-tightness. Typical electrodes are pictured in Fig. 31-6.   Spot welding electrodes are either cast or wrought.

Improper behavior of electrodes can frequently be traced to overheating. One way of meeting this difficulty is to employ refrigeration as a means of cooling. This device has been successfully used in connection with welding heat-treated wrought-aluminum sheet.

The resistance welding processes all employ some modification of the spot welding electrode. The shape or form such contactors take is governed by both the welding process and the weldment material. In seam welding the wheels or rings are made from the same group of materials that are used for spot welding electrodes. Projection welding dies have inserts at the contact points which are analogous to spot welding electrodes. Butt and flash welding dies must have great strength and be capable of withstanding the severe strain to which they are subjected.

Applied Resistance Welding

The Master Chart of Welding Processes[1] classifies resistance welding as spot, seam, projection, flash, upset, and percussion. These classifications can be grouped broadly into the categories of spot welding and butt welding. The basic difference is that in spot welding the seam requires lapped surfaces, while in butt welding the weld is made between abutting faces. In neither case is metal added from an outside source. The resultant weld, therefore, adds no weight to the weldment. A resistance weld has no weight—an important consideration on products where weight saving is critical.

PRODUCT DESIGN

Products designed for resistance welding should be developed for the greatest possible simplicity in joining. The welding requirements should be geared to the use of conventional resistance welding machines as a measure to eliminate difficulties that arise from the use of complicated current-carrying components. The unencumbered welding machine dispenses with involved problems of placing as well as removing the product. Standard electrodes are preferred, since they do not require elaborate water passages and connections.

Resistance welds must be made in short time intervals, since substantial currents, meaning high heat values, are used. The heating time is of short duration as a precaution against warping or burning the weldment. These requisites indicate the reason for the popularity of resistance welding on light-gage material. Heavy weldments with high heat requirements are not adapted to resistance welding as a general rule. There have been some examples of plate welding but such cases are rare. Resistance welding can be used to best advantage by designing a product

[1] American Standard A3.1-49, American Welding Society, New York, 1949.

of sheet metal that requires little surface preparation and is of a shape affording ready access to the weld locations.

Spot Welding. The resistance welding principle finds its widest application in spot welding and its many variations. Where controlled welding has been established, the operation of the machine is automatic once the initiating switch has been closed. There remains, however, a substantial amount of spot welding in which there is slight attention paid to control conditions.

A properly made spot weld results in a "nugget" that, in cross section, approaches the geometry of a sharpened ellipse (Fig. 31-7). The prop-

Fig. 31-7.   Cross section of spot welds, ✕ 10; 0.040-in.-24S-T3 Alclad Aluminum Sheet.   (*Courtesy of The Taylor-Winfield Corp., Warren, Ohio.*)

erties of the nugget are a function of the weld program as well as material, kind, and thickness. The ideal spot weld will show penetration evenly divided between the sheets when the latter are of the same thickness and material.

One feature of the spot welding operation is the resultant shrinkage, which is at maximum value normal to the weld. Surface indentations result largely from weld shrinkage, with electrode marks acting as a contributing factor. The latter can be avoided by using one large electrode contact surface, thereby keeping the dimpling effect on one side of the welded joint. Where dissimilar materials or materials of different gages are to be welded, it is common practice to use electrodes of contrasting diameters as a means of obtaining differential heating as between the two members.

Electrode contacts are designed for both direct and indirect operation. In the usual type of the former setting the electrodes are so placed that they face each other, *i.e.*, one is above the other. The indirect setting, on the other hand, places *both* electrodes on the same side of the joint, separated by a space interval. The welding current travels down through one electrode, then across in a copper shorting block, and up through the second electrode. Setting up such an arrangement requires exact knowledge of welding conditions; care must be taken to prevent the contacted

Fig. 31-8. Multi-electrode, multi-transformer, hydraulically operated spot welder, equipped with 64 spring ring return welding guns and 8 40-kva single-phase water-cooled welding transformers, designed for operation on 0.030 in. clean mild steel. (*Courtesy of National Electric Welding Machines Company, Bay City, Mich.*)

sheet from acting as a shunt for the welding current. Indirect spot welding is not to be confused with multiple spot welding, where several spots are made simultaneously. Some ingenious spot welding machines have been developed as production equipment using the principle of multiple spot welding (Fig. 31-8).

The welding cycle of spot welding machines is varied from a single complete welding operation through pulsation and program welding. Pulsation welding means the reapplication of welding current to a given spot, thus lowering the amount of welding current required. Program welding is applied where heat-treatment of the spot weld is necessary, as in hardenable steels and heat-treatable aluminum alloys. Program welding includes the welding operation plus any post-treatment that the material requires.

The spot welder can be brought to the work by means of portable, or gun-type, equipment. The welding element (Fig. 31-9) is portable and is applied at the point of welding, which lends flexibility; the transformer and control equipment have a more stationary mounting. The design of the gun, which is equipped with electrodes, an application mechanism,

Fig. 31-9. Typical portable welding equipment of the gun-welder type used for welding automotive parts. (*Courtesy of Budd Manufacturing Co., Philadelphia.*)

and water-cooling lines, does not follow a given pattern. The "push" gun type does, in effect, shoot a weld, since its operation is reminiscent of a firearm. Other design types are the scissors, the pinch, the "C" (after C clamp), the swivel, etc. The designations refer to the method of operation or construction of the welding gun.

Spot welding has attained such widespread acceptance in industry as to justify the development of procedure standards. Table 31-1 is included here as an example of the data contained in "Recommended Practices for Resistance Welding (Tentative)."[1] This standard also contains data covering the following: pulsation-welding low-carbon steel; spot-welding stainless steel; pulsation-welding stainless steel; spot-

[1] American Standard C1.1-46T, American Welding Society, New York.

welding annealed nickel, monel, and inconel; and spot-welding hardenable steels (quench and temper method).

TABLE 31-1. SPOT WELDING LOW-CARBON STEEL*

Thickness "T" of thinnest outside piece, in. (Notes 1, 2, 3, and 4 below)	Electrode diameter and shape (Note 5 below)		Net electrode force, lb	Weld time (single impulse), cycles (60 per sec)	Welding current (approx.), amp	Minimum contacting overlap, in.	Minimum weld spacing, in. (see Note 6 below) in. ¢ to ¢	Diameter of fused zone, in., approx. D_w	Minimum shear strength, lb	
									Ultimate tensile strength of metal	
	D, in., min.	d, in., max.							Below 70,000 psi	70,000 psi and above
0.010	3/8	1/8	200	4	4,000	3/8	1/4	0.10	130	180
0.021	3/8	3/16	300	6	6,500	7/16	3/8	0.13	320	440
0.031	3/8	3/16	400	8	8,000	7/16	1/2	0.16	570	800
0.040	1/2	1/4	500	10	9,500	1/2	3/4	0.19	920	1200
0.050	1/2	1/4	650	12	10,500	9/16	7/8	0.22	1,350	
0.062	1/2	1/4	800	14	12,000	5/8	1	0.25	1,850	
0.078	5/8	5/16	1100	17	14,000	11/16	1 1/4	0.29	2,700	
0.094	5/8	5/16	1300	20	15,500	3/4	1 1/2	0.31	3,450	
0.109	5/8	3/8	1600	23	17,500	13/16	1 5/8	0.32	4,150	
0.125	7/8	3/8	1800	26	19,000	7/8	1 3/4	0.33	5,000	

Notes:

1. Type of steel—SAE 1010.

2. Material should be free from scale, oxides, paint, grease and oil.

3. Welding conditions determined by thickness of thinnest outside piece "T."

4. Data for total thickness of pile-up not exceeding 4 "T." Maximum ratio between two thicknesses 3:1.

5. Electrode material, Class 2, minimum conductivity, 75% of copper; minimum hardness, 75 Rockwell B.

6. Minimum weld spacing is that spacing for two pieces for which no special precautions need be taken to compensate for shunted current effect of adjacent welds. For three pieces increase spacing 30 per cent.

* From American Standard C1.1-46T, American Welding Society, New York.

Seam Welding. Welding wheels, or a wheel and a plate, replace the electrodes of a spot welder in seam welding machines. A mechanical drive is provided for the welding wheels. In some designs both wheels are driven, while in others one wheel is driven and the other is an idler. The work is moved forward between the welding wheels at a rate varying from 2 to 50 fpm, depending on such modifications as welding current and material type and thickness. Figure 31-10 shows a diagram of a seam in addition to a spot welding cycle.

Seam welding machines are designed on several basic principles. Where the intended weld is a long seam (Fig. 31-11), the welder is termed a longitudinal type. There is also a circular type, used for welding bottoms into drums and similar jobs. A seam welder wherein the welding wheels can be adapted to both of the previous requirements is referred to as a universal. The mechanism used for driving the welding wheels also gives rise to design types; examples are the gear drive and knurled

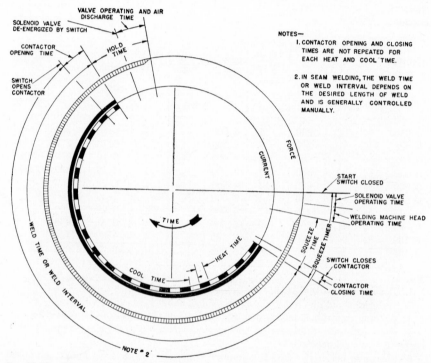

Fig. 31-10. Diagram of welding cycle for seam welding. (*From American Standard A3.0-49, American Welding Society, New York, 1949.*)

drive. In the case of the latter, the welding wheels are friction-driven by a knurled wheel, which in turn derives its motion directly from a motor.

The seam welding considered thus far has involved to lap joints, which are similar to spot welding. There is a further classification of seam welding, known as the butt seam, which is used for welding the longitudinal seam in tubing. The tubing is rolled with an open seam and is guided by that opening into the welding machine. Pressure is exerted from the sides in a closing action on the seam, where the welding wheels supply the necessary current for completing the weld.

Projection Welding. This method of welding is another modification of spot welding. The location of the welds is predetermined by projections or irregularities formed on the weldment parts prior to welding. The projections act as contact points for localizing the weld. In consequence the welding machine is equipped with flat-faced electrodes or dies rather than the usual type of spot welding electrodes. The number of welds that can be made simultaneously is governed by the number of contact surfaces or points that are located within the die area. No previously made welds are in this area, since their presence would act as a shunt for the welding current. This is not to be taken to mean that all projection welds are of the multiple type; there are single ones as well.

Fig. 31-11.   Seam welding operation.   (*Courtesy of Progressive Welder Co., Detroit.*)

Projection welding machines are generally built similarly to press welders. In fact some types are of a design that permits them to be used for either spot or projection welding with only slight equipment changes in shifting from one system to the other. There are also examples of projection welding machines constructed as production or specialized equipment. These designs are predicated on the requirements for a particular welding job and as a result bear slight resemblance in appearance to the standard type of machine. Figure 31-12 shows one example of a production projection welding machine. This equipment is rated at a capacity of 1,000 plates per hr welded to conveyor chain links used in bottling machines.

Flash Welding.   Flash welding is also referred to as flash butt welding. In this method of resistance welding, the weld occurs between abutting surfaces or faces of the parts to be joined. The method has been successful on all materials that can be spot-welded and it also is used for welding dissimilar metals. The shape and size of the weldment parts are of slight consequence, since flash welds are used on sheet metal as they are on bar stock to considerable thicknesses. The all-steel automobile body exemplifies the flash welding technique for joining its component stampings. The flash remaining after welding, when removed, leaves a joint so expertly made that from outward appearance it cannot be detected. In the automotive industry flash welding is a generously used method

Fig. 31-12. Discharge side of projection welding machine, showing plates welded to chain links. (Courtesy of Thomson Electric Welder Company, Lynn, Mass.)

of joining parts of all categories. It is chosen because of its potential in the direction of lower manufacturing costs. As an example, the splined end of a drive shaft is flash welded to the central portion and then the drive pinion is flash welded to the opposite end of this weldment. Thus the drive shaft comprises three parts joined by two flash welds. The saving in material, labor, and machine time of this welding method over making the part from a single piece of steel is a major one. In fact flash welding has been so completely accepted in automotive construction that standard regulations have been established for its application.[1]

[1] "Recommended Practices for Automotive Flash-Butt Welding (Tentative)," American Standards D8.1-46T, American Welding Society, New York, 1946.

The welding heat results from the flashing action, which is produced by forcing tightly together the surfaces or faces to be welded, as a means of establishing current flow in local areas.   This heat concentration in small areas causes localized melting, with the result that molten metal is violently expelled by current behavior.   There is a pronounced showering of sparks and molten metal particles during the flashing period (Fig. 31-13).   The flashing cycle is continued for a period governed by pressure and welding current conditions.   The objective is to heat both pieces to

Fig. 31-13.   *Flash butt welding longitudinal seam on steel pipe.   (Courtesy of A. O. Smith Corp., Milwaukee, Wis.)*

a distance back from the weld face and in an amount that will bring the affected surfaces to a high degree of plasticity.

Upset Welding.   This process holds the distinction of being the forerunner of all the resistance welding methods.   The original patent for resistance welding covered substantially what is now termed upset welding.   Upset welding is unique in that the abutting surfaces are subjected to continuing pressure throughout the entire welding operation. The weld faces are pressed together prior to the release of the welding current.   The pressure continues for the duration of the welding current plus an additional time increment following the cessation of current. The magnitude of the pressure may be variable through the welding cycle, starting with a low value as a means of initially increasing contact resistance. Welding heat is generated entirely by the resistance to current flow. As the weld progresses, resistance decreases, and it actually reaches zero as the weld is completed.

Percussion Welding. Resistance, in the usual sense, plays little part in percussion, or, as it is sometimes termed, percussive welding. The welding heat in this process results from an arc discharge of extremely

Fig. 31-14.   Percussion-type welder.   (*Courtesy of Taylor-Winfield Corp., Warren, Ohio.*)

short duration. The arc is kindled between the faces of the weldments' parts. The current for the arc is obtained from stored electrical energy. The term stored electrical energy is not to be confused with a similar one used in connection with spot welding for the reason that no welding transformer is included in the welding circuit.

Arc duration is on the order of 0.001 sec, whence power expenditure reaches 200 kw. Because of this design the heating effect on the weldment parts is confined to a thin zone on the surface. Immediately upon discharge of the arc, the weldment parts are brought together with percussive force in an action that causes weld completion. Two distinctive characteristics of this process are that (1) dissimilar metals can be welded, since welding heat arises from an arc discharge and resistance plays no part; (2) the pieces to be welded must be individual ones and completely separated (for instance, a closing joint in a ring could not be welded by the percussion welding process). Owing to the nature of the heating process, there is no flash formed at the weld interface.

Welds made by this method are confined to parts of relatively small cross section, among these being wire, rod, and tubing (Fig. 31-14). The possibilities for welding dissimilar metals are interesting when it is realized that, by way of example, brass has been welded to magnesium and stellite to bronze valve stems. Percussion welding is limited primarily to such fields, since it cannot compete with flash welding on the basis of economy.

Survey Questions

31-1. Can resistance welding be classified as a manual method of welding?

31-2. In addition to electrical energy, what other element is essential to resistance welding?

31-3. Is more than one type of heat source possible in resistance welding?

31-4. Why are some metals more difficult to resistance-weld than are others?

31-5. Explain contact resistance.

31-6. Why do electrode tips tend to pick up metal during welding?

31-7. How are resistance welding machines powered from a-c line sources?

31-8. Are all resistance welding machines powered from a-c line sources?

31-9. Where are *ignitrons* and *thyratrons* used in resistance welding?

31-10. Why are single-phase resistance welding machines objectionable as a line load?

31-11. Are stored-energy machines corrective line loads?

31-12. Essentially what is the difference between electrostatic and electromagnetic types of energy storage?

31-13. Describe pulsation welding.

31-14. What three elements must a pulsation timer control?

31-15. In addition to manual pressure, what other pressure systems are used?

31-16. Explain the use of composite electrodes.

31-17. Why are electrode face shapes critical?

31-18. How are spot-welding electrodes secured in the machine?

31-19. Which type of resistance welding has the broadest application?

31-20. What is indirect spot welding?

31-21. Wherein do seam-welding machines differ from spot welders?

31-22. Is all seam welding of the lap-joint type?

31-23. Are projection welding machines equipped with the same style of electrodes as those used on spot welders?

31-24. What joint type is required for flash welding?

31-25. Give some major applications for flash welding.

31-26. Can percussion welding be regarded as a type of resistance welding?

31-27. Is it possible to join dissimilar metals by spot welding?

31-28. Must flux be used in resistance welding?

31-29. Is there any portable resistance welding equipment available?

31-30. Can heavy sections be resistance-welded?

31-31. How is it possible to weld metals of high electrical conductivity?

31-32. Is resistance welding applied to shipbuilding?

31-33. Name at least one manufacturing industry in which resistance welding is prominently used.

31-34. Can mild-steel sections be resistance-welded?

31-35. Is it possible to eliminate spot welding dimples?

31-36. What is program welding?

REFERENCES

Jefferson, T. B.: "Welding Design Handbook," The Welding Engineer, New York, 1948.

Kuntz, George: "Aircraft Spot and Seam Welding," Pitman Publishing Corp., New York, 1942.

"Master Chart of Welding Processes and Process Charts," American Standard A3.1-49, American Welding Society, New York, 1949.

"Recommended Practices for Automotive Flash-Butt Welding (Tentative)," American Standard D8.1-46T, American Welding Society, New York, 1946.

"Recommended Practices for Resistance Welding (Tentative)," American Standard C1.1-46T, American Welding Society, New York, 1946.

"Resistance Welding Manual," Resistance Welder Manufacturing Association, Philadelphia, 1946.

"Standard Welding Terms and Their Definitions," American Standard A3.0-49, American Welding Society, New York, 1949.

Stanley, Wallace A.: "Resistance Welding," McGraw-Hill Book Co., Inc., New York, 1950.

"The Welding Encyclopedia," 11th ed., The Welding Engineer Publishing Company, Chicago, 1943.

CHAPTER 32

AUTOMATIC AND SPECIALIZED WELDING ARCS

Automatic arc welding finds its broadest field of application where production demands are high. This concept of arc welding lacks the versatility and portability characteristic of the manual type. On the other hand, where production requirements justify the installation of automatic arc welding, the resulting costs are extremely favorable and the welding quality is high.

There are several modifications of manual arc welding that are of interest. These employ some type of shielding or some arc operating principles that have been derived from the basic welding arc. In some instances these specialized welding arcs are manually operated, while in others they have been built into mechanical production equipment. Several of the specialized developments have proved of such a spectacular nature as to cause revision of the entire concept of arc welding. Some of these developments were established prior to World War II, others gained recognition during the war, and some have been perfected since the war. From all this it can be conjectured that further substantial developments in welding arcs and their applications are to be expected in the future.

In view of the nature of the developments mentioned above, this chapter will present automatic welding arcs in one section, to be followed by a second section devoted to specialized arcs. It is impossible to draw a sharp line of demarcation between these two since, as noted previously, there is some overlapping.

Automatic Arc Welding

Automatic Bare Electrode Arc Welding. The original interest in automatic arcs was devoted to equipment which merely performed the metallic arc welding function automatically. Equipment of that nature was primarily built for d-c operation and the electrode was of the bare type. Automatic bare metal arc welding consists of equipment which performs all the functions of manual metallic arc welding with bare electrodes. The chief difference between manual and automatic is that closer control is possible with automatic equipment and as a result higher welding speeds and better weld results are achieved.

The electrode wire used with the automatic bare metal arc welding is supplied in coils. The wire is fed automatically through the welding head at a rate to maintain a constant arc length. This wire, although termed bare, actually has a light coating or a dust coating on its surface. The function of this coating is to stabilize the arc. It is not to be confused with other methods in which electrode surfaces are coated to shield the welding arc. In some types the electrode wire is knurled in order to increase the flux capacity of the surface and also to aid in securing a positive drive through the wire feeding rolls of the welding head. The coating that is used varies with different producers of welding wire; however, it has the same general purpose of ionizing the arc stream for arc stability.

The quality of the weld metal deposited by this process is not equal to that obtained where shielding is employed. The deposited metal is susceptible to porosity and brittleness. These shortcomings are to be expected; there is no protection of the arc stream or the deposited metal from the atmosphere, so that iron nitrides and oxides are readily formed. This tendency is not so great as to seriously impair the serviceability of the weld.

Welding performed by the automatic bare metal arc is generally single-pass. Because of this fact, high welding speeds at extremely favorable costs result. Applications of this process are generally limited to gages under $\frac{1}{8}$ in. On such material, welding speeds reach as high as 60 in./min. However, plate thicknesses as great as $\frac{3}{4}$ in. have been welded by this method.

Reasonable precautions must be exercised on edge preparation as well as on fit-up, to obtain good results. One reason for the favorable cost aspect of this method of welding is the fact that, since no shielding material is used on the electrode, there is no deposit of slag on the finished weld and no time is required for slag removal. On occasion automatic bare metal arc welding has been specified as a means of eliminating all possibility of entrapped slag.

A typical automatic bare metal arc welding head is shown in Fig. 32-1. The mechanical as well as electrical construction features of this type of welding head are interesting. The design is such that the arc can be started and maintained automatically. Another important feature is that the arc length remains constant at a predetermined setting. In the welding of irregular surfaces the electrode wire is automatically fed forward or reversed entirely as the condition of work demands. All this is accomplished in the modern arc welding head without the head being unduly complicated.

Automatic Shielded Metallic Arc Welding. As the use of shielded electrodes in manual arc welding developed and the nature of the weld-ments produced by that means became better understood, interest centered in developing automatic equipment to perform similar work. The problem was to find a means of making electrical contact in an automatic arc head through the electrode shielding. In the previously discussed automatic arc this was no problem, since the electrode feed rolls or other attachments acted to conduct current directly to the bare metal wire.

One of the early solutions for using a shielded metal electrode was the "stick" feed. In this method a shielded electrode of standard length is placed in the head and electrical contact is made at the end where the shielding has been removed for the manual electrode holder grip; the electrode is fed into the weld automatically. However, only short welds can be made because as the electrode is consumed the arc is extinguished and a new electrode has to be put into the head.

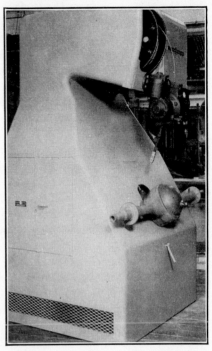

Fig. 32-1. Automatic bare-wire welding head operating in conjunction with weld positioner on automobile rear-end housing. (*Courtesy of General Electric Corp., Schenectady.*)

Another early development employed an automatic head which incorporated a device for wrapping a previously impregnated tape around the bare metal wire in a complete shielding. The tape was made of a combination of textile and fine copper wire woven in an open mesh; it was saturated with a shielding solution whose composition varied with the requirements of the weld. This method proved to be a most versatile one, since the shielding could be changed merely by inserting a different tape into the welding head. Its primary application was on lighter material or as a sealing bead for submerged melt welding. A further advantage of the method was that both the weld rod and the shielding tape were supplied in coils, which meant that there was no limitation on the length of welds that could be made.

A shielded electrode development which had fallen into disuse but is again being employed, with satisfactory results, consists of a woven wire mesh placed concentrically with the electrode, the interstices between them being filled with shielding material. The wire mesh is woven so that the wires pass from the surface of the electrode to the electrode wire and then back to the surface in a continuous pattern. In operation the current conductor of the automatic arc head contacts this fine mesh wire on the outside of the electrode, thereby conveying the current through the shielding to the central welding wire. This method has much to recommend it.

The convenience of using coiled wire for automatic shielded metal arc welding was achieved in still another way. An automatic head was built which contained stationary slitting saws. As the shielded electrode passed through the head it crossed these saws in such a manner that the shielding was slit open, permitting electrical contact to be made with the weld wire at the center of the electrode. One of the features of the construction was the use of rubber-tired feed rolls; these were necessary to avoid cracking the shielding, which was relatively brittle. In other respects the head was designed along the lines of most automatic metal arc welding equipment.

Some automatic heads were equipped with an oscillator. The function of this device is to weave the bead in contradistinction to the stringer type of bead that results from a straight-line motion.

Many further ideas have been proposed in an endeavor to find a satisfactory automatic shielded metal electrode welding method. There was one used in Austria before the war in which the shielding was in the center rather than on the surface of the electrode. Another proposal suggested the use of a bare wire arc operating in a gas shield. All these methods have been forced into the background by the development of the submerged arc method.

Automatic heads are available in a variety of mountings; in some of these the head moves along the weld, while in others the head is stationary and the joint passes under the arc. The electrical design of automatic traveling heads is complicated. The fact that motor speeds must be variable and electrode feed reversible, results in a design that is entirely trustworthy but is likely to present maintenance problems.

Submerged Arc Welding.   As has been indicated, the most significant development in metal arc welding is the submerged arc. The basic principles of this system are illustrated in Fig. 32-2. The welding electrode used is of the bare wire type; it may or may not be copper-coated. It is available in a variety of diameters and is supplied in coils.

The automatic welding head used with this system is about the same as the one used with automatic bare metal arc welding. The main point of difference is that with submerged arc welding a granular material, variously referred to as melt or flux, is fed into the weld by gravity in

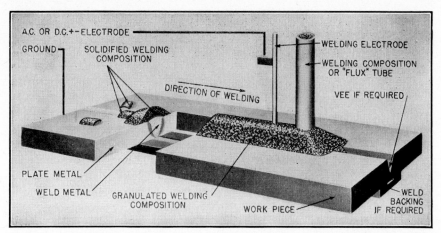

Fig. 32-2. Schematic drawing showing the principles of operation of the submerged melt welding process. (*Courtesy of Linde Air Products Co., New York.*)

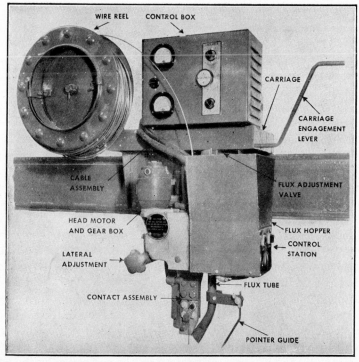

Fig. 32-3. Self-propelled "Lincolnmelt" carriage. This is another type of submerged arc welding equipment. (*Courtesy of The Lincoln Electric Co., Cleveland.*)

an amount sufficient to submerge the arc completely. Figure 32-3 illustrates the pertinent features of one submerged arc welding head design; the flux tube is shown, as well as the hopper and the wire reel from which the bare weld wire is fed.

The operating characteristics of submerged arc welding are different from those of all other methods. Here the arc is established below a blanket of granular flux or melt; this being the case, no arc is visible. Consequently the operator's eyes need no protection from arc rays; they should of course have the protection of clear glass as a safety precaution.

There are two basic submerged arc welding methods. The one pictured in Fig. 32-2 can be adapted to alternating as well as direct current, whereas the equipment shown in Fig. 32-3 is of the d-c variety. There are some differences in operation between the two; however they are fundamentally the same in operating characteristics.

The arc is struck beneath the granular melt, or flux, and as the welding proceeds, this covering material precedes the arc so as to submerge the latter throughout its period of operation, thereby effectively excluding the atmosphere. As the welding continues, some of the granular material becomes fused, while the excess remains unaffected. The latter is picked up by a vacuum device and returned to the hopper for re-use.

The fused material is visibly red at the time of welding; however, upon cooling it changes to a dark color and has a glasslike consistency. It can be readily brushed from the weld. It is interesting to note that the fused material, or slag, forms a substantial blanket over the deposited weld metal, thereby both shielding it and aiding in the control of its cooling rate. The latter feature is of metallurgical importance.

The submerged arc welding process is capable of producing welds of unusually high mechanical properties. This applies to strength as well as ductility. Furthermore, the process has yielded excellent results on low-alloy, high-strength structural steels as well as on firebox steel. Test data indicate that in many instances these welds show properties equal to, and in some instances higher than, those of the base metal. The results, of course, are influenced by the type of wire used in welding.

Welding speeds obtainable from the submerged arc welding process are spectacular, especially when compared to earlier methods. For example, butt welds are made at a rate of 10 to 12 in./min in 1-in. steel plate and at half that rate in plates of 2-in. thickness (Chart 32-1). These welds are completed in one pass. This fact is of great significance, since it means much higher over-all welding speed. Moreover, the addition of filler metal is small with the submerged arc welding process because of the high currents used. There is considerable melting of the base metal, which means that joint preparation need not be as open as in the case of other types of automatic arc welding.

There is some divergence of opinion as to the composition of the granular shielding material. This arises from the question of the function to be performed by that material, which is a product of the electric arc furnace. There has been much experimental work in connection with developing this granular shielding material. Some of the early experiments made use of river sand, among other things. The size of the granules exerts an effect on the operation and results of this welding equipment. The appearance of the welding bead is influenced by the size of the granules used.

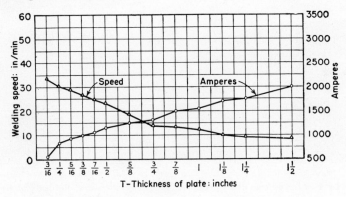

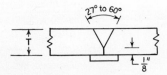

Type of welding groove for one-pass butt weld

Chart 32-1. Typical relationships of welding speed versus plate thickness in low carbon steel material for submerged arc welding. (*Abstracted from Automatic Arc and Gas Welding Processes, American Welding Society, No. D7.2-48T.*)

Submerged arc welding is used primarily in the down-hand position. Because of this limitation, some extremely ingenious weld positioners have been devised. The one shown in Fig. 32-4 is used in welding the roofs of freight cars. Supplementary equipment is not limited to weld positioners; it includes many examples of gear developed for increasing the speed of welding on large as well as complicated equipment. Figure 32-5 is by no means a standardized application; it is used here to give an indication of the elaborateness of some of the installations used in connection with submerged arc welding.

Semiautomatic Submerged Arc Welding. In the previous paragraphs automatic operation of submerged arc welding has been considered. A modification of this method has been developed wherein the actual weld-

Fig. 32-4. Weld positioner for freight-car tops used in conjunction with submerged arc welding. Welding equipment can be seen at the top center. (*Courtesy of American Car and Foundry Co.*)

Fig. 32-5. Mechanical mounting for submerged arc welding. (*Courtesy of American Car and Foundry Co.*)

ing head is manipulated manually (Fig. 32-6). The advantage of the semiautomatic method is increased flexibility. The apparatus approximates manual arc welding in use, except that the welding must be done in the flat position. The advantages of submerged arc welding are incorporated in a manually operated device.

The electrode wire, supplied in coils, is fed into the weld mechanically through a flexible tube that terminates at the welding head. A conically shaped container in which the granular melt is held joins the electrode

Fig. 32-6. Manual submerged arc welding on ½-in. plate, plain butt weld without edge preparation. Weld was made with 5⁄64-in.-diameter electrode at 450 amp. Travel speed 22 in. per min. (*Courtesy of The Lincoln Electric Co., Cleveland.*)

tube at the welding head. The weldor operates the equipment by manipulating controls located within his grasp. He guides the welding head along the joint but is not concerned with the necessity for weaving, as he would be in manual arc welding. Welds are made without edge preparation in plate thicknesses up to ½ in. It is also possible to make fillet welds with the submerged arc welding method. Every advantage of the submerged arc principle is retained in this method, and it also has the versatility that manual manipulation contributes.

Automatic Carbon Arc Welding. Automatic carbon arc welding has been employed in industry for some time. The basic principle is the same as that of the manual carbon arc, excepting that the welding head has been mechanized. Modifications of the automatic carbon arc have been directed toward shielding the arc. Shielding has followed the techniques of automatic metal arc welding. In one type the shielding is accomplished by an impregnated paper tape that is fed into the arc as the welding proceeds (Fig. 32-7). This method has found favor in the welding of sheet steel as well as of nonferrous metals. No provision is made for feeding weld metal into the joint. Flanged joints, and joints in which a metal strip has been placed, are best adapted to this particular type of automatic carbon arc welding head.

Fig. 32-7. Automatic electronic tornado welding head, showing carbon electrode and fibrous flux. (*Courtesy of The Lincoln Electric Co., Cleveland.*)

There are designs in which welding wire is fed into the carbon arc. Controls are provided for regulating the speed of wire feed as well as maintaining desired arc length, which is in turn related to arc voltage. All systems of automatic carbon arc welding are operated with direct current, with the electrode negative. The electrodes are either carbon or graphite, the latter being capable of higher current density per unit of area. The electrode usually rotates and is surrounded by a magnetic field.

In another modification of carbon arc welding the carbon electrode is submerged in a powdered flux. The flux serves as an ionizing agency in addition to acting as a shielding material. If desired, alloying elements can be mixed with the flux in order that they may enter the weld.   Helium gas has also been used as a shielding material for automatic carbon arc welding.

Applications of automatic carbon arc welding are wide in scope.   However, the copper-base alloys are particularly well adapted to this method. The thicknesses that can be welded have not been completely established, but it is generally understood that $\frac{3}{4}$ in. is maximum for carbon steels. Welding speeds, which vary with type of base metal, with thickness, and with current, have reached 50 in./min on steel sheet.   This figure should be considered merely as a maximum; there are too many variables involved to justify anything but a general statement on welding speeds.

Specialized Welding Arcs

When any arc welding method proves itself, it is but a question of time until it is developed into an automatic one.   Hence it seems logical to assume that every manual arc welding process has its automatic counterpart.   It is difficult to make a clear-cut distinction between those processes that should be referred to as automatic, on the one hand, and those that are manual, on the other.   The division made in this chapter is based on the general application of a given process.   It is recognized that both of the following processes are also available in an automatic version although they are not so presented here.

Atomic Hydrogen Welding.   This welding process operates on alternating current with arc voltage ranging between 50 and 100 v.   It is claimed that the atomic hydrogen arc is the "hottest flame on earth" with a temperature potential of 6000°C.   The welding current is taken directly from a power source into a transformer, where output can be regulated to meet the requirements of a given weld.

The distinctive characteristics of this process are, first, that the arc is maintained between two tungsten electrodes, and, second, that the arc is surrounded by hydrogen gas.   The equipment consists of a welding transformer, a hydrogen cylinder with regulator, and an electrode holder (Fig. 32-8).   Fundamentally the atomic hydrogen apparatus is an arc torch.   As such, it merely supplies the heat source for welding; it does not, in itself, supply weld metal.

A unique feature is the use of hydrogen with and in the arc.   Electrodes are supplied in diameters ranging from 0.040 to 0.155 in. in increments of 32ds.   The choice of diameter is governed by the flame size and heat requirements of the welding operation.   Since the arc is completely shielded by hydrogen, no melting of the electrodes occurs; rather they function in a manner similar to the points in a spark plug.   The arc should not be drawn in the absence of the hydrogen shielding lest fouling and melting of the electrodes occur.   The built-in controls of the electrode holder prevent such mishaps. Electrode adjustment and arc length are both critical insofar as correct operation is concerned.

Hydrogen gas, which is supplied as compressed gas from a cylinder, flows through a regulator which establishes a line pressure of 5 psi. The gas is conducted through tubes, which surround the electrodes, into the arc stream. The gas is supplied as molecular hydrogen; in its passage through the arc this is dissociated into atomic hydrogen. Upon completion of travel through the arc, the atomic hydrogen recombines into molecular hydrogen, a reaction that is accompanied by the liberation of heat, which is used for welding. The shape of the arc flame approximates the outline of a fan.

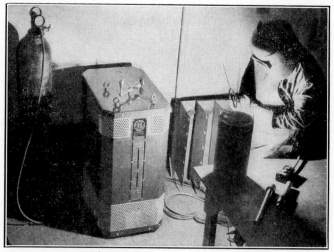

Fig. 32-8. Atomic hydrogen welding; a-c transformer welder and hydrogen equipment are shown at left. (Courtesy of General Electric Co., Schenectady.)

Atomic hydrogen welding can be performed in every position. However, because of the high degree of fluidity imparted to the metal by the operating temperatures, it is difficult to hold metal in vertical or overhead joints. In order to weld at all, the metal pool must be small and the arc removed at frequent intervals to permit the molten metal to chill. This practice tends to cancel the shielding gained by the use of hydrogen.

Edge and corner joints requiring no filler metal are best adapted to this welding process. (A filler rod is required for beveled joints, the rod being fed by the free hand.) The process has a wide range of adaptability, covering both ferrous and nonferrous alloys. The hydrogen shielding obviates the necessity for fluxing the weld excepting only in the case of some of the aluminum- and copper-base alloys. The inherent advantages of atomic hydrogen welding arise from its high temperature potential, which delivers extremely rapid heating coupled with a shielded arc. The method has also been developed for automatic welding; this development finds its greatest application in the welding of sheet metal.

Inert-gas Shielded Metal Arc Welding. The principle of shielding an electric arc with an inert gas, in which the arc is maintained through a nonconsumable electrode, was patented as early as 1930. Since that time there have been some important developments. The basic idea of this process is that of shielding the arc with either helium or argon gas, or both. There is a further development, which will be detailed later in this chapter, in which a consumable electrode is used, employing inert-gas shielding.

Of outstanding significance in connection with this process is the fact that no welding flux is necessary. Thus considerable expense is saved in initial cost and by freedom from the necessity for removal after welding. Further, there need be no fear of residual flux with its corrosive potentials remaining anywhere in the weldment. This is a substantial contribution to the welding of such metals as aluminum and stainless steels. Another matter of importance is the fact that the area of the weld is comparatively small; as a result heating concentration is such as to eliminate many of the distortion difficulties. In the welding of stainless steels a narrow heat zone means less possibility of carbide precipitation.

This process affords an especially good method of shielding and prevention of oxidation, since both the gases used are noncombustible and serve to prevent any air from entering into the arc. The equipment used in inert-gas shielded arc welding consists of a power source, a cylinder of compressed gas equipped with proper regulators, and an electrode holder. The equipment under discussion is that for use in manual operation. There is also equipment for automatic operation.

Two types of electric current are used, alternating and direct, and in the case of direct current, both straight and reverse polarity have their applications. Table 32-1 gives information on current and gas use. When direct current is employed, the usual type of motor-generator set is satisfactory. The use of straight polarity permits higher current values, inasmuch as the heat distribution in the arc results in greater heat on the base metal rather than on the electrode. As noted in the Table 32-1, current values will vary with the diameter of the electrode. Reverse polarity is of interest because of the behavior of the electrical characteristics of the arc, especially in the welding of such materials as aluminum alloys, which readily form surface oxides. Reverse polarity tends to break through these oxides, giving a clean weld. However, welding speeds are considerably less, which means that welding quality is gained at a definite sacrifice of welding speed.

TABLE 32-1.   GAS AND ELECTRICAL CHARACTERISTICS FOR INERT-ARC WELDING*

Diameter of tungsten electrode, in.	Operating current				
	Alternating	Direct, straight polarity		Direct, reverse polarity	
	Argon	Argon	Helium	Argon	Helium
0.040	45	120	100	15	10
$\frac{1}{16}$	60	180	150	20	15
$\frac{3}{32}$	110	240	200	40	30
$\frac{1}{8}$	175	320	275	70	50
$\frac{3}{16}$	250	400	350	100	80
$\frac{1}{4}$	400	450	400	120	100
$\frac{5}{16}$	500	500	450	150	130

* Abstracted from "Inert-arc Welding Process and Equipment," General Electric Company, 1948.

Alternating current is widely used in connection with this process, although this development is of comparatively recent origin. It was discovered early in the development of this equipment that the oxide layer on some metals acted as a rectifier, with the result that alternating current was converted to what amounted to half-cycle, pulsating, direct current of straight polarity. Welds made by alternating current resulting in this rectification were of poor quality, containing oxide inclusions. As a means of overcoming this difficulty, high-frequency current was superimposed on the welding current. This affords only partial relief, since the welding circuit then actually carries a d-c component along with the alternating current. Continuing revisions of circuit design have been directed toward the solution of this difficulty with increasingly satisfactory results. The trend in welding circuits is toward using high frequency imposed on the welding circuit only for starting the arc.

As was noted above, helium and argon are the gases used for shielding. They are used singly, but some work has been done in the direction of using a mixture of the two. Helium is conducive to higher arc voltages than argon. Hence there is more heat when helium is used, arc watts being the product of voltage and amperage.

Both gases are available in quantity. They are supplied in compressed-gas cylinders. Regulators used on the cylinders should be of the flow-meter rather than the straight pressure-reduction type because the volume flow is critical for proper welding and as a means of saving gas. The gas is conducted to the arc-torch through a conventional hose.

Argon mixed with a small volume of oxygen is proving of value because of the better arc penetration that results. This gas mixture can be purchased compressed in cylinders, or two separate cylinders—one of argon and one of oxygen—can be manifolded and the correct gas volume metered from each and used only with consumable electrodes.

The torch used for inert-gas shielded metal arc welding is of rather complicated construction. The exact construction varies with different

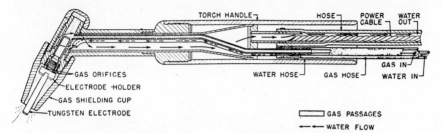

Fig. 32-9. Schematic drawing of a Heliarc torch for inert-gas shielded arc welding. (Courtesy of Linde Air Products Co., New York.)

Fig. 32-10. Heliarc welding aluminum tanks for 10,000-gal.-capacity railroad tank car from 3S aluminum alloy. All seams are welded first with two inside passes; the outside of the joint is then chipped out and welded in one pass. Note method of adding weld metal from independently held filler rod. (Courtesy of Linde Air Products Company, New York.)

manufacturers, although the over-all design is more or less uniform. Figure 32-9 illustrates the construction and operation of the arc-torch generally. Water cooling is provided for the tungsten electrode. The inert gas issues through the shielding cup. The latter is of ceramic material or of stainless steel, depending on the manufacturer.

There is no provision for adding weld metal from the arc-torch; instead, such material is provided from a separate source in the form of a weld rod (Fig. 32-10). Joint design can eliminate the necessity for added weld metal in this process as it can in others.

The rapid strides made in both development and application of this process tend to indicate that much more progress is to be expected. Magnesium, aluminum alloys, and stainless steel have been the principal benefactors thus far. However, it seems assured that the entire category of "hard-to-weld metals" will be handled satisfactorily as the adaptability of this process is extended.

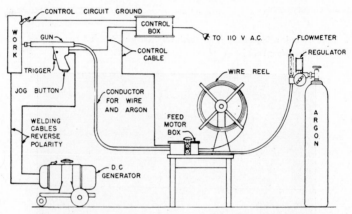

Fig. 32-11.   Schematic diagram of equipment for Aircomatic inert-gas metal arc welding.   (*Courtesy of Air Reduction Sales Co., New York.*)

Consumable Electrode Inert-gas Arc Welding.   The preceding paragraphs have been devoted to an explanation of the inert-gas arc welding system employing a nonconsumable electrode. There is also equipment available in which the electrode is a bare metal wire that functions concurrently as both electrode and filler metal (Fig. 32-11). The weld or electrode wire is fed into the arc mechanically from a reel on which it is coiled.

Other features of the equipment follow the general design of inert-gas arc equipment. The mobility of the welding gun is of distinct advantage for welding in all positions as it is for welding fillets. It has been said of this process that it is manual welding which is, in effect, automatic in operation. The primary application has been for welding aluminum alloys. The equipment is characterized by the use of direct current and argon gas for shielding. There is some evidence of weld spatter, since this is a metal arc welding method. An actual welding operation is shown in Fig. 32-12.

Electric Arc Stud Welding. The idea of end welding stud bolts by an electric arc process was successfully realized in the latter years of the 1930 decade. Stud welding is now regarded as an accepted method. Its definition by the American Welding Society is "an arc welding process wherein coalescence is produced by heating with an electric arc drawn between a metal stud, or similar part, and the other work part until the surfaces to be joined are properly heated, when they are brought together under pressure, and no shielding is used."[1]

Fig. 32-12. Insert-gas metal arc welding of aluminum, using Aircomatic equipment. (*Courtesy of Air Reduction Sales Co., New York.*)

Equipment for stud welding consists of a source of direct current, a time control device, and the stud gun. The stud gun is equipped with a chuck for holding a stud during the welding cycle. Studs are of many designs; at one end they are threaded, blank, or contoured, depending on their use. The opposite, or base, end of the stud, which is the end where the welding occurs, contains flux held beneath a metal cap that gives the base end a conical appearance. A ceramic ferrule fits the welding end of the stud in a way that prevents the spatter of molten metal at the time the weld is actually made. The ferrule also functions as a mold which causes the molten metal at the base of the stud to be cast into a convex fillet.

Welding procedure consists of placing a stud in the gun chuck, placing

[1] "Standard Welding Terms and Their Definitions," Standard A3.0-49, American Welding Society, New York, 1949.

a ferrule in position around the stud, and then setting the stud on its desired location.   The welding cycle is automatic and is controlled by the timer in the circuit.   Depressing the gun trigger draws the stud away from the base metal, thereby establishing an arc and causing melting.   After sufficient melting has occurred, a spring in the stud gun releases, forcing the stud into the pool of molten metal.   This entire operation is automatic; it proceeds to completion upon the pressing of the

Fig. 32-13.   Welding studs in a boiler.   Note ceramic ferrules in position for receiving studs.   (Courtesy of Nelson Stud Welding Division, Morton Gregory Corp., Lorain, Ohio.)

gun trigger.   A stud welding cycle is extremely fast, being on the order of $\frac{1}{20}$ sec for a $\frac{1}{8}$-in.-diameter and $\frac{3}{4}$ sec for a $\frac{3}{4}$-in.-diameter stud.

Studs are used for many types of fastenings, but threaded ones are in the majority.   Figure 32-13 shows a stud gun in operation.   Corrugated metal roofing is fastened by driving the sheet down over a welded stud and then riveting the latter.   Breaker rolls are manufactured by welding pins on a cylinder using a mechanically mounted stud gun and an indexing fixture.

Firecracker Welding.   The principle of making an arc weld with the electrode stationary has been studied for some time, abroad as well as in the United States.   An example of a weld made by this process is shown in Fig. 32-14.   This process has been termed firecracker welding, undoubtedly from the fact that the actual welding operation simulates the burning of a fuse on a firecracker.

The technique consists, in the case of a lap weld, of placing a shielded electrode along the length of the joint. One end of the electrode is connected to the power source. After the electrode has been put in place, it is covered by a holding strip, which is usually copper. This acts to hold the electrode in position and also to cool the electrode, which will become overheated if it is too long. Once the assembly is in position, the arc is started by contacting the electrode with the base metal by means of a piece of carbon or similar material. The length of the arc will be equal to the thickness of the shielding on the electrode. There is difficulty in starting the arc, since there is a tendency for the electrode to stick immediately following the kindling of the arc.

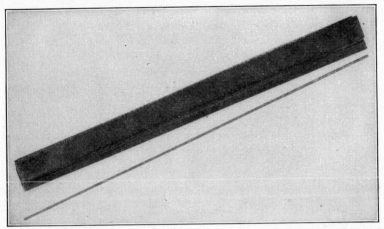

Fig. 32-14. Lap weld made in 2- by $\frac{1}{4}$- in. mild steel with $\frac{5}{32}$ in. shielded electrode of the E6010 classification. Electrode specimen is 36 in. long.

Experiments on this process conducted at the University of Washington led to a solution of the problem of arc starting through tapering the electrode so that the end starting the weld presented but a very small volume of metal. The setup for firecracker welding has been varied by different researchers. Some have included strips of paper in order to increase the shielding on the electrode.

The results obtained by this process were entirely satisfactory in the experiments referred to above. The penetration and soundness of these welds is indicated by Fig. 32-15, which also shows the excellent fusion obtained. There has not been very much application of this technique in American industry. However, Russian writers in 1939 referred to welds made by the firecracker technique.[1] They employed the device of an eccentric coating on the electrode as a means of varying arc length.

[1] Mumrikov, P. V., G. P. Shkliarov, and V. P. Moreev: New Methods of Electric Arc Welding, *Autogenous Work*, 1939.

Electrode Techniques. With the development of heavily coated electrodes, there has been some interest in new manipulation techniques, among them the deep fillet technique. In this method of welding the proper electrode is held close to the work; a high welding current and fast travel speed, used with alternating current, form a combination delivering good penetration.

A similar development has recently been offered in the form of contact welding electrodes, which is a European application. It is claimed for these that they merely need to be touched to the base metal and moved along the joint without any attempt to maintain a given arc length. It

Fig. 32-15.   Cross section of the firecracker weld shown in preceding figure.   ×2.

appears that these electrodes are somewhat similar to our electrode types E6020 and E6030. The disadvantage of the contact electrode is its cost.

Survey Questions

32-1. Where should automatic arc welding be considered?

32-2. Does "bare" automatic arc wire contain a coating?

32-3. How does the quality of weld deposit from bare wire compare with shielded types?

32-4. Mention some advantages for bare-wire automatic arc welding.

32-5. Explain the application of stick feed.

32-6. Has coiled, shielded, automatic arc wire been successful?

32-7. How can weaving be cared for in automatic arc welding?

32-8. In automatics, does the head travel or the work or both?

32-9. In submerged arc welding, is a shielded or bare wire used?

32-10. How is the arc kindled in submerged arc welding?

32-11. Is the submerged arc method ever used manually?

32-12. Can submerged arc welding be used in all positions?

32-13. Give applications for automatic carbon arc welding.

32-14. What electrode material is used in atomic hydrogen welding?

32-15. Does atomic hydrogen welding deposit the electrode as in metal arc welding?

32-16. What type of joints are especially well adapted to atomic hydrogen welding?

32-17. Is atomic hydrogen welding a manual or an automatic welding method, or both?

32-18. What does nonconsumable electrode mean?

32-19. What is the outstanding advantage of inert-gas shielded arc welding?

32-20. Is the choice of shielding gas influenced by the metal being welded?

32-21. How is the shielding gas introduced into the weld area?

32-22. Is inert-arc welding apparatus artificially cooled?

32-23. Are the same regulators used for inert gases as for welding gases?

32-24. In what form is weld metal added in inert-gas welding?

32-25. How is weld metal supplied in consumable electrode inert-gas welding?

32-26. On what type of metals has inert-gas welding proven superior?

32-27. What gases are used for shielding in inert-gas welding?

32-28. State the equipment necessary for electric-arc stud welding.

32-29. Give some specific applications for stud welding.

32-30. Is there any added weld metal in stud welding?

32-31. Can firecracker welding be used for fillets?

32-32. Explain the deep-fillet welding technique.

32-33. How do contact electrodes function?

32-34. Is there a best welding method for heavy steel plates?

32-35. Why are weld positioners used?

32-36. What is the importance of shielding in arc welding?

REFERENCES

Brooking, W. J.: "Arc Welding Engineering and Production Control," McGraw-Hill Book Company, Inc., New York, 1944.

"Procedure Handbook of Arc Welding Design and Practice," 8th ed., The Lincoln Electric Company, Cleveland, 1945.

"Survey of Automatic Arc and Gas Welding Processes as Used in the Automotive Industry," Pub. D7.2-48T, American Welding Society, New York, 1948.

"The Welding Encyclopedia," 11th ed., The Welding Engineer Publishing Company, Chicago, 1943.

"The Welding Handbook," 3d ed., American Welding Society, New York, 1950.

CHAPTER 33

AUXILIARY TORCH AND ARC APPLICATIONS

The flexibility of both the torch and the arc has led to the development of applications which cannot be considered as strictly in the category of welding methods. The utility of these two sources of heat has been a

Fig. 33-1.   Diesel engine base fabricated from flame-cut steel sections.   (*Courtesy of Electro-Motive Corporation, La Grange, Ill.*)

factor in such developments as flame shaping, hard surface overlaying, and heat bending, among others. Torch and arc progress has been such that they are now regarded as inseparable from any broad welding program.

Flame shaping is closely related to welding. Engineering design is employing welded flame-shaped components to an increasing degree (Fig. 33-1). The edge preparation for welding plate is largely a matter of using flame shaping. Arc cutting is increasing in interest for those applications where the flame cannot be used or is ineffective. Materials such as the stainless steels and armor plate are leading examples. Both the torch and the arc have broad application in demolition and in scrap metal preparation.

Hard surfacing, in which both the arc and the torch are used, is accepted as routine by the industry. This process closely resembles welding in that metal is deposited on a base by the combination of a rod and a portable heat source. A further parallel is the recently introduced automatic arc equipment for hard surfacing. This has proved of great value in reclamation, as it has in processing components designed to withstand wear and abrasion.

Flame straightening is widely recognized in shipbuilding, where it has been developed further than in other applications. It is the purpose of this chapter to discuss all these related processes, since their inclusion in a welding program will prove profitable.

Flame Shaping

Flame shaping is not an exact term inasmuch as the flame is an adjunct rather than the primary element in this method. There is some basis for the statement that flame shaping is more accurately described as oxygen shaping, since the basic process, as well as its many modifications, relies upon oxidation for its success. The major application of flame shaping is that of severing steel either at random or for contouring to dimension; consequently such terms as flame cutting and oxygen cutting are also commonly applied to this method.

Theory of Oxygen Cutting. All metallic materials are, in greater or less degree, subject to oxidation. The intensity of oxidation is dependent upon and related to such variables as composition, time, environment, surface condition, and temperature. In general the ferrous group, excepting for those alloys specially compounded for corrosion resistance, are pre-eminently sensitive to oxidation at ordinary temperatures. Mild steel is known to rust as the result of contacting oxygen borne in air and water. This reaction is characterized by the appearance of a red-brown surface overlay resulting from the combination of oxygen and iron and is expressed in the formula

$$2Fe + 3O = Fe_2O_3$$

Oxidation, or rusting, is a continuing process which causes gradual disintegration of the metal being attacked. The speed of this attack is a function of oxygen concentration as well as of temperature.

Pure iron, if heated to its kindling temperature and then subjected to a stream of pure oxygen, will burn violently. This phenomenon is the basis of the use of the shop term "burning" in reference to oxygen cutting. While this shop term may be natural enough, its use is to be discouraged on the ground of inaccuracy, since oxygen-cut steel and burnt steel are not remotely related. The equation given above indicates the necessity for purity of the elements concerned. Any impurities present will tend to retard the reaction; this applies especially to oxygen. The reaction between iron and oxygen occurs at kindling temperature, about 1600°F, as follows:

$$3Fe + 2O_2 = Fe_3O_4 + 26,691 \text{ cal}$$

The resultant material is black oxide of iron.

Fig. 33-2. Manual flame cutting. (*Courtesy of National Cylinder Gas Co., Chicago.*)

The fundamentals of flame shaping consist of heating the metal to its kindling temperature, then directing a blast of oxygen against the heated area, thereby causing rapid oxidation to occur (Fig. 33-2). The success attained is a function of the composition of the base metal. Oxygen cutting cannot be used to shape nonferrous metals, cast irons, or stainless steels. All of these are, in demolition and in emergency repair work, melted by a torch flame. Flame shaping requires a means of developing the necessary kindling temperature. Preheating is the term applied to the procedure of bringing metal to its kindling temperature.

Preheating Flames. A concentrated heat source capable of high temperatures is important to flame cutting. The accepted means of accomplishing preheating is the use of a combination of a combustible gas mixed with oxygen. In theory any combustible gas should be satisfactory for preheating; however, there are practical considerations

such as metal composition, gas cost and availability, and heating time
that must be considered. Frequently the choice of a preheating gas is
predicated on local conditions.

TABLE 33-1. PROPERTIES OF SOME COMBUSTIBLE GASES*

Characteristic	Acetylene C_2H_2	Hydrogen H_2	Methane CH_4	Ethane C_2H_6	Propane C_3H_8	Normal butane C_4H_{10}	Isobutane C_4H_{10}	Manufactured gas	Natural gas
Cubic feet of gas per lb (60°F)...	14.3	187.7	23.64	12.594	8.6	6.5154	6.5154		
Btu per cu ft.....	1,503	323.9	1,008	1,764	2,505	3,274	3,274	550	1,000
Btu per lb........	21,572	60,810	.....	22,216	21,500	21,331	21,331	20,050	21,496

* Compiled from various sources.

Properties of some of the better-known combustible gases are shown in
Table 33-1. The matter of gas selection revolves around relative values.
If rapid preheating time is of importance, as it is when numerous pieces
are to be cut, then that gas giving the highest flame temperature should
be selected. Where cuts of greater duration are the rule, preheating
time loses much of its significance.

The combustion equation for acetylene gas (C_2H_2) is given in Chap. 29.
Similar equations for propane, butane, and hydrogen follow:

Oxy-propane flame Btu/cu ft

Primary: $C_3H_8 + 1\frac{1}{2}O_2 = 3CO + 4H_2$ 430.5
Secondary: $3CO + 1\frac{1}{2}O_2 = 3CO_2$ 961.5
$4H_2 + 2O_2 = 4H_2O$ 1108.0

2500.0

1 volume C_3H_8 requires $5O_2$
Flame temperature, 5300°F

Oxy-butane flame

Primary: $C_4H_{10} + 2O_2 = 4CO + 5H_2$ 574
Secondary: $4CO + 2O_2 = 4CO_2$ 1282
$5H_2 + 2\frac{1}{2}O_2 = 5H_2O$ 1385

1 volume C_4H_{10} requires $6\frac{1}{2}O_2$ 3241
Flame temperature, 5300°F

Oxyhydrogen flame
$H_2 + \frac{1}{2}O_2 = H_2O$ 275.1
Flame temperature, 5400°F

Comparison of the values resulting from combustion of these four gases
shows that the oxy-butane mixture has the highest Btu per cubic foot
potential but is capable of only a 5300°F flame temperature. It also
reveals that the volume of oxygen required for primary combustion is
greatest for butane and lowest for hydrogen. Another consideration

worthy of note is that the oxyacetylene flame is most easily adjusted, a fact of considerable significance where carbon pickup on the edge of the cut is a critical matter.

Fuel Gases Used for Cutting.   Acetylene gas, while it has much to recommend it as a preheating gas, is not pre-eminent.   There is much that can be said for other gases, especially for those in the liquefied petroleum gas field.   Coke oven gas finds favor as a fuel for preheating in steel mill cutting operations.   This gas can be used as manufactured or mixed with blast furnace gas or included in a combination of gases, depending on local conditions.   Natural gas has proved itself as a satisfactory fuel for gas cutting.   Its chief limitations are geographical, since no attempt is made to transport this gas in any other form than bulk pumped through distribution pipe lines.

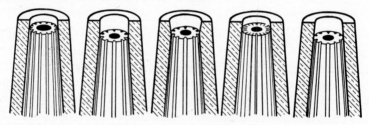

Fig. 33-3.   Sketches showing recessed tips used with liquefied petroleum, manufactured and natural gas.   (*Courtesy of Harris Calorific Company, Cleveland.*)

Propane and butane, single or in combination, are distributed as liquefied gases and, as such, find application as fuel for oxygen cutting. These gases are commonly merchandized under proprietary trade names. The addition of an "odorent" is practiced as a means of calling attention to and locating any leaks or gas escapement.   Liquefied petroleum gases intended for industrial use, in contradistinction to those sold for domestic purposes, are primarily propane.   Liquefied petroleum gases have a lower flame propagation speed than does acetylene gas. Because of this fact, recessed-type torch tips are necessary (Fig. 33-3). The design of these tips is varied to suit different gas characteristics. Manufacturers of oxygen cutting torches are in a position to supply recessed tips that will fit their standard torches.

A unique approach to cutting steel has recently been developed.[1]   In this method the stream of oxygen is used but there is no necessity for continuous heating of the plate by means of an auxiliary heat source. Rather, the oxygen is heated before it strikes the surface of the metal to be cut by being passed through a graphite tube heated, initially, by an electric arc.   If this development gains widespread acceptance, it will mean that cutting can be performed without the use of preheating gases.

[1] Dmitriev, I. S. and N. M. Madatove: report in *Avtogennoe*, May, 1949.

Metallurgical Changes. There is some evidence indicating that a carbon pickup develops at the flame-cut surface. To avoid this, close attention must be given to flame composition during both the preheating and the cutting period. The increase in carbon near the surface even when hydrogen is the fuel gas indicates that circumstances other than flame conditions exist. The reasons for this carbon gain are that the carbon content of the plate back from the cut is lower than the original analysis, indicating a carbon migration is promoted by the heat of the cut.

Cutting Torches. The torch or blowpipe equipment used for flame cutting is designed for manual or machine operation. The former type (Fig. 33-4) is equipped with an angular head, while machine torch heads are commonly of a straight design. A manual cutting torch is similar to a welding torch but it is larger and of heavier construction. Further,

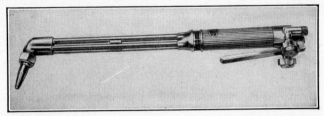

Fig. 33-4. Manual cutting torch. (*Courtesy of Bastian-Blessing Co., Chicago.*)

in addition to the needle valves at the base for regulation of gas flow, there is a third valve, or trigger, for releasing the stream of cutting oxygen. The location of the third valve varies with different manufacturers although its function is the same in all cases.

There is a separate channel for the delivery of the cutting oxygen, which is always through the central part of the tip, regardless of tip design. Figure 33-5 shows the path of travel of the cutting oxygen as well as of the preheating gases. These views are of acetylene equipment as seen from the flush tip ends. The preheating gases are delivered through a series of ports located in a concentric circle surrounding the central oxygen port. The number of preheating ports varies with the size of the piece to be cut; a greater number of preheating flames results in faster heating. The conversion units shown in Fig. 33-5 are attached to a welding torch body as a replacement for the welding head when it is desired to change over from welding to cutting without changing the torch body. A reconverted torch is satisfactory for maintenance and repair but for production and heavy cutting an integrated cutting torch is best from an operational as well as a cost viewpoint.

The machine cutting torch is of straight-line construction with the tip as an extension of the body. Machine cutting blowpipes are constructed for heavier service and differ from the manual models on this account. Extremely heavy-duty cutting blowpipes reach massive proportions; because of their capacity they are water-cooled at the tip (Fig. 33-6). It is sometimes necessary, when heavy cutting is undertaken, to supply cutting oxygen through lines separate from those used in preheating.

Applied Cutting. Regardless of whether the cutting torch is guided manually or mechanically, the fundamental principle of cutting is the same: heating a spot or edge to kindling temperature and then causing an oxygen stream to impinge thereon. Preheating time can be lessened by choosing a corner or edge in preference to a mass of metal as a target.

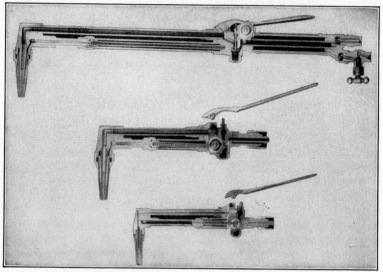

Fig. 33-5.   Cross section of a typical manual cutting torch and torch conversion units.   (*Courtesy of Victor Equipment Co., San Francisco.*)

The device of using a chisel to raise a sliver of metal from a heavy section as a means of rapid preheat will save both time and gas. Once the stream of cutting oxygen is released, rapid oxidation occurs, forming a kerf through the metal in a manner similar to the action of a ripsaw on lumber. The slag from the kerf assists in carrying the cut forward. However, when plates of any thickness are being cut, the cut does not remain perfectly normal to the plate surface, since it does not penetrate the full plate thickness instantaneously. As a result, the kerf cross section assumes a curved shape with the bottom of the cut showing some lag—in cutting terminology, drag. The amount of drag is of small consequence on straight-line cuts, but it is important when contouring is being done or curves are being produced. The amount of drag can be modified by controlling the speed of cut and the gas pressures.

Cutting can be so closely controlled that properly cut plates compare favorably in dimensional accuracy with those produced by machining. The common errors in cutting are shown in Fig. 33-7, which pictures sections of 1-in. plate that have been subjected to some of the variabilities arising in applied cutting; the caption explains the error in each case.

The illustrations in Fig. 33-7 pertain to the vertical cross section of the kerf. Plan views of plate cutting are given in Figure 33-8. Careful

Fig. 33-6. Reducing scrap ingots to charging box size with a heavy-duty machine cutting torch. (*Courtesy of Linde Air Products Co., New York.*)

study of these two figures, together with their accompanying explanations, will familiarize the student with the principles of controlled cutting. Selection of the correct size and style of cutting tip and oxygen pressure should follow the manufacturer's recommendation. The choice of tip size is governed by the type of material to be cut, its surface condition, and its thickness.

Flame shaping is largely confined to mild steel plates because of their adaptability to this process and the welding operations that follow.

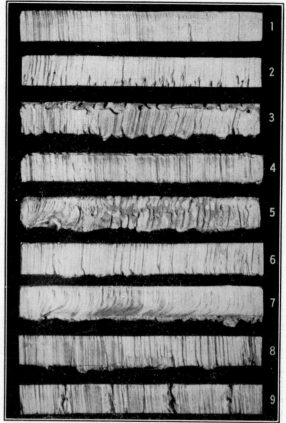

1. This is *a correctly made cut* in 1-in. plate. The edge is square and the draglines are essentially vertical and not too pronounced.

2. *Preheat flames were too small* for this cut: cutting speed was too slow, causing bad gouging at the bottom.

3. *Preheat flames were too long:* top surface has melted over, cut edge is irregular, and there is an excessive amount of adhering slag.

4. *Oxygen pressure was too low:* top edge has melted over because of the too slow cutting speed.

5. *Oxygen pressure was too high* and *nozzle size too small:* entire control of the cut has been lost.

6. *Cutting speed was too slow:* irregularities of the draglines are emphasized.

7. *Cutting speed was too high:* there is a pronounced break to the dragline and the cut edge is irregular.

8. *Blowpipe travel was unsteady:* cut edge is wavy and irregular.

9. *Cut was lost and not carefully restarted:* bad gouges were caused at the restarting point.

Fig. 33-7. Common faults occurring in hand cutting. *(From "The Oxy-Acetylene Handbook," Linde Air Products, New York, 1943.)*

However, the value of oxygen cutting in demolition and scrap preparation is so great that it seems safe to refer to it as one of the most valuable tools in industry. Cast iron is never shape-cut; rather it is cut into sections which are utilized for furnace charges. Cutting cast iron with a torch is difficult, since extremely wide kerfs are necessary in order to circumvent the graphitic carbon constituent. An expedient is to feed a steel rod into the cut in order to provide a greater volume of slag and higher temperature. Another device is to place a steel waster plate on the cast-iron surface, thereby utilizing the molten steel slag as the agency for melting through the cast iron. Somewhat similar ideas have been employed where copper-base alloys required demolition.

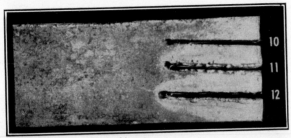

10. *Correct procedure was used* in making this cut.
11. *Too much preheat was used* and *nozzle was held too close to the plate:* a bad melting over of the top edge occurred.
12. *Too little preheat was used and flames were held too far from the plate:* the heat spread opened up the kerf at the top; the kerf is too wide at the top and tapers in.

Fig. 33-8. Plan view of torch cuts in steel plates. (From "The Oxy-Acetylene Handbook," Linde Air Products, New York, 1943.)

Fig. 33-9. Electronic tracing device guiding three cutting torches. (Courtesy of Air Reduction Sales Company, New York.)

Machine Oxygen Cutting. There are many designs of mechanical equipment used for flame shaping. This equipment had its inception in the idea of replacing manual operation with a more precise mechanical movement. The development of machine oxygen cutting equipment has proceeded to the point where automatic operation is accomplished. Equipment development has followed along three basic types, designed respectively for straight-line cuts, circles and contours, and profiling. Each type is available as single- or multiple-torch equipment.

Production cutting frequently employs a templet, or profile, for a tracer guide. The method of holding the tracer element to the guide varies. In some cases friction is depended upon to perform this function; a more positive means is the use of a magnetized element for contacting the steel templet. Electronic control of the tracer element has made possible the use of wooden templates or drawings for a guide. The light beam,

Fig. 33-10.   Track mounted straight-line cutting equipment beveling two plate edges simultaneously. (*Courtesy of Air Reduction Sales Co., New York.*)

which governs the tracer head movement, follows the drawing line or template edge, as the case may be. When electric-eye tracing is available, it is possible to use the drawing as a guide, thereby eliminating the expense and the time required for template construction. Electric-eye tracing has proved satisfactory for quantity production from a given drawing, thereby inaugurating a speedy and economical flame-cutting routine (Fig. 33-9).

The flame cutting of circles is performed with equipment that uses the idea of guiding from a point located at the center of the circle. The cutting torch (or torches) is mounted on a tractor driven by an electric motor. The motor is arranged with a variable drive for optimum operating speeds. The radius arm of the machine is adjusted to fit any circle within the range of the equipment.

Straight-line work constitutes the major part of automatic flame cutting. Plates are cut to size or edges straightened or beveled with automatic equipment (Fig. 33-10).

The various arrangements possible for edge preparation are manifold. It is possible, for example, to set up two torches for concurrent cutting: the leading one is slanted for the desired bevel cut and is followed by a vertical torch that takes off the toe of the bevel and leaves a vertical root for the weld.

Stack Cutting. Duplicate plate or sheet parts can be produced economically by flame shaping. There is no necessity for making an expensive die when production requirements are not sufficient to warrant it. Instead, the sheet steel or plates are stacked and the desired shape is flame-cut through the entire stack thickness. A precaution that must be observed is making sure that the sheets in the stack contact firmly; otherwise the cut will be arrested on passing through one plate or sheet.

SPECIALIZED CUTTING APPLICATIONS

Powder Cutting. Flame-cutting stainless steel has been difficult because the material is specially made to resist oxidation and when melted a tenacious chromium oxide is formed. There have been expedients tried for solving this problem, such as waster plates and increased tip sizes coupled with high gas pressures; however, none of these proved entirely satisfactory. A completely new and successful approach to flame-cutting stainless steel introduces a powdered material into the cutting stream.

Iron powder is used in another method. The powder is blown through the cutting tip by air or nitrogen under pressure. Upon issuing from the tip, the powder enters the preheating flames and burns, with a resulting increase in the flame temperature. Torch tips require additional orifices through which the powder stream can issue prior to entering the flame. Auxiliary equipment for placing the powder under pressure and separate lines for carrying to the torch are requirements of this method.

A different approach to powder cutting consists of introducing a dry flux into the oxygen stream. The action of the flux is considered to be chemical rather than thermal like that of the iron powder. The flux is blown into the cutting stream, where it reacts to produce a very fluid slag stream that results in cutting speeds and quality comparable to mild steel cutting. Figure 33-11 illustrates the stack cutting of stainless steel sheets by the powder method.

Arc Cutting. The principle of arc cutting is merely that of melting a path through the base metal. There is no comparison in quality of cut between torch cutting and arc cutting. The latter produces a very rough kerf and one that is difficult to hold to alignment. Arc cutting has been successfully used on copper-base alloys and other metals that are not easily severed with a cutting torch. It is a ready means of accomplishing demolition work where a torch is unsatisfactory.

Arc cutting has commonly been done with a hard carbon or graphite electrode using direct current, although alternating current has also been employed. The cut is made upward on heavy material in order to keep the bottom of the kerf in the lead. Metal electrodes, both plain and shielded, are used for arc cutting. Shielded electrodes will function adequately, but their cost may be a deterrent. Soaking a gas-type shielded electrode in water will speed up the cutting operation.

Fig. 33-11. Stack cutting twelve 10-gage type 304 stainless steel sheets by powder cutting method. (*Courtesy of Linde Air Products Co., New York.*)

Underwater Cutting. An underwater cutting torch is similar to a standard cutting torch, with the addition of a skirt over the tip (Fig. 33-12) and an additional line to supply compressed air to the skirt or cap. Acetylene gas is used for shallow depths, but on jobs of depth greater than 25 ft, hydrogen is used as the fuel gas because pressure requirements are beyond the safe limits for acetylene.

The tip skirt, or sheath equipped with end vents, is placed against the work and air is turned in. The air acts to hold the water away from the flame and at the same time supplies the secondary oxygen necessary to sustain the preheating flames. The torch can be lighted prior to descent, or an electrical spark-plug arrangement can be incorporated in the tip for lighting the preheating flames. Underwater cutting is also accomplished with an electric arc, using a shielded electrode.

Arc-air Process.   A novel process of gouging and cutting with an arc is termed the arc-air process; this is essentially the melting of metal with an electric arc and the mechanical removal of the molten metal by means of a high-velocity air jet.   Since it does not depend on oxidation, it is used successfully on metals which do not readily oxidize, such as stainless steels and copper alloys.   Its application to structural steel is especially effective for gouging and removal of weld backing beads.

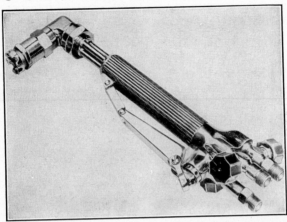

Fig. 33-12.   Underwater cutting torch.   (*Courtesy of Bastian-Blessing Company, Chicago.*)

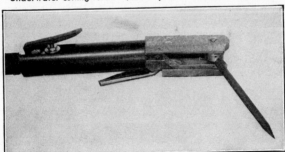

Fig. 33-13.   Arc-air gouging and cutting equipment.   (*Courtesy of Arcair Co., Bremerton, Wash.*)

The torch consists of an external air nozzle which provides a stream of air which is parallel to the electrode and which is maintained in position even though the direction of the electrode is changed.   A valve is provided to control the air "on" and "off," and a coaxial cable to supply the current and air (Fig. 33-13).

Carbon electrodes are usually used with d-c reverse polarity at high current values.   Speed of travel is approximately 24 in./min for a $\frac{3}{8}$-in. groove, but it will vary with the depth and type of cut.   The surface is extremely smooth; though some carburization is present, it is confined to a very thin layer.

Surfacing

Surfacing is defined as the "deposition of filler metal on a metal surface to obtain desired properties or dimensions."[1]   Obviously this definition is subject to some variation in interpretation, since the term deposition can be understood to refer to either coalescence or a mechanical bond.

Hard Facing.   The term hard facing is applied to those welding processes in which a surfacing material is applied for the purpose of increasing resistance to abrasion or corrosion or both.   This development is also referred to as hard surfacing, especially where the object is to produce an edge or surface capable of resisting abrasion.   Oil drilling tools were among the first kinds of equipment to be given this treatment. Hard surfacing is applied to either new or worn parts.   An especially fertile field for this development is the equipment used by contractors, such as dipper teeth and blading for graders.   The useful life of surfaces on switch frogs and crusher liners has been prolonged by overlaying the wearing area with some type of hard-surfacing material.

TABLE 33-2*

Operating requirements	Service and/or production conditions	Recommended surfacing material
Extreme impact...........	Build up and joining 13% Mn steel	Austenitic Mn steel
Severe impact.............	Slight deformation permissible	Pearlitic steel, chrome base, Cr-Mo base
Impact and abrasion.......	Tough, hard deposits of alloy steels that can be forged and heat-treated	Martensitic steels
Impact and abrasion at elevated temperatures	Frictional wear, seizing, galling, and softening to 1100°F	High-speed steels, die steels
Elevated temperatures, corrosion abrasion, some impact	Resistance to hot-gas corrosion up to 2000°F	Cobalt base with high chromium and tungsten
Severe abrasion with light impact	Ball mill liners	Ni-Cr irons, Cr-Mo irons
Severe abrasion under light loads	Plow shares, sand chutes	Austenitic high-chromium irons
Extreme abrasion.........	Sharp cutting edges	Tungsten carbide

* Abstracted and compiled from manufacturers' publications.

The development of surfacing materials has kept pace with the broadening demand, with the result that there is now an extensive selection of materials available for every condition of service and method of applica-

[1] Standard A3.0-49, American Welding Society, New York, 1949.

tion.   The information in Table 33-2 is included as a guide to the selection of proper hard-surfacing materials.   The tabulation shows that surfacing materials include many highly alloyed steel types as well as carbides and nonferrous compositions, some of which were discussed in Chap. 2.

Hard facing cannot be applied indiscriminately to all metals; this applies especially to the nonferrous group.   The light metals are not suitable because of their low melting points.   Copper-base alloys are rarely considered for hard-surfacing treatment, since they also have melting points below those of the surfacing materials.   Monel metal is an exception in that it is readily adaptable to hard surfacing.

As a general rule it can be stated that those steels which are readily weldable offer no difficulty for hard surfacing (Fig. 33-14).   When,

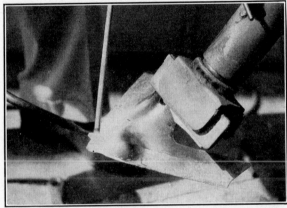

Fig. 33-14.   Manual hard-facing of a cultivator sweep.   (Courtesy of Stoody Co., Whittier, Calif.)

however, carbon contents increase, precautions such as preheating and postheating are necessary as a means of avoiding cracking and shrinkage difficulties.   The more complex steel compositions, such as high-speed and stainless types, require individual consideration as to procedures and techniques.

Hard facing is not confined to engineering manufacture.   The petroleum industry offers a diversity of applications.   Processing industries where eroding materials are handled offer outlets for overlay work. Agricultural equipment, especially plowshares and other items of tillage equipment, are among the prominent subjects for hard facing.

Application Procedures.   Hard-surfacing materials are supplied in the form of weld rods and electrodes.   They are, therefore, applied to the base metal by any of the commonly known welding methods.   The original method of application was by the use of a gas torch with the hard-facing material in the form of a weld rod.   This method continues in popularity, especially with oxyacetylene as the heat source.   There is a considerable amount of knowledge required for best results, since heats range from melting of the base metal down to temperatures just below or approaching fusion.   Hard surfacing with a torch is a flux-free operation as a general thing.

Deposits vary in thickness to a considerable extent, a minimum layer being $\frac{1}{16}$ in.   When heavy build-up is necessary, it is common practice to use a low-priced material for the backup material, and to top it with a high-quality surfacing.

Fig. 33-15.   Automatic arc hard-surfacing.   (*Courtesy of Stoody Co., Whittier, Calif.*)

Hard-surfacing materials are available in electrode form suitable for application by arc welding.   Some of these are solid electrodes, either bare or shielded.   Others are in the form of tubing in which the surfacing material is in fragments held within the tube.   This scheme solves the problem of physical form preparation of such materials as the carbide types and permits the use of particles whose cost is substantially lower than those requiring more elaborate preparation.

A noteworthy achievement in arc application of hard surfacing (Fig. 33-15), has been the automatic arc.   Hard-surfacing material has been developed into wire that is supplied in coils for use in an automatic arc welding head.   Where such components as rollers and the like are to be processed, the entire operation can be mechanized, with genuine savings in over-all costs.

Soft Facing. Not all overlay work is done with materials designed to increase surface hardness. On the contrary, there is considerable application for copper-base alloys as surfacing materials. Primarily the use of bronze overlays is restricted to areas subject to wear by friction. In some instances, build-up surfaces are repaired by bronze. There are examples of shafts being built up oversize and then machined to bearing diameter. An interesting application of bronze was the resurfacing of valve seats in a motor block. Bronze overlays are not confined to wearing surfaces, since these have properties of corrosion resistance that can be exploited. Another application can be found in the direction of resisting erosion, as in valve seats or drawing dies, by way of example. Monel has proved itself as a facing material in steam turbine casings where steam-flow action causes erosion.

Sprayed Metal Coatings

Metal spraying lends itself to two main fields of application. One is metal-sprayed coatings designed for improving surface conditions, as for corrosion resistance; maintenance and repair comprise the second. Sprayed coatings for decorative effects on such diverse materials as wood, glass, and ceramics are still another outlet.

Equipment. A spray gun is the essential part of a metalizing installation. The spray gun serves as a device for atomizing the coating material and then delivering it through a nozzle in the form of a spray possessing sufficient velocity to cause impact on contact with the bare surface (Fig. 33-16). The gun is serviced by a source of heat—either oxyacetylene or some other combustible gas, such as propane or hydrogen. The material to form the metal spray is commonly fed to the gun in wire form; there are instances where powder is used, but in these cases distinctive equipment is necessary. Compressed air is connected to an air turbine in the spray gun as a means of feeding the wire; it also serves to atomize the molten metal and blow it out through the nozzle.

Nozzles and attendant equipment are available in a range of sizes that will accommodate wire diameters up to and inclusive of $\frac{1}{8}$ in. The speed of wire feed is controlled by a needle valve in the turbine air line or by a governor. Nozzles must be selected to operate with the particular type of fuel gas in use (Fig. 33-17). Operation of the spray gun is continuous with the metalizing wire being fed into the gas flame where it is melted. The molten globules are atomized by the compressed-air jet operating at 60 to 70 psi, and blown out through the orifice in the nozzle.

Preparation of Surface. The surface to be sprayed must be properly prepared. All foreign matter must be removed as a preliminary to subjecting the surface to some form of roughening treatment. The surface texture must be such that it will offer anchoring points for the spray particles. It is important to note that the *bond between the spray*

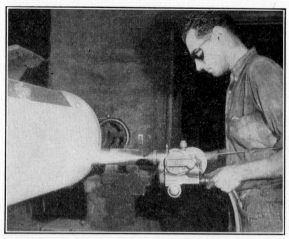

Fig. 33-16. Metal spraying cylindrical surface. (*Courtesy of Metallizing Engineering Co., Inc., Long Island City, N.Y.*)

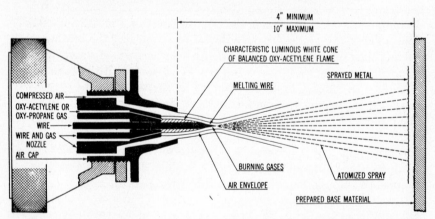

Fig. 33-17. Wire nozzle and air cap cross-section metal spray gun. (*Courtesy of Metallizing Engineering Co., Inc., Long Island City, N.Y.*)

coating and the surface metal in a mechanical one. This being the case, every effort must be directed toward making the surface roughness of such a character that when the spray strikes it will adhere firmly.

Several methods of surface preparation are general; of these, grit blasting offers the least complications. The choice of method is dependent upon the shape and size of the part to be sprayed. Circular components, such as shafting, are mounted in a lathe, and a coarse, rough thread is cut on the surface (Fig. 33-18). When this treatment fails to produce proper keying points, it is common practice to run a knurling tool over the thread crests in order to flatten them in a manner that leaves an undercut effect on the part.

Another technique for preparation consists of using an electric arc to roughen the surface in place of either a blast or a machining operation. An interesting development is that of a metalizing wire which requires no surface preparation—it can be sprayed on any clean area.

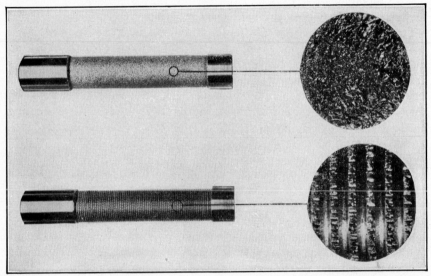

Fig. 33-18. Surface preparation for metal spraying. Photomicrograph of grit-blasted surface shown above, machined surface below. ✕ 10. *(Courtesy of Metallizing Engineering Co., Inc., Long Island City, N.Y.)*

Spraying Procedures. Metal coatings should be sprayed in light layers with the gun nozzle held 4 to 10 in. from the surface. The desired thickness is obtained by applying a sufficient number of layers. This procedure is preferred to applying a single heavy layer, since heavy layers are subject to stratification difficulties. Spraying can be done by manual manipulation with the smaller, portable guns; when heavier equipment is used, the gun is mechanically mounted. Placing a shaft in a lathe and mounting the spray gun in the tool post is the ideal and economical setup for spraying. On the other hand, spraying the inside surfaces of a tank for corrosion resistance is a manual operation.

The metalized surface can be finished by machining to dimension. Components that have been machined undersize are built up by metal spraying. They can then be machined to desired dimensions. Worn surfaces are similarly treated. The machinist doing this work should be cautioned, since a sprayed metal surface reacts differently from solid material to machining operations. Tool positions, feed, and speeds are different for machining sprayed surfaces.

Metal Spray Applications. The field of application for metalizing is being extended constantly. Substituting powder for wire makes it possible to use coating materials that cannot be produced as wire. Powder spraying is accomplished by equipment so constructed that the powder is drawn into the nozzle by suction. The base material need not be metallic. For example, the plating that was formerly used for carbon brushes has been supplanted by spraying with copper.

Sprayed metal coatings are used for joining in what amounts to a brazing operation. The faying surfaces are sprayed with the bonding metal; surfaces are assembled and placed in a furnace, where temperatures are raised to the flow point of the sprayed metal. The resultant weld is on occasion referred to as a spray weld. This development, as well as the method of using hard-surfacing materials for wire and of making hard-faced overlays by metal spraying, is known to the industry.

Contraction

The author makes no claim for originality in the matter of employing contraction as a tool for correcting distorted or bent sections in ductile metal members. On the contrary, he recognizes the pioneering work in this field as having been done by Joseph Holt and published in a copyrighted pamphlet more than a decade ago.[1] However, the author has had considerable experience with the Holt method working individually as well as with the originator of this technique for contraction bending.

Heat Bending. The basic principle in using contraction as an easy means of causing metal to move is that of upsetting a section in such a manner and in such a position that subsequent cooling will cause contraction to be effective at a chosen point or region. A member is heated differentially so that expansion is confined and as a result the area of elevated temperature cannot elongate but upsets. Heating must follow a carefully chosen pattern, since a member cannot be heated completely across its section lest no upsetting action occur. The heated area is of a conformation that permits the remainder of the cross section being straightened to remain at normal temperature. The cool section acts as the restraint which causes the upsetting behavior of the heated area. Figure 33-19 shows diagrammatically the manner in which a flat steel bar can be bent by the application of these principles.

[1] Holt, Joseph: "Contraction as a Friend in Need," Seattle, 1938. Permission has been granted the author for use of any material appearing in this publication.

Initial heating is applied at point *A*, located approximately one-third the distance in from the edge *DE*. When using a welding flame, it should be positioned so that it points toward *BC* or in the direction in which the heat is to travel. *Heating should be done rapidly and uniformly* by moving the flame in a sidewise path over a triangular area whose apex is located at *A* and whose base is formed by *BC*. Special care should be exercised in heating, since failure to confine the heated area will defeat the entire objective. If, for example, the heat effect is permitted to wander from point *A* toward the edge *DE*, the entire bar will elongate

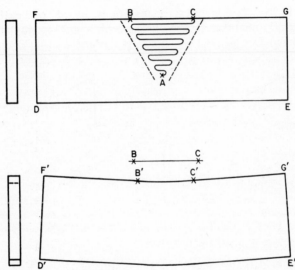

Fig. 33-19.   Heat bending applied to a flat bar of uniform cross section.   Top, primary heat affected area within dotted lines.   Continuous line shows path of torch flame and area of upset.

and the desired positioned upsetting effect will be nullified because the area of the bar adjacent to the edge *DE* will not act as a restraining force against elongation. There must be a portion of the metal remaining at a temperature lower than the heated area if localized upsetting is to occur.

After the triangular area is heated rapidly, the heat source is withdrawn. The metal within the heated area cannot expand longitudinally owing to the restraint of the cooler metal adjacent to the edge *DE*. In consequence, edge *FG* has not elongated; rather, the area bounded by *A, B, C* has expanded into itself, causing increased thickening or upsetting of the metal in that area. Upon cooling, this critical area will contract, causing a shortening of the edge *FG* to the length *F'G'*. Obviously this shortening causes the entire bar to bend toward that edge.

The amount of bending resulting from a single heat application is dependent upon the temperature of both the heated and the restraint area. As a general rule, several small and rapid heat applications are preferable to one extended effort. Good results follow from the correct placing of heats and control of temperatures, and these are matters requiring the exercise of judgment. There is no point in heating steel to scaling temperature; as a matter of fact, a black heat, in contradistinction to a red one, will suffice for some applications.

The basic principles of heat bending, which have been explained above, apply equally well to any section. An example of bending a steel angle is sketched in Fig. 33-20a and 20b. In the first case, one entire leg acts as the restraining metal in a manner that will cause the angle to be bent toward edge BC. Figure 33-20b shows the angle bending in the opposite direction. Only the metal adjacent to A can act as restraint here, since

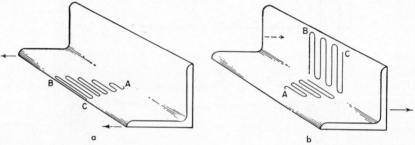

Fig. 33-20. Heat bending applied to equal-leg steel angles. Arrows indicate direction of bend upon cooling after heat has caused upsetting action.

the heated area extends across the remainder of the section. It might prove desirable to use a second torch on leg BC in order to meet the basic requirement of rapid heating.

Heat Straightening. The greatest utility of the heat bending process lies in straightening bent members. Potential applications are legion for this method. Considerable recognition has been given this method in straightening bent members of highway bridges damaged by blows or through the action of floods. Evidence of the successful straightening of bridge members is given in Fig. 33-21. In Fig. 33-21, top, the buckled cross bracing is shown. Some of these members were more than 3 ft out of line. Figure 33-21, bottom, shows the same members after straightening. It should be borne in mind that straightening was accomplished entirely by heat, employing the principles explained in this section.

Another view of the same bridge, showing other damaged members can be seen in Fig. 33-22a; the same view with the damaged members heat straightened is shown in Fig. 33-22b. In order to save time and reduce cost, mechanical force is sometimes applied as a supplement to heat straightening. Obviously, judgment of a high order is needed on a bridge job, since improperly placed heat applications can lead to disastrous results. It should be stressed that experience must be gained by a thorough grounding in fundamentals on simple members before complicated applications are attempted.

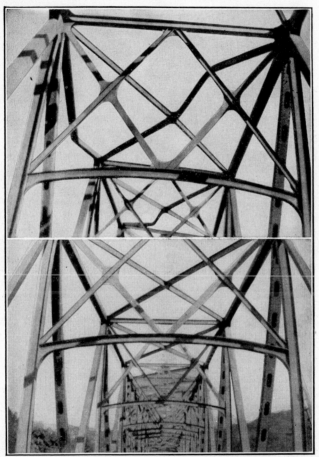

Fig. 33-21. *Top*—Note buckled upper members. *Bottom*—Same bridge, with upper members straightened by use of flame method. (*Courtesy of Joseph Holt, Seattle.*)

The use of heat straightening is not confined to structural steel members. The machine shop and assembly floor frequently have need of this method. Distorted castings of ductile metal offer a further field of application. In every instance it is essential that heat be applied at the correct location.

Small heats give closer control and better results. Heating a large area will frequently result in complete failure, since no restraining area remains. A cool restraining area is as necessary to success as is the heating feature of the heat-straightening method.

Fig. 33-22. Bridge located on U.S. Highway 99 where it crosses the Umpqua River near Roseburg, Ore. *a*, note bent bridge member in foreground; *b*, same bridge with bent member flame-straightened. (*Courtesy of Joseph Holt, Seattle.*)

Survey Questions

33-1. State some of the terms that are used to describe flame shaping.

33-2. Explain kindling temperature.

33-3. Is oxygen necessary in all flame-shaping operations?

33-4. List the most commonly used combustible gases in flame shaping.

33-5. Can the same style of tip be used for the different fuel gases?

33-6. How can flame shaping develop metallurgical changes in steel plate?

33-7. Can welding torches be used for flame shaping?

33-8. Why is a narrow kerf desirable?

33-9. Are cutting machines equipped with single or multiple torches?

33-10. Do all cutting machines operate from a template?

33-11. When is stack cutting competitive with die blanking?

33-12. On what material is powder cutting used?

33-13. For surface finish, is flame or arc cutting better?

33-14. Is it possible to use welding electrodes for arc cutting?

33-15. Wherein does an underwater cutting torch differ from conventional types?

33-16. Is there a method for arc-cutting stainless steel?

33-17. Give some applications for hard facing.

33-18. Is hard facing accomplished with the torch or arc or both?

33-19. What is soft facing? Give some applications.

33-20. How are surfaces prepared for metal-spray coating?

33-21. Mention some objectives for metal spraying.

33-22. Can metal be sprayed on nonmetallic surfaces satisfactorily?

33-23. Is a metalized bond characterized by fusion?

33-24. If a part is undersize, can it be built up by metalizing for subsequent machining?

33-25. Can metalizing be used as an auxiliary for brazing?

33-26. Is it possible to straighten a distorted or bent steel member with heat alone?

33-27. What heating precautions are necessary for flame straightening or bending?

33-28. Can distortion in steel castings be corrected by flame applications?

33-29. What methods can be used for steel-plate edge preparation prior to welding?

33-30. Is there a rapid means for starting a cut in a steel shaft?

33-31. Steel plates can be flame-shaped; does this also apply to cast-iron components?

33-32. How are risers generally removed from steel castings?

33-33. Is dimensional accuracy possible with flame cutting?

33-34. When is flame de-scaling applicable?

33-35. What is the purpose of shrinking as applied in shipbuilding?

33-36. Are nonferrous metals prepared by flame shaping?

33-37. Distinguish between preheating as used in welding and when used in flame cutting.

33-38. Is there any similarity between the apparatus used for metalizing and welding torches?

33-39. Of what material are cutting torch tips made?

33-40. Can machine elements be completely fabricated by flame cutting? If so, give some specific applications.

REFERENCES

Avery, Howard S.: "Hard Surfacing by Fusion Welding," The American Brake Shoe Company, New York, 1947.

Bullard, W. H.: "Metal Spraying and Sprayed Metal," 3d ed., Charles Griffin & Co., Ltd., London, 1948.

"Hard-Facing by the Oxy-Acetylene Process," International Acetylene Association, New York, 1936.

Holt, Joseph: "Contraction as a Friend in Need," a pamphlet, Seattle, 1938.

Holt, Joseph: Directional Welding to Minimize or Eliminate Distortion in Weldments and Control Residual Stresses, The Welding Journal, Vol. 26, No. 10, October, 1947.

"Instructions in Oxyacetylene Welding and Cutting Processes," Air Reduction Company, New York, 1940.

"Liquefied Gases," Standard Oil Company of California, San Francisco, 1939.

"The Oxy-Acetylene Handbook," The Linde Air Products Company, New York, 1943.

Plumley, Stuart: "Oxy-Acetylene and Arc Welding," 3d ed., University Printing Company, Minneapolis, 1939.

Spraragen, W., and W. G. Ettinger: "Shrinkage Distortion in Welding," The Welding Journal, Research Supplement, Vol. XV, New York, 1950.

"Welding and Cutting Manual," The Linde Air Products Company, New York, 1949.

"The Welding Handbook," 3d ed., American Welding Society, New York, 1950.

LIST OF VISUAL AIDS

The motion pictures and filmstrips listed in this visual bibliography can be used to supplement the material presented in this book. It is recommended, however, that each film be reviewed before using in order to determine its suitability for a particular group. For the convenience of users, the films have been correlated with particular chapters in the book. Some films may, of course, be used in the study of different chapters.

Both motion pictures and filmstrips are included in this visual bibliography, and the character of each is indicated by the self-explanatory abbreviations, "MP" and "FS." Immediately following this identification is the name of the producer. If the distributor is different from the producer, the name of the distributor follows. Abbreviations are identified in the list of sources at the end of the bibliography. In most instances, the films can be borrowed or rented from local or state 16-mm. film libraries, a nationwide list of which is given in "A Directory of 2002 16mm Film Libraries," available for 30 cents from the Superintendent of Documents, Washington 25, D.C. Unless otherwise indicated, the motion pictures are 16-mm. black-and-white sound films and the filmstrips are 35-mm. black-and-white silent.

This bibliography is suggestive only, and film users should examine the latest annual edition of, and quarterly supplements to "Educational Film Guide," a catalog of some 10,000 films published by the H. W. Wilson Co., New York. The "Guide," a standard reference book, is available in most college and public libraries.

MANUFACTURING MATERIALS

Alloy Steel (MP, Beth, 43 min). Describes new techniques (1949) used in producing alloy steels and shows various steelmaking processes.

The Drama of Steel (MP, USBM, 30 min). Shows the uses of steel in homes, industry, and national defense; portrays early methods of making steel and, in contrast, scenes of modern open-pit mining of iron ore and its conversion to steel in modern furnaces and mills. Reviews the industrial uses of steel. Sponsored by Inland Steel Co.

Iron—Product of the Blast Furnace (MP, Acad, 11 min). Shows the preparation of iron ore, limestone, and coke for the blast furnace and, by animation, the process of making pig iron within the furnace.

Metal Crystals (MP, Am Soc Metals, 33 min, silent). Defines and illustrates crystalline and noncrystalline substances, demonstrates microscopic techniques with metal specimens, and explains the characteristics of metals during changes in temperature.

Plastics (MP series, USOE/UWF). A series of 10 motion pictures and 10 correlated filmstrips having the same titles, demonstrating various processes in the manufacture of plastics. The titles and running times of the individual films are:

1. *Origin and Synthesis of Plastic Materials* (MP, 16 min, FS, 68 fr).
2. *Methods of Processing Plastics Materials* (MP, 25 min, FS, 68 fr).
3. *Compression Molding. Part 1: Prepairing the Charge and Loading the Mold* (MP, 11 min, FS, 39 fr).
4. *Compression Molding. Part 2: Molding a Simple Part* (MP, 10 min, FS, 42 fr).
5. *Transfer Molding: Molding a Part with Inserts* (MP, 10 min, FS, 35 fr).
6. *Semiautomatic and Hand Molding of Intricate Parts* (MP, 16 min, FS, 40 fr).
7. *Injection Molding. Part 1: Setting Up the Press and Molding a Part* (MP, 16 min, FS, 37 fr).
8. *Injection Molding. Part 2: Cleaning and Servicing the Press* (MP, 12 min, FS, 34 fr).
9. *Finishing Molded Parts* (MP, 14 min, FS, 42 fr).
10. *Machining Laminated Plastics* (MP, 19 min, FS, 39 fr).

A Story of Lead (MP, USBM, 29 min). Portrays mining operations in the lead belt of southeast Missouri; the crushing of ore, smelting, refining, and other steps in the production of pig lead for industrial use. Sponsored by St. Joseph Lead Co.

This Is Aluminum (MP, USBM, 29 min). Shows many phases of aluminum, including its abundance, mining operations, processing of bauxite to obtain metallic aluminum, molding, casting, alloying, rolling, annealing, testing of fabricated parts, and manufacturing aluminum articles. Sponsored by Aluminum Co. of America.

Treasure from the Sea (MP, USBM, 11 min, color). Portrays by animation and live-action photography the characteristics and uses of magnesium. Emphasizes the importance of its lightness and its source, which is sea water. Sponsored by Dow Chemical Co.

Zinc, Its Mining, Milling, and Smelting (MP, USBM, 30 min). Locates zinc-ore areas in the United States, describes the process of mining the ore, transporting it to the mill, and smelting the ore to produce zinc oxide and metallic zinc. Illustrates some of the principal industrial uses of zinc. Sponsored by St. Joseph Lead Co.

PATTERNMAKING

Fundamentals of Patternmaking (MP series, USOE/UWF). A series of 11 motion pictures and 11 correlated filmstrips having the same titles, demonstrating fundamental processes in patternmaking. The titles and running times of the individual films are:

1. *Making a One-piece Flat Pattern* (MP, 22 min, FS, 37 fr).
2. *Making a Pattern with a Vertical Core* (MP, 14 min, FS, 46 fr).
3. *Making a Pattern with a Horizontal Core* (MP, 14 min, FS, 41 fr).
4. *Making a Pattern with a Tail Print* (MP, 19 min, FS, 31 fr).
4a. *Making a Core Box for a Tail Print* (MP, 18 min, FS, 34 fr).
5. *Making a Segmented Pattern* (MP, 22 min, FS, 52 fr).
6. *Making a Pattern for a Three-part Mold* (MP, 20 min, FS, 40 fr).
7. *Making a Pattern for a Flanged Pipe Elbow* (MP, 18 min, FS, 41 fr).
8. *Making a Matchboard Pattern* (MP, 21 min, FS, 41 fr).
9. *Making a Core Box for a Vertical Core* (MP, 19 min, FS, 32 fr).
10. *Making a Core Box for a Flanged Pipe Elbow* (MP, 21 min, FS, 40 fr).

Problems in Patternmaking (MP series, USOE/UWF). A series of 10 motion pictures and 10 correlated filmstrips having the same titles, presenting typical problems faced by a patternmaker, and the methods used to meet these problems in the design and construction of patterns. The titles and running times of the individual films are:

Making a Pattern Using a Green- and a Dry-sand Core (MP, 14 min, FS, 31 fr).
Making a Pattern Requiring a Cover Core (MP, 14 min, FS, 35 fr).
Making a Pattern Requiring Box Construction (MP, 17 min, FS, 31 fr).
Making a Core Box for a Machine Base (MP, 12 min, FS, 26 fr).
Making a Pattern Requiring Segmental Construction (MP, 13 min, FS, 30 fr).
Redesigning a Pattern for Production Purposes (MP, 11 min, FS, 32 fr).
Designing a Pattern for a Water-cooled Motor Block (MP, 15 min, FS, 41 fr).
Designing Core Boxes for a Water-cooled Motor Block (MP, 12 min, FS, 30 fr).
Making Pattern, Core Boxes, and Assembling Cores for a Water-cooled Motor Block (MP, 15 min, FS, 32 fr).
Making a Pattern for a Machine-molded Steel Globe and Angle Valve (MP, 14 min, FS, 36 fr).

CASTING AND MELTING METALS

Foundry Practice (MP, USOE/UWF). A series of 14 motion pictures and 14 correlated filmstrips having the same titles, presenting typical operations and processes in the casting and melting of metals. The titles and running times of the individual films are:

Bench Molding

1. *Molding with a Loose Pattern* (MP, 21 min, FS, 37 fr).
2. *Making a Simple Core* (MP, 15 min, FS, 31 fr).
3. *Molding Part Having a Vertical Core* (MP, 19 min, FS, 38 fr).
4. *Molding with a Split Pattern* (MP, 19 min, FS, 26 fr).
5. *Molding with a Gated Pattern* (MP, 11 min, FS, 30 fr).

Floor Molding

1. *Molding with a Loose Pattern (Floor)* (MP, 24 min, FS, 35 fr).
2. *Molding Part with Deep Green-sand Core* (MP, 25 min, FS, 30 fr).
3. *Molding a Valve Body* (MP, 26 min, FS, 33 fr).
4. *Molding a Horizontal Cored Part* (MP, 22 min, FS, 37 fr).
5. *Molding with a Three-part Flask* (MP, 35 min, FS, 33 fr).

Machine Molding

Molding on a Jolt Squeeze Machine (MP, 10 min, FS, 49 fr).
Molding on a Jolt Roll-over Pattern Draw Machine (MP, 23 min, FS, 47 fr).

Melting Practice

Preparing a Cupola for Charging (MP, 21 min, FS, 48 fr).
Charging and Operating a Cupola (MP, 14 min, FS, 44 fr).
Foundry Progress (MP, Modern Equip, 15 min, color). Shows a complete pouring operation from the time the metal is tapped out of the cupola until it is poured into the mold.
Steel with a Thousand Qualities (MP, MTP, 38 min color). Show the processing of steel castings from blueprint stages to the testing of completed samples, and describes the uses of such castings in industry. Sponsored by Lebanon Steel Foundry.

FORGING AND HEAT-TREATING

Forging (MP series, USOE/UWF). A series of three motion pictures and three correlated filmstrips having the same titles, demonstrating forging operations with particular reference to farm work. The titles and running times of the individual films are:

1. *Forging with a Hand Forge* (MP, 13 min, FS, 48 fr).
2. *Forge Welding* (MP 12 min, FS, 26 fr).
3. *Sharpening and Tempering Farm Tools* (MP, 17 min, FS, 34 fr).

Heat-treatment of Aluminum. Film 1 (MP, USOE/UWF, 19 min).   Purpose of heat-treatment, microstructure changes during heat-treatment, procedure of heat-treatment, aging or precipitation hardening, effects of heat-treatment on the physical properties of aluminum.   (Correlated filmstrip, same title, 47 fr, also available.)

Heat-treatment of Aluminum. Film 2 (MP, USOE/UWF, 24 min).   Nature of cold-working operations, microstructure changes during cold working and annealing, cold-working and annealing operations.   (Correlated filmstrip, some title, 41 fr, also available.)

Heat-treatment of Steel (MP series, USOE UWF).   A series of three motion pictures and three correlated filmstrips having the same titles, portraying the hardening, tempering, annealing, and normalizing of steel.   The titles and running times of the individual films are:

1. *Elements of Hardening* (MP, 15 min, FS, 40 fr).
2. *Elements of Tempering, Normalizing, and Annealing* (MP, 15 min, FS, 31 fr).
3. *Elements of Surface Hardening* (MP, 14 min, FS, 36 fr).

MACHINING

Machine Shop Work (MP series, USOE/UWF).   A series of over 100 motion pictures, each one with a correlated filmstrip, demonstrating various machining operations.   Because of space limitations, titles of the individual films are not reproduced here, but film users may obtain a list of the titles and descriptions from the U.S. Office of Education, Washington 25, D.C.   Titles of the various sub-series and the number of films in each such series are:

Basic Machines (4 films).
Bench Work (8 films).
Carbide Cutting Tools (5 films).
Operations on a Broaching Machine (3 films).
Operations on the Center-type Grinder (5 films).
Operations on the Centerless Grinding Machine (5 films).
Operations on the Cutter Grinder (5 films).
Operations on the Drill Press (5 films).
Operations on the Engine Lathe (17 films).
Operations on the Gear Hobbing Machine (5 films).
Operations on the Horizontal Boring Mill (5 films).
Operations on the Internal Grinder (5 films).
Operations on the Milling Machine (10 films).
Operations on the Planer (2 films).
Operations on the Shaper (3 films).
Operations on the Surface Grinder (5 films).
Operations on the Turret Lathe (7 films).
Operations on the Vertical Boring Mill (3 films).
Operations on the Vertical Milling Machine (5 films).
Single-point Cutting Tools (2 films).

PRECISION MEASURING

Measurement with Light Waves (MP, USOE/UWF, 15 min).   Principles of measurement with light waves, nature of light waves, cause of interference bands, and use of these bands in ultra-precision measurement.   Procedures used in gage block inspection.   (Correlated filmstrip, same title, 50 fr, also available.)

Precisely So (MP, GM, 20 min). The development of modern standards of accuracy and illustrations of scientific instruments for precision jobs.

Precision Measurement (MP series, USOE/UWF). A series of eight motion pictures and eight correlated filmstrips having the same titles, covering the uses of various measuring instruments. Titles and running times of the individual films are:

1. *The Steel Rule* (MP, 14 min, FS, 52 fr).
2. *The Micrometer* (MP, 15 min, FS, 38 fr).
3. *Fixed Gages* (MP, 17 min, FS, 35 fr).
4. *Verniers* (MP, 19 min, FS, 37 fr).
5. *Height Gages and Test Indicators* (MP, 12 min, FS, 34 fr).
6. *Precision Gage Blocks* (MP, 18 min, FS, 28 fr).
7. *The Bevel Protractor* (MP, 15 min, FS, 34 fr).
8. *Gage Blocks and Accessories* (MP, 23 min, FS, 33 fr).

WELDING AND BRAZING

Arc Welding at Work (MP, GE, 27 min, color). Explains and demonstrates metal arc welding, atomic-hydrogen arc welding, and insert arc welding.

Brazing Carbide Tools (MP, USOE/UWF, 18 min). Characteristics of carbide tools; how to braze carbide tools with silver solder, how to make a sandwich braze, how to braze by other methods, and how to remove the carbide tip from the shank. (Correlated filmstrip, same title, 41 fr, also available.)

How to Braze Aluminum (MP, USBM, 7 min). Demonstrates the process of joining thin aluminum sections by means of brazing, shows the importance of preparing the aluminum surfaces, describes automatic temperature control in heating furnace, and discusses alloys and temperature differentials. Sponsored by Aluminum Co. of America.

How to Weld Aluminum (MP series, USBM). A series of three motion pictures demonstrating various welding processes. Titles and running times of the individual films are:

Arc Welding (10 min).
Resistance Welding (12 min).
Torch Welding (17 min).

The Oxyacetylene Flame, Master of Metals (MP, USBM, 19 min, color). Shows how oxygen and acetylene are blended to form a flame to cut, weld, solder, braze, and harden metal. Demonstrates the forming of teeth on tractor gears, welding gray cast iron, hardening the working edge of plows, and joining metals by fusing melted bronze. Sponsored by International Acetylene Association.

DIRECTORY OF SOURCES

Acad—Academy Films, Box 3088, Hollywood, Calif.
Am Soc Metals—American Society for Metals, 7301 Euclid Ave., Cleveland 3.
Beth—Bethlehem Steel Company, Bethlehem, Pa.
GE—General Electric Company, 1 River Rd., Schenectady 5.
GM—General Motors Corporation, 3044 West Grand Blvd., Detroit 2.
Modern Equip—Modern Equipment Company, Port Washington, Wis.
MTP—Modern Talking Picture Service, Inc., 45 Rockefeller Plaza, New York 20.
USBM—U.S. Bureau of Mines, 4800 Forbes St., Pittsburgh 13.
USOE—U.S. Office of Education, Washington 25, D.C. (Films sold via government
    contract by United World Flms, Inc.)
UWF—United World Films, Inc., 1445 Park Ave., New York 29.

INDEX

C

"C" process, 87
Calcium carbide, 497
Calipers, 455
  micrometer, 456
  vernier, 458
Can making, 139
Carburizing, 188
Case hardening, 188
Castings, 80
  centrifugal, 89
  centrifuged, 89
  permanent-mold, 91
  precision, 98
Catalysts, 32
Cellini, Benvenuto, 98
Cemented carbide, 320
  columbian, 447
  tantalum, 446
  titanium, 447
  tungsten, 446
Cementite, 178
Centers, 215
  self-mounting, 249
Cerium, 10
Chamfering, 224
Cheek, 81
Chill, 75
Chip, 440
Chip breaker, 441
Chipping, 122
Choke, 73
Chuck, 213
  collet, 249
  drill, 361
  magnetic, 394
Chucking machines, 253
Clad plate, 155
Clad sheet, 22, 155
Cogging, 158
Coining, 126
Cold strip mills, 14
Cold weld, 472
Cold working, 125
Combined cut, 237
Contact resistance, 530
Contraction, 592
Coolant, 439
Cope, 81
Copper, 19
Copper-base alloys, 20–21
Core baking, 69
Core blower, 68
Core oil, 67
Cores, 50–52
Corn flour, 63
Corrosion, intergranular, 206

Corundum, 376
Counterbore, 363
Countersink, 364
Croning process, 87
Cross rolling, 155
Crucible, 111
Cutting, arc, 573
  arc-air, 585
  powder, 583
  torch, 577
  underwater, 584
Cyanide, 189
Cycle index, 260

D

Davy, Sir Humphrey, 467
De Lauvand, D. S., 90
Diamond, 376
Diamond tools, 450
Diamond wheels, 386
Die broaching, 169
Die casting, cold-chamber, 94
  gravity, 91
  submerged-plunger, 95
Die heads, 280
  chasers, 277
  rotating, 276
  self-opening, 275
  stationary, 276
Die set, 148
Die typing, 169
Dies, blanking, 148
  extrusion, 168
  forging, 168
  solid-thread, 279
Dietert, Harry W., 58
Direct-current, 480
D-c generators, 481
D-c rectifiers, 480
D-c welding methods, 485
Directional solidification, 47
Distortion, 194
Dividing head, 330
  hypoid-type, 331
Dog plate, 213
Dowmetal, 25
Draft, 42
Drag, 41
Draw spike, 84
Drawbench, 132
Drawing, 180
  cold, 128
  deep, 138
Drill point, 358
  angle, 359
  chisel edge, 359
Drill sharpening, 359